Register Now for to Your B

Your print purchase of *Suicide Assessment and Treatment, Second Edition*, **includes online access to the contents of your book**—increasing accessibility, portability, and searchability!

Access today at:

http://connect.springerpub.com/content/book/978-0-8261-3515-5
or scan the QR code at the right with your smartphone
and enter the access code below.

DL92NBXU

Scan here for quick access.

SPC

SPRINGER PUBLISHING COMPANY
View all our products at springerpub.com

SUICIDE ASSESSMENT
AND TREATMENT

Dana Alonzo, PhD, LCSW, is an associate professor at Fordham University, New York. She has a wide range of clinical experience working with individuals with mood disorders and suicidality in outpatient, inpatient, and psychiatric emergency room settings. Dr. Alonzo has been conducting research for more than 16 years, examining risk and protective factors related to suicidal behavior and the treatment engagement and mental health service utilization of individuals at risk for suicide across psychiatric disorders and ethnicities. Based on the findings of her research, Dr. Alonzo has published approximately 40 peer-reviewed scientific articles and has developed an intervention to help patients move from intake and assessment to engagement in a successful course of outpatient mental health treatment. Dr. Alonzo has been awarded funding from the American Foundation for Suicide Prevention (AFSP) and the National Alliance for Research on Schizophrenia and Depression (NARSAD) to examine the treatment engagement and adherence of suicidal individuals, which is a sorely neglected area in the field of suicidology. Dr. Alonzo has also established the Suicide Prevention Research Program through which she has received funding from the Mental Health Association of New York State (MHANYS) and the Office of Mental Health of New York State (OMH-NYS) to further develop her intervention and to test its efficacy across high-risk, vulnerable populations.

Robin E. Gearing, PhD, LCSW, is an associate professor and director of the Center for Mental Health Research and Innovations in Treatment Engagement and Service at the University of Houston. Dr. Gearing's research focuses on improving the mental health outcomes of adolescents and young adults with serious mental illnesses, and their families. His research is driven by an interest in informing and improving engagement and adherence to empirically supported psychosocial and medication treatment, and developing evidence-based interventions. This interest is the result of more than 20 years of clinical work with adolescents and young adults, of having firsthand professional knowledge of the needs and gaps in the field, and of seeing uneven efforts to manage the devastating functional, emotional, and fiscal costs of serious mental health conditions. His research nationally and internationally concentrates on treatment engagement and adherence in relation to mental health treatment, cultural adaptation, service delivery, and service utilization. Specifically, Dr. Gearing has conducted a series of research studies examining and operationalizing the multidimensional components of adherence; identifying the barriers, promoters, and temporal patterns of adherence; and investigating the development, cultural adaptation, and promotion of treatment adherence strategies and interventions. Dr. Gearing's research continues to focus on developing and testing interventions and improving treatment engagement and adherence in medical and community-based settings. In addition to other forums, findings from Dr. Gearing's research have appeared in over 60 peer-reviewed journal publications.

SUICIDE ASSESSMENT AND TREATMENT

Empirical and Evidence-Based Practices

SECOND EDITION

Dana Alonzo, PhD, LCSW

Robin E. Gearing, PhD, LCSW

SPRINGER PUBLISHING COMPANY

Springer Publishing Company, LLC
11 West 42nd Street
New York, NY 10036
www.springerpub.com

Acquisitions Editor: Debra Riegert
Compositor: Westchester Publishing Services

ISBN: 978-0-8261-3514-8
ebook ISBN: 978-0-8261-3515-5

Instructor's Materials: Qualified instructors may request supplements by emailing textbook@ springerpub.com:
Answer Key for KATs: 978-0-8261-3517-9

17 18 19 20 21 / 5 4 3 2 1

Library of Congress Cataloging-in-Publication Data
Names: Alonzo, Dana, author. | Gearing, Robin E., author.
Title: Suicide assessment and treatment : empirical and evidence-based practices / Dana Alonzo, Robin E. Gearing.
Description: Second edition. | New York, NY : Springer Publishing Company, LLC, [2018] | Includes bibliographical references and index.
Identifiers: LCCN 2017034227 (print) | LCCN 2017036287 (ebook) | ISBN 9780826135155 (ebook) | ISBN 9780826135148 (hard copy : alk. paper) | ISBN 9780826135155 (e-book)
Subjects: | MESH: Suicide—psychology | Suicide—prevention & control | Risk Assessment | Psychotherapy—methods
Classification: LCC RC569 (ebook) | LCC RC569 (print) | NLM WM 165 | DDC 616.85/8445—dc23
LC record available at https://lccn.loc.gov/2017034227

Contact us to receive discount rates on bulk purchases.
We can also customize our books to meet your needs.
For more information please contact: sales@springerpub.com

Printed in the United States of America.

To every individual who has struggled with suicidality;

to supportive family and friends who have struggled with them;

and, to all mental health professionals, health care practitioners, and social service clinicians who work each day in the field.

CONTENTS

PART II. SUICIDALITY ACROSS THE LIFE SPAN

PART III. SUICIDE AND MENTAL ILLNESS

PART V. ASSESSING SUICIDE

PART VI. EVIDENCE-BASED TREATMENTS

PART VII. SURVIVING SUICIDE

PREFACE

Suicide is an event that cannot be ignored, minimized, or untreated. Each year in the United States over 400,000 individuals attempt suicide, with approximately 40,000 taking their own lives. Effective assessment and empirically supported treatment of suicidality can directly reduce these rates. However, all too often mental health professionals, health care practitioners, and social service clinicians feel ill-prepared to assess and treat this phenomenon. This text is designed to practically transfer the growing empirically supported knowledge and evidence-based treatments to front line and future professionals who will often encounter suicidal clients throughout their careers, and to educators teaching and training future clinicians. Although every suicide may not be predicted or prevented, empirical knowledge derived from current research can provide a deeper foundation for mental health professionals who encounter suicidal clients.

While suicide is the ultimate act we work to prevent, practitioners must also effectively intervene with nonfatal suicidal behaviors that occur with higher frequency. These include suicidal ideation or thoughts, intentional self-harm, and suicide attempts. Empirical research on suicidality indicates that nonfatal suicidal behaviors are often most effectively reduced via systematic focus and specialized intervention strategies. Knowledge of these strategies and evidence-based interventions is essential. This research-driven text provides empirically grounded knowledge on suicide identification, assessment, and evidence-based treatments with specific practical and clinically based learning tools and teaching exercises.

INTENDED AUDIENCE

This text is designed to provide mental health students and professionals, health care practitioners, and social service clinicians with the essential empirically supported knowledge in the following areas: (1) incidence and prevalence rates of suicidal behaviors in various demographic and diagnostic groups; (2) ethical considerations and implications related to suicidality; (3) the significance of culture, race, and ethnicity on suicidal behaviors; (4) religious, spiritual, and philosophical influences on suicide; (5) risk and identification of suicidal behaviors across the life cycle (children/adolescents, adults, older adults); (6) suicide risk across major diagnostic categories; (7) the components of comprehensive suicide assessments; (8) evidence-based treatment interventions (i.e., crisis intervention, cognitive-behavioral therapy [CBT], dialectical behavior therapy [DBT], interpersonal psychotherapy [IPT]); motivational interviewing [MI]); (9) suicide across at-risk populations; and (10) the impact of suicide on survivors (family, friends, and mental health professionals). As such it is an ideal text for graduate and advanced undergraduate courses in suicide assessment and prevention, crisis intervention, crisis counseling or assessment, or advanced techniques taught in social work, counseling, psychology, public health, nursing, and medicine. The book is also appropriate for mental health and health professionals in these areas.

FEATURES OF THIS BOOK

Throughout the text, several recurring features offer readers a chance to better understand and apply the material with their students, or in their own clinical practice.

Each chapter begins with a clear set of *Goals and Objectives* that are covered within that chapter.

Individual Exercises allow readers to consider their personal reactions to the material under discussion and how those reactions might impact their clinical practice.

Small Group Exercises encourage readers to compare their own reactions with others and discuss why and how differences may arise.

Case Examples depict realistic client scenarios that readers may encounter in practice, followed by questions for discussion.

Role-Plays offer readers a chance to act out the common (and often difficult) conversations and scenarios that may arise when working with suicidal clients.

A Closer Look offers more additional information and an in-depth focus on a specific topic within some sections of the text.

Key Points at the end of each chapter summarize the primary issues covered within that chapter.

Electronic Resources offer a wide variety of useful websites for further information.

Knowledge Acquisition Tests in each chapter offer readers a chance to confirm their comprehension of the material. Each test includes true-or-false, short-answer, and multiple-choice questions.

In summary, this text offers readers comprehensive, empirically grounded knowledge regarding suicidality. It is our hope that it provides a strong foundation for mental health professionals and students who may encounter and work with suicidal clients and those interested in this area. It is essential to recognize that this text does not take the place of effective supervision and training, but it can serve as a useful, practical, clinical reference.

NEW TO THIS EDITION

- Expanded coverage of the relationship between suicide and mental illness including updating to address changes introduced with the *DSM 5*. This edition also expands its coverage of suicide within the context of bipolar disorder and adds a new chapter that focuses on personality disorders.
- Expanded coverage of at-risk populations. Two new chapters have been added, highlighting the prevalence of suicide, risk and protective factors for suicide, and key issues for assessment of suicide within the veteran and military personnel and LGBTQ populations.

- New and expanded chapters examining evidence- and empirically based treatments for suicide. A new chapter on motivational interviewing and an updated and expanded chapter on interpersonal therapy explore how these treatments can be modified to address suicidality and present the most recent data regarding the effectiveness of the two approaches.
- Expanded coverage of surviving a suicide. This new edition provides a more extensive examination of the assessment, treatment, and management of suicide survivors from the perspective of both close loved ones and mental health professionals.

PART I: INTRODUCTION

Suicidal behavior is a complex phenomenon that resonates across societal and individual ethics, philosophies, cultures, ethnicities, and religions. It is important for practitioners to consider the influences and implications of the larger systems and contexts in which individual clients function and reside. Part I specifically focuses on how these larger factors relate to suicidal behavior and how they inform clinical practice and treatment. These factors are often overlooked in the assessment and treatment of suicidal individuals. However, the three chapters in Part I illustrate why it is imperative to have a clear awareness of these issues.

Chapter 1, "Ethical and Philosophical Issues in Suicide," examines the important role of ethical considerations and dilemmas related to client suicidality and clinical assessment and treatment. Chapter 2, "The Role of Culture, Race, and Ethnicity in Suicide," highlights how culture, race, and ethnicity can serve as both risk and protective factors for suicide, and it emphasizes treating suicidality from a culturally competent perspective. Chapter 3, "Religion and Suicide," considers the differential impact of Christianity, Islam, Hinduism, and Judaism as they relate to suicidal behavior, assessment, and treatment.

The issues raised in Part I are complex and can be challenging to discuss and explore. However, it is essential for a practitioner to consider not only how these factors impact his or her clients but also how they inform the manner in which the practitioner experiences, views, and understands the world as this directly influences suicide assessment and treatment.

PART II: SUICIDALITY ACROSS THE LIFE SPAN

Suicidality is experienced across the life span. The nature, risk, and protective factors of suicidality differ among the various stages of life. The assessment and treatment of suicidality is directly related to the age, developmental stage, and experiences of the client. Part II consists of three chapters that explore suicidality among children and adolescents, adults, and older adults.

Chapter 4, "Child and Adolescent Suicide," explores the identification of unique and common risk and protective factors for suicide among youth. Chapter 5, "Adult Suicide," examines the epidemiological trends, prevalence, and incident rates of adult suicidality as well as unique risk and protective factors for suicide in this age group. Chapter 6, "Older Adult Suicide," focuses on the identification of risk and protective factors unique to the aging population, which has the highest rate of suicide. Each chapter also deconstructs myths and misconceptions related to suicide within that age group.

The importance of age should not be underestimated. Age not only impacts the risk and protective factors related to a client's suicidality, but it can positively or negatively influence mental health professionals in their approach to and treatment of suicidal clients.

PART III: SUICIDE AND MENTAL ILLNESS

It is important to recognize that not everyone with a psychiatric illness is going to experience suicidality. However, 90% of individuals who complete suicide have a psychiatric diagnosis. Consequently, Part III centers on suicide across three high-risk diagnostic categories. Although many psychiatric disorders are associated with an elevated risk of suicide attempts and completions, Part III focuses specifically on mood disorders, psychotic disorders, substance disorders, and personality disorders.

Chapter 7, "Depressive and Bipolar Disorders and Suicide," examines the relationship between depression, bipolar disorder, and suicide as mood disorders are the most common psychiatric disorders associated with suicide. Chapter 8, "Schizophrenia and Suicide," provides a focused presentation of the suicide risk associated with schizophrenia. Chapter 9, "Substance-Related Disorders and Suicide," explores the relationship between substance-related disorders and risk of suicidality. Lastly, Chapter 10, "Personality Disorders and Suicide," provides a review of the relationship between personality disorders, specifically borderline personality disorder, and suicide. Knowledge of the influence of psychiatric disorders is a critical component in the assessment of suicide risk and is fundamentally related to the treatment of suicidality. Mental health practitioners need to be aware of the interaction between psychiatric symptomatology, treatment, and adherence issues when working with a suicidal client.

PART IV: AT-RISK POPULATIONS

The risk of suicide varies across individuals and groups. Certain groups of individuals are uniquely vulnerable toward and affected by suicidality. It is important for mental health professionals to have specific knowledge and awareness of these vulnerable populations.

Part IV highlights several vulnerable groups. Chapter 11, "Active Military Personnel and Veterans," focuses on the prevalence rates, risk, and protective factors and treatment considerations unique to this population. Chapter 12, "Lesbian, Gay, Bisexual, Transgender, and Queer/Questioning," similarly focuses on the prevalence rates, risk, and protective factors and treatment considerations unique to the LGBTQ population. Chapter 13, "At-Risk Groups," focuses on a number of specific groups within society that are at an elevated risk for suicidality: the homeless, Native Americans, and incarcerated individuals. These at-risk groups often experience high levels of stigma and isolation from society, frequently due to disenfranchisement, separateness, exclusion, or sociodemographic characteristics. It is essential for mental health professionals working with suicidal clients to be aware of and understand the larger context with which individuals within these groups interact.

PART V: ASSESSING SUICIDE

Effective clinical work in the field of mental health requires knowledge of suicide assessment. Although there is no universal assessment format, there are a number of key components essential to every suicide assessment. Chapter 14, "Guidelines for Suicide Risk Assessment," presents core guidelines and key components of assessing suicide risk.

PART VI: EVIDENCE-BASED TREATMENTS

Although many different approaches to suicide treatment exist, Part VI focuses on empirically supported, evidence-based psychosocial practices. The science of suicide assessment and treatment has improved dramatically in recent years leading to the establishment of several rigorous and efficacious evidence-based treatments. Part VI presents five widely used psychosocial evidence-based treatments for suicidality.

Psychopharmacology has a unique role in the treatment of suicidality. Although there is no medication that can directly prevent suicide, psychotropic medications have been successful at treating a wide number of symptoms related to suicidality, including depressed mood, hallucinations, and anxiety. These medications are often most effective in conjunction with psychosocial evidence-based treatments. Research has often found that the joint treatment approach of utilizing psychopharmacology and psychosocial evidence-based treatments can be more effective than using either one alone. The scope of Part VI is on psychosocial evidence-based practices in the assessment and treatment of suicidality.

Part VI contains five chapters. Chapter 15, "Crisis Intervention and Suicide," presents the key stages and strategies of crisis intervention. Chapter 16, "Cognitive Behavioral Therapy and Suicide," presents the core elements and techniques of cognitive behavioral therapy (CBT) in working with suicidal clients. Chapter 17, "Dialectical Behavioral Therapy and Suicide," introduces dialectical behavior therapy (DBT) as a treatment model to address suicidal individuals. Chapter 18, "Interpersonal Psychotherapy and Suicide," describes the preliminary adaptation of this emergent model of intervention with individuals experiencing suicidality. Chapter 19, "Motivational Interviewing and Suicide," explores how this evidence-based treatment has been adapted to address suicidal behavior. Part VI offers a comprehensive description of these five psychosocial evidence-based treatments for suicidality. The core elements of working from these approaches are presented in relation to the unique challenges of assessing and treating suicidality. Clinical practice expertise requires ongoing training and supervision.

PART VII: SURVIVING SUICIDE

Suicide can affect anyone. Yet, its impact is not equal across groups. Every death due to suicide has a direct and indirect effect on others. While this text focuses intensively on the assessment and treatment of suicidality, it is fundamentally important for mental health professionals to work with and support survivors of suicide, be it family members or professional colleagues. Chapter 20, "Family Survivors," examines family and friend survivors of suicide with a special focus on the grief process and approaches to working with family survivors. Chapter 21, "Professional Survivors," examines the impact of client suicide on treating clinicians.

An Answer Key for the Knowledge Acquisition Tests is available for all qualified instructors. Email textbook@springerpub.com to access the Answer Key.

PART I

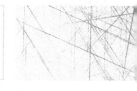

Introduction

CHAPTER ONE

ETHICAL AND PHILOSOPHICAL ISSUES IN SUICIDE

Each individual, including mental health professionals, has an ethical and philosophical stance on suicide. Perceptions and bias, which are not made explicit by the practitioner, undoubtedly will influence professional conduct (Frankena, 1980). Thus, this chapter presents ethical and philosophical issues and concerns from multiple perspectives. Specific attention is given to the issues of philosophical perspectives related to suicide, rational suicide, suicide and the law, euthanasia and physician-assisted suicide, professional ethics and suicide, media and suicide ethics, and ethics in the aftermath of a client suicide. Personal and professional conflicts are explored in relation to clinical practice throughout this chapter.

GOALS AND OBJECTIVES

An understanding of:

- The importance of personal ethical, moral, and value beliefs regarding end-of-life care in clinical practice
- The meaning of rational suicide
- The practitioners' legal and ethical responsibilities
- The professional standard of care
- The four types of euthanasia: passive, active, voluntary, and involuntary
- The implications of physician-assisted suicide (PAS)
- The professional ethical principles of autonomy or self-determination, informed consent, duty to protect, beneficence, nonmaleficence, and confidentiality in relation to end-of-life decisions
- The role of the media in suicidality
- The ethical issues related to professional conduct following the suicide of a client
- The importance of ethics when working with clients at risk for suicide

---

What do you think, feel, or believe when considering the concept of suicide? Your ethical, moral, and philosophical conceptualization of suicide will have direct and indirect influences on your clinical practice. While the act of suicide itself may be readily defined, it raises challenging and complex problems due to the numerous situations, conditions, and circumstances that can lead to it (Carasevici, 2016). Suicide has been considered noble, an important freedom, unacceptable, morally wrong, an indication of mental illness, a crime, and an offense against God (Mishna, Antle, & Regehr, 2002). In working with suicidal individuals, it is essential to candidly consider and openly understand your own ethics, morals, values, and beliefs relating to suicide, and the impact of those thoughts and attitudes on your own practice.

These questions could remain relegated to a hypothetical, theoretical, or intellectual argument if suicides or suicide attempts were uncommon occurrences rarely experienced by practitioners in their clinical practice. Although it is hoped that suicides are scarce and all can be prevented, the reality is most mental health professionals will experience at least one client suicide over the course of their careers. Studies have begun to research the phenomenon of client suicides. In survey research, 86% of community mental health teams, 46% to 67% of psychiatrists, 35% of social workers, and 22% to 40% of psychologists have reported experiencing one or more patient suicides (Alexander, Klein, Gray, Dewar, & Eagles, 2000; Chemtob, Hamada, Bauer, Kinney, & Torigoe, 1988; Chemtob, Hamada, Bauer, Torigoe, & Kinney, 1988; Kleespies, 1993; Linke, Wojciak, & Day, 2002; Ruskin, Sakinofsky, Bagby, Dickens, & Sousa, 2004).

Research has also found that experiencing a client suicide during professional training is common (Coverdale, Roberts, & Louie, 2007; Dewar, Eagles, Klein, Gray, & Alexander, 2000; Kleespies, 1993; Ruskin et al., 2004). Consequently, it is fundamentally important to be aware of your ethical and philosophical beliefs and conceptualizations, as well as the direct and indirect impact of these beliefs on your practice. While this chapter focuses on ethical and philosophical considerations and perceptions, the implications of surviving a client's suicide are explored in Chapters 20 and 21.

Individual Exercise 1.1

1. Develop a list of your personal values and beliefs as they relate to suicide (i.e., always unacceptable, acceptable under certain circumstances). In considering this list, do you feel people close to you (e.g., colleagues, peers, family) would recognize these values and beliefs in you?
2. How do you think these values and beliefs will influence your clinical practice, both positively and negatively?
3. Have your personal values remained constant over time, or have they evolved or changed over time? If they have changed, based on what?
4. Should a practitioner's values change as a result of his or her work with clients? Why or why not?

CAN SUICIDE EVER BE CONSIDERED AN ACCEPTABLE ACTION?

Can suicide be an act of competency, or is every suicide a result of a client's lack of competence (Pinch & Dougherty, 1993)? Does an individual ever have a right to die by ending his or her own life? Can suicide or suicide intervention be moral (Lester & Leenaars, 1996)? When, if ever, is suicide ethically acceptable? What is our professional duty to protect a client from himself or herself? Each practitioner will have different responses to these questions, and those responses may be subject to change over time, raising some important ethical and practical considerations.

PHILOSOPHICAL PERSPECTIVES RELATED TO SUICIDE

Philosophers have strived to conceptualize and define suicide. There are two dominant philosophical paradigms in suicidality: the Kantian and the Utilitarian perspectives (Hill, 1983; Maris, Berman, & Silverman, 2000; Mayo, 1984; Regan, 1983). According to the *Kantian perspective*, a person is a rational agent with autonomy of will, and suicide is a violation of one's duty to himself or herself (Maris et al., 2000). Therefore, individuals who complete suicide are acting in violation of the moral law and their duty to protect themselves (Brassington, 2006; Maris et al., 2000).

The *Utilitarian perspective* considers the consequences of the suicide, including the impact on family members, others, and larger society in determining the moral or ethical judgment of the action (Maris et al., 2000; Mayo, 1984; Schramme, 2013). A client's suicide that reduces pain or suffering to self and others may be morally acceptable; however, if the suicide causes more harm than good, the act is construed to be morally wrong.

These philosophical perspectives are generally thought to be in opposition, rather than on a spectrum. In clinical practice with suicidal clients and their families, it is important to consider how your philosophical perspective impacts your work.

Individual Exercise 1.2

1. Which philosophical perspective, Kantian or Utilitarian, resonates more with your personal values and beliefs?
2. Which philosophical perspective, Kantian or Utilitarian, resonates more with your professional values and beliefs?
3. How may your personal and professional philosophical perspectives conflict?
4. How might this conflict influence your work with clients expressing suicidality?
5. How would you work to resolve this discrepancy?

RATIONAL SUICIDE

Depending on their philosophical and ethical stance, individuals may argue that suicide is morally wrong and that allowing an individual to suicide or failing to prevent suicide is no different from killing that individual (Donagan, 1977; Hendin, 1982; Heyd & Bloch, 1999; Ho, 2014; Mishara & Weisstub, 2013; Schwyn, 1976). Such individuals would argue that under no circumstances is suicide an acceptable solution. Furthermore, suicide is generally perceived as an act committed by irrational individuals affected by psychiatric illness or by those under the influence of an illicit substance. Several studies, in fact, found that as many as 90% of those who committed suicide were mentally ill at their time of death (Barraclough, Bunch, Nelson, & Salisbury, 1974; Brent et al., 1993; Hendin, 1982; Isometsa et al., 1995; Kaplan & Harrow, 1996; Robins, 1981; Strakowski, McElroy, Keck, & West, 1996). Additionally, research indicates that there tends to be a great deal of ambivalence among individuals who attempt suicide (Daigle, 2005; Erazo, Baumert, & Ladwig, 2005; Litman, 1996; Lynch, Cheavens, Morse, & Rosenthal, 2004) and that a suicide attempt is often a means to communicate a problem (Lizardi et al., 2007; Organization, 2007; Paris, 2002). Is it not imperative, then, to intervene in every instance of attempted suicide, given the chance that mental illness may have influenced the decision to commit the suicidal act or that some ambivalence may be present in the individual? Should we not explore the ambivalence and support problem-solving and coping skills?

Despite the evidence, some still argue that suicide may actually be a rational decision and should be a matter of individual choice (Brock, 1985; Fintzy, 1993; Leeman, 2004; Maris, 1982; Motto, 1999; Szasz, 1999; Werth, 1999). The case of Nico Speijers is often used to exemplify the concept of *rational suicide*. In 1981, Speijers, a suicidologist and suicide prevention advocate, committed suicide, leaving behind a suicide note expressing his decision to end his life in the face of terminal illness and debilitating pain. Speijers had just the year prior published a (1980) book, *Aiding Suicide*, detailing circumstances under which suicide should not be prevented (Motto, 1999). These conditions are the following:

1. The decision to commit suicide is not made under pressure but rather as a result of free will.
2. The individual is suffering from unbearable pain with no relief expected.
3. The wish to end one's life is ongoing.
4. The individual is competent at the time the decision is made.
5. No unnecessary or preventable harm to others is caused by the act.
6. The helper should be a qualified health practitioner or MD if drugs are utilized.
7. The helper should seek advice/consultation from colleagues.
8. The process of the suicide should be documented and the documents submitted to the proper authorities.

Are these conditions sufficient to suggest that intervention should not be taken when a client expresses suicidality? Who should decide the answers to these questions, the client or the practitioner? In considering the concept of rational suicide, it is imperative to understand the legality of suicide and one's legal responsibility as a helping professional. Further review of one's professional code of ethics should also contribute to determining an answer to these questions.

Case Vignette 1.1

As a mental health clinician within the Crisis Team in a large and busy urban hospital, you are frequently called into the Emergency Department to conduct mental health assessments. After being paged to the emergency room (ER), the attending physician informs you that the referred patient has been medically cleared after a significant overdose attempt. The patient, a 64-year-old male, has no prior reported psychiatric history or past suicide attempts. The attempt would have been lethal had not his adult daughter and son-in-law, with whom he resides, unexpectedly returned home early from visiting friends in a nearby town and discovered the patient, unresponsive in his room, wearing a suit. Beside him on his nightstand were sealed letters to each of his family members, his organized bank records, and his will. The ER doctor noted that the patient is stable and oriented. He has slept off the effects of the overdose and charcoal he received upon admission. His blood results are fine and his toxicology report is clear, with no trace of alcohol or illicit narcotics.

In reading his medical chart and receiving a complete update from the attending physician and ER nurse, you learned that the patient has a chronic and deteriorating pain condition. The patient has managed his condition for 21 years. Over the years, his ability to work or engage in functions of daily living has continued to worsen. He is now on exceptionally strong pain medications and can rarely manage to leave his room to eat, watch television, or interact with his family. His condition is terminal and will continue to decline, perhaps for many years. His constant level of pain will continue to escalate. His wife passed away 8 years earlier due to cancer, at which time he moved in with his daughter and her family. The ER nurse stated that the patient, Lee, is a nice and gentle man in a tremendous amount of physical pain. The doctor noted that Lee is a very strong and dignified individual who has managed his pain well over the years. The doctor also stated that, beyond his pain condition, Lee is in good health and that he expected him to live for many more years. However, the doctor did think Lee would have to be placed in a nursing home within a year. The doctor noted that if the patient had not been brought to the hospital, he would not have survived another hour or two.

In the examination room, you find Lee in a hospital bed, sitting up with his hair combed, gently talking to his adult daughter, who is sitting in a bedside chair. After introducing yourself and describing your role of conducting an assessment, the daughter, Karen, recounts that her father has always been a strong and independent person until recently. She tells of finding him yesterday after returning early from visiting friends. She notes how fortunate it was that her friend's son had become very ill during their visit, and that she and her husband had come home hours before they had intended. Both report that he has never attempted suicide nor experienced any psychiatric or mental health problems. While it is clearly observable that he is in pain, Lee contributes to the assessment. After a few minutes, Lee states in a quiet voice how much he loves his daughter and her family and then requests continuing the assessment alone. Karen, holding back tears, kisses her father on his forehead and leaves the room.

Lee states that he had fully intended to die and was disheartened that his daughter had returned unexpectedly early and found him. In fact, he had carefully planned his death for nearly 3 months. He describes suicide as a morally and personally repugnant idea, but it was best for everyone. Twenty-one years ago, when he was diagnosed with his condition, he knew this moment would come. Over the years, he struggled to maintain a normal and productive life, but, with each passing year, his condition deteriorated and his pain increased.

When his wife was diagnosed with cancer, they had agreed that he would continue to support their children and grandchildren until he became a burden. After she died, he noted that he wanted to end his life, but was determined to honor his wife's request to support and care for the family. Four months ago, his treating doctor had informed him that he would soon have to be placed in an expensive nursing home. Also, his pain medications, which were becoming increasingly stronger, were no longer blocking much of the pain. Recently, his daughter spoke of quitting her job to be better able to care for him. Lee states that she has her own family to look after, and while he loves his daughter, the time has come for him to die. Lee tells you that he understands your job is to assess him and prevent his suicide. He agrees to accept any treatment options; however, he also notes that regardless of what you plan, he would quietly and effectively complete suicide over the next few weeks.

1. *Is this an example of rational suicide? Why or why not?*
2. *Which of Speijers's eight conditions of rational suicide are present in the aforementioned case vignette?*
3. *What action would you take as a professional practitioner in this case vignette?*
4. *Would your stance in regard to Lee change if you were his friend? His family member? If so, how?*
5. *Would your personal ethics, values, and beliefs create any potential dilemmas in regard to your professional obligation?*
6. *How would you support this practitioner, if you were his or her supervisor?*

ROLE-PLAY 1.1

Using Case Vignette 1.1 of Lee, engage in a role-play in which you would propose and present a discharge plan and treatment options to Lee.

SUICIDE AND THE LAW

The past decades have seen a dramatic shift in malpractice lawsuits regarding suicide from a focus largely on inpatient institutions and practitioners toward an overrepresentation of lawsuits against outpatient practitioners (Jobes & Berman, 1993; Litman, 1982). It is critical to be aware of your legal and ethical responsibilities as a practitioner, particularly concerning malpractice liability (S. R. Feldman, Moritz, & Benjamin, 2005).

Determining Liability

Regardless of personal values or ethics, practitioners are legally expected to actively prevent the suicide of a client. Practitioners are expected to uphold their standard of care or duty to care, which includes making reasonable efforts to prevent suicide of a client. The standard of care is legally defined as the duty to employ the degree of skill and care as would be used by a typical practitioner in a similar circumstance (Gutheil, 1992; Jobes & Berman, 1993).

As the act of suicide is nearly impossible to predict, four key elements are often present for a claim of malpractice to be supported. These are (a) the presence of a professional relationship, (b) a violation of the standard of care, (c) the violation resulting in damages or harm, and (d) a direct causal relationship between the practitioner's omissions and the suicidal act of the client (Berman, 2006; Bongar, 2002; Bongar & Greaney, 1994; Cantor & McDermott, 1994).

In malpractice suits, the standard of care is evaluated retrospectively via review of clinical records and available testimony. There are several areas that are considered failures of the standard of care that can result in a practitioner being held liable for malpractice (Bongar, Maris, Berman, & Litman, 1992; Gutheil, 1992; Waltzer, 1980). These include failures to perform the following:

1. Assess risk as the most obvious violation of the standard of care.
2. Keep accurate, up-to-date records.
3. Assess for suicide risk at the time of the last professional contact.
4. Conduct or refer client for a psychological evaluation.
5. Secure records from prior psychiatric treatment.
6. Develop an adequate treatment plan.
7. Provide adequate treatment.
8. Refer to inpatient hospitalization, voluntarily or involuntarily, when indicated.
9. Protect patient from known danger to self.
10. Possess the training, knowledge, and skill necessary to treat and assess for suicidality.

Recommendations to Minimize Risk of Malpractice

Essential guidelines have been developed as a result of the proliferation of suicide malpractice lawsuits in outpatient care settings (Bongar, 1991). Key recommendations that should not be overlooked include the following:

1. Conduct an assessment of suicide risk with every patient. As suicidal behavior cannot be predicted, no client can be determined to be free of risk without a thorough assessment.
2. Maintain comprehensive records. A lack of documentation can be damaging to a practitioner's defense as there will be no evidence of the standard of care he or she maintained in respect to the client's treatment.
3. Seek records from client's prior treatment experiences. Proper assessment of the suicide risk must include consideration of prior suicidal behavior. Relying on a client's personal report of suicide history is insufficient when it has been established that prior treatment existed.
4. Suicide risk is increased in offspring of individuals with psychiatric illness and a history of suicidality (Brent et al., 1994; Gould, Fisher, Parides, Flory, & Shaffer, 1996; Kovacs, Obrosky, Gatsonis, & Richards, 1997; Schulsinger, Kety, Rosenthal, &

Wender, 1979; Tsuang, 1983; Weissman, Fendrich, Warner, & Wickramaratne, 1992; Wender et al., 1986). Thus, proper evaluation of a client's risk for suicide should include assessment of family history of mental disorders and psychiatric hospitalization.

5. Establish relevant *Diagnostic and Statistical Manual of Mental Disorders* (5th ed.; *DSM-5*; American Psychiatric Association, 2013) diagnoses. There is a differential risk of suicide associated with psychiatric illnesses (see Part IV). Comprehensive assessment of *DSM-5* psychiatric disorders will shed light on the degree of suicide risk in relation to other psychosocial characteristics with which the client presents.

Small Group Exercise 1.1

1. In groups of four to five, use Case Vignette 1.2 (later in the chapter) to discuss whether the prescribing physician could be considered liable for malpractice.
2. What violations of the standards of care (listed earlier) might apply, if any?
3. If you were a mental health practitioner on the physician's team, what steps could you have engaged in to prevent Sam's action (use Case Vignette 1.2 provided later in the chapter)?

EUTHANASIA AND PHYSICIAN-ASSISTED SUICIDE

There are four types of euthanasia: passive, active, voluntary, and involuntary. *Passive euthanasia* involves the withdrawal or withholding of artificial life-support or medical treatments that may prolong life, whereas *active euthanasia* is an act taken to shorten life (Smokowski & Wodarski, 1996). An individual requesting assistance from anyone in ending his or her life is considered to be engaging in *voluntary euthanasia*; however, intentionally causing the death of an individual, whether, competent, incompetent, or unaware, without informed consent or explicit request, is considered *involuntary euthanasia* (Csikai, 1999). Only passive euthanasia is widely accepted by health care practitioners, family members, society, and the law. *Physician-assisted suicide (PAS)* is the provision of suicidal means, such as prescribed medications, to an individual who is otherwise able to suicide (Csikai, 1999; Smokowski & Wodarski, 1996). If a physician administers the lethal dose following the request of the patient, this is considered active voluntary euthanasia (Smokowski & Wodarski, 1996).

Euthanasia, PAS, and the Law

Across the United States and throughout the world, the increasing legalization of euthanasia and PAS has challenged the attitudes and practices of health care providers and the larger public. In the United States, as of 2016, five states (California, Oregon, Montana, Vermont, and Washington) have passed laws supporting PAS, but not euthanasia. Globally, euthanasia or PAS can be legally practiced in Canada, Colombia, Belgium, Luxembourg, and the Netherlands, with Switzerland allowing only PAS (Emanuel, 2016). Reportedly, fewer than 20% of U.S. physicians described having received requests for euthanasia or PAS, whereas in the Netherlands and Belgium, over 50% of physicians reported receiving such requests (Emanuel, 2016). Beyond the five states of the United States, countries that have discussed, debated, and have passed laws related to euthanasia and PAS currently include Argentina, Australia, Chile, Croatia, Cyprus, Denmark, Estonia, Finland, France, Germany, Greece, India, Israel, Italy, Poland, Spain, Sweden, Taiwan, Uganda, United Kingdom, and West Indies (Bendiane et al., 2009; Gielen, 2008; Giese, 2009; Levene, 2011; Rosenfeld, 2004; Schoonman, van Thiel, & van Delden, 2014; Snijdewind,

2014; Sorta-Bilajac, 2008; Tamayo-Velazquez, Simon-Lorda, & Cruz-Piqueras, 2012; Trankle, 2014).

In 1997, the U.S. Supreme Court unanimously ruled (*Washington v. Glucksberg; Vaccpo v. Quill*) that there is neither a constitutional prohibition nor a constitutional right to euthanasia and PAS (Breitbart & Rosenfeld, 1999; Emanuel, 2002). The Ninth and Second U.S. Circuit Courts of Appeals in Washington State and New York State have also ruled in lawsuits brought before them that laws prohibiting PAS are unconstitutional (Drickamer, Lee, & Ganzini, 1997). In 1998, Oregon passed the Death With Dignity Act legalizing PAS for state residents with a terminal illness who voluntarily request these actions (Quill, Meier, Block, & Billings, 1998; Sullivan, Hedberg, & Fleming, 2000).

Euthanasia, PAS, and Attitudes

In their analysis of opinion polls between 1936 and 2002, Allen and colleagues (2006) found that Americans supported euthanasia and PAS. Since 1973, the majority of polled Americans, when asked "when a person has a disease that cannot be cured, do you think doctors should be allowed by law to end the patient's life by some painless means if the patient and his family request it?" supported this position (Allen et al., 2006). In a similar survey study among terminally ill patients and their caregivers, a majority supported PAS, but only a small proportion seriously considered taking such actions themselves (Emanuel, Fairclough, & Emanuel, 2000). This is consistent with other research that found that only approximately 10% of the patients in palliative care report suicidal thoughts (Mosich & Müller-Busch, 2014).

For some, there is a moral distinction between killing or ending-a-life (e.g., withdrawing life-supporting or life-sustaining treatment) and allowing-to-die (e.g., withholding life-supporting or life-sustaining treatment). Some individuals posit that PAS or physician withdrawal of life-sustaining treatment cannot be morally equated to voluntary active euthanasia (Huddle, 2013). This concept of "doing" versus "allowing" remains one of the critical aspects of the debate around active euthanasia and PAS (Bishop, 2006a, 2006b; Huddle, 2013; McLachlan, 2010; Shaw, 2007). In a study comparing the general public to mental health professionals (physicians and nurses), results found that, in general, life-ending actions are more acceptable to lay people than to the health professionals; however, for both groups acceptability is highest when the patient is experiencing enduring physical suffering, is higher when patients end their own lives rather than when physicians complete the act, and, when physicians are completing the act, is higher when patients have clearly expressed a desire to die rather than when they have not (voluntary vs. involuntary euthanasia; Guedj et al., 2005).

It is important to consider whether the condition or illness that the client is managing is acute versus a potential chronically debilitating condition. Some argue that a distinction should be made between those individuals suffering from severe psychiatric disorders and lacking mental capacity and competent patients suffering from enduring pain and incurable physical illness seeking to end their suffering (Macleod, 2012). It has been argued that a person with a serious mental disorder (SMI) is nonautonomous, and therefore, suicide prevention is likely to be deemed legally and morally justified. Further, because some consider psychogenic pain as less real than physical pain, the presence of a mental illness invariably means that a desire to die is irrational and inauthentic (Hewitt, 2013). However, research has shown that some people managing mental illnesses can be rational and that psychological pain is of equal significance to physical suffering (Hewitt, 2013). In accordance, there is a call for greater incorporation of mental health professionals into end-of-life decisions and considerations made by medical professionals (Deschepper, Distelmans, & Bilsen, 2014; Groenewoud et al., 2004; Kelly & McLoughlin, 2002; Macleod, 2012; Sjöberg & Lindholm, 2003). Thus, should individuals managing a serious mental illness, who are rational and in significant pain, not have the option of *rational suicide*?

Not relegated to public opinion, the debate over euthanasia and PAS has been waged for many decades across a number of fields including, but not limited to, medicine, health care, mental health, individual rights, human rights, religion, professional codes of ethics, and the law. Each practitioner holds very specific personal ethical beliefs regarding euthanasia and PAS. As such, health care and mental health practitioners may face a number of ethical dilemmas stemming from clients considering euthanasia and PAS and should be aware of these issues and their own personal ethics and values. It is necessary to realize that what you believe will directly and indirectly impact your practice. For example, in a survey on the attitudes of nurses, 75% personally felt that PAS may be justified in select cases, but only 46% would be willing to participate if PAS were legalized (Kowalski, 1997). A similar survey with U.S. oncologists found that a willingness to perform PAS was lower than the support for the procedure (Emanuel, Fairclough, Clarridge, et al., 2000; Hilden et al., 2001). Others found that 80% of geriatricians, but only 52% of intensive care physicians, considered active voluntary euthanasia as never justified ethically (Dickinson, Lancaster, Clark, Ahmedzai, & Noble, 2002).

Individual Exercise 1.3

1. Do you agree with the law regarding PAS? Why or why not?
2. If you do support PAS, what are the boundaries or limits of your support? For example, do you feel all clients have a right to choose suicide? Is it limited to those who are terminal and in pain? Does the client's physical versus mental nature of his or her illness influence your determination?
3. Would you participate in PAS? Why or why not?
4. How would you work with a client requesting PAS in a state where it is legal?

Euthanasia, PAS, and Guidelines for Ethical Practice

Many mental health professional organizations, such as the American Psychiatric Association, American Psychological Association, National Association of Social Workers (NASW), and American Counseling Association, are beginning to develop guidelines for members working with clients considering PAS (Werth, 1999). However, each organization has a different perspective on addressing these ethical issues. It is important to understand the professional stance of your governing body.

For example, the National Association of Social Workers (NASW) *Code of Ethics* (2000), Standard 1.02, states that social workers have a responsibility to help clients assert their rights of self-determination (NASW, 2000). According to Mackelprang and Mackelprang (2005), this "suggests that, for terminally ill people who are capable of making decisions, the ethical responsibility to promote self-determination outweighs the social workers' responsibilities to avoid harm" (Mackelprang & Mackelprang, 2005; p. 321). While self-determination is a primary principle, Csikai (1999) iterates that social workers "must be well informed of and comply with the laws of their states concerning end-of-life decisions, including living wills, durable powers of attorney for health care, and laws concerning physician assisted suicide" (pp. 55–56). NASW also dictates that social workers should discuss all options with clients and families in end-of-life situations (Csikai, 1999).

However, the NASW does not articulate clear procedures or provide guidance for when social workers should become involved with terminally ill clients (Allen et al., 2006). Consequently, in working with terminally ill patients considering PAS, social workers may need, at minimum, to (a) understand the implications of their own personal ethics; (b) determine informed consent; (c) assess the client's self-determination and his or her individual and family's wishes; (d) review all options with client and family; (e) work with the larger health care team; (f) consult with their supervisor, professional organization, and workplace policy and procedures; (g) understand the laws governing their state; and, if necessary, (h) consult with legal counsel.

PROFESSIONAL ETHICS AND SUICIDE

Clearly, the law overwhelmingly obliges practitioners to intervene to prevent suicidal acts. Professional values, those we accept when we choose to enter a profession, serve as yet another guideline for proper behavior that practitioners are expected to follow. Professional codes of ethics define a practitioner's ethical obligations as helping professionals. Ethical codes consist of multiple principles that serve to protect a client (Rosenbluth, Kleinman, & Lowy, 1995; Wagle, Ede, Craig, & Bottum, 2004) and to guide a practitioner through times of conflict involving morals, values, and beliefs (Sasson, 2000). While differences exist, the fundamental principles proposed by the main codes of ethics of the helping professions (social work, psychology, psychiatry, and medicine) share several fundamental features. The ethical principles most relevant when considering a suicidal patient include *autonomy* or *self-determination, informed consent, duty to protect, beneficence, nonmaleficence*, and *confidentiality*.

Autonomy

Autonomy is one of the foremost principles that affect a practitioner's course of action regarding a suicidal client. The principle of self-determination involves the client's right to take action rooted in his or her own goals, desires, and wishes (Reamer, 1983). Suicide often occurs in those with mental illness. Thus, granting autonomy to individuals to act on suicidal thoughts and/or feelings is considered, by some, allowing a noncompetent individual to make life-threatening decisions. Respecting one's individual rights might be better served by recognizing their vulnerability and strengthening their resources. In fact, the NASW *Code of Ethics* (2000) permits social workers to limit clients' self-determination when their action or potential actions pose a serious, foreseeable, and imminent risk to themselves or to others.

Informed Consent

The principle of autonomy grows directly out of the doctrine of informed consent, having competent understanding of risks, benefits, and alternatives from which a client can make a decision regarding an appropriate course of action (Beauchamp, 1999). The process of informed consent recognizes the importance of autonomy, of individuals making their own decisions (Bell & Clark, 1998). Prevention of suicide is ethically justified by suggesting that the suicidal person is not competent to give informed consent and to make decisions regarding his or her care (Chadwick & Tadd, 1992), as suicidal behavior is considered to be the byproduct of mental illness (Barraclough et al., 1974; Brent et al., 1993; Chadwick & Tadd, 1992; Hendin, 1982; Isometsa et al., 1995; Kaplan & Harrow, 1996; Robins, 1981; Strakowski, McElroy, Keck, & West, 1996).

Duty to Protect

In entering a therapeutic relationship with a client, practitioners accept certain responsibilities, including the duty to protect the client from harming himself or herself

(Packman & Harris, 1998; Welfel, 2002; Werth & Rogers, 2005). However, how each practitioner applies this duty to protect with a client who is suicidal varies considerably. It has been argued that practitioners should always intervene to protect when a client raises the possibility of self-harm or suicide (Elitzur, 1995). Conversely, psychiatrist Thomas Szasz forwarded the position that clients have a right to decide for themselves whether they wish to die without the protection and intervention of a practitioner (Maris et al., 2000).

Clearly, how one ethically or professionally understands this duty to protect is open to interpretation. Werth and Rogers (2005) have provided some guidelines for the determination of this duty. Specifically, they propose that (a) this duty should apply when a client is engaging in serious self-harm or death within a short period of time, and (b) the best method to protect is to assess for impaired judgment and apply appropriate treatment interventions (Werth & Rogers, 2005).

Confidentiality

Confidentiality is a major area for practitioners as far as suicide is concerned. Most codes of ethics require practitioners to breach confidentiality if their clients represent a danger to themselves or others. Therapists are ethically, and in all states legally, obligated to disclose if the client is homicidal. The responsibility of protecting individuals from harm that may be inflicted by another individual does not frequently pose as an ethical dilemma. However, breaching confidentiality when one poses a threat to self, as is the case with suicide, often results in an ethical conflict (Rosenbluth, Kleinman, & Lowy, 1995; Wagle, Ede, Craig, & Bottum, 2004). In these instances, the principles of beneficence and nonmaleficence can guide the practitioner.

Beneficence

This principle represents the concept of doing the greatest good possible. Practitioners have an ethical responsibility to strive for the well-being of clients. Beneficence should take precedence over autonomy, as the death of an individual would not generally be considered a "good" action (Rosenbluth, Kleinman, & Lowy, 1995; Wagle, Ede, Craig, & Bottum, 2004).

Nonmaleficence

Practitioners have a legal and ethical obligation to protect clients from harm. The principle of nonmaleficence, minimizing or preventing harm, requires a practitioner to take whatever action necessary to prevent a client from taking his or her own life. The practitioner is obligated to work toward the improvement of a client's quality of life and well-being, although this responsibility often conflicts with a client's ability to be independent and make decisions about his or her own life. In the case of a suicidal client, practitioners often find themselves in a paternalistic position (Abramson, 1985; Kelly, 1994). Reamer (1983) provides a framework for making ethical decisions in times of conflict particularly regarding the conflict between supporting and limiting one's autonomy. He suggests that while social workers should carefully avoid excessive intrusion into the lives of clients, paternalism may be justified in certain circumstances. These circumstances include when (a) harmful consequences may result from supporting a client's autonomy that may be irreversible, (b) placing temporary restrictions may potentially generate a wider degree of freedom for the client, and (c) the immediate need to rescue a client from harm exists. Suicidal behavior certainly would fall among these categories. Understanding fully one's responsibilities as dictated by law and one's professional code of ethics can guide a practitioner to take action to prevent a client from acting on suicidal impulses and to feel justified in doing so.

1. According to your personal perspective, rank in order the ethical principles (autonomy or self-determination, informed consent, duty to protect, beneficence, nonmaleficence, and confidentiality) from most important to least important.
2. Justify your ordering of the ethical principles.
3. Consider the implications of your answers for your work with suicidal clients, who may have very different personal perspectives.

Case Vignette 1.2

Samantha, who prefers to go by Sam, is a 46-year-old White female widow with no prior psychiatric history. She was admitted to the adult inpatient psychiatry unit of an urban hospital following an attempted suicide. As the social worker on the unit, your role is to conduct meetings with the client and her family about the factors that led up to her inpatient admission. Prior to scheduling a meeting with significant others in Sam's life, you meet with Sam to conduct an assessment to further understand Sam's presenting situation and to determine who would be the most appropriate member to invite to a family session. Sam has been on the unit for less than a day when you meet with her in the small interview room on the unit. She is disheveled, makes poor eye contact, and is hesitant to meet with you. After describing your role, Sam's first words to you are "you've got the wrong gal. I have no one to ask to come to meet with you." Upon further exploration you learn the following:

Sam is the only child. Her parents, now deceased, were her closest friends growing up. Her mother, Anne, a stay-at-home mom, and her father, Benjamin, a tailor, were loving, warm, supportive, hardworking individuals. Sam was encouraged to be hardworking, to value the importance of education. Neither Sam's mother nor father had attended college, and Sam was groomed to be the first in the family who would do so. Sam, in fact, was very dedicated to her studies and despite the fact that she held a job, managed to graduate from college in 3 years. College was a very happy time in Sam's life. She recalls having a full social network. College is also where she met Richard, her future husband. Richard was Sam's first serious boyfriend. He was an artist and her complete opposite. She adored Richard and felt he was the "love of her life."

After college, Sam got a job in an investment banking firm. While she did not receive an MBA, she managed to work her way up through the company to the position of Managing Director and earned nearly a million dollars a year. Richard continued with his art. It came as a great surprise to Sam when Richard informed her that he had a "once in a lifetime job opportunity" to run a small art gallery in the Southwest. They knew no one there and Sam would have to leave her job. It would be the first time in 32 years she would be unemployed. While the idea was scary, she would do anything to support Richard. The move was the "greatest thing that could have happened." Sam, for the first time in her life, felt truly at ease. She decided not to find a job and instead developed her own hobby, literature. Sam became an avid reader and even dabbled at writing.

Sam and Richard lived a very quiet life. They never had any children and never felt like they were missing out on anything, "We were all we needed." They never made any close friends in the town to which they moved but that was also not something they missed. Sam felt they had the "perfect life. But perfect never lasts."

Five years after they moved, Richard became ill and was diagnosed with a terminal illness. The doctors gave him 2 to 3 years to live but the illness progressed rapidly and within 8 months of his diagnosis he died. Sam "died that day, too." She never recovered from his death which, at the time of admission, was 2 years earlier. She moved back to the city they had left 7 years prior but could not manage to get a job and make any friends. She lived a solitary life; the life built around Richard was gone. She struggled for 2 years to make meaning out of his death and to figure out what she "was being punished for." She could no longer find a reason to live.

Three weeks prior to her admission, Sam decided she would end her life. She came up with an elaborate plan. She went to the dentist complaining of terrible sensitivity to pain in one of her teeth, and was informed that she needed a root canal. After having the procedure, she saved up the prescribed pain medication. A week later, she called her physician to explain that she had just had a root canal and that her dentist was out of town for the next week but that she continued to experience severe pain. Her doctor prescribed pain medication on the condition that Sam see her dentist upon his return from vacation. She then spent the next week paying all of her bills, reviewing photos of her husband, and mailing his artwork to the gallery in the Southwest. Sam became at ease with the idea that her life was going to end and felt she would finally be reunited with Richard. The night prior to her admission, she overdosed on pain medications.

Sam's well-planned suicide would have been successful had her superintendent not entered her apartment to check for a suspected leak in Sam's bathroom. Sam does not regret her attempted suicide and is "angry" that the superintendent interrupted her. She understands that some may find suicide to be the "easy way out" but she feels it "is the only thing that makes sense." Sam explains that there is no one on whom she can call to attend a family session because "the only people she ever cared about are dead." She understands that medication and therapy can make some people feel better but feels strongly that she has "nothing to feel better about, so why bother." She is unwilling to comply with the treatment team's decision to begin medication, and a decision has to be made as to whether or not to seek court-ordered treatment to medicate her against her will.

1. *Should a court-order mandating treatment be obtained? Why or why not?*
2. *What professional values and ethics guide your decision?*
3. *How would your personal ethics, values, and beliefs influence your decision?*
4. *How can you support Sam's right to self-determination and informed consent while still upholding your professional responsibilities?*

ROLE-PLAY 1.2

Using Case Vignette 1.2 of Sam, engage in a role-play in which you would present the possibility of court-ordered mandated treatment to Sam. One participant plays the role of Sam, the other plays the role of a mental health practitioner discussing the treatment.

MEDIA AND SUICIDE ETHICS

Can a newspaper article, television news story, or video clip on the Internet cause or encourage an individual to attempt suicide? A recent review identified 28 countries where media guidelines on suicide reporting exist, but fewer than 20 countries' recommendations were listed in the national press codex (Erlangsen, 2013). In and of itself, reading or viewing a story about someone else attempting or committing suicide is generally not sufficient to cause an individual to attempt suicide (World Health Organization [WHO], 2000). However, research informs us that if an individual has a preexisting vulnerability to suicide, such as a mental illness, he or she may be more sensitive to suicide reporting and may be more inclined to attempt suicide, as a result of exposure to a suicide report (Etzersdirfer & Sonneck, 1998; Pirkis & Blood, 2001). Research has also indicated an increase in the rate of suicide as suicide reports in newspapers and television increase (Motto, 1967, 1970; Phillips, 1974, 1982; Wasserman, 1984). In particular, researchers found a substantial increase in the number of suicides within the 10-day period following the highlighting of a suicide in television news. What, then, is the ethical responsibility of the media in regard to suicide? Can editorial freedom cross the line into an ethical violation?

Clearly, in an era dominated by 24-hour news, the Internet, and webcasts, the media plays a crucial role in the transfer of knowledge. Social media, including Facebook, Twitter, Snapchat, Instagram, and others, has brought new challenges as messages are distributed to large numbers of recipients by people unaware of any press-reporting guidelines on suicide (Erlangsen, 2013). How the media reports information and transfers knowledge has become a source of much contention, particularly as it relates to reports of suicide in newspapers, television, and, increasingly, in social media. Concerns center on the detailed accounts of suicide events (attempted suicide and completed suicide) and the fear that such reports will motivate vulnerable individuals to copy those events, often referred to as the "contagion" or "Werther effect" (Alvarez, 1975; Phillips, 1974). There is a fear that, in an attempt to grab readers, sensational headlines, photos of the deceased and glorified accounts of death may lead to more unnecessary deaths by suicide (Blood & Pirkis, 2007; Motto, 1970; Wasserman, 1984). Additionally, in the rush to meet deadlines and put out a story, information may be presented as fact that has not actually been confirmed. Are these ethical violations or just detailed news required in an increasingly competitive market?

The effect of media is not limited to newspapers, radio, and television. In this ever-growing electronic era, the impact of the Internet is undeniable (Alao, Soderberg, Pohl, & Alao, 2006; Baume, Cantor, & Rolfe, 1997). Websites posting specific instructions on how to attempt suicide by various means can be found in multiples. With a simple click of a mouse, an individual can be directed to a web page that accurately describes how to end one's life. Evidence-based research on the influence of the Internet on suicide attempt risk is limited but should be the focus of future research as the Internet continues to grow and its influence expands to new and younger audiences.

A recent discussion paper on media recommendations by Maloney and colleagues (2013) on reporting suicide noted that fewer than 25% of media recommendations include the following factors that may prevent imitation:

- Not mentioning the name and characteristics of the suicidal person
- Not citing or printing photographs of suicide notes
- Not referring to online suicide forums
- Not mentioning suicide pacts
- Not mentioning suicides that are close in time or space (suicide clusters)
- Not mentioning an accumulation of suicidal acts at certain locations (hot spots)
- Not mentioning positive consequences of suicidal behavior
- Referring to self-help groups

According to the WHO, minimizing media reporting of suicide is one of its key strategies for suicide prevention. The media is in a position to decrease the incidence of tragic deaths due to suicide by reporting suicide in an appropriate and accurate manner (WHO, 2000). Furthermore, the media can report on the warning signs for suicide and convey the means for seeking help. This suggests that when reports of suicide do not follow these guidelines, ethical boundaries are in fact being crossed, as the reason for the reporting has shifted from conveying matters of public interest to vying for customers.

Guidelines for Ethical Suicide Reporting in the Media

In light of these findings, several main principles have been proposed as guidelines to follow for ethical reporting of suicide. These include avoiding the following:

1. Sensationalizing headlines
2. Describing the means employed in the suicide event

3. Mentioning names or publishing photos to limit the perception that suicide is a means to draw attention to oneself
4. Oversimplifying the cause of suicide; suicide is complex and often is the result of a combination of factors
5. Sanitizing when mental illness and/or substance abuse are involved
6. Describing the suicide event as a "success" or as a "solution" (Canadian Association for Suicide Prevention, 2003; The Samaritans, 2005; WHO, 2000).

ETHICS IN THE AFTERMATH OF A CLIENT SUICIDE

What happens to the practitioner when a client completes suicide? Although professionals are very effective in assessing and treating suicidal patients, there will be clients in treatment who successfully complete suicide. This phenomenon is often neglected or minimized in practice, and literature regarding how professionals manage a client's suicide is limited (Gitlin, 1999). Following a client's suicide, practitioners' reactions may vary from grief, shock, denial, distress, depression, isolation, self-blame, a sense of failure, strain on their personal and professional lives, fear of another suicide, and loss of confidence, to avoidance of triggering stimuli (Alexander et al., 2000; Cooper, 1995; Dewar et al., 2000; Eagles, Klein, Gray, Dewar, & Alexander, 2001; Halligan & Corcoran, 2001; Maltsberger, 1992; Spiegelman & Werth, 2005; Strom-Gottfried & Mowbray, 2006).

Though the literature is relatively limited on ethically managing this issue, a number of professions, including social workers (D. Feldman, 1987; Strom-Gottfried & Mowbray, 2006; Ting, Sanders, Jacobson, & Power, 2006), medical doctors (Alexander et al., 2000; Dewar et al., 2000; Eagles et al., 2001; Halligan & Corcoran, 2001; Talseth & Gilje, 2007), nurses (Cooper, 1995; Gilje, Talseth, & Norberg, 2005), and psychologists (Kleespies, 1993; Spiegelman & Werth, 2005), have begun to investigate the impact of a client suicide on practitioners. Please go to Chapter 21 for a full discussion of this important issue.

SUMMARY

The majority of clinical practitioners will encounter a suicidal client in the course of their careers. It is essential to be aware of personal values, ethics and philosophical beliefs, professional ethical responsibilities, legal obligations, and the manner in which these factors interact to influence the course of action that would be taken when faced with a suicidal client. The personal and professional stance of providers can be a significant ethical challenge as providers weigh the expressions of patient wishes versus their own views of beneficence, nonmaleficence, and professional integrity (Venkat & Drori, 2014). Ethics matter.

KEY POINTS

1. In working with a suicidal client, it is essential to candidly consider and openly understand your own ethics, morals, values, and beliefs relating to suicide and the impact of these thoughts and attitudes on your own practice.
2. Some argue that suicide may be a rational decision under certain circumstances and should be a matter of individual choice.
3. It is critical to be aware of the legal and ethical responsibilities related to the role of a practitioner, particularly concerning malpractice liability.

(continued)

KEY POINTS (*continued*)

4. Practitioners are expected to uphold their professional standard of care, despite their personal beliefs.
5. Regardless of personal values or ethics, practitioners are legally expected to actively prevent the suicide of a client.
6. There are four types of euthanasia: passive, active, voluntary, and involuntary.
7. There is neither a constitutional prohibition nor a constitutional right to euthanasia and PAS.
8. The ethical principles most relevant when considering a suicidal patient include autonomy or self-determination, informed consent, duty to protect, beneficence, nonmaleficence, and confidentiality.
9. Minimizing unethical media reporting of suicide is one of the key strategies for suicide prevention.
10. The media has the potential to play an important role in reducing suicide by reporting on warning signs and how/where to seek treatment.

ELECTRONIC RESOURCES

RATIONAL SUICIDE

Suicide prevention, awareness, and support

www.suicide.org

Suicide and crisis support information in 10 languages, suicide support from Befrienders International

www.suicideinfo.org

American Association of Suicidology

www.suicidology.org

SUICIDE AND THE LAW

Developments in New York law

http://tswartz1.typepad.com/new_york_legal_update/2007/07/suicide-and-psy.html

Practice Pointers, the NASW Assurance Services

www.naswassurance.org

Ethics and malpractice

www.kspope.com/ethics/index.php

Psychiatry and law updates

www.reidpsychiatry.com

Search engine for medical literature

www.ncbi.nlm.nih.gov/entrez/query.fcgi

American Association of Suicidology

www.suicidology.org

EUTHANASIA

Death With Dignity National Center
www.deathwithdignity.org
Euthanasia Research & Guidance Organization
www.finalexit.org
Voluntary Euthanasia Society of London, England
www.dignityindying.org.uk
Hemlock Society USA
www.endoflifechoices.org
Compassion and Choices
www.compassionandchoices.org
World Federation of Right to Die Societies
www.worldrtd.net
Exit International
www.exitinternational.net

CODE OF ETHICS

American Psychiatric Association
www.psych.org/psych_pract/ethics/ethics.cfm
American Psychological Association
www.apa.org/ethics/code2002.html
NASW
www.socialworkers.org/pubs/code/code.asp
www.iap.org.au/ethics.htm
Links to additional ethics codes
www.kspope.com/ethcodes/index.php

MEDIA

International World Health Organization's resource
www.who.int/mental_health/resources/suicide/en
American Foundation for Suicide Prevention—Reporting on Suicide
https://afsp.org
www.mindframe-media.info/ (Further information)
Project on Death in America
http://www.soros.org/death
Social Workers in End-of-Life and Palliative Care
www.swlda.org
National Association of Social Workers End-of-Life Care
www.socialworkers.org/research/naswResearch/EndofLifeCare

KNOWLEDGE ACQUISITION TEST (KAT)

True or False

1. According to the Kantian perspective, a client's suicide that reduces pain or suffering to self and others may be morally acceptable.
2. The majority of those who commit suicide have a mental illness at the time of their death.
3. Experiencing a client suicide during professional training is not common.
4. The Death With Dignity Act of 1998 legalized PAS in all states.
5. An individual may be more inclined to attempt suicide as a result of exposure to a suicide report when he or she has a mental illness.
6. Nonmaleficence represents the concept of doing the greatest good possible.
7. Involuntary euthanasia exists only when the client is incompetent.
8. It is acceptable, under certain circumstances, to allow one's personal values to influence one's professional actions.
9. Social media abides by the same suicide-reporting guidelines as television and print media.
10. Only 25% of identified media includes limiting reporting on identifiable core factors that may prevent imitation.

Short Answer

11. What are the four key elements to support a claim of malpractice?
12. Under what circumstances can you as a practitioner breach confidentiality?
13. Is failure to secure previous records a breach of standard care practices?
14. What are three key ways to minimize risk of malpractice? If someone is going to commit suicide, can media reporting encourage or discourage their decision-making process? Why or why not?
16. Which ethical principles support an individual's right to commit suicide?
17. What is the difference between voluntary and involuntary euthanasia?
18. What are the core factors that may prevent imitation and are recommended to be considered when media reports on suicide?
19. How has social media challenged suicide reporting?

Multiple Choice

20. Which if the following is an ethical principle that does not support an individual's right to suicide?
    A. Informed consent
    B. Self-determination
    C. Confidentiality
    D. Duty to protect
    E. None of the above
    F. All of the above
21. Reamer's (1983) framework for ethical decision making proposes that limiting a client's autonomy is justifiable under which of the following circumstances:
    A. The client's family requests the assistance of the practitioner in facilitating the suicidal act.
    B. Harmful consequences that may be irreversible are likely to result should the client's autonomy be supported.
    C. There is potential that at some point in the future the need to rescue a client from harm may exist.

  D. When a colleague expresses that limiting the client's autonomy would be appropriate.

  E. None of the above.

  F. All of the above.

22. Which of the following is a definition of voluntary euthanasia?

  A. An act taken to shorten life

  B. The withdrawal or withholding of artificial life-support or medical treatments that may prolong life

  C. Individuals requesting assistance from anyone in ending their lives

  D. Intentionally causing the death of an individual without informed consent or explicit request

  E. None of the above

  F. All of the above

23. Failures to uphold the standard of care include:

  A. Keeping accurate, up-to-date records

  B. Assessing suicide risk during the last clinical contact

  C. Securing records from prior psychiatric treatment

  D. Developing an adequate treatment plan

  E. None of the above

  F. All of the above

24. In considering ethical issues related to suicide, a practitioner must:

  A. Maintain current knowledge of relevant governing laws.

  B. Have self-awareness regarding personal ethics, values, beliefs concerning suicide.

  C. Possess mastery of professional obligations as defined in relevant professional code of ethics.

  D. Take adequate steps to minimize risk of malpractice liability should a client suicide.

  E. None of the above.

  F. All of the above.

25. Which of the following media recommendations are intended to prevent suicide imitations?

  A. Not referring to online suicide forums

  B. Not mentioning suicide pacts

  C. Not mentioning suicides that are close in time or space

  D. Not mentioning an accumulation of suicidal acts at certain locations

  E. All of the above

  F. None of the above

REFERENCES

Abramson, M. (1985). The autonomy-paternalism dilemma in social work practice. *Social Casework, 66*, 387–393.

Alao, A. O., Soderberg, M., Pohl, E. L., & Alao, A. L. (2006). Cybersuicide: Review of the role of the internet on suicide. *Cyberpsychological Behavior, 9*(4), 489–493.

Alexander, D. A., Klein, S., Gray, N. M., Dewar, I. G., & Eagles, J. M. (2000). Suicide by patients: Questionnaire study of its effect on consultant psychiatrists. *British Medical Journal, 320*, 1571–1574.

Allen, J., Chavez, S., DeSimone, S., Howard, D., Johnson, K., LaPierre, L., Montero, D., Sanders, J. (2006). Americans' attitudes toward euthanasia and physician-assisted suicide, 1936–2002. *Journal of Sociology & Social Welfare, 3*(2), 5–23.

Alvarez, A. (1975). Literature in the nineteenth and twentieth centuries. In S. Perlin (Ed.), *A handbook for the study of suicide* (pp. 153–178). New York, NY: Oxford University Press.

Barraclough, B., Bunch, J., Nelson, B., & Salisbury, P. (1974). A hundred cases of suicide: Clinical Aspects. *British Journal of Psychiatry, 125*, 355–373.

Baume, P., Cantor, C. H., & Rolfe, A. (1997). Cybersuicide: The role of interactive suicide notes on the internet. *Crisis, 18*(2), 73–79.

Beauchamp, T. L. (1999). The philosophical basis of psychiatric ethics. In S. Bloch, P. Chodoff, & S. A. Green (Eds.), *Psychiatric ethics* (3rd ed., pp. 25–48). Oxford, UK: Oxford University Press.

Bell, C. C., & Clark, D. C. (1998). Adolescent suicide. *Pediatric Clinics of North America, 45*(2), 365–380.

Bendiane, M. K., Bouhnik, A. D., Galinier, A., Favre, R., Obadia, Y., & Peretti-Watel, P. (2009). French hospital nurses' opinions about euthanasia and physician-assisted suicide: A national phone survey. *Journal of Medical Ethics, 35*(4), 238–244.

Berman, A. L. (2006). Risk management with suicidal patients. *Journal of Clinical Psychology, 62*(2), 171–184.

Bishop, J. P. (2006a). Euthanasia, efficiency, and the historical distinction between killing a patient and allowing a patient to die. *Journal of Medical Ethics, 32*(4), 220–224.

Bishop, J. P. (2006b). Framing euthanasia. *Journal of Medical Ethics, 32*(4), 225–228.

Blood, R. W., & Pirkis, J. (2007). Media reporting of suicide methods: An Australian perspective. *Crisis, 28*(Suppl. 1), 64–69.

Bongar, B. (2002). *The suicidal patient: Clinical and legal standards of care* (2nd ed.). Washington, DC: American Psychological Association.

Bongar, B., & Greaney, S. A. (1994). Essential clinical and legal issues when working with the suicidal patient. *Death Studies, 18*(5), 529–548.

Bongar, B., Maris, R. W., Berman, A. L., & Litman, R. E. (1992). Outpatient standards of care and the suicidal patient. *Suicide and Life-Threatening Behavior, 22*(4), 453–478.

Bongar, B. M. (1991). Suicide: Legal perspectives. In B. M. Bongar (Ed.), *The suicidal patient: Clinical and legal standards of care* (pp. 33–59). Washington, DC: American Psychological Association.

Brassington, I. (2006). Killing people: What Kant could have said about suicide and euthanasia but did not. *Journal of Medical Ethics, 32*, 571–574.

Breitbart, W., & Rosenfeld, B. D. (1999). Physician-assisted suicide: The influence of psychosocial issues. *Cancer Control, 6*(2), 146–161.

Brent, D., Perper, J., Moritz, G., Baugher, M., Schweers, J., & Roth, C. (1993). Firearms and adolescent suicide: A community case-control study. *American Journal of Disorders of Childhood, 147*, 1066–1071.

Brent, D. A., Perper, J. A., Moritz, G., Liotus, L., Scheweers, J., Balach, L., Roth, C. (1994). Familial risk factors for adolescent suicide: A case-control study. *Acta Psychiatrica Scandinavica, 89*, 52–58.

Brock, D. W. (1985). Taking human life. *Ethics, 95*(4), 851–865.

Canadian Association for Suicide Prevention. (2003). Media guidelines. Retrieved from https://www .suicideprevention.ca/understanding/for-media/

Cantor, C. H., & McDermott, P. M. (1994). Suicide litigation: From legal to clinical wisdom. *Australian & New Zealand Journal of Psychiatry, 28*(3), 431–437.

Carasevici, B. (2016). Dilemmas in the attitude towards suicide. *Revista Medico-Chirurgicală A Societății De Medici Şi Naturaliști Din Iaşi, 120*(1), 152–157.

Chadwick, R., & Tadd, W. (1992). *Ethics and nursing practice*. London, UK: The Macmillan Press.

Chemtob, C. M., Hamada, R. S., Bauer, G., Kinney, B., & Torigoe, R. Y. (1988). Patients' suicides: Frequency and impact on psychiatrists. *American Journal of Psychiatry, 145*(2), 224–228.

Chemtob, C. M., Hamada, R. S., Bauer, G., Torigoe, R. Y., & Kinney, B. (1988). Patient suicide: Frequency and impact on psychologists. *Professional Psychology: Research and Practice, 19*(4), 416–420.

Chochilnov, H. M., & Breitbart, W. (2000). *Handbook of Psychiatry in Palliative Medicine.* New York, NY: Oxford University Press.

Cooper, C. (1995). Patient suicide and assault: Their impact on psychiatric hospital staff. *Journal of Psychosocial Nursing and Mental Health Services, 33*(6), 26–29.

Coverdale, J. H., Roberts, L. W., & Louie, A. K. (2007). Encountering patient suicide: Emotional responses, ethics, and implications for training programs. *Academic Psychiatry, 31*(5), 329–332.

Csikai, E. L. (1999). Euthanasia and assisted suicide: Issues for social work practice. *Journal of Gerontological Social Work, 31*(3–4), 49–63.

Daigle, M. S. (2005). Suicide prevention through means restriction: Assessing the risk of substitution: A critical review and synthesis. *Accident Analysis Prevent, 37*(4), 625–632.

Deschepper, R., Distelmans, W., & Bilsen, J. (2014). Requests for euthanasia/physician-assisted suicide on the basis of mental suffering: Vulnerable patients or vulnerable physicians. *Journal of the American Medical Association Psychiatry, 71*(6), 617–618.

Dewar, I. G., Eagles, J. M., Klein, S., Gray, N., & Alexander, D. A. (2000). Psychiatric trainees' experiences of, and reactions to, patient suicide. *Psychiatric Bulletin, 24*(1), 20–23.

Dickinson, G. E., Lancaster, C. J., Clark, D., Ahmedzai, S. H., & Noble, W. (2002). U.K. physicians' attitudes toward active voluntary euthanasia and physician-assisted suicide. *Death Studies, 26*(6): 479–490.

Donagan, A. (1977). *The theory of morality.* Chicago, IL: University of Chicago Press.

Drickamer, M. A., Lee, M. A., & Ganzini, L. (1997). Practical issues in physician-assisted suicide. *Annals of Internal Medicine, 126*(2), 146–151.

Eagles, J. M., Klein, S., Gray, N. M., Dewar, I. G., & Alexander, D. A. (2001). Role of psychiatrists in the prediction and prevention of suicide: A perspective from north-east Scotland. *British Journal of Psychiatry, 178,* 494–496.

Elitzur, A. C. (1995). In defense of life: On the mental-health professions' failure to confront the suicide epidemic *OMEGA: The Journal of Death and Dying, 31*(4), 305–310.

Emanuel, E. J. (2002). Euthanasia and physician-assisted suicide: A review of the empirical data from the United States. *Archives of Internal Medicine, 162,* 142–152.

Emanuel, E. J. (2016). Attitudes and practices of euthanasia and physician-assisted suicide in the United States, Canada, and Europe. *Journal of the American Medical Association, 316*(1), 79–90.

Emanuel, E. J., Fairclough, D., Clarridge, B. C., Blum, D., Bruera, E., Penley, W. C., . . . Mayer, R. J. (2000). Attitudes and practices of U.S. oncologists regarding euthanasia and physician-assisted suicide. *Annals of Internal Medicine, 133*(7), 527–532.

Emanuel, E. J., Fairclough, D. L., & Emanuel, L. L. (2000). Attitudes and desires related to euthanasia and physician-assisted suicide among terminally ill patients and their caregivers. *Journal of the American Medical Association, 284,* 2460–2468.

Erazo, N., Baumert, J. J., & Ladwig, K. H. (2005). Factors associated with failed and completed railway suicides. *Journal of Affect Disorders, 88*(2), 137–143.

Erlangsen, A. (2013). Media reporting on suicide: Challenges and opportunities. *Acta Psychiatrica Scandinavica, 128,* 316–317.

Etzersdirfer, E., & Sonneck, G. (1998). Preventing suicide by influencing mass-media reporting: The Viennese Experience 1980–1996. *Archives of Suicide Research, 4*(1), 67–74.

Feldman, D. (1987). A social work student's reaction to client suicide. *Social Casework, 68,* 184–187.

Feldman, S. R., Moritz, S. H., & Benjamin, G. (2005). Suicide and the law: A practical overview for mental health professionals. *Women & Therapy, 28*(1), 95–103.

Fintzy, R. T. (1993). The dangers of legalizing physician assisted suicide. *American Journal of Psychiatry, 150*(12), 1901–1904.

Frankena, W. K. (1980). *Thinking about morality.* Ann Arbor: University of Michigan Press.

Gielen, J. (2008). Attitudes of European physicians toward euthanasia and physician-assisted suicide: A review of the recent literature. *Journal of Palliative Care, 24*(3), 173–184.

Giese, C. (2009). German nurses, euthanasia and terminal care: A personal perspective. *Nursing Ethics, 16*(2), 231–237.

Gilje, F., Talseth, A. G., & Norberg, A. (2005). Psychiatric nurses' response to suicidal psychiatric inpatients: Struggling with self and sufferer. *Journal of Psychiatric and Mental Health Nursing, 12*(5), 519–526.

Gitlin, M. J. (1999). A psychiatrist's reaction to a patient's suicide. *American Journal of Psychiatry, 156*(10), 1630–1634.

Gould, M., Fisher, P., Parides, M., Flory, M., & Shaffer, D. (1996). Psychosocial risk factors of child and adolescent completed suicide. *Archives of General Psychiatry, 53,* 1155–1162.

Groenewoud, J. H., Van Der Heide, A., Tholen, A. J., Schudel, W. J., Hengeveld, M. W., Onwuteaka-Philipsen, B. D., . . . Van Der Wal, G. (2004). Psychiatric consultation with regard to requests for euthanasia or physician-assisted suicide. *General Hospital Psychiatry, 26*(4), 323–330.

Guedj, M., Gibert, M., Maudet, A., Munoz, S., Mullet, E., & Sorum, P. (2005). The acceptability of ending a patient's life. *Journal of Medical Ethics, 31*, 311–317.

Gutheil, T. G. (1992). *Suicide and clinical practice.* Washington, DC: American Psychiatric Press.

Halligan, P., & Corcoran, P. (2001). The impact of patient suicide on rural general practitioners. *British Journal of General Practice, 51*(465), 295–296.

Hendin, H. (1982). *Suicide in America.* New York, NY: Norton.

Hewitt, J. (2013). Why are people with mental illness excluded from the rational suicide debate? *International Journal of Law and Psychiatry, 363*, 58–65.

Heyd, D., & Bloch, S. (1999). The ethics of suicide. In S. Bloch, P. Chodoff, & S. Green (Eds.), *Psychiatric ethics* (pp. 441–460). Oxford, UK: Oxford University Press.

Hilden, J. M., Emanuel, E. J., Fairclough, D. L., Link, M. P., Foley, K. M., Clarridge, B. C., . . . Mayer, R. J. (2001). Attitudes and practices among pediatric oncologists regarding end-of-life care: Results of the 1998 American Society of Clinical Oncology survey. *Journal of Clinical Oncology, 19*(1), 205–212.

Hill, T. E. (1983). Self-regarding suicide: A modified Kantian view. *Suicide and Life-Threatening Behavior, 13*(4), 254–275.

Ho, A. O. (2014). Suicide: Rationality and responsibility for life. *Canadian Journal of Psychiatry, 59*, 141–147.

Huddle, T. S. (2013). Moral fiction or moral fact? The distinction between doing and allowing in medical ethics. *Bioethics, 27*(5), 257–262.

Isometsa, E., Henrikksson, M., Marttunen, M., Heikkinen, M., Aro, H., Kuoppasalmi, K., & Lonnqvist, J. (1995). Mental disorders in young and middle aged men who commit suicide. *British Medical Journal, 310*, 1366–1367.

Jobes, D. A., & Berman, A. L. (1993). Suicide and malpractice liability: Assessing and revising policies, procedures, and practice in outpatient settings. *Professional Psychology, Research and Practice, 24*(1), 91–99.

Kaplan, K. J., & Harrow, M. (1996). Positive and negative symptoms as risk factors for later suicidal activity in schizophrenics versus depressives. *Suicide and Life-Threatening Behavior, 26*(2), 105–120.

Kelly, B., & McLoughlin, D. M. (2002). Euthanasia, assisted suicide and psychiatry: A Pandora's box. *The British Journal of Psychiatry, 181*, 278–279.

Kelly, T. B. (1994). Paternalism and the marginally competent: An ethical dilemma, no easy answers. *Journal of Gerontological Social Work, 23*(1/2), 67–84.

Kleespies, P. M. (1993). The stress of patient suicidal behavior: Implications for interns and training programs in psychology. *Professional Psychology: Research and Practice, 24*(4), 477–482.

Kovacs, M., Obrosky, S., Gatsonis, C., & Richards, C. (1997). First-episode major depressive and dysthymic disorder in childhood: Clinical and sociodemographic factors in recovery. *Journal of the American Academy of Child & Adolescent Psychiatry, 36*(6), 777–784.

Kowalski, S. D. (1997). Nevada nurses' attitudes regarding physician-assisted suicide. *Clinical Nurse Specialist, 11*(3), 109–115.

Leeman, C. P. (2004). Commentary on Elger and Harding: Can suicide be rational in persons who are not terminally ill? *General Hospital Psychiatry, 26*(2), 145–146.

Lester, D., & Leenaars, A. A. (1996). The ethics of suicide and suicide prevention. *Death Studies, 20*, 163–184.

Levene, I. (2011). Prevalence of depression in granted and refused requests for euthanasia and assisted suicide: A systematic review. *Journal of Medical Ethics: Journal of the Institute of Medical Ethics, 37*(4), 205–211.

Linke, S., Wojciak, J., & Day, S. (2002). The impact of suicide on community mental health teams findings and recommendations. *Psychiatric Bulletin, 26*, 50–52.

Litman, R. E. (1982). Hospital suicides: Lawsuits and standards. *Suicide and Life-Threatening Behavior, 12*, 212–220.

Litman, R. E. (1996). Suicidology: A look backward and ahead. *Suicide and Life-Threatening Behavior, 26*(1), 1–7.

Lizardi, D., Currier, D., Galfalvy, H., Sher, L., Burke, A., Mann, J. J., & Oquendo, M. (2007). Perceived reasons for living at index hospitalization and future suicide attempt. *Journal of Nervous and Mental Disease, 195*(5), 451–455.

Lynch, T. R., Cheavens, J. S., Morse, J. Q., & Rosenthal, M. Z. (2004). A model predicting suicidal ideation and hopelessness in depressed older adults: The impact of emotion inhibition and affect intensity. *Aging and Mental Health, 8*(6), 486–497.

Mackelprang, R. W., & Mackelprang, R. D. (2005). Historical and contemporary issues in end-of-life deci-sions: Implications for social work. *Social Work, 50*(4), 315–324.

Macleod, S. (2012). Assisted dying in liberalized jurisdictions and the role of psychiatry: A clinician's view. *Australian and New Zealand Journal of Psychiatry, 46*(10), 936–945.

Maloney, J., Pfuhlmann, B., Arensman, E., Coffey, C., Gusmão, R., Poštuvan, V., . . . Schmidtke, A. (2013). Media recommendations on reporting suicidal behaviour and suggestions for optimisation. *Acta Psychiatrica Scandinavica, 128*, 314–315.

Maltsberger, J. T. (1992). The implications of patient suicide for the surviving psychotherapist. In D. Jacobs (Ed.), *Suicide and clinical practice* (Vol. Clinical Practice Number 21, pp. 169–182). Washington, DC: American Psychiatric Press.

Maris, R. W. (1982). Rational suicide: An impoverished self-transformation. *Suicide and Life-Threatening Behavior, 12*, 3–16.

Maris, R. W., Berman, A. L., & Silverman, M. M. (2000). *Comprehensive textbook of suicidology.* New York, NY: Guilford Press.

Mayo, D. J. (1984). Confidentiality in crisis counseling: A philosophical perspective. *Suicide and Life-Threatening Behavior, 14*(2), 96–112.

McLachlan, H. V. (2010). Assisted suicide and the killing of people? Maybe. Physician-assisted suicide and the killing of patients? No: The rejection of Shaw's new prospective on euthanasia. *Journal of Medical Ethics: Journal of the Institute of Medical Ethics, 36*(5), 306–309.

Mishara, B. L., & Weisstub, D. N. (2013). Premises and evidence in the rhetoric of assisted suicide and euthanasia. *International Journal of Law and Psychiatry, 36*(5–6), 427–435.

Mishna, F., Antle, B. J., & Regehr, C. (2002). Social work with clients contemplating suicide: Complexity and ambiguity in the clinical, ethical, and legal considerations. *Clinical Social Work Journal, 30*(3), 265–280.

Mosich, V., & Müller-Busch, H. C. (2014). Suicidal drug overdose while receiving palliative home care: A case report. *Wiener Medizinische Wochenschrift, 164*(9–10), 184–188.

Motto, J. (1967). Suicide and suggestibility. *American Journal of Psychiatry, 124*, 252–256.

Motto, J. (1970). Newspaper influence on suicide: A controlled study. *Archives of General Psychiatry, 23*, 143–148.

Motto, J. A. (1999). A psychiatric perspective on rational suicide: 24 points of view. In J. L. Werth (Ed.), *Contemporary perspectives on rational suicide*, (pp. 121–125). Philadelphia, PA: Brunner/Mazel.

National Association of Social Workers. (2000). *Code of ethics.* Washington, DC: NASW Press. Retrieved from http://www.socialworkers.org/pubs/code/code.asp

Overholser, J. C. (2006). Treatment of suicidal patients: A risk-benefit analysis. *Behavioral Sciences & the Law, 13*(1), 81–92.

Packman, W. L., & Harris, E. A. (1998). Legal issues and risk management in suicidal patients. In B. Bonger, A. L. Berman, R. W. Maris, M. M. Silverman, E. A. Harris, & W. L. Packman (Eds.), *Risk management with suicidal patients*, (pp. 150–186). New York, NY: Guilford Press.

Paris, J. (2002). Chronic suicidality among patients with borderline personality disorder. *Psychiatric Ser-vices, 53*, 738–742.

Phillips, D. P. (1974). The influence of suggestion on suicide: Substantive and theoretical implications of the Werther effect. *American Sociological Review, 39*(3), 340–354.

Phillips, D. P. (1982). The impact of fictional television stories on US adult fatalities: New evidence on the effect of the mass media on violence. *American Journal of Sociology, 87*, 1340–1359.

Pinch, W. J., & Dougherty, C. J. (1993). Competency after a suicide attempt: An ethical reflection. *Dimen-sions of Critical Care Nursing, 12*(4), 206–211.

Pirkis, J., & Blood, R. W. (2001). Suicide and the media part 1: Reportage in nonfictional media. *Crisis, 22*(4), 146–154.

Quill, T. E., Meier, D. E., Block, S. D., & Billings, J. A. (1998). The debate over physician-assisted suicide: Empirical data and convergent views. *Annals of Internal Medicine, 128*(7), 552–558.

Reamer, F. G. (1983). The concept of paternalism in social work. *Social Service Review, 57*, 254–271.

Regan, D. H. (1983). Suicide and the failure of modern moral theory. *Suicide and Life-Threatening Behavior, 13*(4), 276–292.

Robins, E. (1981). *The final months: A study of the lives of 134 persons who committed suicide.* New York, NY: Oxford University Press.

Rosenbluth, M., Kleinman, I., & Lowy, F. (1995). Suicide: The interaction of clinical and ethical issues. *Psychiatric Services, 46*(9), 919–921.

Rosenfeld, B. (2004). *Assisted suicide and the right to die: The interface of social science, public policy, and medi-cal ethics.* Washington, DC: American Psychological Association.

Ruskin, R., Sakinofsky, I., Bagby, R. M., Dickens, S., & Sousa, G. (2004). Impact of patient suicide on psychiatrists and psychiatric trainees. *Academic Psychiatry, 28*(2), 104–110.

Samaritans. (2005). Media guidelines: Portrayals of suicide. Retrieved from https://www.samaritans.org/media-centre/media-guidelines-reporting-suicide

Sasson, S. (2000). Beneficence versus respect for autonomy: An ethical dilemma in social work practice. *Journal of Gerontological Social Work, 33*(1), 5–16.

Schoonman, M. K., van Thiel, G. J., & van Delden J. J. (2014). Non-physician-assisted suicide in The Netherlands: A cross-sectional survey among the general public. *Journal of Medical Ethics, 40*, 842–848.

Schramme, T. (2013). Rational suicide, assisted suicide, and indirect legal paternalism. *International Journal of Law and Psychiatry, 36*(5–6), 477–484.

Schulsinger, F., Kety, S. S., Rosenthal, D., & Wender, P. H. (1979). A family study of suicide. In M. Schou & E. Stromgren (Eds.), *Origin, prevention and treatment of affective disorders*, (pp. 277–287). Orlando, FL: Academic Press.

Schwyn, E. (1976). Ethical norms of suicide prevention and crisis intervention. *Mental Health and Society, 393*(40), 142–147.

Shaw, D. (2007). The body as unwarranted life support: A new perspective on euthanasia. *Journal of Medical Ethics, 33*, 519–521.

Sjöberg, R. L., & Lindholm, T. (2003). Decision-making and euthanasia. *The British Journal of Psychiatry, 182*, 172.

Smokowski, P. R., & Wodarski, J. S. (1996). Euthanasia and physician assisted suicide: A social work update. *Social Work in Health Care, 23*(1), 53–65.

Snijdewind, M. (2014). Complexities in euthanasia or physician-assisted suicide as perceived by Dutch physicians and patients' relatives. *Journal of Pain and Symptom Management, 48*(6), 1125–1134.

Sorta-Bilajac, I. (2008). Croatian physicians' and nurses' experience with ethical issues in clinical practice. *Journal of Medical Ethics: Journal of the Institute of Medical Ethics, 34*(6), 450–455.

Spiegelman, J. S., & Werth, J. L. (2005). Don't forget about me: The experiences of therapists-in-training after a client has attempted or died by suicide. *Women & Therapy, 28*(1), 35–57.

Strakowski, S. M., McElroy, S. L., Keck, P. E., & West, S. A. (1996). Suicidality among patients with mixed and manic bipolar disorder. *American Journal of Psychiatry, 153*, 674–676.

Strom-Gottfried, K., & Mowbray, N. D. (2006). Who heals the helper? Facilitating the social worker's grief. *Families in Society, 87*(1), 9–15.

Sullivan, A. D., Hedberg, K., & Fleming, D. W. (2000). Legalized physician-assisted suicide in Oregon: The second year. *New England Journal of Medicine, 342*(8), 598–604.

Szasz, T. S. (1999). *Fatal freedom: The ethics and politics of suicide*. Westport, CT: Praeger/Greenwood Publishing Group.

Talseth, A. G., & Gilje, F. (2007). Unburdening suffering: Responses of psychiatrists to patients' suicide deaths. *Nursing Ethics: An International Journal for Health Care Professionals, 14*(5), 620–636.

Tamayo-Velazquez, M., Simon-Lorda, P., & Cruz-Piqueras, M. (2012). Euthanasia and physician-assisted suicide: Knowledge, attitudes and experiences of nurses in Andalusia. *Nursing Ethics, 19*(5), 677–691.

Ting, L., Sanders, S., Jacobson, J. M., & Power, J. R. (2006). Dealing with the aftermath: A qualitative analysis of mental health social workers' reactions after a client suicide. *Social Work, 51*(1), 329–341.

Trankle, S. A. (2014). Decisions that hasten death: Double effect and the experiences of physicians in Australia. *BioMed Central Medical Ethics, 15*, 26. doi: 10.1186/1472-6939-15-26

Tsuang, M. T. (1983). Risk of suicide in relatives of schizophrenics, manics, depressives, and controls. *Journal of Clinical Psychiatry, 44*, 396–400.

Venkat, A., & Drori, J. (2014). When to say when: Responding to a suicide attempt in the acute care setting. *Narrative Inquiry in Bioethics, 4*, 263–270.

Wagle, R. K., Ede, K., Craig, J., & Bottum, K. (2004). An ethical dilemma: When the family wants the withdrawal of care. *Journal of Psychiatric Practice, 10*(5), 334–336.

Waltzer, H. (1980). Malpractice liability in a patient's suicide. *American Journal of Psychotherapy, 34*(1), 89–98.

Wasserman, I. (1984). Imitation and suicide: A reexamination of the Werther effect. *American Sociological Review, 49*, 427–436.

Weissman, M. M., Fendrich, M., Warner, V., & Wickramaratne, P. (1992). Incidence of psychiatric disorder in offspring at high and low risk for depression. *Journal of the American Academy of Child & Adolescent Psychiatry, 31*, 640–648.

Welfel, E. R. (2002). *Ethics in counseling and psychotherapy: Standards, research, and emerging issues* (2nd ed.). Pacific Grove, CA: Brooks/Cole.

Wender, P. H., Kety, S. S., Rosenthal, D., Schulsinger, F., Ortmann, J., & Lunde, I. (1986). Psychiatric disorders in the biological and adoptive families of adopted individuals with affective disorders. *Archives of General Psychiatry, 43*, 923–929.

Werth, J. L. (1999). Mental health professionals and assisted death: Perceived ethical obligations and proposed guidelines for practice. *Ethics and Behavior, 9*(2), 159–183.

Werth, J. L., & Rogers, J. R. (2005). Assessing for impaired judgment as a means of meeting the "duty to protect" when a client is a potential harm-to-self: Implications for clients making end-of-life decisions. *Mortality, 10*(1), 7–21.

World Health Organization. (2000). Preventing suicide: A resource for media professionals. Retrieved from http://www.who.int/mental_health/media/en/426.pdf

CHAPTER TWO

THE ROLE OF CULTURE, RACE, AND ETHNICITY IN SUICIDE

Accurate identification and assessment of suicide risk requires an understanding of the influence of culture, ethnicity, and race in relation to suicidality. If culture, race, and ethnicity are overlooked, and it may be assumed that individuals from all backgrounds experience the world in the same way, intervention and prevention efforts will remain largely unsuccessful at reducing suicide rates. In this chapter, culturally relevant risk and protective factors for suicide are explored and epidemiological data and contextual findings on suicidality across cultures and nationalities are presented. International trends regarding suicide prevalence are examined, as well as the impact of immigration, acculturation, and assimilation on suicide risk. A model of culturally relevant suicide intervention and prevention strategies is described, including a discussion of differences in attitudes toward suicide and suicide acceptability across cultures.

GOALS AND OBJECTIVES

An understanding of:

- Trends in suicide rates across culture, race, and ethnicity
- Epidemiology of suicide across culture, race, and ethnicity
- Influence of immigration on suicide
- Influence of acculturation and assimilation on suicide
- Transcultural risk factors and protective factors
- Culture-specific risk factors and protective factors
- Core theories related to suicidal behavior
- International perspectives and attitudes on suicide
- Influence of the culture of the provider on assessment and treatment
- Culturally competent and evidence-based approach to practice with diverse populations

---

The past decades have seen major improvements in the recognition and treatment of suicide, depression, and other mental health concerns, as well as the introduction of safer and more effective psychotropic medications. Notwithstanding, global suicide rates have been steadily increasing and are predicted to increase to 1.53 million by the year 2020 (Khan, 2005). It is important to recognize that suicide rates vary by ethnicity and geographic location. Further, race and ethnicity have consistently been shown to be related to suicidal behavior and ideation (Beck-Cross & Cooper, 2015; Castle, Conner, Kaukeinen, & Tu, 2011; Eaton et al., 2011). It is essential to understand the unique risk and protective factors for suicide among diverse populations and to adapt prevention and intervention efforts for each specific population in order for such efforts to be more focused and effective.

Our personal values and beliefs impact the nature and quality of the interactions we have with our clients. In addition to understanding the universal and culture-specific risk and protective factors for suicide, it is necessary, as clinicians treating suicidal individuals from diverse backgrounds, to be aware of any cultural and ethnic preconceptions, stereotypes, and/or biases we may hold in order to ensure that they do not interfere with effective, professional treatment of our clients.

Individual Exercise 2.1

1. What is your cultural background? How would you describe your degree of *cultural affiliation*/identification?
2. What is the attitude toward suicide from your culture(s) of origin? Is your attitude toward suicide the same as that of your culture(s) of origin? If it differs, how do you reconcile those differences?
3. Is your culture considered a minority or majority culture? How does this impact your experience of the world?
4. Considering your answers to questions 1 to 3, how may these factors influence your work (positively or negatively) with suicidal individuals from diverse backgrounds?

STATISTICS, EPIDEMIOLOGY, AND TRENDS IN SUICIDE BY CULTURE, RACE, AND ETHNICITY

To understand the larger contextual issues related to suicidality and culture and ethnicity, it is important to focus on the trends in suicide rates among Caucasians, African Americans, Latinos, and Asians in the United States (due to the high suicide rate among this group; suicidality among Native Americans is discussed in Chapter 14). International trends in suicide are subsequently examined. In addition, theories are presented that provide an understanding of the differences in suicide rates transculturally.

Trends in Suicide Rates Among the Major Ethnic/Cultural Groups in the United States

Caucasians. It is estimated that by the year 2050, Caucasians will no longer be the majority population in the United States (Passel & Cohn, 2011). Currently, Caucasian males have a higher rate of suicide than Caucasian females, and Caucasian males aged 85 years and older have the highest rate of suicide in the United States (Joe, Baser, Breeden, Neighbors, & Jackson, 2006). In general, Caucasians have a higher rate of suicide than African Americans. This trend is more pronounced with age, with elderly Caucasian male suicide rates exceeding elderly Black male suicide rates by more than 2 to 1 (Joe et al., 2006). The trend is even more pronounced with gender; Caucasian male suicide rates exceed African American female suicide rates as high as 18 to 1 (Joe et al., 2006). Among Caucasian adolescents, approximately 20% consider suicide and make a plan, while 8% report making an attempt (Centers for Disease Control and Prevention [CDC], 2015). Suicide is the third leading cause of death among Caucasian adolescents (CDC, 2002). Caucasian adolescents have a higher rate of completed suicide than African Americans and Hispanics (Lorenzo-Luaces & Phillips, 2014; Rutter & Behrendt, 2004).

African Americans. Among African Americans, females have a lower rate of suicide than African American males (1 to 3; Joe et al., 2006). African American females also have a lower rate of suicide than Caucasian females (1 to 2; Joe et al., 2006). Historically, African American youths have had lower suicide rates than have Caucasians, and while this remains true, the gap between the groups appears to be narrowing (Borowsky, Ireland, & Resnick, 2001; CDC, 2006; Garlow, Purselle, & Heninger, 2005; Joe et al., 2006; Joe & Kaplan, 2001; Rockett, 2010), due largely to a sharp increase in suicide rates among young African Americans aged 15 to 24 years during the past two decades (Borowsky et al., 2001). However, it is important to note that African American females have a much higher rate of suicide attempt than either African American males or Caucasian females (Joe et al., 2006).

Hispanics. As a group, Hispanics have a lower rate of suicide than Caucasians and a higher rate than African Americans (Lorenzo-Luaces & Phillips, 2014; Rockett, 2010). Evidence shows that Hispanics report less suicidal ideation and make lower lethality attempts than non-Hispanics despite having similar suicide intent (Oquendo et al., 2005). Among Hispanic subgroups, the rates of suicidal behavior vary greatly. Cuban Americans have the lowest rate of lifetime suicide attempt (2%) followed by Mexican Americans (3%; Oquendo, Lizardi, Greenwald, Weissman, & Mann, 2004). Puerto Ricans have the highest rate of suicide attempt (9.1%; Oquendo et. al., 2004; Ungemack & Guarnaccia, 1998). Yet, the completed suicide rate for Puerto Ricans is lower than the completed suicide rates for other Hispanic ethnic subgroups and for Caucasians (Oquendo et al., 2001). Mexican Americans also have a lower rate of completed suicide than Caucasians (Oquendo et al., 2001). Among Hispanics, Latina adolescents have the highest rate of suicide attempts of all age groups (Zayas, Lester, Cabassa, & Fortuna, 2005). Despite similar levels of psychopathology, Latina adolescents have a higher rate of suicide attempts than adolescent females from other ethnic groups (Kuhlberg, Pena, & Zayas, 2010; Zayas, Aguilar-Gaxiola, Yoon, & Rey, 2012; Zayas et al., 2005; Zayas & Gulbas, 2012).

Asians. Among Asians, females and older individuals tend to have higher suicide rates. However, results have been shown to vary based on the place of birth. Specifically, U.S.-born Asian American women have been shown to have a higher prevalence of suicidal ideation and *suicide plan* than U.S.-born Asian American men and immigrant Asian American men and women (Duldulao, Takeuchi, & Seunghye, 2009). Overall, Asians have a lower rate of suicidal behavior than their Caucasian counterparts (Evans, Hawton, Rodham, & Deeks, 2005; Sue, 2012). This is especially the case for Asian adolescents (Evans et al., 2005). However, more Asian females engage in suicide than Caucasian and African American females (Shiang, Bonger, Stephens, Allison, & Schatzberg, 1997). This finding is more pronounced among elderly female Asians than elderly females from other ethnic groups (Shiang et al., 1997). East Asian American women have the highest suicide rate among all American women over the age of 65 years (McKenzie, Serfaty, & Crawford, 2003).

International Trends in Suicide Rates

Internationally, there is a distinct variance in suicide rates across regions, due in part to the limited availability of data from many regions regarding the incidence and prevalence of suicidal behavior. For example, suicide rates in the Mediterranean are among the lowest in the world (3.5 per 100,000; Goldney, 2002; Marusic & Farmer, 2001) as is the suicide rate in Egypt (Kahn, 2005; Lester, 1997b). Conversely, the suicide rate in Russia has been consistently reported as high (Goldney, 2002; World Health Organization, 1994); it is currently estimated to be three times the suicide rate in the United States (Pridemore & Spivak, 2003). The suicide rate in Hungary has also been consistently high (Goldney, 2002; Lester, 1997b; Schmidtke, 1997).

The suicide rate in China is among the highest in the world, with rates approximating 300,000 suicides per year (Phillips, Liu, & Zhang, 1999). China is one of the few countries in which the rate of suicide among females exceeds the rate of suicide among males (Aaron et al., 2004; Baillargeon et al., 2003; Bhugra, Desai, & Baldwin, 1999; Goldney, 2002; Ji & Kleinman, 2001; Lester, 1997b; Phillips et al., 1999; Raleigh, 1996; Qin & Mortensen, 2001; Yip, 1996; Zhang, 2014). Rural suicide rates are dramatically higher than urban rates, and suicide rates are lower for adolescent females (Phillips et al., 1999; Qin & Mortensen, 2001; Kleinman & Becker, 2001; Zhang, Li, Tu, Xiao, & Jia, 2011). Malaysians have a lower rate of suicide than the Chinese (Chen, Lee, Wong, & Kaur, 2005), and, in general, South Asian populations have a lower rate of suicidality than other Asian populations (Bhugra, 2002; Burr, 2002). In general, China has a higher proportion of suicide cases in which individuals do not have a psychiatric diagnosis as compared to North America and Europe (Milner, Sveticic, & De Leo, 2013).

There is very little information on suicide in most developing countries and, specifically, in the Indian subcontinent, which consists of eight countries: India, Pakistan, Nepal, Sri Lanka, Afghanistan, Bhutan, Bangladesh, and the Maldives (Khan, 2002). The limited data that does exist indicates that 10% of suicides in this region occur in India, Sri Lanka, and Pakistan (Khan, 2002). In particular, the suicide rate in Sri Lanka is extremely high (Bolz, 2002; Goldney, 2002; Lester, 1997b). The suicide rate among women in this region is high, particularly in India, where the male to female ratio of suicides is much smaller compared to that of the rest of the world (Aaron et al., 2004; Khan, 2005; Mayer & Zianian, 2002). Like China, India has a higher proportion of suicides with no psychiatric diagnosis as compared to the United States, Canada, and Europe (Milner et al., 2013).

Based on the limited data available, the rate of suicide among Arab populations is quite low (Morad, Merrick, Schwarz, & Merrick, 2005); however, it appears to be on the rise (Pritchard & Amanullah, 2007). This may reflect Islamic cultural beliefs that strongly sanction taking one's own life (Morad et al., 2005) and a legal perspective that often views suicide as a crime (Khan, 2005; Khan & Hyder, 2006; Morad et al., 2005). In Israel, suicide rates in youth and adults are among the lowest in the world (Kohn, Levav, Chang, Halperin, & Zadka, 1997), and, in contrast to most other countries, the overall rate of suicide in this country does not appear to be on the rise (Kohn et al., 1997).

Core Theories Explaining Suicidal Behavior

While there is no universally accepted explanation for suicidality, some theories have been posited to explain the presence or absence of suicidal behavior. For example, Lester (1987) proposed a *physiological theory of suicidal behavior*. According to the theory, differences in suicide rates may be explained by variances in physiology across cultures, specifically regarding the inheritance of psychiatric disorders and concentrations of neurotransmitters. One study, for example, found that biological markers for endogenous depressive disorders in residents of eight countries were significantly associated with the suicide rates in those eight countries (Lester, 1991). Thus, according to this theory, differences in rates of suicidal behavior can, at least in part, be due to differences in the physiological makeup of individuals from different cultures.

More recently, a *stress-diathesis model* of suicidal behavior has been proposed (Goldney, 2002; Mann, Waternaux, Haas, & Malone, 1999). This model proposes that triggers or stressors exist that can be considered state-dependent, which present only during certain periods of time. Additionally, a threshold or diathesis exists that is more trait-dependent, which is constantly present. When risk factors from only one of these domains are present, it is not sufficient to elicit suicidal behavior. However, when risk factors from both domains are present, their combined effect increases the likelihood of suicidal behavior. The resultant suicidal behavior can be seen as the result of either a decrease in internal restraints against such behaviors or as the result of increased external stressors magnifying the suicidal impulse (Malone, Haas, Sweeny, & Mann, 1995).

Individuals who engage in suicidal actions have a vulnerability or lower threshold for such behaviors than those who do not attempt suicide (Malone et al., 1995). This vulnerability may be innate, as a result of genetic or familial factors, such as having a first-degree relative with a history of suicide attempts (Malone et al., 2000; Mann et al., 1999; Pfeffer, Normandin, & Kakuma, 1994; Roy, 1983, 1986; Roy, Segal, Centerwall, & Robinette, 1999), or it may be the result of trauma early in life, such as parental loss or childhood physical and/or sexual abuse (Adam, Bouckoms, & Streiner, 1982; Briere & Runtz, 1990; Farber, Herbert, & Reviere, 1996; Levi, Fales, Stein, & Sharp, 1966). Other factors may develop later in life, such as alcoholism or substance abuse, which may contribute to this vulnerability (Malone et al., 1995) and may further decrease the threshold for suicidal behavior (Mann et al., 1999). Additionally, research has indicated that trait-related factors such as aggression and impulsivity are related to suicidal behavior (Malone et al., 1995; Mann et al., 1999). Individuals with an aggressive-impulsive trait appear to have a lower threshold for suicidal behavior, which perhaps is an external expression of their self-directed aggressive, destructive thoughts (Malone et al., 1995).

This theory allows for variance in several areas that may account for the differential rates of suicidal behavior seen across cultures and ethnicities. Both state- and trait-related factors are subject to cultural influences. For example, substance abuse, physical abuse, sexual abuse, aggression, impulsivity, unemployment, undereducation all occur in varying rates across cultures and have a direct influence on an individual's vulnerability toward suicidal acts.

IMMIGRATION AND THE RISK OF SUICIDE

Because the act and process of immigrating to another country is a stressful life event, it is not surprising that *immigration* is associated with increased levels of stress and mental health illnesses (Shoval, Schoen, Vardi, & Zalsman, 2007), and can even be considered a crisis event (Ponizovsky & Ritsner, 1999). Individuals who migrate from one country to another are faced with not only the transition and the acculturation process but also with a number of potential risk factors and the withdrawal of some previously established protective factors. Immigrants generally lack a well-developed support system and frequently may experience the loss of their previously established support network (Sorenson & Shen, 1996). Also, immigrants tend to earn less money, are less likely to seek mental health care when needed, and may face a number of linguistic barriers (Sorenson & Shen, 1996). Immigrants are also confronted with prejudice and discrimination that may contribute to increased suicide risk (Shoval et al., 2007).

The research on migration and suicide is inconsistent. For example, research has often identified that among American-born ethnicities, non-Hispanic Whites have a higher suicide ideation and attempt rate, followed by Hispanics, Blacks, and Asians. However, research has found that within these ethnic groups, the overall suicide risk was lower among immigrants prior to migration compared to native U.S. born, but that such differences equalize over time after migration (Borges, Orozco, Rafful, Miller, & Breslau, 2012).

Also, while the linkage between suicide and immigration has been studied across a number of countries, the results are conflicting (Shoval et al., 2007). A seminal work by Kushner (1991) found that during the mid-20th century, migration increased the risk of suicide; specifically, foreign-born persons had nearly twice the suicide rate of native-born persons (Kushner, 1991). Kushner (1991) proposed that foreign-born persons from countries with higher suicide rates maintain a higher suicide risk after immigration. This association between the suicide rate of immigrants and rates of suicide in their country of origin has received further research support (Lester, 1997b, 1998; Spallek & Razum, 2015).

In Nordic studies, being foreign-born instead of native-born was a significant risk factor for suicide in both sexes and in all age groups except for males aged 30 to 49 years (Johansson et al., 1997). Similarly, a Canadian study found an over-representation of foreign-born suicide among psychiatric patients, but recognized that unemployment and poor social integration may have been confounding factors (Chandrasena, Beddage, & Fernando, 1991). In contrast, another Canadian study found immigrant adolescents had a lower suicide rate than nonimmigrant peers (Greenfield et al., 2006). In a study of Ghanaian immigrants to the United States, a significant association was found between the length of residency in the United States and negative suicide attitudes, and also between psychological acculturation and negative suicide attitudes (Eshun, 2006). These findings may indicate that other factors may confound any clear association between immigration and suicide risk.

In their seminal study, Sorenson and Shen (1996) investigated nearly 33,000 death certificates in California between 1970 and 1992 to assess suicide trends and ethnic group risk. Immigration is an important issue in California, as for several decades beginning in 1976, it was the leading state of residence for authorized and unauthorized immigrant populations in the United States (Sorenson & Shen, 1996). Sorenson and Shen (1996) found that foreign-born persons are generally at lower risk of suicide than U.S.-born persons. Although there was a higher risk for foreign-born Caucasians than for native-born Caucasians, foreign-born Hispanics had lower risk, and foreign-born Blacks and Asians shared similar risks with native-born persons (Sorenson & Shen, 1996). In interpreting their findings, the following four potential hypotheses that may mediate any suicide risk were suggested:

1. Culture of origin effects are protective factors derived from an individual's culture of origin that are brought with them to the new culture. For example, Catholicism's belief regarding suicide (values life, views suicide as a sin) and Confucianism's belief regarding suicide (values self-sacrifice, potentially views suicide as a virtue) may mitigate suicide risk among immigrants.
2. Country of destination factors, such as crowded housing arrangements, which may lead to discovering suicide attempts sooner, or availability of suicide method (e.g., firearms) may be protective or risk factors.
3. Personal characteristics of immigrants may be protective factors; for example, immigrants are often healthier and less depressed than the U.S.-born population (Stephen, Foote, Hendershot, & Schoenborn, 1994).
4. Migration selectivity efforts recognize that migration is a process in which only certain people elect or are selected to immigrate. Migration selectivity is a more established theory that posits only healthy individuals, who have a good chance of succeeding in the new country and may be able to bring over the rest of the family and/or send money back to their country of origin, are supported or encouraged to migrate (Sorenson & Shen, 1996). Similarly, individuals who are not likely to succeed may not be selected by the new country as candidates for immigration (Marmot, Adelstein, & Bulusu, 1984). Consequently, individuals prone to suicidality are less likely to immigrate and more likely to return to their country of origin (Sorenson & Shen, 1996).

Small Group Exercise 2.1

Complete the answers first individually, then discuss in groups of two to three.

1. What are some of your personal and/or family's cultural, bicultural, or multicultural customs, traditions, and effects that may positively or negatively impact your ability to integrate into the larger dominant culture?
2. How have some of these cultural customs and traditions changed or evolved over generations or time? For example, would your parents' older generation or a

younger generation hold the same perspectives as you now possess; and how might these differences influence your current treatment approach or how clients receive your care?

3. In considering questions 1 and 2, what are some potential problems (and strengths) that may emerge and how might you manage them?

THE ROLE OF ACCULTURATION AND ASSIMILATION IN SUICIDE

Acculturation is known as the process through which immigrants pass as they move to a new country. It is characterized by the struggle to maintain one's cultural identity, traditions, values, and customs while adapting to and embracing the values and customs of the mainstream culture to which they have emigrated, their host culture. This period can, for some, prove to be a time of great conflict that can result in heightened feelings of depression, anxiety, isolation, and suicidality (Hovey & King, 1997). The resultant distress is often referred to as "acculturative stress" (Berry & Kim, 1988; Hovey & King, 1996; 1997; Lester, 1999; Padilla, Cervantes, Maldonado, & Garcia, 1988; Williams & Berry, 1991).

In general, suicide rates are positively associated with acculturative stress and negatively associated with traditional integration (Lester, 1997a, 1998). Several factors have been identified that may serve as risk or protective factors for acculturative stress and ensuing suicidality. These factors include availability of social supports in the new community, level of familial support from both immediate and extended family networks, socioeconomic status (i.e., work status changes, education, employment), language ability, expectations toward the future, and pre-immigration level of cognitive/coping skills (Hovey & King, 1997; Williams & Berry, 1991).

Counterintuitively, evidence suggests that for many ethnicities, individuals with higher levels of acculturation are at higher risk for engaging in suicidal behavior than those with lower levels of acculturation. Among Native Americans, for example, acculturative stress is a strong predictor of suicide (Gray & McCullagh, 2014; Lester, 1999). Similarly, greater acculturation has also been found to be associated with increased risk of suicidal ideation among African Americans (Eaton et al., 2011). Gomez, Miranda, and Polanco (2011) also found acculturative stress to be related to increased odds of lifetime suicide attempt, with African Americans at the highest risk and Asian Americans at the lowest risk (Gomez et al., 2011). More so than ethnicity, strong cultural affiliation is a risk factor for suicide attempts among native-Hawaiian adolescents (Yuen, Nahulu, Hishinuma, & Miyamoto, 2000).

Acculturative stress has also been found to be a risk factor for suicide among several cultural subgroups. Among Hispanics (Gutierrez, Osman, Kopper, & Barrios, 2000; Vega, Gil, Warheit, Apospori, & Zimmerman, 1993; Zayas, 1987), for example, Mexican Americans born in the United States have higher rates of suicide and suicidal ideation than Mexican Americans born in Mexico (Sorenson & Golding, 1988; Swanson, Linskey, Quintero-Salinas, Pumariega, & Holzer, 1992). High levels of acculturative stress have also been found to be a risk factor for suicide among Central Americans (Hovey, 2000) and Puerto Ricans (Oquendo et al., 2004; Monk & Warshauer, 1974).

On the other hand, some have found that acculturation is related to suicidal ideation but not to suicidal behavior (Kennedy, Parhar, Samra, & Gorzalka, 2005; Lessenger, 1997). Kennedy and colleagues (2005) found that suicidal ideation, plans, and attempts did not vary by generational level or overall ethnic group among European, Chinese, and Indo-Asians.

In summary, it is essential to consider not only the rates and trends in suicide among various ethnic groups but equally, if not even more important, to consider the level of acculturation and degree of cultural affiliation of each client and how these might impact that client's suicide risk. When evaluating and treating suicidal individuals, a comprehensive assessment should be conducted concerning the process of immigration for individuals and their families, the acculturation process and signs of acculturative stress, their degree of cultural affiliation to their culture of origin, and their level of connection to their host culture.

In a large community mental health agency, a family is referred to you for counseling. The parents emigrated from Norway in the early 1990s. He is a skilled computer engineer and she is a chartered accountant. Both parents are successful and loving. They had three children, Anna, Peter, and Elise, soon after moving to the United States. The family has always been close. Although the family has maintained many cultural traditions from Norway, they consider America their home and are well integrated into the mainstream culture. The eldest daughter, Anna, is completing her master's degree out of state. Elisa, the youngest child, is finishing high school and had been accepted to a business program at a nearby college. Peter has been increasingly depressed and has recently experienced some vague suicidal ideation. The entire family, excluding Anna who resides in another state, wants to help and support Peter. Although everyone is busy, they have all agreed to come to family counseling.

1. *During your assessment of Peter, what are some questions that you might ask him?*
2. *What questions might you ask the other family members?*
3. *How might your assessment or treatment recommendations differ from those of a native-born U.S. family with a similar problem?*
4. *If the answer to question 3 was there is no difference in your assessment or treatment recommendations, what does it mean to your practice or for your client?*

TRANSCULTURAL RISK AND PROTECTIVE FACTORS

Increasingly, research is examining and identifying risk and protective factors that may be generalizable across cultures and ethnicities. However, only a few such factors have been identified. A history of previous suicide attempt is the most consistent risk factor for repeat attempts across ethnic groups (e.g., Hispanics, African Americans, and Caucasians), particularly for males (Borowsky et al., 2001; Colucci & Martin, 2007). Other risk factors that appear to be universal include youth or old age, low-socioeconomic standing, substance use, and recent stressful life events. Exposure to the suicide of a family member or friend appears to be another universal risk factor for suicide (Colucci & Martin, 2007; Rew, Thomas, Horner, Resnick, & Beuhring, 2001). However, much more research is needed in this area to further demonstrate and understand this relationship. Among adolescents, parent–family connectedness has been identified as a protective factor for attempting suicide that appears to be universal (Borowsky et al., 2001).

Research in this area is fraught with difficulty. Given the tremendous influence that social (attitudes toward suicide, gender norms and roles, socioeconomic status, etc.) and interpersonal factors (quality of familial functioning, peer support, marriage, etc.) have on the risk of suicidality and how greatly these factors are affected and vary by culture, race, and ethnicity, it is unlikely that many universal risk factors exist. Additionally, it is unlikely that prevention or intervention efforts based solely on transcultural risk factors can effectively reduce suicidal behavior.

CULTURE-SPECIFIC RISK AND PROTECTIVE FACTORS

It is essential to consider the unique risk and protective factors among specific ethnic groups to ensure that assessment, prevention, and intervention efforts target the most prevalent, significant issues.

Caucasians. More often than African Americans, Caucasians who engage in suicidal behavior are older and have anxiety disorders (Garlow et al., 2005; Vanderwerker et al., 2007). Caucasians also commit suicide more frequently in the context of a major depressive episode than do African Americans (Hollis, 1996; Malone et al., 2000; Oquendo et al., 2001; Shaffer et al., 1996). A major risk factor for suicide among Caucasians is disrupted family environment (Handy, Chithiramohan, Ballard, & Silveira, 1991). Suicide attempts among Caucasians have also been shown to be associated with alcohol use (Groves, Stanley, & Sher, 2007; Vanderwerker et al., 2007), with Caucasians consuming alcohol before committing suicide twice as often as African Americans (Groves et al., 2007). Loss of a family member or friend to suicide (Borowsky et al., 2001; Brent, Bridge, Johnson, & Connolly, 1996, Brent et al., 1993), access to firearms (Brent, Perper, Moritz, Baugher, et al., 1993), and female gender (Grossman, Milligan, & Deyo, 1991; Lefebvre, Lesage, Cyr, & Toupin, 1998; Moscicki et al., 1988; Pirkis, Burgess, & Dunt, 2000; Schmidtke et al., 1996; Suominen, Isometsa, Haukka, & Lonnqvist, 2004; Woods et al., 1997) have also been identified as risk factors among Caucasians. Particularly among elderly Caucasians, physical illness has also been shown to be associated with increased risk of suicidality (Vanderwerker et al., 2007). Further, low income has been demonstrated to be associated with increased risk of suicidal ideation and behavior among non-Hispanic Whites (McMillan, Enns, Asmundson, & Sareen, 2010; Purselle, Heninger, Hanzlick, & Garlow, 2009).

Major protective factors against suicide for Caucasians include marriage, female gender, low levels of aggression and impulsivity, and religiosity (Oquendo et al., 2004, 2005). Among Caucasian youths, family cohesion has been identified as a major protective factor against suicidality (Borowsky et al., 2001).

African Americans. Interpersonal conflict, male gender, and younger age have been shown to be consistent predictors of suicide among African Americans (Gibbs, 1997; Groves et al., 2007).

In general, negative family interaction has been found to be associated with increased odds of suicide ideation among African Americans (Lincoln, Taylor, Chatters, & Joe, 2012). For example, African American youth who experience parental conflict are approximately seven times more likely to engage in suicidal behavior than those who do not experience parental conflict (Groves et al., 2007). Overall, African Americans are twice as likely as Caucasians to choose a violent method of suicide (Stack & Wasserman, 2005). For example, African Americans aged 15 years and older are twice as likely as Caucasians to commit suicide via the use of firearms (Joe, Marcus, & Kaplan, 2007). African Americans who engage in suicidal behaviors are more likely than their Caucasian peers to use cocaine (Garlow, 2002). Increased risk of suicidal ideation among African Americans has also been shown to be associated with substance use, specifically alcohol and marijuana (Lorenzo-Luaces & Phillips, 2014). In terms of socioeconomic status, lower levels of education have been found to be associated with increased suicide risk (Kellerman et al., 1992), and African Americans are more likely than Caucasians to have lower levels of education (U.S. Census Bureau, 2015). Additionally, unemployed individuals have more than twice the suicide risk of employed white-collar workers (Cubbin, LeClere, & Smith, 2000), and both African American males and females are more likely to be unemployed than their Caucasian counterparts (Bureau of Labor Statistics, 2004).

Yet, African Americans, in general, have a lower rate of suicide than Caucasians and Hispanics and report greater reasons for living than Caucasians, particularly regarding moral objections to suicide and survival- and coping-related beliefs (Molock & Barksdale, 2013; Morrison & Downey, 2000; Yip, Callanan, & Yuen, 2000). Strong religious ties and family cohesiveness have been identified as protective factors (Ali & Maharajh, 2005; Hirsch, Webb, & Kaslow, 2014; June, Segal, Coolidge, & Klebe, 2009; Walker, 2007) among African Americans.

Hispanics. Acculturative stress has been found to be a risk factor for suicide ideation and behavior among Hispanics, specifically adolescents (Cervantes, Goldbach, Varela, &

Santisteban, 2014; Humensky et al., 2013; Smokowski, David-Ferdon, & Stroupe, 2009; Vega et al., 1993). The impact of acculturative stress on suicide risk is increased in the presence of substance use (Vega et al., 1993). Young age is a risk factor for suicide among Puerto Ricans and Mexicans. Fatalism, or the belief that life is predetermined by fate, is a risk factor for suicide among Hispanics, as it places the locus of control outside of the individual and reduces an individual's desire to cope with and manage stressors (Hoppe & Martin, 1986; Hovey & King, 1997; Sorenson SB & Golding, 1988). Among Hispanic adolescent males, acculturative stress is associated with suicidal thoughts, while discrimination stress is associated with both suicidal thoughts and self-harm behavior; whereas for females, acculturation stress and immigration stress are associated with self-harm behaviors (Cervantes et al., 2014).

Among Latina adolescents, research has examined the relationship between their notably high rate of suicide attempts and the quality/nature of the mother–daughter relationship. Consistently, research indicates that underlying their suicide attempts is often a cultural discontinuity in which Latina adolescents struggle to reconcile traditional Hispanic gender role expectations with their own modern Western societal values and beliefs. This discontinuity often results in tension and conflict between daughter and mother that lead to escalating stress that triggers a suicide attempt (Zayas, Aguilar-Gaxiola, Yoon, & Rey, 2015; Zayas & Gulbas, 2012; Zayas, Gulbas, Fedoravicius, & Cabassa, 2010; Zayas, Hausmann-Stabile, & De Luca, 2015).

Familism, which emphasizes close relationships with immediate family and extended family networks, serves as a protective factor against suicide for Hispanics (Hovey & King, 1997; Kuhlberg et al., 2010; Oquendo et al., 2005; Polanco-Roman & Miranda, 2013) and Hispanics have been shown to endorse greater responsibility toward family than their non-Hispanic counterparts (Oquendo et al., 2005). Moral objections to suicide, and survival and coping beliefs are also stronger among Hispanics than non-Hispanics (Oquendo et al., 2005). Religious activities, in general, have been shown to be protective against suicidality (Dervic et al., 2004; Neeleman, Halpern, Leon, & Lewis, 1997) and have been shown to lead to greater coping skills (Morrison & Downey, 2000; Neeleman & Wessely, 1999). Among Hispanics, in particular, religiosity is a protective factor against suicide (Oquendo et al., 2005). Old age is also a protective factor against suicide among Hispanics (Group for the Advancement of Psychiatry, 1989).

Asian Americans. Among Asian adolescents, a diagnosis of depression leads to a four-fold increase in suicidality as compared to other psychiatric disorders (Groves et al., 2007). High parental conflict increases suicide risk by as much as 30-fold as compared to low parental conflict (Groves et al., 2007; Lau, Jernewall, Zane, & Myers, 2002). A lower level of acculturation is an additional risk factor for suicidality among Asian Americans, particularly in the presence of parental conflict (Lau et al., 2002). Hopelessness is predictive of suicide among the Chinese, in particular (Stewart et al., 2005).

Risk factors for suicide among the Chinese are related primarily to psychiatric illness and poor health (Zhang, Conwell, ZHou, & Jiang, 2004). Secondary predictors include a lack of social support, negative life events, lower socioeconomic status (SES), religious affiliation, and family conflict (Zhang et al., 2004). Among young rural Chinese women, for example, recent negative life events related to family relations, love affairs, and marital issues were most likely to precede a suicide (Zhang, 2014). Some suggest that political and social environment may be more influential risk factors than economic factors for Asian populations (Yip, 1996). Among female Chinese, traditional values of obedience and respect have been found to be protective against suicide attempts, independent of quality of family relationships (Lam et al., 2004). Impulsivity is a risk factor for suicide among Chinese females (Pearson, Phillip, He, & Ji, 2002). Risk factors for suicide in South Asians include domestic violence, negative family environment, and depression (Ahmed & Mohan, 2007; Hicks & Bhugra, 2003). Academic stress is a risk factor for suicide among Koreans (Dawkins, 1996).

Case Vignette 2.2

You are scheduled to do an intake with a new client who you learn is a 16-year-old first-generation Mexican-American female. Your new client, Lourdes, was referred by her school guidance counselor after her gym teacher overheard her in the locker-room at school telling her friend, in a very distressed tone, that she felt like killing herself. The gym teacher had noticed that lately Lourdes had seemed more withdrawn, less energetic, and lacking in concentration and attention. Upon hearing this statement, the gym teacher notified the school guidance counselor who then met with Lourdes. Lourdes expressed feeling "stressed" over increasing conflicts with her mother that centered largely on their disagreements over curfews, dating, dropping grades, going to church, and having to take care of her two younger brothers (aged 5 and 11 years). Lourdes explained that her father was "cool." He understood and cared for her, but her mother was more concerned about what other people would think and did not take the time to understand what Lourdes wanted. "She's too stuck back in Mexico and doesn't realize this is LA!" Lourdes explained that she had great friends and their parents understood them, they didn't have curfews and were allowed to date. She just wished her mom could be like them but since that would never happen, "What's the point?" The guidance counselor was very concerned about the seriousness of Lourdes's suicidal ideation and promptly made a referral for outpatient services.

1. *What risk factors are present in the Case Vignette?*
2. *What protective factors are present in the Case Vignette?*
3. *What areas would you target for treatment with this client?*
4. *How would your answers to questions 1 to 3 be different or similar if the client was a Latino rather than a Latina?*

ROLE-PLAY 2.1

Using Case Vignette 2.2 of Lourdes, engage in a role-play in which you would assess for culturally relevant risk and protective factors for suicidal behavior. Have one person take on the role of the clinician and the other, that of Lourdes.

INTERNATIONAL PERSPECTIVES AND ATTITUDES ON SUICIDE

Lay theories are intrinsic or commonsense beliefs held by lay persons (Walker, Lester, & Sean, 2006). Lay beliefs and acceptability of suicide differ across cultural, ethnic, and societal groups (Angermeyer & Matschinger, 1999; Knight, Furnham, & Lester, 2000). In some cultures, suicide is a positive moral act, and, in other cultures, suicide is an unaccepted forbidden act that is equated with a mental disorder.

Cultural differences within cultures also exert influence on beliefs about and attitudes toward suicide (Pridmore & Walter, 2013). For example, in the Indian subcontinent, female suicide rates are among the highest in the world (Bhugra, 2005; Thompson & Bhugra, 2000). Traditional and cultural beliefs regarding rigid roles and position of women contribute to their increased suicide risk. Deference to males, arranged marriages, viewing women as the property of males, restricted life opportunities, limited access to mental health services, high rates of domestic violence, and the ritual act Sati or burning themselves on their husband's funeral pyre influence the attitudes of women toward suicide (Bhugra, 2005; Thompson & Bhugra, 2000).

In Japan, where being part of the society is more important than being an individual, there is a traditional acceptance of suicide (jisatsu) as an acceptable and appropriate behavior in certain circumstances (Pfeffer, 1991). Also, suicide in not interpreted as a denial of life, but rather an affirmation of the value of one's moral duty to others (giri; Young, 2002). Also, there is less traditional sanctioning for double suicide (shinju; e.g., parent–child suicide or husband–wife) or youth suicide (Pfeffer, 1991). The collectivist values of Japan are distinctly different from the autonomous values held in North America, thereby influencing the respective cultures' perspective on suicide.

Ethnic and cultural groups within the United States may hold different beliefs on who has greater influence and control over their lives (e.g., God, individual, the government), and what circumstances may dictate when suicide is an option (e.g., intrapsychic, interpersonal, or societal difficulties; Walker et al., 2006). According to Walker and colleagues (2006), European Americans are more likely than African Americans to attribute suicidal thoughts to interpersonal problems (e.g., conflict, work stress, broken home). In addition, European Americans attribute ownership of life to the individual or government, whereas African Americans attribute ownership of life to God.

This suggests that when working with individuals, irrespective of their origin of birth, it is important to explore and assess the impact of their culture(s) on their beliefs, attitudes, and values toward life and death, specifically in relation to suicide. The process of collecting this information may not only facilitate and strengthen the engagement and therapeutic alliance with the individual but can also provide valuable information on potential protective and/or risk factors that may be incorporated into treatment strategies.

In a recent multilevel cross-national analysis on culture and suicide acceptability, Stack & Rockett (2016) examined the relationship across countries of survivalism (e.g., intolerance, mistrust of others) versus self-expressionism (e.g., tolerance, trust of others) and suicide acceptability. Results found that nations high in self-expressionism were also relatively high in suicide acceptability. Results of this study also suggest that there may exist a general cultural shift throughout the world from survivalism to self-expressionism. Such a shift could signify a notable challenge to current and future suicide prevention efforts as it may indicate a changing global view of the acceptability of suicide (Stack & Rockett, 2016).

Small Group Exercise 2.2

Complete the answers first individually, then discuss in groups of four to six.

1. Is your work with a client whose cultural background supports suicide as an acceptable behavior different from your work with a client whose cultural background clearly sanctions suicide? Explain.
2. How would your answer to question 1 differ if the client were of the same cultural/ethnic background as you, yet still held differing views on suicide?
3. Is it appropriate to initiate a discussion with clients regarding their cultural beliefs/attitudes toward suicide as an acceptable or unacceptable practice? Explain. If yes, under what circumstances? Explain.

ROLE-PLAY 2.2

Divide into pairs. Have one person take on the role of the clinician and the other, the role of a client. Role-play how you would engage your client in a discussion regarding his or her cultural beliefs toward suicide.

EVIDENCE-BASED CULTURAL COMPETENCY IN WORKING WITH DIVERSE POPULATIONS

It is estimated that by the year 2050, half of the U.S. population will be people of color (Dalton, 2005). It is important to recognize that in the United States and other countries, minorities typically underutilize mental health services, particularly if they are depressed or suicidal. Researchers and practitioners have noted, with regret, the lack of ethnocultural comparative studies that are needed to develop culturally responsive prevention and intervention strategies in the field of suicidality (Colucci & Martin, 2007). Evidence-based cultural competency in working with diverse populations is a developing field. Although evidence-based practices (EBP) are increasingly being developed for specific populations (e.g., gender, developmental stage, age) and issues (e.g., diagnosis, presenting problems, social concerns), there is a gap in the development of EBPs that target specific populations and cultures. Increasingly, however, clinical and intervention researchers are investigating the adaptation of existing EBPs to targeted cultures and groups (see Chapters 5–8 for EBPs within suicidality). Researchers in the field of suicidality are finding that each culture exerts positive and negative influences on suicidality, and interventions will need to incorporate these cultural differences as they emerge and are identified (Bhugra & Mastrogianni, 2004). It is also recommended that evidence-based research needs a finer focus on the ethnic group and that research findings need to be placed into a sociopolitical and cultural context (Colucci & Martin, 2007).

Clinicians are increasingly recognizing the importance of practicing with cultural competency. It is essential that clinicians be sensitive to the cultural expectations and issues of clients and of the cultural differences between the clients and themselves (Dalton, 2005). According to Derald Sue and colleagues (Sue & Sue, 2003), cultural competence requires practitioners to work toward several goals (Sue et al., 1982; Sue, Arredondo, & McDavis, 1992; Sue & Sue, 2003). Specifically, practitioners must:

1. Actively and continually seek to become aware of their own assumptions, biases, values, and personal limitations;
2. Recognize that their worldview is different from their clients;
3. Be in the process of actively developing practicing appropriate, sensitive, and relevant intervention strategies and skills in working with culturally diverse clients (Sue & Sue, 2003).

Research has indicated that the ability to work from a culturally competent perspective remains an area of concern in the field of suicidality. Burr's (2002) study on mental health care professionals' explanation for patterns of suicide in South Asian communities found that stereotypes have been taken as facts, potentially resulting in misdiagnosis and treatment. Cultural competency is an active process in which the practitioner remains engaged with the individual in front of him or her and does not presuppose an understanding of the client based on an awareness of his or her cultural group. Practitioners and researchers have warned that by emphasizing cultural differences one may run the risk of increasing prejudice toward different cultures and reinforcing overgeneralizations (Takahashi, 1997).

Small Group Exercise 2.3

Complete the answers first individually, then discuss in groups of two to three.

1. List the cultural groups that you are most familiar working with. Be specific.
2. List the cultural groups that you are least familiar working with. Again be specific.
3. What are some of the advantages of being familiar with/knowledgeable about the cultural groups with which you may work?
4. What are some of the disadvantages of being familiar with/knowledgeable about the cultural groups with which you may work?
5. What are some of the advantages of being unfamiliar with/less knowledgeable about the cultural groups with which you may work?
6. What are some of the disadvantages of being unfamiliar with/less knowledgeable about the cultural groups with which you may work?
7. Are there groups that you might feel less comfortable working with? Explain.

Small Group Exercise 2.4

After discussing your answers to Small Group Exercise 2.3, consider the following questions.

1. Were there any similarities and/or differences that emerged between your answers?
2. What may account for these patterns or differences? What does this mean for your work with clients whose cultural background is similar to yours? What does this mean for your work with clients who come from a cultural background different from yours?
3. What did you learn or can take away from this exercise?

Small Group Exercise 2.5

In a large group, discuss your observations from Small Group Exercises 2.3 and 2.4, including answers that you expected or did not expect. How might this knowledge improve your cultural competency and practice?

SUMMARY

Despite improved treatments for the psychiatric illnesses most associated with suicidal behavior, suicide continues to be a growing problem in the United States and the world. In order for prevention and intervention efforts to be successful, they must take into consideration the impact of culture, race, and ethnicity. There remains an urgent need to continue to investigate risk and protective factors and treatment implications relating to ethnic and cultural differences and suicidology (Stansfeld, 2012). As risk and protective factors vary across ethnicities, so do attitudes and perspectives regarding suicide acceptability.

Intervention efforts should stem from a culturally competent approach, and prevention efforts should be guided by culturally relevant risk and protective factors for suicide and attitudes toward suicide among the target population.

KEY POINTS

1. The overall number of suicides in the United States remained relatively stable over the past decade until recently when the rates have increased, particularly among certain ethnic and gender groups.
2. World suicide rates over the past 50 years have steadily increased.
3. Globally, prevention efforts remain largely ineffective at addressing the growing problem of suicide.
4. Immigration is a complex phenomenon that has the potential to affect suicide risk.
5. Acculturation stress is a major risk factor for suicide among certain cultural/ ethnic groups.
6. Attitudes and beliefs toward suicide vary across cultures and ethnicities and exert a direct influence on suicide risk.
7. When assessing for suicide risk with clients, it is essential to consider culture, race, and ethnicity to accurately identify relevant risk factors that may contribute to increased suicidality.
8. Protective factors that promote resilience vary by culture, race, and ethnicity.
9. Empirically supported treatment and EBPs are increasingly being developed and adapted for specific populations and presenting problems; however, there is a gap in the development of specific treatments that uniquely intersect populations, issues, and cultures.
10. Culturally competent practice is an active and ongoing process on the part of the practitioner who requires remaining engaged with the individual in front of him or her and not assuming an understanding of the client based on an awareness of his or her cultural group.

ELECTRONIC RESOURCES

LATINOS

http://www.pacificclinics.org
http://healthymindsnetwork.org
www.immigrationforum.org
http://alianzas.us

ASIANS

http://www.sprc.org/populations/asian-pacific-islanders
www.asian-nation.org/headlines/2007/05/when-too-much-pressure-leads-to-suicide

NATIVE AMERICANS

www.turtleisland.org/healing/healing-suicide.htm
www.ahf.ca

MULTICULTURAL RESOURCES
CENTER FOR MULTICULTURAL HUMAN SERVICES
www.cmhsweb.org

NATIONAL ORGANIZATION FOR PEOPLE OF COLOR AGAINST SUICIDE
www.nopcas.com

MENTAL HEALTH: RACE, CULTURE AND ETHNICITY A SUPPLEMENT TO MENTAL HEALTH: A REPORT OF THE SURGEON GENERAL
www.surgeongeneral.gov/library/mentalhealth/cre

SUICIDE FACT SHEETS SPECIFIC FOR FOUR AMERICAN POPULATIONS
http://library.sprc.org/browse.php?catid=116637

KNOWLEDGE ACQUISITION TEST (KAT)

True or False

1. Suicide rates in developing countries are lower than in developed countries.
2. Crowded housing can be a protective factor against suicide for immigrants.
3. First-generation immigrants are at more risk of suicide death than second-generation immigrants.
4. Regardless of the culture, suicide is universally perceived as an unacceptable action.
5. Immigration is a stressful life event.
6. Psychiatric illness is not a universal risk factor for suicide across cultures.
7. There is an association between suicide rates of immigrants and rates of suicide from their country of origin.
8. Old age is a protective factor against suicide across all ethnicities.
9. Providers' culture has no influence on their ability to assess or treat clients from different cultural/ethnic backgrounds.
10. Higher levels of acculturation are associated with reduced suicide risk across cultures.
11. Old age is a universal risk factor for suicide.

Short Answer

12. What are the four possible hypotheses that may mitigate suicide risk in immigrants identified in the research? Is it hypotheses or immigrants that are identified in the research?
13. In the acculturation process, describe how maintaining elements from one's old culture may be both a protective and risk factor for suicide?
14. How might an individual's beliefs regarding who controls life (e.g., God, individual, the government) influence his or her perception of suicide?
15. What accounts for the lack of suicide data that exists from developing countries?
16. What are the evidence-based universal risk and protective factors for suicide?
17. What is the stress–diathesis model of suicide?
18. What are three characteristics of a culturally competent practitioner?
19. Why is culturally competent practice particularly important when working with clients expressing suicidal thoughts and/or engaging in suicidal behavior?

Multiple Choice

20. What experience will immigrants generally not face in their new country?
    A. Linguistic barriers
    B. Prejudice and discrimination
    C. A well-developed support network
    D. Unequal access to mental health care
    E. None of the above
    F. All of the above
21. Examples of culture of origin effects that may mitigate suicide in immigrants include:
    A. The importance of establishing and maintaining strong social networks
    B. Religious beliefs
    C. Belief that suicide is unacceptable
    D. Help-seeking behavior

     E. None of the above

     F. All of the above

22. The theory of migration selectivity recognizes the following:
    A. Healthier individuals elect to migrate.
    B. Families assist and support healthier members to migrate.
    C. Individuals who are more likely to succeed are selected to immigrate.
    D. Individuals with mental health problems are less likely to immigrate and/or more likely to return to their home country.
    E. None of the above.
    F. All of the above.

23. Evidence reports a higher rate of suicide among males as compared to females in all countries EXCEPT:
    A. India
    B. America
    C. Norway
    D. Australia
    E. England
    F. Spain

24. Adolescents from which ethnicity have the highest rate of suicide?
    A. Caucasian
    B. Hispanic
    C. African American
    D. Native American
    E. None of the above
    F. All of the above

25. Country of destination factors for suicide do not generally include which of the following?
    A. Crowded housing arrangements
    B. Availability of firearms
    C. Access to medication
    D. Gender
    E. None of the above
    F. All of the above

REFERENCES

Aaron, R., Joseph, A., Abraham, S., Muliyil, J., George, K., Prasad, J., . . . Bose, A. (2004). Suicides in young people in rural southern India. *Lancet, 363*(9415), 1117–1118.

Adam, K. S., Bouckoms, A., & Streiner, D. (1982). Parental loss and family stability in attempted suicide. *Archives of General Psychiatry, 39,* 1081–1085.

Ahmed, K., & Mohan, R. A. (2007). Self-harm in South Asian women: A literature review informed approach to assessment and formulation. *American Journal of Psychotherapy, 61*(1), 71–81.

Ali, A., & Maharajh, H. D. (2005). Social predictors of suicidal behaviour in adolescents in Trinidad and Tobago. *Social Psychiatry and Psychiatric Epidemiology, 40*(3), 186–191.

Angermeyer, M. C., & Matschinger, H. (1999). Lay beliefs about mental disorders: A comparison between the western and the eastern parts of Germany. *Social Psychiatry and Psychiatric Epidemiology, 34*(5), 275–281.

Baillargeon, J., Ducate, S., Pulvino, J., Bradshaw, P., Murray, O., & Olvera, R. (2003). The association of psychiatric disorders and HIV infection in the correctional setting. *Annals of Epidemiology, 13*(9), 606–612.

Beck-Cross, C., & Cooper, R. (2015). Micro- and macrosystem predictors of high school male suicidal behaviors. *Children and Schools, 37*(4), 231–239.

Berry, J. W., & Kim, U. (1988). *Acculturation and mental health.* London, UK: Sage.

Bhugra, D. (2002). Suicidal behavior in South Asians in the UK. *Crisis: Journal of Crisis Intervention and Suicide, 23*(3), 108–113.

Bhugra, D. (2005). Sati: A type of non-psychiatric suicide. *Crisis: The Journal of Crisis Intervention and Suicide Prevention, 26*(2):73–77.

Bhugra, D., Desai, M., & Baldwin, D. S. (1999). Attempted suicide in west London, I. Rates across ethnic communities. *Psychological Medicine, 29*(5), 1125–1130.

Bhugra, D., & Mastrogianni, A. (2004). Globalization and mental disorders: Overview with relation to depression. *British Journal of Psychiatry—Supplementum, 184,* 10–20.

Bolz, W. (2002). Psychological analysis of the Sri Lankan conflict culture with special reference to the high suicide rate. *Crisis: The Journal of Crisis Intervention and Suicide Prevention, 23*(4), 167–170.

Borges, G., Orozco, R., Rafful, C., Miller, E., & Breslau, J. (2012). Suicidality, ethnicity and immigration in the USA. *Psychological Medicine, 42,* 1175–1184.

Borowsky, I. W., Ireland, M., & Resnick, M. D. (2001). Adolescent suicide attempts: Risks and protectors. *Pediatrics, 107,* 485–493.

Brent, D. A., Bridge, J., Johnson, B. A., & Connolly, J. (1996). Suicidal behavior runs in families: A controlled family study of adolescent suicide victims. *Archives of General Psychiatry, 53*(12), 1145–1152.

Brent, D. A., Perper, J. A., Moritz, G., Allman, C., Schweers, J., Roth, C., . . . Liotus, L. (1993). Psychiatric sequelae to the loss of an adolescent peer to suicide. *Journal of the American Academy of Child & Adolescent Psychiatry, 32,* 509–517.

Brent, D. A., Perper, J., Moritz, G., Baugher, M., Schweers, J., & Roth, C. (1993). Firearms and adolescent suicide: A community case-control study. *American Journal of Disorders of Childhood, 147,* 1066–1071.

Briere, J., & Runtz, M. (1990). Differential adult symptomatology associated with three types of child abuse histories. *Child Abuse and Neglect, 14,* 357–364.

Bureau of Labor Statistics. (2004). *Unemployed persons by marital status, race, Hispanic or Latino ethnicity, age, and sex.* Washington, DC: U.S. Department of Labor. Retrieved from https://www.bls.gov/cps/cpsaat24.htm

Burr, J. (2002). Cultural stereotypes of women from South Asian communities: Mental health care professionals' explanations for patterns of suicide and depression. *Social Science & Medicine, 55*(5), 835–845.

Castle, K., Conner, K., Kaukeinen, K., & Tu, X. (2011). Perceived racism, discrimination, and acculturation in suicidal ideation and suicide attempts among Black young adults. *Suicide and Life-Threatening Behavior, 41*(3), 342–351.

Centers for Disease Control and Prevention. (2006). National Center for Injury Prevention and Control. Retrieved from http://www.cdc.gov/ncipc/factsheets/suifacts.htm

Cervantes, R., Goldbach, J. T., Varela, A., & Santisteban, D. A. (2014). Self-harm among Hispanic adolescents: Investigating the role of culture-related stressors. *Journal of Adolescent Health, 55*(5), 633–639.

Chandrasena, R., Beddage, V., & Fernando, M. L. (1991). Suicide among immigrant psychiatric patients in Canada. *British Journal of Psychiatry—Supplementum, 159,* 707–709.

Chen, P. C., Lee, L. K., Wong, K. C., & Kaur, J. (2005). Factors related to adolescent suicidal behavior: A cross-sectional Malaysian school survey. *Journal of Adolescent Health, 37*(4), 337.e11–337.e16.

Colucci, E., & Martin, G. (2007). Ethnocultural aspects of suicide in young people: A systematic literature review part 2: Risk factors, precipitating agents, and attitudes toward suicide. *Suicide and Life-Threatening Behavior, 37*(2), 222–237.

Cubbin, C., LeClere, F. B., & Smith, G. S. (2000). Socioeconomic status and the occurrence of fatal and nonfatal injury in the United States. *American Journal of Public Health, 90,* 70–77.

Dalton, B. (2005). Teaching cultural assessment. *Journal of Teaching in Social Work, 25*(3–4), 45–61.

Dawkins, K. (1996). The interaction of ethnicity, sociocultural factors, and gender in clinical psychopharmacology. *Psychopharmacology Bulletin, 32*(2), 283–289.

Department of Health and Human Services (2002). *Youth Risk Behavior Survey.* Washington, DC: Center for Disease Control. Retrieved from https://www.cdc.gov/mmwr/pdf/ss/ss6104.pdf

Dervic, K., Oquendo, M. A., Grunebaum, M. F., Ellis, S., Burke, A. K., & Mann, J. J. (2004). Religious affiliation and suicide attempt. *American Journal of Psychiatry, 161*(12), 2303–2308.

Duldulao, A. A., Takeuchi, D. T., & Seunghye, H. (2009). Correlates of suicidal behaviors among Asian Americans. *Archives of Suicide Research, 13*(3), 277–290.

Eaton, D. K., Foti, K., Brener, N. D., Crosby, A. E., Flores, G., & Kann, L. (2011). Associations between risk behaviors and suicidal ideation and suicide attempts: Do racial/ethnic variations in associations account for increased risk of suicidal behaviors among Hispanic/Latina 9th- to 12th-grade female students? *Archives of Suicide Research, 15*(2), 113–126.

Eshun, S. (2006). Acculturation and suicide attitudes: A study of perceptions about suicide among a sample of Ghanaian immigrants in the United States. *Psychological Reports, 99*(1), 295–304.

Evans, E., Hawton, K., Rodham, K., & Deeks, J. (2005). The prevalence of suicidal phenomena in adolescents: A systematic review of population-based studies. *Suicide and Life-Threatening Behavior, 35*(3), 239–250.

Farber, E. W., Herbert, S. E., & Reviere, S. L. (1996). Child abuse and suicidality in obstetrics patients in a hospital-based urban prenatal clinic. *General Hospital Psychiatry, 18,* 56–60.

Garlow, S. J. (2002). Age, gender, and ethnicity differences in patterns of cocaine and ethanol use preceding suicide. *American Journal of Psychiatry, 159,* 615–619.

Garlow, S. J., Purselle, D., & Heninger, M. (2005). Ethnic differences in patterns of suicide across the life cycle. *American Journal of Psychiatry, 162,* 319–323.

Gibbs, J. T. (1997). African-American suicide: A cultural paradox. *Suicide and Life-Threatening Behavior, 27,* 68–79.

Goldney, R. D. (2002). A global view of suicidal behaviour. *Emergency Medicine, 14,* 24–34.

Gomez, J., Miranda, R., & Polanco, L. (2011). Acculturative stress, perceived discrimination, and vulnerability to suicide attempts among emerging adults. *Journal of Youth and Adolescence, 40*(11), 1465.

Gray, J. S., & McCullagh, J. A. (2014). Suicide in Indian country: The continuing epidemic in rural Native American communities. *Journal of Rural Mental Health, 38*(2), 79–86.

Greenfield, B., Rousseau, C., Slatkoff, J., Lewkowski, M., Davis, M., Dube, S., . . . Harnden, B. (2006). Profile of a metropolitan North American immigrant suicidal adolescent population. *Canadian Journal of Psychiatry, 51,* 155–159.

Grossman, D. C., Milligan, B. C., & Deyo, R. A. (1991). Risk factors for suicide attempts among Navajo adolescents. *American Journal of Public Health, 81,* 870–874.

Group for the Advancement of Psychiatry (1989). Suicide and ethnicity in the United States. *Committee on Cultural Psychiatry, 128,* 1–131.

Groves, S. A., Stanley, B., & Sher, L. (2007). Ethnicity and the relationship between adolescent alcohol use and suicidal behavior. *International Journal of Adolescent Medicine & Health, 19*(1), 19–25.

Gutierrez, P. M., Osman, A., Kopper, B. A., & Barrios, F. X. (2000). Why young people do not kill themselves: The reasons for living inventory for adolescents. *Journal of Clinical Child Psychology, 29,* 177–187.

Handy, S., Chithiramohan, R. N., Ballard, C. G., & Silveira, W. R. (1991). Ethnic differences in adolescent self-poisoning: A comparison of Asian and Caucasian groups. *Journal of Adolescence, 14*(2), 157–162.

Hicks, M. H. R., & Bhugra, D. (2003). Perceived causes of suicide attempts by U.K. South Asian women. *American Journal of Orthopsychiatry, 73*(4), 455–462.

Hirsch, J. K., Webb, J. R., & Kaslow, N. J. (2014). Daily hassles and suicide ideation in African American female suicide attempters: Moderating effect of spiritual well-being. *Mental Health, Religion & Culture, 17*(5), 529–541.

Hollis, C. (1996). Depression, family environment, and adolescent suicidal behavior. *Journal of the American Academy of Child & Adolescent Psychiatry, 35,* 622–630.

Hoppe, S. K., & Martin, H. W. (1986). Patterns of suicide among Mexican Americans and Anglos, 1960–1980. *Social Psychiatry, 21,* 83–88.

Hovey, J. D. (2000). Acculturative stress, depression, and suicidal ideation among Central American immigrants. *Suicide and Life-Threatening Behavior, 30*(2), 125–139.

Hovey, J. D., & King, C. A. (1996). Acculturative stress, depression, and suicidal ideation among immigrant and second-generation Latino adolescents. *Journal of the American Academy of Child & Adolescent Psychiatry, 35*(9), 1183–1192.

Hovey, J. D., & King, C. A. (1997). Suicidality among acculturating Mexican Americans: Current knowledge and directions for research. *Suicide and Life-Threatening Behavior, 27*(1), 92–103.

Humensky, J. L., Gil, R., Coronel, B., Cifre, R., Mazzula, S., & Lewis-Fernandez, R. (2013). Life is precious: Reducing suicidal behavior in Latinas. *Ethnicity and Inequalities in Health and Social Care, 6*(2–3), 54–61.

Ji, J., & Kleinman, A. (2001). Suicide in contemporary China: A review of China's distinctive suicide demographics in their sociocultural context. *Harvard Review of Psychiatry, 9*(1), 1–12.

Joe, S., Baser, R. E., Breeden, G., Neighbors, H. W., & Jackson, J. S. (2006). Prevalence of and risk factors for lifetime suicide attempts among Blacks in the United States. *Journal of the American Medical Academy, 296,* 2112–2123.

Joe, S., Marcus, S. C., & Kaplan, M. S. (2007). Racial differences in the characteristics of firearm suicide decedents in the United States. *American Journal of Orthopsychiatry, 77*(1), 124–130.

Johansson, L., M., Sundquist, J., Johansson, S. E., Bergman, B., Qvist, J., & Traskman-Bendz, L. (1997). Suicide among foreign-born minorities and native Swedes: An epidemiological follow-up study of a defined population. *Social Science & Medicine, 44*(2), 181–187.

June, A., Segal, D. L., Coolidge, F. L., & Klebe, K. (2009). Religiousness, social support and reasons for living in African American and European American older adults: An exploratory study. *Aging & Mental Health, 13*(5), 753–760.

Kellermann, A. L., Rivara, F. P., Somes, G., Reay, D. T., Francisco, J., Banton, J. G., . . . Hackman, B. B. (1992). Suicide in the home in relation to gun ownership. *The New England Journal of Medicine, 327*(7), 467–472.

Kennedy, M. A., Parhar, K. K., Samra, J., & Gorzalka, B. (2005). Suicide ideation in different generations of immigrants. *Canadian Journal of Psychiatry, 50*(6), 353–356.

Khan, M. M. (2002). Suicide on the Indian subcontinent. *Crisis: The Journal of Crisis Intervention and Suicide Prevention, 23*(3), 104–107.

Khan, M. M. (2005). Suicide prevention and developing countries. *Journal of the Royal Society of Medicine, 98,* 459–463.

Khan, M. M., & Hyder, A. A. (2006). Suicides in the developing world: Case study from Pakistan. *Suicide and Life-Threatening Behavior, 36,* 76–81.

Kleinman, J. J., & Becker, A. E. (2001). Suicide in contemporary China: A review of China's distinctive suicide demographics in their sociocultural context. *Harvard Review of Psychiatry, 9*(1), 1–12.

Knight, M. T. D., Furnham, A. F., & Lester, D. (2000). Lay theories of suicide. *Personality and Individual Differences, 29*(3), 453–457.

Kohn, R., Levav, I., Chang, B., Halperin, B., & Zadka, P. (1997). Epidemiology of youth in Israel. *Journal of the American Academy of Child & Adolescent Psychiatry, 36*(11), 1537–1542.

Kuhlberg, J. A., Pena, J. B., & Zayas, L. H. (2010). Familism, parent-adolescent conflict, self-esteem, internalizing behaviors and suicide attempts among adolescent Latinas. *Child Psychiatry & Human Development, 41*(4), 425–440.

Kushner, H. I. (1991). *American suicide: A psychocultural exploration.* New Brunswick, NJ: Rutger University Press.

Lam, T. H., Stewart, S. M., Yip, P. S., Leung, G. M., Ho, L. M., Ho, S. Y., & Lee, P. W. (2004). Suicidality and cultural values among Hong Kong adolescents. *Social Science & Medicine, 58*(3), 487–498.

Lau, A. S., Jernewall, N. M., Zane, N., & Myers, H. F. (2002). Correlates of suicidal behaviors among Asian American outpatient youth. *Cultural Diversity & Ethnic Minority Psychology, 8*(3), 199–213.

Lefebvre, F., Lesage, A., Cyr, M., & Toupin, J. (1998). Factors related to utilization of services for mental health reasons in Montreal, Canada. *Social Psychiatry and Psychiatric Epidemiology, 33,* 291–298.

Lessenger, L. H. (1997). Use of acculturation rating scale for Mexican Americans-II with substance abuse patients. *Hispanic Journal of Behavioral Sciences, 19*(3), 387–399.

Lester, D. (1987). National distribution of blood groups, personal violence (suicide and homicide), and national character. *Personality and Individual Differences, 8,* 575–576.

Lester, D. (1991). The association between platelet imipramine binding sites and suicide. *Pharmacopsychiatry, 24,* 232.

Lester, D. (1997a). Suicide in America: A nation of immigrants. *Suicide and Life-Threatening Behavior, 27*(1), 50–59.

Lester, D. (1997b). Suicide in an international perspective. *Suicide and Life-Threatening Behavior, 27*(1), 104–111.

Lester, D. (1998). Suicide rates of immigrants. *Psychological Reports, 82*(1), 50.

Lester, D. (1999). Native American suicide rates, acculturation stress and traditional integration. *Psychological Reports, 84*(2), 398.

Levi, L. D., Fales, C. H., Stein, M., & Sharp, V. H. (1966). Separation and attempted suicide. *Archives of General Psychiatry, 15,* 158–164.

Lincoln, K. D., Taylor, R. J., Chatters, L. M., & Joe, S. (2012). Suicide, negative interaction and emotional support among Black Americans. *Social Psychiatry and Psychiatric Epidemiology, 47*(12), 1947–1958.

Lorenzo-Luaces, L., & Phillips, J. (2014). Racial and ethnic differences in risk factors associated with suicidal behavior among young adults in the U.S.A. *Ethnicity and Health, 19*(4), 458–477.

Malone, K. M., Haas, G. L., Sweeny, J. A., & Mann, J. J. (1995). Major depression and the risk of attempted suicide. *Journal of Affective Disorders, 34,* 173–185.

Malone, K. M., Oquendo, M. A., Haas, G. L., Ellis, S. P., Li, S., & Mann, J. J. (2000). Protective factors against suicidal acts in major depression: Reasons for living. *American Journal of Psychiatry, 157,* 1084–1088.

Mann, J. J., Waternaux, C., Haas, G. L., & Malone, K. M. (1999). Towards a clinical model of suicidal behavior in psychiatric patients. *American Journal of Psychiatry, 156,* 181–189.

Marmot, M. G., Adelstein, A. M., & Bulusu, L. (1984). Lessons from the study of immigrant mortality. *Lancet, 1*(8392), 1455–1457.

Marusic, A., & Farmer, A. (2001). Genetic risk factors as possible causes of the variation in European suicide rates. *The British Journal of Psychiatry, 179,* 194–196.

Mayer, P., & Zianian, T. (2002). Suicide, gender, and age variations in India: Are women in Indian society protected from suicide? *Crisis: The Journal of Crisis Intervention and Prevention Suicide, 23*(3), 98–103.

McKenzie, K., Serfaty, M., & Crawford, M. (2003). Suicide in ethnic minority groups. *British Journal of Psychiatry—Supplementum, 183*(2), 100–101.

McMillan, K. A., Enns, M. W., Asmundson, G. J. G., & Sareen, J. (2010). The association between income and distress, mental disorders, and suicidal ideation and attempts: Findings from the collaborative psychiatric epidemiology surveys. *The Journal of Clinical Psychiatry, 71*(9), 1168–1175.

Milner, A., Sveticic, J., & De Leo, D. (2013). Suicide in the absence of mental disorder? A review of psychological autopsy studies across countries. *International Journal of Social Psychiatry, 59*(6), 545–554.

Molock, S., & Barksdale, C. (2013). Relationship between religiosity and conduct problems among African American and Caucasian adolescents. *Journal of Child and Family Studies, 22*(1), 4–14.

Monk, M., & Warshauer, M. E. (1974). Completed and attempted suicide in three ethnic groups. *American Journal of Epidemiology, 130,* 348–360.

Morad, M., Merrick, E., Schwarz, A., & Merrick, J. (2005). A review of suicide behavior among Arab adolescents. *The Scientific World Journal, 5,*674–679.

Morrison, L. L., & Downey, D. L. (2000). Racial differences in self-disclosure of suicidal ideation and reasons for living: Implications for training. *Cultural Diversity & Ethnic Minority Psychology, 6,* 374–386.

Moscicki, E. K., O'Carroll, P., Rae, D. S., Locke, B. Z., Roy, A., & Regier, D. A. (1988). Suicide attempts in the Epidemiologic Catchment Area Study. *Yale Journal of Biology and Medicine, 61,* 259–268.

Neeleman, J., Halpern, D., Leon, D., & Lewis, G. T. (1997). Tolerance of suicide, religion, and suicide rates: An ecological and individual study in 19 Western countries. *Psychological Medicine, 227,* 1165–1171.

Neeleman, J., & Wessely, S. (1999). Ethnic minority suicide: A small geographical study in south London. *Psychological Medicine, 29*(2), 429–436.

Oquendo, M. A., Dragatsi, D., Harkavy-Friedman, J., Dervic, K., Currier, D., Burke, A. K, . . . Mann, J. J. (2005). Protective factors against suicidal behavior in Latinos. *Journal of Nervous and Mental Disease, 193,* 438–443.

Oquendo, M. A., Ellis, S. P., Greenwald, S., Malone, K. M., Weissman, M. M., & Mann, J. J. (2001). Ethnic and sex differences in suicide rates relative to major depression in the United States. *American Journal of Psychiatry, 158*(10), 1652–1658.

Oquendo, M. A., Lizardi, D., Greenwald, S., Weissman, M. M., & Mann, J. J. (2004). Rates of lifetime suicide attempt and rates of lifetime major depression in different ethnic groups in the United States. *Acta Psychiatrica Scandinavica, 110*(6), 446–451.

Padilla, A. M., Cervantes, R. C., Maldonado, M., & Garcia, R. E. (1988). Coping responses to psychosocial stressors among Mexican and Central American immigrants. *Journal of Community Psychology, 16,* 418–427.

Passel, J. S., & Cohn, D. (2011). U.S. population projections: 2005–2050. Pew Research: Hispanic Trends. Retrieved from http://www.pewhispanic.org/2008/02/11/us-population-projections-2005-2050.

Pearson, V., Phillip, M. R., He, F., & Ji, H. (2002). Attempted suicide among young rural women in the People's Republic of China: Possibilities for prevention. *Suicide and Life-Threatening Behavior, 32*(4), 359–369.

Pfeffer, C. R. (1991). Suicide in Japan. *Journal of the American Academy of Child and Adolescent Psychiatry, 30*(5), 847–848.

Pfeffer, C. R., Normandin, L., & Kakuma, T. (1994). Suicidal children grow up: Suicidal behavior and psychiatric disorders among relatives. *Journal of the American Academy of Child & Adolescent Psychiatry, 33*(8), 1087–1097.

Phillips, M. R., Liu, H., & Zhang, Y. (1999). Suicide and social change in China. *Culture, Medicine and Psychiatry, 23*(1), 25–50.

Pirkis, J., Burgess, P., & Dunt, D. (2000). Suicidal ideation and suicide attempts among Australian adults. *Crisis: The Journal of Crisis Intervention and Suicide Prevention, 21*(1), 16–25.

Polanco-Roman, L., & Miranda, R. (2013). Culturally related stress, hopelessness, and vulnerability to depressive symptoms and suicidal ideation in emergencing adulthood. *Behavior Therapy, 44*(1), 75–87.

Ponizovsky, A. M., & Ritsner, M. S. (1999). Suicide ideation among recent immigrants to Israel from the former Soviet Union: An epidemiological survey of prevalence and risk factors. *Suicide and Life-Threatening Behavior, 29,* 376–392.

Pridemore, W. A., & Spivak, A. L. (2003). Patterns of suicide mortality in Russia. *Suicide and Life-Threatening Behavior, 33*(2), 132–150.

Pridmore, S., & Walter, G. (2013). Culture and suicide set points. *German Journal of Psychiatry, 16*(4), 143–151.

Pritchard, C., & Amanullah, S. (2007). An analysis of suicide and undetermined deaths in 17 predominantly Islamic countries contrasted with the UK. *Psychological Medicine, 37,* 421–430.

Purselle, D. C., Heninger, M., Hanzlick, R., & Garlow, S. J. (2009). Differential association of socioeconomic status in ethnic and age-defined suicides. *Psychiatry Research, 167,* 258–265.

Qin, P., & Mortensen, P. (2001). Specific characteristics of suicide in China. *Acta Psychiatrica Scandinavica, 103*(2), 117–121.

Raleigh, V. S. (1996). Suicide patterns and trends in people of Indian subcontinent and Caribbean origin in England and Wales. *Ethnicity & Health, 1*(1), 55–63.

Rew, L., Thomas, N., Horner, S. D., Resnick, M. D., & Beuhring, T. (2001). Correlates of recent suicide attempts in a tri-ethnic group of adolescents. *Journal of Nursing Scholarship, 33,* 361–367.

Rockett, I. R. (2010). Counting suicides and making suicide count as a public health problem. *Crisis, 31*(5), 227–330.

Roy, A. (1983). Family history of suicide. *Archives of General Psychiatry, 40,* 971–974.

Roy, A., & Linnoila, M. (1986). Alcoholism and suicide. *Suicide and Life-Threatening Behavior, 16,* 244–273.

Roy, A., Segal, N. L., Centerwall, B. S., & Robinette, C. D. (1991). Suicide in twins. *Archives of General Psychiatry, 48,* 29–32.

Rutter, P. A., & Behrendt, A. E. (2004). Adolescent suicide risk: Four psychosocial factors. *Adolescence, 39,* 295–302.

Schmidtke, A. (1997). Perspective: Suicide in Europe. *Suicide and Life-Threatening Behavior, 27,* 127–136.

Schmidtke, A., Bille-Brahe, U., DeLeo, D., Kerkhof, A., Bjerke, T., Crepet, P., . . . Sampaio-Faria, J. G. (1996). Attempted suicide in Europe: Rates, trends and sociodemographic characteristics of suicide attempters during the period 1989–1992. Results of the WHO/EURO Multicentre Study on Parasuicide. *Acta Psychiatrica Scandinavica, 93*(5), 327–338.

Shaffer, D., Gould, M., Fisher, P., Trautman, P., Moreau, D., & Kleinman, M. (1996). Psychiatric diagnosis in child and adolescent suicide. *Archives of General Psychiatry, 53,* 339–348.

Shiang, J. R. B., Bonger, B., Stephens, B., Allison, D., & Schatzberg, A. (1997). Suicide in San Francisco CA: A comparison of Caucasian and Asian groups, 1987–1994. *Suicide and Life-Threatening Behavior, 28*(4), 338–354.

Shoval, G., Schoen, G., Vardi, N., & Zalsman, G. (2007). Suicide in Ethiopian immigrants in Israel: A case for study of the genetic-environmental relation in suicide. *Archives of Suicide Research, 11*(3), 247–253.

Smokowski, P. R., David-Ferdon, C., & Stroupe, N. (2009). Acculturation and violence in minority adolescents: A review of the empirical literature. *The Journal of Primary Prevention, 30*(3–4), 215–263.

Sorenson, S. B., & Golding, J. M. (1988). Prevalence of suicide attempts in a Mexican-American population: Prevention implications of immigration and cultural issues. *Suicide and Life-Threatening Behavior, 18*, 322–333.

Sorenson, S. B., & Shen, H. (1996). Youth suicide trends in California: An examination of immigrant and ethnic group risk. *Suicide and Life-Threatening Behavior, 26*(2), 143–154.

Spallek, J., & Razum, O. (2015). Migration and gender. *Public Health Forum, 23*(2), 73–75.

Stack, S., & Rockett, I. R. (2016). Are suicide note writers representative of all suicides? Analysis of the National Violent Death Reporting System. *Suicide and Life-Threatening Behavior.* Advance online publication. doi: 0.1111/sltb.12320

Stack, S., & Wasserman, I. (2005). Race and method of suicide: Culture and opportunity. *Archives of Suicide Research, 9*(1), 57–68.

Stansfeld, S. (2012). The complexity of explaining ethnic differences in suicide and suicidal behaviours. *Ethnicity & Health, 17*(1–2), 3–6.

Stephen, E. H., Foote, K., Hendershot, G. E., & Schoenborn, C. A. (1994). Health of the foreign-born population: United States, 1989–1990. *Advanced Data, 14*, 1–12.

Stewart, S. M., Kennard, B. D., Lee, P. W., Mayes, T., Hughes, C. W., & Emslie, G. (2005). Hopelessness and suicidal ideation among adolescents in two cultures. *The Journal of Child Psychology and Psychiatry and Allied Disciplines, 46*(4), 364–372.

Sue, D. W., Arredondo, P., & McDavis, R. J. (1992). Multicultural counseling competencies and standards: A call to the profession. *Journal of Counseling and Development, 70*(4), 477–486.

Sue, D. W., Bernier, J. E., Durran, A., Feinberg, L., Pedersen, P., Smith, E. J., & Vasquez-Nuttall, E. (1982). Position paper: Cross-cultural counseling competencies. *Counseling Psychologist, 10*(2), 45–52.

Sue, D. W., & Sue, D. (2003). *Counseling the culturally diverse: Theory and practice.* New York, NY: John Wiley.

Suominen, K., Isometsa, E., Haukka, J., & Lonnqvist, J. (2004). Substance use and male gender as risk factors for deaths and suicide: A 5-year follow-up study after deliberate self-harm. *Social Psychiatry and Psychiatric Epidemiology, 39*(9), 720–724.

Swanson, J. W., Linskey, A. O., Quintero-Salinas, R., Pumariega, A. J., & Holzer, C. E. (1992). A binational school survey of depressive symptoms, drug use, and suicidal ideation. *Journal of the American Academy of Child and Adolescent Psychiatry, 31*, 669–678.

Takahashi, Y. (1997). Culture and suicide: From a Japanese psychiatrist's perspective. *Suicide and Life-Threatening Behavior, 27*(1), 137–145.

Thompson, N., & Bhugra, D. (2000). Rates of deliberate self-harm in Asians: Findings and models. *International Review of Psychiatry, 12*(1), 37–43.

Ungemack, J. A., & Guarnaccia, P. J. (1998). Suicidal ideation and suicide attempts among Mexican Americans, Puerto Ricans and Cuban Americans. *Transcultural Psychiatry, 35*, 307–327.

U.S. Census Bureau. (2015). Educational attainment of the population 15 years and over, by age, sex, race, and Hispanic origin. Retrieved from: https://www.census.gov/content/dam/Census/library/publications/2016/demo/p20-578.pdf

Vanderwerker, L. L., Chen, J. H., Charpentier, P., Paulk, M. E., Michalski, M., & Prigerson, H. G. (2007). Differences in risk factors for suicidality between African American and White patients vulnerable to suicide. *Suicide and Life-Threatening Behavior, 37*(1), 1–9.

Vega, W. A., Gil, A., Warheit, G., Apospori, E., & Zimmerman, R. (1993). The relationship of drug use to suicide ideation and attempts among African American, Hispanic, and White non-Hispanic male adolescents. *Suicide and Life-Threatening Behavior, 23*(2), 110–119.

Walker, R. L. (2007). Acculturation and acculturative stress as indicators for suicide risk among African Americans. *American Journal of Orthopsychiatry, 77*(3), 386–391.

Walker, R. L., Lester, D., & Sean, J. (2006). Lay theories of suicide: An examination of culturally relevant suicide beliefs and attributions among African Americans and European Americans. *Journal of Black Psychology, 32*(3), 320–334.

Williams, C. L., & Berry, J. W. (1991). Primary prevention of acculturative stress among refugees: Application of psychological theory and practice. *American Psychologist, 46*(6), 632–641.

Woods, E. R., Lin, Y. G., Middleman, A., Beckford, P., Chase, L., & DuRant, R. H. (1997). The associations of suicide attempts in adolescents. *Pediatrics, 99*, 791–796.

World Health Organization. (1994). *World health statistic annual: Health for all 2000 database.* Geneva, Switzerland: Author.

Yip, P. S. (1996). Suicides in Hong Kong, Taiwan and Beijing. *British Journal of Clinical Psychiatry, 169*(4), 495–500.

Yip, P. S., Callanan, C., & Yuen, H. P. (2000). Urban/rural and gender differentials in suicide rates: East and west. *Journal of Affective Disorders, 57*(1–3), 99–106.

Young, J. (2002). Morals, suicide, and psychiatry: A view from Japan. *Bioethics, 16*(5), 412–424.

Yuen, N. Y., Nahulu, L. B., Hishinuma, E. S., & Miyamoto, R. H. (2000). Cultural identification and attempted suicide in native Hawaiian adolescents. *Journal of the American Academy of Child & Adolescent Psychiatry, 39*(3), 360–367.

Zayas, L H.. (1987). Toward an understanding of suicide risks in youth Hispanic females. *Journal of Adolescent Research, 2*(1), 1–11.

Zayas, L. H., Aguilar-Gaxiola, S., Yoon, H., & Rey, G. N. (2015). The distress of citizen-children with detained and deported parents. *Journal of Child and Family Studies, 24*(11), 3213–3223.

Zayas, L. H., & Gulbas, L. E. (2012). Are suicide attempts by young Latinas a cultural idiom of distress? *Transcultural Psychiatry, 49*(5), 718–734.

Zayas, L. H., Gulbas, L. E., Fedoravicius, N., & Cabassa, L. J. (2010). Patterns of distress, precipitating events, and reflections on suicide attempts by young Latinas. *Social Science & Medicine, 70*(11), 1773–1779.

Zayas, L. H., Hausmann-Stabile, C., & De Luca, S. M. (2015). Suicidal behaviors and U.S. Hispanic youth: Social, psychological, and cultural factors and challenges for interventions. In D. A. Lamis, N. J. Kaslow, D. A. Lamis, & N. J. Kaslow (Eds.), *Advancing the science of suicidal behavior: Understanding and intervention* (pp. 269–282). Hauppauge, NY: Nova Science Publishers.

Zayas, L. H., Lester, R. J., Cabassa, L. J., & Fortuna, L. R. (2005). Why do so many Latina teens attempt suicide? A conceptual model for research. *American Journal of Orthopsychiatry, 75*(2), 275–287.

Zhang, J. (2014). The gender ratio of Chinese suicide rates: An explanation in Confucianism. *Sex Roles, 70* (3–4), 146–154.

Zhang, J., Conwell, Y., ZHou, L., & Jiang, C. (2004). Culture, risk factors and suicide in rural China: A psychological autopsy case control study. *Acta Psychiatrica Scandinavica, 110*(6), 430–437.

Zhang, J., Li, N., Tu, X. M., Xiao, S., & Jia, C. (2011). Risk factors for rural young suicide in China: A case-control study. *Journal of Affective Disorders, 129*(1–3), 244–251.

CHAPTER THREE

RELIGION AND SUICIDE

Research has found that religion is associated with suicidality. Specifically, an individual's degree of religiosity can potentially serve as a protective factor against suicidal behavior. It is imperative to be aware of and understand the role of religion in relation to suicidality in order to more accurately identify and assess the risk of suicide and to determine the resources to facilitate and enhance treatment of suicidal individuals. While it is recognized that a number of factors, such as gender, age, ethnicity, and/or culture, are interrelated with one's religiosity, the influence of these factors on suicide are explored in more depth in other chapters. This chapter intentionally focuses on the key risk and protective factors of religion as it relates to suicidality. Although spirituality is related to religiosity, this chapter focuses on five dominant religions in the United States and across the world. The relationship between suicide and Christianity, Islam, Hinduism, Buddhism, and Judaism, as well as important factors of religiosity related to suicide assessment and treatment are described in this chapter.

GOALS AND OBJECTIVES

An understanding of:

- Influence of religion on suicidality
- Importance of assessing an individual's religiosity
- Protective role of religion against suicidal behavior
- Risk factors within religions
- Protective factors within religions
- Suicide trends and rates within religions
- Christianity and suicidality
- Hinduism and suicidality
- Islam and suicidality
- Buddhism and suicidality
- Judaism and suicidality

Research has consistently shown a relationship between religion and suicide. Evidence indicates that the rate of suicide varies across religious denominations (Gearing & Lizardi, 2009; Lizardi & Gearing, 2010). However, across religious denominations, a higher degree of religiosity is associated with decreased suicide risk (Dervic et al., 2004; Martin, 1984). Research establishing a relationship between high levels of religiosity and decreased suicide risk dates back over 40 years (Kranitz, Abrahams, Spiegel, & KeithSpiegel, 1968). Individuals who attend church more frequently are four times less likely to commit suicide than those who never attend (Martin, 1984). The relationship between religiosity and suicide appears to vary by gender. Among males, higher suicide rates are associated with lower levels of religious belief and religious attendance. This relationship has not been demonstrated among females (Neeleman, Halpern, Leon, Lewis, 1997).

Among the most common religious groups in the United States, Protestants have the highest suicide rate, followed by Roman Catholics. Jewish individuals have the lowest rate of suicide (Maris, Berman, & Silverman, 2000). There are lower recorded rates of suicidal behavior found among Muslims when compared to other religions, such as Christianity or Hinduism (Abdel-Khalek, 2004; Ineichen, 1998).

Emile Durkheim, in 1897, first proposed that spiritual commitment may contribute to emotional well-being, providing a source of meaning and order in the world (Durkheim, 1951). Given the potential protective impact of religious affiliation and commitment against suicide risk, it is essential to include an evaluation of religion in any psychosocial assessment, particularly with suicidal clients. An accurate understanding of a client's degree of religious affiliation and level of participation in religious activities may indicate potential suicide risk. It may also help to identify the potential areas that treatment may target to enhance life-affirming beliefs and expectations.

As highlighted in the previous chapters, our personal values and beliefs impact how we assess, treat, and interact with our clients. A study that assessed clinicians' religious worldviews found that most clinicians were open to asking patients about their religious or spiritual beliefs and encouraging patients to pray or participate in faith communities, even when their positions on these practices differed modestly (Peteet & Balboni, 2013). In addition to understanding the relationship between religion and suicide, as a clinician treating suicidal individuals from diverse religious backgrounds, it is necessary to be aware of any religious stereotypes and/or biases. It is essential to become aware of your personal attitudes and assumptions regarding religion to fully understand how they may impact your work with your clients.

Individual Exercise 3.1

1. What is your religious background, if any? How would you describe your degree of religious affiliation/identification?
2. What is your understanding of your religion's belief and attitude toward suicide? Is your perspective on suicide the same as that of your religion? If it differs, how do you reconcile those differences?
3. Considering your answers to questions 1 and 2, how may these factors influence your work with suicidal individuals from diverse religious backgrounds and differing degrees of religious faith?

RELIGION AS A PROTECTIVE FACTOR AGAINST SUICIDE

Religiosity has been shown to be associated with a reduced risk of suicidality (Colucci, 2008; Dervic et al., 2004; Lizardi et al., 2007; Lizardi & Gearing, 2010; Rasic et al., 2009; Stack, 1983). Studies have reported that suicide rates in religious countries are lower than suicide rates in secular countries (Breault, 1993; Dervic et al., 2004; Stack, 1983). Furthermore, intensity of religious commitment has been shown to be related to suicidal behaviors (Nelson, 1977). These findings are not specific to particular religious denominations (Dervic et al., 2004; Lizardi et al., 2007; Stack, 1983). Some studies have identified that individuals with lower religious orientation versus higher religious orientation may be at increased suicide risk, but this finding was associated with gender (Ozdel et al., 2009). A recent cross-national analysis of religion and suicide found that individuals who are religiously committed, engaged within their religious community network, and residing in countries with high levels of religiosity are found to be lower in suicide acceptability (Stack & Kposowa, 2011).

Moral and religious objections to suicide have a unique association with suicidal behavior. The life-saving beliefs associated with religious commitment may protect against suicide (Dervic et al., 2004; Lizardi et al., 2007; Koenig, McCullough, & Larson, 2001; Neeleman et al., 1997; Stack, 1983). Studies indicate that individuals with low moral and religious objections to suicide are more likely to have a lifetime history of suicide attempts (Dervic et al., 2004; Lizardi et al., 2007; Neeleman et al., 1997; Stack, 1983), while individuals with higher moral and religious objections to suicide perceive more reasons for living.

The protective role of religiosity includes a number of mechanisms. Most religions have strong sanctions against suicide; thus, those individuals who report stronger commitment to those religions would be less likely to resort to suicide. In addition to condoning suicide, involvement in organized religions provides the opportunity to develop an extended support network in congregation members and clergy, which has been shown to be a protective factor against suicidality (Cheng, Chen, Chen, & Jenkins, 2000; Gould, Fisher, Parides, Flory, & Shaffer, 1996; Greening & Stoppelbein, 2002; Koenig et al., 2001; Mann, 2002; Szanto, Mulsant, Houck, Dew, & Reynolds, 2003). Religiosity has also been shown to be associated with lower levels of aggression and hostility (Koenig et al., 2001; Mann et al., 2005; Malone, Haas, Sweeny, & Mann, 1995; Oquendo et al., 2000), which consistently have been shown to be related to suicidal behavior. Additionally, many religions proscribe elicit behaviors such as substance abuse (Hilton, Fellingham, & Lyon, 2002) and smoking (Martin et al., 2003), which have an established relationship to suicide. Thus, high levels of religiosity could have an indirect protective effect on suicide via the prohibition of substance use (Hilton et al., 2002).

Further, the motivation to commit suicide involves considerable ambivalence, and suicidal individuals often experience an internal struggle between wanting to live and wanting to die (Shneidman & Farberow, 1957). Given that the moral objections to suicide are founded in traditional religious beliefs (Linehan, Goodstein, Nielsen, & Chiles, 1983), religious values and optimism may be important considerations for many individuals contemplating suicide (Linehan et al., 1983) and may serve to positively influence the decision to live (Pinto, Whisman, & Conwell, 1998). Further studies with more comprehensive assessment of religiosity are needed to clarify the relationship between suicidality and religiosity.

ROLE-PLAY 3.1

Taking turns as client and practitioner, engage in a role-play in which you would assess for your client's degree of religious affiliation and commitment.

1. Does the individual's religious faith and an understanding of his or her religion contain any real or perceived protective factors for the client? Remember this is from the client's perspective, not the practitioner's.
2. Does the individual's religion or religious community offer any support for, or obstacles against, treatment?

CHRISTIANITY AND SUICIDE

The word suicide does not appear in the Bible; however, there are several examples of individuals committing suicide, such as Judas, King Saul, and Samson (Maris et al., 2000;

Phipps, 1985). Biblical writers neither condemn nor praise those whom they recorded as having taken their own lives. The Christian perspective on suicide has remained relatively stable since the fifth century (Phipps, 1985). St. Augustine argued in the fifth century that suicide was a violation of the commandment, "Thou shalt not kill" (Kennedy, 2000; Maris et al., 2000; Phipps, 1985; Retterstol, 1993). He argued that this applied to one's own life as well as the lives of others, and all life should be preserved (Kennedy, 2000; Phipps, 1985; Retterstol, 1993). St. Thomas Aquinas, a Catholic theologian, expanded on Augustine's perspective and described suicide as a sin against self, neighbor, and God (Aquinas, 1225–1274). Aquinas claimed that every living organism naturally desires to preserve its life, thus suicide is against nature. Aquinas also claimed that suicide is contrary to religious rights in that only God has the right to decide when a person will live or die. Further, Aquinas believed that confession of sins must be made prior to departing from the world in order to enter heaven. Consequently, suicide is one of the most serious of all sins because the individual who completes suicide is unable to confess to the act and repent (Kennedy, 2000; Phipps, 1985).

The view of suicide as a sin dominates current Christian attitudes across the various denominations (e.g., Catholics, Baptists, and Protestants). The sin of suicide is equated with other forms of taking life such as abortion and murder (Maris et al., 2000; Wogaman, 1990). According to the *Catechism of the Catholic Church* (Inc-Libreria Editrice Vaticana, 1994), one has to be mentally competent to understand that the act in which he or she partakes is a sin. Thus, if one considers suicide an act of the mentally ill, it cannot simultaneously be viewed as a sin. When an individual dies, he or she faces judgment by God, and only God can decide if the individual will go to heaven, hell, or purgatory (Inc-Libreria Editrice Vaticana, 1994). Historically, those who committed suicide were unable to be buried in Catholic cemeteries (Phipps, 1985); however, this is now a rarely practiced custom within Catholicism.

There are 2.2 billion Christians worldwide. Among the dominant Christian denominations (Catholics, Baptists, and Protestants), the lowest suicide rates are found among Catholics and evangelical Baptists, with higher incidence occurring among Protestant faiths (Pescosolido & Georgianna, 1989; Torgler & Schaltegger, 2014). Researchers indicate that Catholics and Baptists are more likely to be actively involved in church activities and, therefore, may benefit more from expanded social support networks (Pescosolido & Georgianna, 1989; Torgler & Schaltegger, 2014). However, it is important to note that research examining the role of level of church attendance as a proxy for religiosity did not find an association between low church attendance and increased suicide risk (O'Reilly & Rosato, 2015). This research suggests that the lower engagement in general risk behaviors and alcohol use may be more likely to explain the lower suicide rates found among conservative Christians rather than their tendency to attend church more frequently (O'Reilly & Rosato, 2015).

Additionally, Catholic countries have lower suicide rates than Protestant ones, and within Protestant countries, areas with a preponderance of Catholics have lower suicide rates (Hood-Williams, 1996). However, there are significantly higher suicide rates in men and in the elderly in Catholic and Christian orthodox countries, compared to rates in non-Catholic and orthodox countries (Pritchard & Baldwin, 2001).

HINDUISM AND SUICIDE

There are an estimated 1 billion Hindus in the world, predominantly in the Indian subcontinent. Unlike Muslim or Christian writings, Hindu scriptures are relatively ambivalent on the issue of suicide (Ineichen, 1998). Also, Hindu philosophies of reincarnation and karma mean that, for Hindus, life does not end at death, as death leads to rebirth (Hassan, 1983; Ineichen, 1998). Thus, it has been purported by some that the Hindu religion may be more tolerant toward suicide (Hassan, 1983; Ineichen, 1998; Kamal & Loewenthal, 2002).

There is limited research on suicidality and Hindus. In a study examining suicide beliefs and behavior among Hindus and Muslims living in the United Kingdom, it was found that Hindus less strongly endorsed moral objections and survival-and-coping reasons for living than Muslims (Kamal & Loewenthal, 2002). Another survey study found a higher rate of suicide among Hindus than Muslims (Ineichen, 1998). Research seems to indicate that males have higher rates of suicide than females, and the majority of suicide attempters studied had a psychiatric diagnosis (Latha, Bhat, & D'Souza, 1996).

The centuries-old Hindu practice of Sati is a ritual act of suicide in which widows self-immolate on the funeral pyre of their husbands. Although this ritual is now illegal, it continues to be practiced in some areas of the Indian subcontinent (Kelly, 2011; Kumar, 2003). Research has found little evidence that women who engage in Sati have a psychiatric disorder (Bhugra, 2005). It is important to recognize that Sati is not a religious act nor is it related to psychiatric illness; rather this form of suicide appears more related to social, gender, and cultural factors (Bhugra, 2005).

ISLAM AND SUICIDE

Worldwide, there are approximately 1.6 billion adherents to Islam, representing about 23% of the global population (Pew Research Center, 2017). The impact and influence of the Islamic faith on suicidality remains difficult to determine, due to the limited research in the area (Cosar, Kocal, Arikan, & Isik, 1997; Khan & Reza, 2000; Rezaeian, 2009). No Middle Eastern country has reported mortality data to the World Health Organization (WHO) since 1989 (Lester, 2006), and very few Islamic countries record suicide or report suicide rates (Khan & Hyder, 2006; Pritchard & Amanullah, 2007). It is important to separate the concept of suicide from martyrdom. The focus here is on suicide, the self-inflicted intentional act designed to end one's own life, not on martyrdom, which involves using one's death in defense of one's homeland by inflicting losses on an enemy (Abdel-Khalek, 2004).

Results of the limited extant research examining suicide among Muslims indicate that a high degree of religious affiliation acts as a protective factor against suicidal behavior, and that rates of suicide are similar among males and females (Kazi & Naidoo, 2016). Limited research also indicates that suicide rates are lower in predominantly Islamic countries in comparison to other countries (Abdel-Khalek, 2004; Gal et al., 2012). Similarly, there are lower recorded rates of suicidality found among Muslims when compared to other religions, such as Christianity or Hinduism (Abdel-Khalek, 2004; Ineichen, 1998; Kamal & Loewenthal, 2002; Mohyuddin, 2008; Shah & Chandia, 2010).

In studies that have focused on psychological disorders and traits such as depression, anxiety, obsessive compulsion, neuroticism, pessimism, and death obsession, samples from Islamic countries have scored higher than those from Western countries (Abdel-Khalek, 2004, 2006; Abdel-Khalek & Lester, 1999, 2003).

Studies examining this phenomenon of low suicide rates, but higher levels of psychological distress scores, have proposed several explanations. One, higher rates of religiosity among Muslims act as a buffer to suicidality (Thorson, Powell, Abdel-Khalek, & Beshai, 1997); however, religiosity is associated with lower levels of depression and anxiety (Abdel-Khalek, 2007). Two, Islam is firmer in regard to the sinfulness of suicide as compared to other religions (Ineichen, 1998; Lester, 2006; Pritchard & Amanullah, 2007). The seriousness of the sin is such that people are frequently not allowed to offer the funeral prayer for someone who has completed suicide (Jahangir, Rehman, & Jan, 1998). Three, the social stigma of suicidality in predominantly Islamic countries artificially lowers the reported rates (Lester & Akande, 1994; Sarfraz & Castle, 2002). It has been suggested that the reported rareness of Muslim suicide is a myth (Sarfraz & Castle, 2002), because of such underreporting (Lester & Akande, 1994; Sarfraz & Castle, 2002).

In the Holy Qu'ran, suicide is expressly forbidden in Surah 4, verses 29 and 30, which state "do not kill or destroy yourself," with eternal punishment for suicide resulting in the individual burning in hell. Similar to the Christian Bible, however, the Qu'ran is interpreted differently across various (Islamic) countries, regions, and sects (Pritchard & Amanullah, 2007). Furthermore, as many Islamic countries have incorporated the Sharia (Islamic law) into their legal system, such as in Saudi Arabia, Pakistan, or Kuwait, suicide and suicide attempts remain criminal offenses (Al-Jahdali et al., 2004; Khan & Hyder, 2006; Pridmore & Pasha, 2004; Sarfraz & Castle, 2002; Suleiman, Moussa, & El-Islam, 1989).

Some research, however, has indicated an increasing suicide trend in Islamic countries (Khan, 2007; Khan & Hyder, 2006). For example, the number of suicides has reportedly increased in the Sindh region in Pakistan between 1987 and 1999 (Khan & Hyder, 2006). Another study surveying suicide ideation among Pakistani college students found high overall rates equally in both men and women (Khokher & Khan, 2005). Notwithstanding the strict religious prohibition on suicide, researchers in Muslim majority countries (e.g., Iran, Pakistan) are increasingly calling for nonreligious preventative efforts, including school-based programs (Sadr, 2013; Syed, 2008) to be directed to individuals experiencing suicidality. Research investigating suicide in predominantly Islamic countries has found suicidality to be both a reality and a growing concern (Al-Jahdali et al., 2004; Cosar et al., 1997; Khan & Reza, 2000; Rezaeian, 2010).

According to Pritchard and Amanullah's (2007) analysis comparing suicide and undetermined deaths in 17 Islamic countries, patterns of suicide (e.g., increased risk with age) similar to those in Western countries have been found. Similarities in respect to gender have also been found, with women being at higher risk for suicide attempts and lower risk for suicide completions (Canetto, 2015). Additionally, research has found that Muslim women's suicide is often viewed as a protest against oppressive regulation and extreme abuse endured within families and society (Canetto, 2015).

Although suicide in Islamic countries has been found to be a significant problem (Pritchard & Amanullah, 2007), there are few mental health or social services in predominantly Islamic countries for individuals who are suicidal, and fewer for survivors and family members following a suicide (Khan & Hyder, 2006; Sarfraz & Castle, 2002). Often individuals who have attempted suicide and their families will avoid going to public hospitals, which will report the event as a crime to the police (Khan, 2007; Khan & Hyder, 2006). Surviving family members are stigmatized and often ostracized in traditional Muslim communities (Sarfraz & Castle, 2002). Muslim graveyards are often reluctant to bury an individual after a suicide, which is considered a *haram* or forbidden death (Sarfraz & Castle, 2002).

To date, research on Muslim suicidality remains limited not only in reported data but also across religious subgroups. Islam is not a single unified religion; rather it comprises many competing sects (Lester, 2006). Yet, there is little investigation or empirical data across the various Islamic sects of the Sunni or Shia, or the smaller sects of the Ahmadi, Alawai, Druze, Islaili, Qadiani, Sufi, or Yezidi (Lester, 2006).

BUDDHISM AND SUICIDE

In the United States, Buddhism is the third most practiced religion, following Christianity and Judaism (Pew Forum's U.S. Religious Landscape Survey, 2008). Across the world, an estimated 535 million individuals practice Buddhism, which represents approximately 500 million followers or 7% of the global population. In the United States, approximately 5,973,446 Americans or 2% of the U.S. population ascribe to the Buddhist faith (Pew Research Center, 2017). Less research on suicidality and Buddhism is available, limiting the reported data on the incidence and prevalence of suicide among practicing Buddhists.

There are two major branches within Buddhism: Theravada (also called Hinayana) and Mahayana. Buddhism was founded and remains the dominant religion in India. Theravada Buddhism has also been a central religion in Sri Lanka, Thailand, Cambodia, Myanmar, and Laos, whereas Mahayana Buddhism is a significant religion in China, Japan, Taiwan, Tibet, Nepal, Mongolia, Korea, and Vietnam (Lizardi & Gearing, 2010).

Central to Buddhist faith, life and death are a cycle that does not end until one reaches Nirvana, the state that is characterized by the cessation of desire and suffering and epitomizes bliss and peace. If Nirvana is reached by an individual, death is considered another beginning in the ongoing cycle of pain and suffering on the path to Nirvana. Within the Buddhist doctrine, the Four Noble Truths teach the message that life is full of dissatisfactions (Disayavanish & Disayavanish, 2007). All life's stages, including life itself, birth, ageing, sickness, and death, are composed with want and desire that are considered conditions of suffering. The Buddhist faith teaches that the end to a dissatisfactory life is possible only through the Noble Eightfold Path.

The mind in the Buddhist faith is considered to be the cause of suffering and of happiness. Mental states based on craving result in actions that lead to increased suffering and decreased happiness (Disayavanish & Disayavanish, 2007). Thus, these mental states and their subsequent actions are called "unskillful" (Sangharakshita, 2007). In contrast, actions that are based on contentment are termed "skillful" and result in increased happiness (Sangharakshita, 2001). Accordingly, if one attempts to end suffering by taking one's life via suicide, rather than by purifying the mind through meditation and following the eightfold path, the result is rebirth into a lower level of life (Disayavanish & Disayavanish, 2007), Karmic retribution, not relief from suffering.

Further, another core Buddhist tenet by which Buddhists must abide is the principle of abstaining from harm, termed "ahiṁsā" (Sangharakshita, 1996). Thus, to suicide constitutes a variation of killing a living being and, therefore, is seen in a negative light as yet another cause of suffering (Sangharakshita, 1996). It is further proposed that "moha," or delusion, is the core motivation of suicide, and is a failure to appreciate that death is the greatest suffering (Keown, 1996).

JUDAISM AND SUICIDE

Judaism strictly sanctions suicide and regards suicide as a criminal act, likened to murder. According to Jewish doctrine, an individual does not have the right to wound his or her own body, let alone to take his or her own life (Bailey & Stein, 1995; Schwartz & Kaplan, 1992). Jewish law does not consider the commandment, "Thou shalt not kill," as applying to suicide (Jacobs, 1995). However, it does value the preservation of human life above all else (Jacobs, 1995), and thus condemns suicide.

According to Kaplan and Schoenberg (1988), Judaic principles ascribe a great spiritual consequence to suicide. When an individual commits suicide, the soul has nowhere to go (Kaplan & Schoenberg, 1988). It cannot return to the body, because the body has been destroyed. It cannot be let into any of the soul worlds, because its time has not come. Thus, it is in a state of limbo, which is very painful. A person may commit suicide because he or she wants to escape, but, in reality, the result is a far worse situation. While problems have the opportunity to be resolved in this world, after death, there are no more opportunities, only consequences. According to strict Judaic belief, individuals who commit suicide are unable to receive traditional postdeath rituals such as a proper burial and blessings (Kaplan & Schoenberg, 1988).

Across the world, 16 million people identify themselves as Jewish. Suicide rates among Jewish individuals in the United States and Israel have historically been noted to be low

(Dublin, 1963; Levav & Aisenberg, 1989; Miller, 1976) with suicide rates in Israel being lower than suicide rates in the United States (Levav & Aisenberg, 1989). Overall, Jewish individuals have the lowest rate of suicide in the United States as compared to Christians and Protestants (Maris et al., 2000). Several studies have also reported that suicide rates are lower among Jews as compared to the general population in predominantly Protestant communities (Danto & Danto, 1983; Goss & Reed, 1971; Levav, Magnes, Aisenberg, Rosenblum, & Gil, 1988; Williams, 1997). Additionally, in a study of the United States examining the proportion of the Jewish population and corresponding suicide rates across 50 states, a significant negative correlation was found (Bailey & Stein, 1995).

In Israel, suicide rates among the Jewish population are among the lowest in the world (Kohn, 1997), yet they are higher for Jewish individuals than for Muslims (Levav & Aisenberg, 1989; Lubin, Glasser, Boyko, & Barell, 2001). Among the Jewish population, suicide rates are higher for men than for women (Lubin et al., 2001) and increase directly with age. In addition, the suicide rate for Jewish males in Israel is increasing, particularly in the 18- to 21-year-old age group. Rates of suicide are found to differ according to marital status. The highest rates were in married individuals (Nachman et al., 2002). An increase in the use of firearms has also been cited (Lubin et al., 2001).

ROLE-PLAY 3.2

With another colleague, taking turns as a client and a practitioner, engage in a role-play in which the client asks about your religion.

1. How can you facilitate an answer without proselytizing or influencing the client's existing religiosity?
2. Why might the client ask this question?
3. How can your answer negatively or positively influence your client and the established therapeutic alliance between you and the client?
4. How can your response assist or limit the client's ability to explore this issue?

Case Vignette 3.1

A young woman was brought by a friend to a local emergency department of a community hospital due to an overdose attempt. She was hysterical, broke a picture in the hospital hallway, and tried to use a shard of glass to cut her wrists. She was subsequently restrained. You are the mental health clinician called to work with her family who, upon arrival, has asked that she be immediately discharged. Reportedly, the patient is in love with a young man of a different religion and her traditional family has barred her from seeing him again.

1. *The young women and her family are Muslim and her boyfriend is Hindu. How would you engage the family?*
2. *How would your assessment and treatment recommendations be different if religion were not a core factor in this case?*
3. *What personal issues may affect your professional practice?*
4. *Complete questions 1 to 3, but change the young woman and her family's religion to Christianity and her boyfriend's religion to Islam. Are your responses the same or different? Why?*

Small Group Exercise 3.1

Considering Case Study 3.1, please complete the answers first individually, then discuss in groups of four to six.

1. When working with individuals with different religions, what combinations of religions would be the easiest for you to work with and why?
2. What combinations of religions would be the hardest for you to work with and why?

ROLE-PLAY 3.3

Role-play the assessment and discharge planning of Case Study 3.1. One person takes the role of the clinician, one of the young woman, and one a member of her family. You may alternate religions (and degree of affiliation/commitment) and the gender of the participants.

SUMMARY

The act of suicide is condemned by most major religious sects. Research has established that the degree of religiosity is directly related to the degree of suicidality, with greater religiosity predicting a decreased risk of suicidal behavior. Several mechanisms have been attributed to the protective role of religion, including a decrease of aggression and hostility and an increase in reasons for living. The protective role of religion can be found across major religious denominations; thus, assessing a client's degree of religious affiliation may serve as an effective indicator of suicide risk.

KEY POINTS

1. Assessing and, when appropriate, supporting a suicidal patient's religiosity and religion may contribute to the effectiveness of psychosocial interventions. (This is about supporting an existing religiosity, not proselytizing. Note: This is from the client's identified religiosity, and not the practitioner's perspective.)
2. Many religions foster extended social support networks that are protective factors against suicide.
3. Religion plays a protective role against suicide via the strict sanctions against taking one's life in most major religions (among other mechanisms).
4. In Christianity, suicide is a sin and, in some denominations (e.g., Catholicism), results in the individual's inability to enter heaven.
5. While more tolerant toward individuals who suicide, Hindu scriptures denounce suicide.
6. Islam sects traditionally hold a very strict interpretation of suicide as an unforgivable sin. For example, Sharia or Islamic law has been incorporated into many

(continued)

KEY POINTS (*continued*)

   Islamic countries' legal systems where suicide and suicide attempt are criminal offenses.
7. Judaism equates suicide with murder and views it as unacceptable under any conditions.
8. According to Buddhism, if an individual attempts to end suffering by taking one's life via suicide, the result is rebirth into a lower level of life as a form of Karmic retribution.
9. Suicide is condemned across Christianity, Hinduism, Islam, Buddhism, and Judaism, but the strictness of this condemnation varies across religions and within each religion's denominations or sects.
10. Individuals with more traditional or orthodox religiosity tend to have lower rates of suicide.

ELECTRONIC RESOURCES

GENERAL

National and World Religion Statistics—Church Statistics—World Religions
www.adherents.com
Religious Tolerance
www.religioustolerance.org
Religions of the Word, Minnesota State University
www.mnsu.edu/emuseum/cultural/religion
http://libguides.mnsu.edu/religion

CHRISTIANITY

American Baptist Churches
www.abc-usa.org
Roman Catholicism
www.catholic.org
The Presbyterian Coalition
https://presbycoalition.wordpress.com
Youth for Christ
www.yfc.org
World Vision International
www.wvi.org
Campus Crusade for Christ International
www.ccci.org

HINDUISM

The Hindu Universe
www.hindunet.org

Hinduism Today
www.hinduismtoday.com
Hindu Website
www.hinduwebsite.com/hinduindex.asp

ISLAM
Islam 101
http://islam101.net

BUDDHISM
About Buddhism
www.aboutbuddhism.org
Buddhism Religious Facts
www.religionfacts.com/buddhism
Buddhist Core Beliefs
www.sapphyr.net/buddhist/buddhist-core.htm

JUDAISM
B'nai B'rith International
www.bnaibrith.org
Memorial Foundation for Jewish Culture
www.mfjc.org/mission.html
United Jewish Communities
www.ujc.org
World Jewish Congress
www.worldjewishcongress.org

KNOWLEDGE ACQUISITION TEST (KAT)

True or False

1. Religiosity is associated with lower levels of aggression and hostility.
2. Strong religious commitment is not related to the extent of social support networks.
3. Moral objections to suicide protect against suicidal behavior.
4. Judaism views suicide as acceptable under certain circumstances.
5. Modern Catholicism prevents individuals who committed suicide from receiving a Catholic funeral.
6. Muslims have higher rates of suicide than Christians.
7. Individuals residing in predominantly Islamic countries have higher rates of psychological distress than individuals in Western countries.
8. Buddhism takes no position on suicide.
9. Individuals following Buddhism can advance their Karma through rebirth; therefore, suicide is a fully acceptable and positive act.
10. Hinduism fully accepts suicide as a natural form of death.
11. Suicide in old age is more tolerated in world religions.

Short Answer

12. What are two ways in which religiosity may protect against suicidal behavior?
13. Describe the predominant Christian view of suicide.
14. On what principles did St. Thomas Aquinas determine suicide to be a sin?
15. In Judaism, what value comes before all else and how does this relate to Judaic attitudes toward suicide?
16. What are the potential reasons for the lower suicide rates among Muslims?
17. How is the life and death cycle central to the Buddhist faith?
18. Describe how the Four Noble Truths taught in the Buddhist doctrine may relate to suicidality?
19. Why is Sati considered a type of nonpsychiatric suicide?

Multiple Choice

20. Suicide and religion are associated through which of the following?
    A. Hopelessness
    B. Impulsivity
    C. Aggression
    D. All of the above
    E. None of the above
21. Religiosity may protect against suicide because:
    A. Most major religions forbid suicide.
    B. Religious activities build social support networks.
    C. Moral objections to suicide are related to reasons for living.
    D. All of the above.
    E. None of the above.
22. Reported lower rates of suicide in predominantly Islamic countries may result because:
    A. Islam is a strong protective religion against suicide.
    B. Islam is firmer in regard to the sinfulness of suicide.
    C. The social stigma of suicidality in Islam may artificially lower suicide rates.

D. All of the above.
E. None of the above.
23. Suicide is acceptable in what major religion:
    A. Christianity
    B. Hinduism
    C. Buddhism
    D. Judaism
    E. None of the above
24. In Hinduism, Sati is:
    A. A purification rite
    B. A religious ritual for men before marriage
    C. An act where women self-immolate on the funeral pyre of their husbands
    D. A religious text condemning suicide
    E. None of the above
25. When assessing for a client's religiosity, a practitioner should consider:
    A. The number of times the client attends formal services
    B. The way in which a client defines his or her religious affiliation
    C. The client's perception of the potential benefits of his or her religious commitment
    D. All of the above
    E. None of the above

REFERENCES

Abdel-Khalek, A. (2004). Neither altruistic suicide, nor terrorism but martyrdom: A Muslim perspective. *Archives of Suicide Research, 8*(1), 99–113.

Abdel-Khalek, A. (2006). Optimism and pessimism in Kuwaiti and American college students. *International Journal of Social Psychiatry, 52*(2), 110–126.

Abdel-Khalek, A., & Lester, D. (1999). Obsession-compulsion in college students in the United States and Kuwait. *Psychological Reports, 85*, 799–800.

Abdel-Khalek, A., & Lester, D. (2003). Death obsession in Kuwaiti and American college students. *Death Studies, 27*(6), 541–553.

Al-Jahdali, H., Al-Johani, A., Al-Hakawi, A., Arabi, Y., Ahmed, Q. A., Altowirky, J., . . . Binsalih, S. (2004). Pattern and risk factors for intentional drug overdose in Saudi Arabia. *Canadian Journal of Psychiatry, 49*(5), 331–334.

Aquinas, T. (1225–1274). *The Summa Theologica of St. Thomas Aquinas - Treatise on Law: XC-XCVII.* Chicago, IL: University of Chicago Bookstore.

Bailey, W. T., & Stein, L. B. (1995). Jewish affiliation in relation to suicide rates. *Psychological Reports, 76*(2), 561–562.

Bhugra, D. (2005). Sati: A type of nonpsychiatric suicide. *Crisis: The Journal of Crisis Intervention and Suicide Prevention, 26*(2), 73–77.

Breault, K. D. (1993). Suicide in America: A test of Durkheim's theory of religious family integration, 1933–1980. *American Journal of Sociology, 92*, 628–656.

Canetto, S. S. (2015). Suicidal behaviors among Muslim women: Patterns, pathways, meanings and prevention. *Crisis: The Journal of Crisis Intervention and Suicide Prevention, 35*(6), 447–458.

Cheng, A., Chen, T., Chen, C., & Jenkins, R. (2000). Psychosocial and psychiatric risk factors for suicide: Case-control psychological autopsy study. *British Journal of Psychiatry, 177*, 360–365.

Colucci, E. (2008). Religion and spirituality along the suicidal path. *Suicide and Life-Threatening Behavior, 38*(2), 229–244.

Cosar, B., Kocal, N., Arikan, Z., & Isik, E. (1997). Suicide attempts among Turkish psychiatric patients. *Canadian Journal of Psychiatry, 42*, 1072–1075.

Danto, B. L., & Danto, J. M. (1983). Jewish and non-Jewish suicide in Oakland County, Michigan. *Crisis, 4*, 33–60.

Dervic, K., Oquendo, M. A., Grunebaum, M. F., Ellis, S., Burke, A. K., & Mann, J. J. (2004). Religious affiliation and suicide attempt. *American Journal of Psychiatry, 161*(12), 2303–2308.

Disayavanish, C., & Disayavanish, P. (2007). A Buddhist approach to suicide prevention. *Journal of the Medical Association of Thailand, 90*, 1680–1688.

Dublin, L. I. (1963). *Suicide in Jewish History. In suicide: A sociological and statistical study.* New York, NY: The Ronald Press.

Durkheim, E. (1951). *Suicide: A study in sociology* (J. A. Spaulding & G. Simpson, Trans.). New York, NY: Free Press.

Gal, G., Goldberger, N., Kabaha, A., Haklai, Z., Geraisy, N., Gross, R., & Levav, I. (2012). Suicidal behavior among Muslim Arabs in Israel. *Social Psychiatry and Psychiatric Epidemiology, 47*(1), 11–17.

Gearing, R. E., & Lizardi, D. (2009). Religion and suicide. *Journal of Religion and Health, 48*(3), 332–341.

Goss, M., & Reed, J. (1971). Suicide and religion: A study of white adults in New York City, 1963-67. *Life Threatening Behaviour, 1*, 163–177.

Gould, M. S., Fisher, P., Parides, M., Flory, M., & Shaffer, D. (1996). Psychosocial risk factors of child and adolescent completed suicides. *Archives of General Psychiatry, 53*, 1155–1162.

Greening, L., & Stoppelbein, L. (2002). Religiosity, attributional style, and social support as psychosocial buffers for African American and White adolescents' perceived risk for suicide. *Suicide and Life-Threatening Behavior, 32*, 404–417.

Hassan, R. (1983). *A way of dying: Suicide in Singapore.* Kuala Lumpur, Malaysia: Oxford University Press.

Hilton, S. C., Fellingham, G. W., & Lyon, J. L. (2002). Suicide rates and religious commitment in young adult males in Utah. *Journal of Epidemiology and Community Health, 155*(5), 413–419.

Hood-Williams, J. (1996). Studying suicide. *Health & Place, 2*, 167–177.

Ineichen, B. (1998). The influence of religion on the suicide rate: Islam and Hinduism compared. *Mental Health, Religion & Culture, 1*, 31–36.

Jacobs, L. (1995). *The Jewish religion: A companion.* Oxford, UK: Oxford University Press.

Jahangir, F., Rehman, H., & Jan, T. (1998). Degree of religiosity and vulnerability to suicidal attempt/plans in depressive patients among Afghan refugees. *International Journal of the Psychology of Religion, 8*(4), 265–269.

Kamal, Z., & Loewenthal, K. M. (2002). Suicide beliefs and behaviour among young Muslims and Hindus in the UK. *Mental Health, Religion & Culture, 5*(2), 111–118.

Kaplan, S. J., & Schoenberg, L. A. (1988). Defining suicide: Importance and implications for Judaism. *Journal of Religion & Health, 27*(2), 154–156.

Kazi, T. B., & Naidoo, S. (2016). Does religiosity mediate suicidal tendencies? A south African study of Muslim tertiary students. *Journal of Religion & Health, 55*(3), 1010–1023.

Kelly, B. (2011). Self-immolation, suicide and self-harm in Buddhist & Western traditions. *Transcultural Psychiatry, 48*(3), 299–317.

Keown, D. (1996). Buddhism and suicide: The case of Channa. *Journal of Buddhist Ethics, 3*, 8–31.

Kennedy, T. D. (2000). Suicide and the silence of scripture. *Christianity Today*. Retrieved from http://www.christianitytoday.com/ct/2000/julyweb-only/42.0.html?start=1

Khan, M. M. (2007). Suicide prevention in Pakistan: An impossible challenge? *Journal of Pakistan Medical Association, 57*(10), 478–480.

Khan, M. M., & Hyder, A. A. (2006). Suicides in the developing world: Case study from Pakistan. *Suicide and Life-Threatening Behavior, 36*(1), 76–81.

Khan, M. M., & Reza, H. (2000). The pattern of suicide in Pakistan. *Crisis, 21*(1), 31–35.

Khokher, S., & Khan, M. M. (2005). Suicidal ideation in Pakistani college students. *Crisis, 26*(3), 125–127.

Koenig, H. G., McCullough, M. E., & Larson, D. B. (2001). *Handbook of religion and health*. New York, NY: Oxford University Press.

Kranitz, L., Abrahams, J., Spiegel, D., & KeithSpiegel, P. (1968). Religious beliefs of suicidal patients. *Psychological Reports, 22*, 936.

Kumar, V. (2003). Burnt wives—A study of suicides. *Burns, 29*(1), 31–51.

Latha, K. S., Bhat, S. M., & D'Souza, P. (1996). Suicide attempters in a general hospital unit in India: Their socio-demographic and clinical profile—emphasis on cross-cultural aspects. *Acta Psychiatrica Scandinavica, 94*(1), 26–30.

Lester, D. (2006). Suicide and Islam. *Archives of Suicide Research, 10*, 77–97.

Lester, D., & Akande, A. (1994). Attitudes about suicide among the Yoruba of Nigeria. *The Journal of Social Psychology, 134*, 851–853.

Levav, I., & Aisenberg, E. (1989). Suicide in Israel: Crossnational comparisons. *Acta Psychiatrica Scandinavica, 79*, 468–473.

Levav, I., Magnes, J., Aisenberg, E., Rosenblum, I., & Gil, R. (1988). Sociodemographic correlates of suicidal ideation and reported attempts: A brief report on a community survey. *Israel Journal of Psychiatry and Related Sciences, 25*(1), 38–45.

Libreria Editrice Vaticana. (1994). *Catechism of the catholic church*. Washington, DC: United States Conference of Catholic Bishops.

Linehan, M. M., Goodstein, J. L., Nielsen, S. L., & Chiles, J. A. (1983). Reasons for staying alive when you are thinking of killing yourself: The reasons for living inventory. *Journal of Consulting and Clinical Psychology, 51*, 276–286.

Lizardi, D., Currier, D., Galfalvy, H., Sher, L., Burke, A., Mann, J. J., & Oquendo, M. (2007). Perceived reasons for living at index hospitalization and future suicide attempt. *Journal of Nervous and Mental Disease, 195*(5), 451–455.

Lizardi, D., & Gearing, R. E. (2010). Religion and suicide: Buddhism, Native American and African religions, atheism, and agnosticism. *Journal of Religion and Health, 49*(3), 377–384.

Lubin, G., Glasser, S., Boyko, V., & Barell, V. (2001). Epidemiology of suicide in Israel: A nationwide population study. *Social Psychiatry and Psychiatric Epidemiology, 36*, 123–127.

Malone, K. M., Haas, G. L., Sweeny, J. A., & Mann, J. J. (1995). Major depression and the risk of attempted suicide. *Journal of Affective Disorders, 34*, 173–185.

Mann, J. J. (2002). A current perspective of suicide and attempted suicide. *Annals of Internal Medicine, 136*, 302–311.

Mann, J. J., Bortinger, J., Oquendo, M. A., Currier, D., Li, S., & Brent, D. A. (2005). Family history of suicidal behavior and mood disorders in probands with mood disorders. *American Journal of Psychiatry, 162*(9), 1672–1679.

Maris, R. W., Berman, A. L., & Silverman, M. M. (2000). *Comprehensive textbook of suicidology*. New York, NY: Guilford Press.

Martin, W. T. (1984). Religiosity and United States suicide rates, 1972–1978. *Journal of Clinical Psychology, 40*, 1166–1169.

Mohyuddin, F. (2008). Suicide in the Muslim world. *International Journal of Child Health and Human Development, 1*(3, spec iss), 273–279.

Miller, L. (1976). Some data on suicide and attempted suicide of the Jewish population in Israel. *Mental Health and Society, 3*, 178–181.

Nachman, R., Yanai, O., Goldin, L., Swartz, M., Barak, Y., & Hiss, J. (2002). Suicide in Israel: 1985–1997. *Journal of Psychiatry & Neuroscience, 27*, 423–428.

Neeleman, J., Halpern, D., Leon, D., & Lewis, G. T. (1997). Tolerance of suicide, religion, and suicide rates: An ecological and individual study in 19 Western countries. *Psychological Medicine, 227*, 1165–1171.

Nelson, F. L. (1977). Religiosity and self-destructive crises in the institutionalized elderly. *Suicide and Life-Threatening Behavior, 7*, 67–74.

Oquendo, M., Waternaux, C., Brodsky, B., Parsons, B., Haas, G. L., Malone, K. M., & Mann J. J. (2000). Suicidal behavior in bipolar mood disorder: Clinical characteristics of attempters and non-attempters. *Journal of Affective Disorders, 59*, 107–117.

O'Reilly, D., & Rosato, M. (2015). Religion and the risk of suicide: Longitudinal study of over 1 million people. *The British Journal of Psychiatry, 206*(6), 466–470.

Ozdel, O., Varma, G., Atesci, F. C., Oguzhanoglu, N. K., Karadag, F., & Amuk, T. (2009). Characteristics of suicidal behavior in a Turkish sample. *The Journal of Crisis Intervention and Suicide Prevention, 30*(2), 90–93.

Pescosolido, B. A., & Georgianna, S. (1989). Durkheim, suicide, and religion: Toward a network theory of suicide. *American Sociological Review, 54*, 33–48.

Peteet, J. R., & Balboni, M. J. (2013). Spirituality and religion in oncology. *CA: A Cancer Journal for Clinicians, 63*, 280–289. doi:10.3322/caac.21187

Pew Forum's U.S Religious Landscape Survey. (2008). Retrieved from http://www.pewforum.org/files/2013/05/report-religious-landscape-study-full.pdf

Pew Research Center (2017a). Muslims and Islam: Key findings in the U.S. and around the world. Retrieved from http://www.pewresearch.org/fact-tank/2017/08/09/muslims-and-islam-key-findings-in-the-u-s-and-around-the-world/

Pew Research Center (2017b). The global religious landscape: Buddhists. Retrieved from http://www.pewforum.org/2012/12/18/global-religious-landscape-buddhist

Phipps, W. (1985, October 30). Christian perspectives on suicide. *The Christian Century*, 970–972.

Pinto, A., Whisman, M. A., & Conwell, Y. (1998). Reasons for living in a clinical sample of adolescents. *Journal of Adolescence, 21*, 397–405.

Pridmore, S., & Pasha, M. I. (2004). Psychiatry and Islam. *Australasian Psychiatry, 12*(4), 380–385. doi:10.1111/j.1440-1665.2004.02131.x

Pritchard, C., & Amanullah, S. (2007). An analysis of suicide and undetermined deaths in 17 predominantly Islamic countries contrasted with the UK. *Psychological Medicine, 37*, 421–430.

Pritchard, C., & Baldwin, D. (2001). Effects of age and gender on elderly suicide rates in catholic and orthodox countries: An inadvertent neglect? *International Journal of Geriatric Psychiatry, 15*, 904–910.

Rasic, D., Belik, S. L., Elias, B., Katz, L. Y., Enns, M., & Sareen, J. (2009). Spirituality, religion, and suicidal behavior in a nationally represented sample. *Journal of Affective Disorders, 114*(1–3), 32–40.

Retterstol, N. (1993). *Suicide: A European perspective* (R. Williams, Trans.). Cambridge, UK: Cambridge University Press.

Rezaeian, M. (2009). Islam and suicide: A short personal communication. *Journal of Death and Dying, 58*(1), 77–85.

Rezaeian, M. (2010). Suicide among young Middle Eastern Muslim females. *Crisis, 31*, 36–42.

Sadr, S., Habil, H., Zahiroddin, A., Bejanzadeh, S., Seghatoleslam, N., Arkdakani, A., & Rashid, R. (2013). Risk factors for multiple suicide attempts: A critical appraisal of Iranian psychology. *International Medical Journal, 20*(1), 418–422.

Sangharakshita. (1996). *The ten pillars of Buddhism*. Birmingham, UK: Windhorse Publications.

Sangharakshita. (2007). *The Buddha's noble eightfold path* (Rev. ed.). Cambridge, UK: Windhorse Publications.

Sarfraz, A., & Castle, D. J. (2002). A Muslim suicide. *Australasian Psychiatry, 10*(1), 48–50.

Schwartz, M., & Kaplan, K. J. (1992). Judaism, Masada, and suicide: A critical analysis. *Journal of Death and Dying, 25*(2), 127–132.

Shah, A., & Chandia, M. (2010) The relationship between suicide and Islam: A cross-national study. *Journal of Injury and Violence Research, 2*(2), 93–97.

Shneidman, E. S., & Farberow, N. L. (1957). Some comparisons between genuine and simulated suicide notes in terms of Mowrer's concepts of discomfort and relief. *Journal of General Psychology, 56,* 251–256.

Stack, S. (1983). The effect of religious commitment on suicide: A cross-national analysis. *Journal of Health and Social Behavior, 24,* 362–374.

Stack, S., & Kposowa, A. J. (2011). Religion and suicide acceptability: A cross-national analysis. *Journal for the Scientific Study of Religion, 50*(2), 289–306.

Suleiman, M. A., Moussa, M. A., & El-Islam, M. F. (1989). The profile of parasuicide repeaters in Kuwait. *International Journal of Social Psychiatry, 235*(2), 146–155.

Syed, E. U. (2008). Pattern of deliberate self-harm in young people in Karachi, Pakistan. *Crisis: The Journal of Crisis Intervention and Suicide Prevention, 29*(3), 159–163.

Szanto, K., Mulsant, B. H., Houck, P., Dew, M. A., & Reynolds, C. F. (2003). Occurrence and course of suicidality during short-term treatment of late-life depression. *Archives of General Psychiatry, 60,* 610–617.

Thorson, J. A., Powell, F. C., Abdel-Khalek, A., & Beshai, J. A. (1997). Constructions of religiosity and death anxiety in two cultures: The United States and Kuwait. *Journal of Psychology and Theology, 25*(374–383).

Torgler, B., & Schaltegger, C. (2014). Suicide and religion: New evidence on the differences between Protestantism and Catholicism. *Journal for the Scientific Study of Religion, 53*(2), 316–340.

Williams, M. (1997). *Cry of pain: Understanding suicide and self-harm.* Harmondsworth, UK: Penguin.

Wogaman, P. J. (1990). *Ethical perspectives for the community.* Westminster, UK: John Knox Press.

PART II

Suicidality Across the Life Span

CHAPTER FOUR

CHILD AND ADOLESCENT SUICIDE

The rising rate of suicide attempts and completions in children and adolescents is a significant and growing concern. Since 2000, the number of children and adolescents presenting to the emergency room in psychiatric crisis has nearly doubled, with suicidality among the most common presenting problems (Carubia, Becker, & Levine, 2016). In order to work with this population, it is important to understand the epidemiological trends, prevalence, and incidence rates of child and adolescent suicidality and to identify unique and common risk and protective factors. This chapter addresses these issues, deconstructs myths and misconceptions related to suicide among children and adolescents, and highlights the importance of developmental issues with this population. It also provides an overview of empirically grounded strategies for effective assessment and treatment of this population.

GOALS AND OBJECTIVES

An understanding of:

- Epidemiology of child and adolescent suicidality
- Rates of completed suicide, attempted suicide, and suicidal ideation
- Impact of age and gender on suicidality
- Risk factors for child and adolescent suicide
- Protective factors against child and adolescent suicide
- Influence of family systems on child and adolescent suicide
- Social learning theory of transmission of suicidal behavior
- Parental psychiatric illness and its impact on offspring suicide
- The dominant myths and misconceptions of child and adolescent suicidality
- Importance and impact of child and adolescent development on the risk of suicide

---

The death of any individual due to suicide is tragic. The terrible impact of such an event seems to exponentially increase when the individual is a child. Despite the rareness of the event, child and adolescent suicide exerts considerable impact on families, society, and the treating clinician(s). Although completed suicides in this population may be rare, attempts and ideation are far more common in children and adolescents. Approximately 2 million U.S. adolescents attempt suicide annually, with almost 700,000 receiving medical attention for their attempt (American Academy of Child and Adolescent Psychiatry [AACAP], 2001).

It is clinically beneficial for mental health professionals to understand suicidality across the life span for two fundamental reasons. One, professional awareness of the epidemiology, risk and protective factors, misconceptions, developmental issues, and interventions that are unique to the specific age group can guide clinicians in their practice. Two, personal awareness to your response, thoughts, and beliefs connected to suicidality and a specific age equally impact your clinical assessment, interaction, and treatment of clients.

Individual Exercise 4.1

The suicide of a patient in which of the following demographics would be the hardest for you to accept? Please rank in order of impact (1 representing the most impactful to 8 the least impactful):

_____ 39-year-old female   _____ 78-year-old male
_____ 17-year-old male   _____ 23- year-old male
_____ 13-year-old male   _____ 57-year-old female
_____ 64-year-old female   _____ 15-year-old female

Individual Exercise 4.2

Describe at least three reasons for your following answers from individual exercise 4.1:

1. What were your reasons for selecting number 1 (the most impactful)?
2. What were your reasons for selecting number 2 (the second most impactful)?
3. What were your reasons for selecting number 8 (the least impactful of the group)?
4. Was this exercise more difficult or less difficult than you anticipated? Explain your rationale.
5. What lessons did you learn from this exercise?

Small Group Exercise 4.1

In small groups of two to three, please discuss, as you are comfortable, your responses to Individual Exercises 4.1 and 4.2. Remember, answers are personal and there are no correct or incorrect answers.

1. What were the response similarities in your group?
2. What were the response differences in your group?
3. Did you find any surprises in the group discussion? If so, what were they and how were you surprised?

STATISTICS, EPIDEMIOLOGY, AND TRENDS IN CHILD AND ADOLESCENT SUICIDE

Completed Suicide

As individuals grow from childhood into adolescence and then into adulthood and their senior years, so, too, does the risk of suicide. Suicide is the third highest cause of death among youths (Centers for Disease Control and Prevention [CDC], 2015; Wintersteen, Diamond, & Fein, 2007). Completed suicides in children under the age of 10 years are exceptionally rare (CDC, 2015). For example, in 1992, there were no reported suicides for children under 4 years of age and there were only 10 completed suicides in children 5 through 9 years of age (Maris, Berman, & Silverman, 2000). However, according to epidemiological research, it is estimated that each year approximately 2,000 U.S. adolescents aged 13 to 19 years complete suicide (Martin, Kochanek, Strobino, Guyer, & MacDorman, 2005; National Center for Health Statistics, 2000).

For children between the ages of 10 and 14 years, studies have found that the rate of completed suicide has doubled since 1979 (CDC, 2015; National Center for Health Statistics, 2000). However, according to the World Health Organization Mortality Database, worldwide suicide rates for children aged 10 to 14 years across two decades (1990–1999 and 2000–2009) show that the suicide rate per 100,000 in boys aged 10 to 14 years in 81 countries has experienced a minor decline (from 1.61 to 1.52), whereas in girls it has shown a slight increase (from 0.85 to 0.94; Kõlves & De Leo, 2014). Although the average rate has not changed significantly, rates have decreased in Europe and increased in South America (Kõlves & De Leo, 2014).

A recent study examining suicide trends among U.S. elementary school–aged children found the suicide rate among children aged 5 to 11 years remained stable between 1993 and 1997 and between 2008 and 2012 (from 1.18 to 1.09 per 1 million; Bridge et al., 2015). In examining racial–ethnic differences, the suicide rate increased significantly in Black children (from 1.36 to 2.54 per 1 million) and decreased in White children (from 1.14 to 0.77 per 1 million; Bridge et al., 2015). In comparing worldwide suicide trends for youths 10 to 14 years of age in the past two decades (1990–1999 and 2000–2009), research has found the suicide rate in boys has shown a minor decline (from 1.61 to 1.52 per 100,000), whereas in girls it has shown a slight increase (from 0.85 to 0.94 per 100,000; Kõlves & De Leo, 2014).

Among adolescents 15 through 19 years of age, the suicide rate is 8.2 per 100,000 suicides (CDC, 2015; National Center for Health Statistics, 2000). This age group comprises approximately 6% of the overall U.S. population, but accounts for 6.6% of all completed suicides (CDC, 2015; National Center for Health Statistics, 2000). In this age range, the completed suicide rate among males was 15.2 per 100,000 and among females, 3.4 per 100,000 (National Center for Health Statistics, 2000). Since the 1960s, the suicide rate among all adolescents 15 to 19 years of age has tripled, but the female rate has changed little (National Center for Health Statistics, 2000; Peters, Kochanek, & Murphy, 1998). Reportedly, in 2001, of all U.S. youth (15–24 years of age) suicide deaths, 86% were male and only 14% were female (Anderson & Smith, 2003). In young adults aged 20 to 24 years, the suicide rate continues to increase to 12.5 suicides per 100,000 (CDC, 2006).

Among adolescents, males are typically four to six times more likely than females to complete suicide (CDC, 2006). A number of theories and studies have been proposed that investigated this distinct gender disparity in completed suicide, including (a) males use more lethal means (e.g., firearms); (b) females have higher rates of depression for which they receive treatment, whereas males have higher rates of substance use/abuse and do not receive the same levels of mental health treatment; and (c) socialization of genders, where suicide is viewed as more masculine and attempting is seen as more feminine (Canetto & Sakinofsky, 1998; Moscicki, 1994). Additionally, differences in help-seeking behaviors of males and females may partially explain the higher rate of suicide attempts among females and completed suicides among males. Women more often seek help for psychosocial distress and emotional difficulties (Galdas, Cheater, & Marshall, 2005; Möller-Leimkühler, 2002), whereas men more often seek treatment when physical symptoms are present (Corney, 1998; Galdas et al., 2005; Möller-Leimkühler, 2002; NHS Executive, 1998). Furthermore, men have more difficulty than females expressing emotions (Good & Sherrod, 2001), fearing the appearance of being weak, and lacking masculinity (Chapple et al., 2006; Gascoigne & Whitear, 1999; Good, Dell, & Mintz, 1989; Good & Mintz, 1990; Pleck, 1995; Richardson & Rabiee, 2001; Wisch, Mahalik, Hayes, & Nutt, 1995).

Research on the methods of suicide indicates that younger people are more likely to use firearms, suffocation, and poisoning than other methods. However, while adolescents and young adults are more likely to use firearms than suffocation, children are dramatically more likely to use suffocation (CDC, 2015). One study that examined all cases of suicide by poison ingestion among youths aged 9 to 18 years reported to a Toxicology Information Center (Zakharov, Navratil, & Pelclova, 2013) determined that drugs were used as the type of poison in just under 98% of cases. The most common drugs used were those affecting the nervous system and anti-inflammatory nonsteroidals. The dose was evaluated as toxic in 73%, severely toxic in 3%, and unknown in 11% of cases. Only one in 10 children did not use a toxic dose. Girls used nontoxic doses more often than boys (Zakharov et al., 2013).

Suicide Attempt and Ideation

Suicide attempts across all age groups have a higher prevalence rate than completed suicide. In the general population, men and the elderly are more likely to have fatal attempts than are women and youths (Moscicki, 2001). For every completed suicide, approximately eight to 25 nonfatal suicide attempts occur (CDC, 2006; Moscicki, 2001).

According to Evans, Hawton, Rodham, and Deeks's (2005) systematic review of population-based studies, approximately 10% of adolescents reported attempting suicide and 30% reported that they had thought about suicide at some point (Evans et al., 2005). In a study examining all children aged 12 years and younger presenting for hospital emergency services in 1 year, 17% reported a history of suicidal ideation and/or behaviors with the prevalence rate increasingly higher in Whites, Latinos, and Blacks, respectively. Of those presenting with suicidality, 65% were diagnosed with a behavioral disorder, 26% were diagnosed with a mood disorder, 4% with a psychotic disorder, and 5% with another disorder (Joe, Banks, & Belue, 2016).

Some research suggests gender differences in the relationship between suicidal ideation and suicide attempts among youths. For example, suicidal ideation has been found to be a significant predictor of subsequent suicide attempts for girls, but not for boys (Czyz & King, 2015; King, Jiang, Czyz, & Kerr, 2014).

The ratio of nonfatal attempts to completed suicide in children and adolescents has been found to be significantly higher than among older persons (Moscicki, 1995). In adolescents, males are more likely to complete suicide than females (Canetto & Sakinofsky, 1998; CDC, 2015); however, adolescent females are more likely to attempt suicide (CDC, 2015; Schmidtke, Bille-Brahe, DeLeo, & Kerkhof, 1996). Across studies, research has found that adolescent females have a 1.25 times higher prevalence of suicidal ideation than males and attempt suicide at least twice as often as males (Evans et al., 2005).

Some research has examined the trajectories of suicide risk in youths as they transition into adulthood. Among youths who initially presented as at low risk, most remained at low risk across the 7-year follow-up. Additionally, although some youths initially classified as at high risk transitioned to a lower risk group 7 years later, the majority remained at high risk. Further results demonstrated that the probability of making a suicide attempt was higher for those youths who were initially classified as high risk both at 1 and 7 years earlier (Thompson, Kuruwita, & Foster, 2009).

RISK AND PROTECTIVE FACTORS

Over the past 30 years, research has extensively investigated characteristics associated with child and adolescent suicide. Four major categories of risk have been identified: (a) psychiatric; (b) demographic; (c) relational; and (d) other risk factors.

Psychiatric Risk Factors

Psychiatric illness, particularly depression, is the greatest known risk factor for suicide among children and adolescents (Brent, Perper, & Moritz, 1993; Breton et al., 2015; Garrison, Jackson, Addy, McKeown, & Waller, 1991; Harrington et al., 1994; Hollis, 1996; Kovacs, Goldston, & Catsonis, 1993; Pfeffer, 1991; Pfeffer et al., 1993; Tsypes & Gibb, 2016). Depressed youths are six times more likely to make suicide attempts than nondepressed adolescents (Stewart et al., 2015). However, there are age differences within youths regarding the risk posed by depression. That is, among youths presenting to the emergency department for suicidal behavior, 12- to 18-year-olds most often had a mood disorder, whereas younger children under 12 years more often had attention deficit hyperactivity disorder (ADHD; Ben-Yehuda, 2012).

Other psychiatric disorders associated with an increased risk of suicide among youths include substance abuse, conduct disorders, anxiety disorders, oppositional defiant disorder, ADHD, and schizophrenia (Andrews & Lewinsohn, 1992; Beautrais, Joyce, & Mulder, 1998b; Brent et al., 1988, 1993; Bushe & Savill, 2013; Chronis-Tuscano et al., 2010; Fergusson & Lynskey, 1995b; Fombonne, 1998; Joffe, Offord, & Boyle, 1988; Karaman & Durukan, 2013; Lesage et al., 1994; Mayes et al., 2015; Patton et al., 1997; Shaffer et al., 1996; Shafi, Steltz-Lenarsky, Derrick, Beckner, & Whittinghill, 1988). Please refer to Part IV for a detailed discussion of psychiatric disorders and suicide.

Parental psychiatric illness is also a risk factor for suicide in child and adolescent offspring (Brent et al., 2002, 2004; Brent & Mann, 2005; Egeland & Sussex, 1985; Garfinkel, Froese, & Hood, 1982; Linkowski, de Maertelaer, & Mendlewicz, 1985; Roy, Segal, Centerwall, & Robinette, 1991; Roy, Segal, & Sarchiapone, 1995; Runeson, 1998; Sorenson & Rutter, 1991; Tsuang, 1983). This issue is discussed later in the chapter under Family System.

Interpersonal Risk Factors

Family conflict is a significant risk factor for suicide among children and adolescents (Adams, Overholser, & Lehnert, 1994; Asarnow, Carlson, & Mintz, 1988; de Wilde, Kienhorst, Diekstra, & Waters, 1992; Hollis, 1996; Kosky, Silburn, & Zubrick, 1990; Randell, Wang, Herting, & Eggert, 2006; Soole & Kõlves, 2015; Taylor & Stansfeld, 1984; Zalsman & Mann, 2005), with negative mother–child relationship and lack of family warmth highly associated with increased suicide risk (Hollis, 1996). Furthermore, research has indicated that suicidal youths are more likely to have increased family instability and chaos (Adam, Bouckoms, & Streiner, 1982; de Jong, 1992). In a study examining the role of conflicted family environments, results showed that children living in quarrelsome families showed a 3.7-fold risk of suicidal ideation compared with children in harmonious families. A 27-fold increased suicidal ideation risk was also observed among depressed children living in a quarrelsome family environment, compared with nondepressed children living in a harmonious family environment (Lin, Lin, Hsieh, & Chang, 2014). Additionally, parental separation and divorce are also significant risk factors for suicide among youths (Fergusson, Woodward, & Harwood, 2000; Gould & Kramer, 2001; Rubenstein, Halton, Kasten, Rubin, & Stechler, 1998).

Adverse childhood experiences including various forms of maltreatment, dysfunctional household environments, and trauma can have an immediate and long-term effect on development. In terms of adolescents, early adverse experiences during childhood have been shown to increase the risk of suicide ideation (Diamond, Creed, Gillham, Gallop, & Hamilton, 2012; Fuller-Thomson, Baird, Dhrodia, & Brennenstuhl (2016); Greger, Myhre, Lydersen, & Jozefiak (2015); Thompson et al., 2012) and attempt during adolescence (Araújo & Lara, 2016; Coohey, Dirks-Bihun, Renner, & Baller, 2014; Enns et al., 2006; Molnar, Berkman, & Buka, 2001; Perez, Jennings, Piquero, & Baglivio, 2016). Exposure to physical and sexual abuse (Beautrais, Joyce, Mulder, Fergusson, Deavoll, & Nightingale, 1996;

Brodsky & Stanley, 2008; de Wilde, Kienhorst, Diekstra, & Waters, 1992; Evans et al., 2005; Fergusson et al., 2000; Gould, Fisher, Parides, Flory, & Shaffer, 1996; Salzinger, Rosario, Feldman, & Ng-Mak, 2007; Shaunessey, Cohen, Plummer, & Berman, 1993; Thompson et al. 2012; Stewart, Vigod, & Riazantseva, 2016; Wherry, Baldwin, Junco, & Floyd, 2013; Zalsman & Mann, 2005) and family violence (Hawton, O'Grady, Osborn, & Cole, 1982; Kosky, 1983) is associated with increased suicide risk among children and adolescents. One systematic review of the literature examining childhood maltreatment found that childhood sexual abuse, physical abuse, emotional abuse, and neglect are all associated with adolescent suicidal ideation and attempts across community, clinical, and high-risk samples, using cross-sectional and longitudinal research designs (Miller, Esposito-Smythers, Weismoore, & Renshaw, 2013). Results of the review also found that these associations remain significant even after controlling for covariates such as youth demographics, mental health issues, family characteristics, and peer-related variables (Miller et al., 2013). Each form of maltreatment makes a unique contribution and has an additive effect on adolescent suicide risk (Greger, Myhre, Lydersen, & Jozefiak, 2016; Miller et al., 2013; Serafini et al., 2015). The risk of suicide attempt among adolescents who experienced adverse childhood events is further increased when the adolescent's personality is characterized by aggression and impulsivity and when the adolescent experiences problem behaviors including school difficulties and/or substance abuse (Perez, 2016). A study by Soylu and & Alpaslan (2013) examining suicidal ideation and attempts in sexually abused adolescents found that suicidal ideation developed in 63% of the individuals, and 25% of them attempted suicide (Soylu & Alpaslan, 2013). Another study examining only female adolescents who experienced sexual abuse found that 26% had attempted suicide, 52% had suicidal ideation, and 24% had nonsuicidal self-injury during the postabuse period (Unlu & Cakaloz, 2016). Research has also found a link between younger childhood sexual abuse in females and increased risk of suicide attempts (Rabinovitch, Kerr, Leve, & Chamberlain, 2015). See Chapter 5 for a discussion of the long-term effects of early adverse experiences on adult suicide risk.

The relationship between perceived social support and adolescent suicide risk has received much attention (Miller, Esposito-Smythers, & Leichtweis, 2015). Lower perceived parental support has been shown to predict a lifetime history of suicide attempt among adolescents even after controlling for perceptions of support received from school and close friends (Miller et al., 2015; Wolff et al., 2013). Further, perceptions of lower school support have been shown to predict greater severity of suicidal ideation among adolescents, even after controlling for perceptions of support received from parents and close friends (Miller et al., 2015). This relationship is even stronger among those adolescents who also report lower perceived parental support (Miller et al., 2015). Research also has demonstrated that after controlling for demographics, diagnostic status, past history of attempt, and life event stress, chronic stress in family relationships and close friendships predicted suicidal ideation among adolescents, and chronic close friendship stress predicted suicide intent among attempters (Pettit, Green, Grover, Schatte, & Morgan, 2011). Social exclusion, in general, during early adolescence has also been associated with an elevated risk in suicide attempts (Wilczynska-Kwiatek, 2011). However, others have found that the level of suicide risk based on perceived connectedness to parents varies according to which parent is the focus of the perceived support. More specifically, increased perceived connectedness to father but not to mother was associated with a lower risk of suicidal thoughts and behaviors (Conner et al., 2016).

Other research has also identified that having a friend with a past history of attempted and completed suicide was significantly associated with increased odds of suicide attempts among youths (Nanayakkara, Misch, Chang, & Henry, 2013; Thompson & Light, 2011). Further, exposure to a friend or family member's suicide attempt or completed suicide contributes significantly to the risk of suicide for adolescents, independent of the adolescent's level of depression (Nanayakkara et al., 2013). However, some research has found that these positive associations between exposure to peer suicide or suicidal behavior and individual suicide behavior become smaller and less significant after controlling for environmental confounders (Ali, Dwyer, & Rizzo, 2011), that the effects fade over time (Abrutyn & Mueller, 2014), and that the effect is stronger among female adolescents than among male adolescents (Abrutyn & Mueller, 2014).

Bullying has consistently been identified as a risk factor for suicidal ideation and behavior (El Asam & Samara, 2016; Flannery et al., 2016; Geoffroy et al., 2016; Gini & Espelage, 2014; Hanley & Gibb, 2011; Holt et al., 2015; Hong, Kral, & Sterzing, 2015; Shpiegel, Klomek, & Apter, 2015; Sinclair, Bauman, Poteat, Koenig, & Russell, 2012; Williams, & Guerra, 2007). Bullying can manifest in many formats. Verbal, physical, and cyberbullying have all been found to be associated with increased suicide risk (Hanley & Gibb, 2011; Hirschtritt, Ordóñez, Rico, & LeWinn, 2015; Kodish et al., 2016); however, verbal bullying has been shown to be uniquely associated with suicide attempt (Hanley & Gibb, 2011; Kodish et al., 2016). Research has also found an association between cyberbullying and suicidal thoughts (Mirsky & Omar, 2015). One study on cyberbullying examined the impact of role (cyber-victim, cyberbully, and cyberbully-victim) and of viewing suicide-related web content on suicide risk (Görzig, 2016). Results demonstrated that compared with those not involved in cyberbullying, the viewing of web content related to suicide was higher among cyber-victims and cyberbully-victims than for cyberbullies. The viewing of web content related to suicide was higher across all cyberbullying roles, and highest for cyberbully-victims. Rates of emotional problems were higher among cyber-victims and cyberbully-victims, whereas rates of peer problems were higher for cyber-victims, and rates of conduct problems were higher for all cyberbullies. Moreover, the links between cyberbullying role and viewing of suicide-related web content remained even after controlling for psychiatric symptoms. Research has also suggested that early intervention for adolescents frequently involved in bullying may reduce the onset of substance use and other mental disorders (Kelly et al., 2015).

Sociodemographic Risk Factors

Several demographic characteristics are significantly associated with child adolescent suicide. Low socioeconomic status and low educational achievement have been found to increase the risk of suicidal behavior among youths (Andrews & Lewinsohn, 1992; Beautrais, Joyce, & Mulder, 1998a; Bucca et al., 1994; Dubow, Kausch, Blum, Reed, & Bush, 1989; Fergusson & Lynskey, 1995a; Gould et al., 1996; Lesage et al., 1994). However, research in this area has been inconsistent as some studies have failed to find any association between low socioeconomic status and youth suicidality (Brent et al., 1988; Pelkonen, Marttunen, Pulkkinen, Laippala, & Aro, 1997).

Additionally, research has consistently demonstrated that sexual orientation, specifically identifying as gay, lesbian, or bisexual, may result in an increased risk for suicidal behavior among adolescents (Bagley & Tremblay, 2000; Borowsky, Ireland, & Resnick, 2001; Button, O'Connell, & Gealt, 2012; Eisenberg & Resnick, 2006; Gould & Kramer, 2001; Mustanski, Andrews, Herrick, Stall, & Schnarrs, 2014; Saewyc, Heinz, Bearinger, Blum, & Resnick, 1998; Stronski-Huwiler & Remafedi, 1998). Further, research indicates that the rate of suicide attempts among gay, lesbian, and bisexual adolescents is as much as four times higher than the rate of suicide attempts among heterosexual adolescents (Bagley & Tremblay, 2000; Bostwick et al., 2014; Eisenberg & Resnick, 2006; Gould & Kramer, 2001; Saewyc, Heinz, Bearinger, Blum, & Resnick, 1998; Stronski-Huwiler & Remafedi, 1998). This is discussed in more detail in Chapter 12.

Another potential risk factor increasingly being investigated in the literature is the relationship between body weight and suicidal behaviors. Results suggest that self-perceived and measured overweight or obese status may increase a female adolescent's probability of suicidal ideation (Minor Ali, & Rizzo,, 2016).

Lastly, gender is another major risk factor for suicide among adolescents. Among older adolescents (15 years and older), females have been consistently shown to be at greater risk for suicide than males (Evans et al., 2005). Please refer to Chapter 2 for a review of ethnic/cultural risk and protective factors among adolescents.

Other Risk Factors

A number of other risk factors have been associated with suicidality in youths. Research has found that heavy episodic drinking is a distinct risk factor for suicidal behavior among younger adolescents, even when controlling for depression (Aseltine, Schilling, James, Glanovsky, & Jacobs., 2009). However, research has found that children are much less likely to consume alcohol prior to an attempt than are adolescents (Soole, 2015).

Low self-esteem has also been associated with an increased risk for suicidal behaviors among adolescents (Sharaf, Thompson, & Walsh, 2010). Research has found that low self-esteem moderates the relationship between several key risk factors and suicidal ideation. For example, the relationship between depression and suicidal ideation has been found to be significantly moderated by self-esteem (Brausch & Decker, 2014), and the relationship between peer victimization and suicidal ideation has been found to be both moderated (Jones, Bilge-Johnson, Rabinovitch, & Fishel, 2014) and mediated by self-esteem (Hong et al., 2015).

Research with suicidal adolescents has also examined whether extreme self-reliance is a risk factor that may prevent youths from reaching out for help or engaging in mental health services. A study posited that a commonly reported reason for not seeking help is the perception of youths that they should solve problems on their own (Labouliere, Kleinman, & Gould, 2015). The study, whose hypothesis was supported by its preliminary findings, concluded with the recommendation that attitudes that reinforce extremely self-reliant behavior may be an important target for youth suicide prevention programs (Labouliere, Kleinman, & Gould, 2015).

As is the case with adults, cigarette smoking is associated with increased risk of suicidal behavior among adolescents (Gart & Kelly, 2015; Riala, Hakko, & Räsänen, 2009). For example, research has found a more than fourfold increase in the risk of suicide attempts among female adolescents with a high level of nicotine dependence even after adjusting for adolescents' age and psychiatric diagnoses (Riala et al., 2009). Other research has found that current smoking increases the likelihood of suicidality at least fivefold among Black adolescent smokers (Gilreath, Connell, & Leventhal, 2012).

Research has suggested an association between sleep problems and suicidal ideations in adolescence (Franić, Kralj, Marčinko, Knez, & Kardum, 2014; Kaplan, Ali, Simpson, Britt, & McCall, 2014; Lee, Ma, Yen, Huang, & Chiang, 2012; Winsler, Deutsch, Vorona, Payne, & Szklo-Coxe, 2015). This factor requires further study as two-thirds of adolescent students reported insufficient sleep (McKnight-Eily et al., 2011), and insomnia symptoms are reported by one-third of adolescents in the general population (Blank et al., 2015). It is recommended that clinicians should consider evaluating sleep disturbances in youths, specifically sleep amount and quality, as they might be a marker of increased risk for suicidality (Bernert, Kim, Iwata, & Perlis, 2015; Bernert & Nadorff, 2015; Franić et al., 2014; Kim, Park, Lee, & Yoo, 2015; Malik et al., 2014).

Lastly, research has examined the role of child welfare systems in relation to suicide risk. Children and adolescents in child welfare care are at a greater risk of completed suicide and attempting suicide than those who are not in care (Anderson, 2011; Katz et al., 2011). Rates of suicide attempts and hospital admissions within the youth in-care population are highest before entry into care and decrease thereafter (Katz et al., 2011). Further, among youths involved with the child welfare system, those with a stronger connection to caregivers are much less likely to report suicidal ideation, whereas those with stronger deviant peer relationships are significantly more likely to report such ideation (He,

Fulginiti, & Finno-Velasquez, 2015). Youths with multiple placements are also at a higher risk (Taussig et al., 2014).

Risk factors for repeat attempts among adolescents have also been examined. Studies have shown that adolescents with a history of both suicide attempts and nonsuicidal self-harm report more mental health problems and other psychosocial problems than adolescents who report only one or none of these behaviors (Tørmoen, Rossow, Mork, & Mehlum, 2014). Research demonstrates that when the adolescent was alone during his or her index attempt, when he or she reports having had a serious wish to die prior to the index attempt, and when he or she planned the index attempt for an hour or more, the risk of a repeat attempt is significantly increased (Miranda, Jaegere, Restifo, & Shaffer, 2014). Among adolescents who have experienced a suicide attempt, maternal hostility and paternal anger and arguing predicted increased risk of future suicide attempts.

Among parents of adolescents who have made suicide attempts, mothers report feeling increased sadness, caring, anxiety, guilt, fear, and being overwhelmed, while fathers report increased sadness, anxiety, and fear (Greene-Palmer et al., 2015). Parents also have reported that most important to them following their child's suicide attempt is first keeping their child safe, followed by identifying what caused or triggered the suicide attempt, building strategies to prevent another suicide attempt, and improving communication and building trust for the future (Hickey, Rossetti, Strom, & Bryant, 2015).

Protective Factors Against Suicide

Research examining protective factors against youth suicide is much more limited in comparison to the literature examining risk factors. Having a strong social support network, particularly family cohesion, is the strongest protective factor against suicide in children and adolescents (Armstrong & Manion, 2006; Borowsky, Ireland, & Resnick, 2001; Eisenberg, Ackard, & Rsenick, 2007; Eisenberg & Resnick, 2006; Hall-Lande, Eisenberg, Christenson, & Neumark-Sztainer, 2007; Rubenstein, Heeren, Housman, Rubin, & Stechler, 1989; Sharaf et al., 2010; Taliaferro & Muehlenkamp, 2014; van Heeringen, 2001). For example, sharing frequent family meals together has been associated with reduced suicide ideation and attempt in youths (Utter et al., 2013).

Researchers have specified the importance of perceived social support, in particular, as compared to family cohesion alone as a protective factor against suicide among youths (Chioqueta & Stiles, 20 07). Peer relationships have been demonstrated to have an indirect protective effect against suicidality among adolescents (Rubenstein et al., 1989).

The presence of a caring adult has also been shown to be a protective factor against youth suicide (Borowsky, Ireland, & Resnick, 1991; Eisenberg, Ackard, & Resnick, 2007; Eisenberg & Resnick, 2006; Resnick et al., 1997). Additionally, a safe school environment, including teacher caring, has been shown to be protective against suicidal behavior in youths (Borowsky, Ireland, & Resnick, 1991; Eisenberg, Ackard, & Resnick, 2007; Eisenberg & Resnick, 2006).

Protective effects of self-esteem have also been found to influence youth suicidal behaviors (Sharaf, Thompson, & Walsh, 2009). Research has demonstrated, however, that family support moderates the impact of self-esteem on suicide risk. That is, the protective effect of self-esteem is stronger among adolescents with low family support as compared to those who report high family support (Sharaf, Thompson, & Walsh, 2009). More often, research has examined the effects of low self-esteem as a risk factor, as described earlier.

Effective coping skills serve as a protective factor for youths experiencing suicidal ideation. Research has identified that suicidal youths use effective coping mechanisms less frequently than healthy controls; they also experience communication problems and problem-solving difficulties within the family (Fidan, Ceyhun, & Kirpinar, 2011). According to McMahon and colleagues (2013), emotion-oriented coping was strongly associated with poorer mental health and self-harm thoughts and acts, whereas problem-oriented coping was associated with better mental health (McMahon et al., 2013). Research has identified a number of coping strategies, including problem solving, emotional regulation, support seeking, and acceptance, as predicting a reduction in suicidal ideation among both male and female youths (Khurana & Romer, 2012).

As was mentioned earlier, religiosity has been shown to be associated with reduced risk of suicidality in adults (Dervic et al., 2004; Lizardi et al., 2007; Stack, 1983). Research investigating religion as a protective factor for adolescents has been mixed, but is beginning to demonstrate stronger evidence that it may also serve as a protective factor for suicidal risk in youths (Amit et al., 2014; Greening & Stoppelbein, 2002; Hilton, Fellingham, & Lyon, 2002; Hoffman & Marsiglia, 2014).

Research investigating the influence of emotional intelligence (EI; the ability to perceive, integrate into thoughts, understand, and manage one's emotions) on suicidal ideation and attempts in youths found EI to be a protective factor for both suicidal ideation and attempts (Cha & Nock, 2009). Specifically, Cha and colleagues (2009) identified that the protective effect of EI was driven primarily by differences in strategic EI (e.g., ability to understand and manage emotions), but not experiential EI (e.g., ability to perceive emotions and integrate emotions into thoughts; Cha et al., 2009). Another study examining the moderating role of emotional intelligence in the relationship between perceived stress and suicidal ideation found that emotional intelligence serves as a buffer in the relationship between perceived stress and suicidal ideation (Abdollahi, Carlbring, Khanbani, & Ghahfarokhi, 2016).

Physical activity has also been examined as a protective factor against suicidal ideations and behaviors (Babiss & Gangwisch, 2009; Gunn & Lester, 2014; Sibold, Edwards, Murray-Close, & Hudziak, 2015; Stein & Dubowitz, 2015). Research has found a relationship between high levels of physical activity/exercise and decreased risk of suicidal ideation and behaviors as well as nonsuicidal self-injury (Boone & Brausch, 2016). A strong association has been found between increased physical activity, depressive symptoms, and suicidality in bullied adolescents (Sibold, Edwards, Murray-Close, & Hudziak, 2015). More specifically, exercise for 4 or more days per week has been found to be associated with an approximately 23% reduction in suicidal ideation and attempt in youths who are victims of bullying (Sibold, 2016). Other studies have examined sports participation, finding that as sports participation increases, the odds of suffering from depression decrease by 25% and the odds of suicidal ideation decrease by 12%, even after controlling for sex, age, race/ethnicity, public assistance, and physical limitations (Babiss & Gangwisch, 2009). Further, research shows that youths involved in sports in both middle and high schools were less likely to experience suicidal ideation during high school than nonparticipants. Youths who discontinued sports participation after middle school had higher odds of attempting suicide during high school than nonparticipants (Taliaferro, Eisenberg, Johnson, Nelson, & Neumark-Sztainer, 2011). However, other research suggests that participation in sports can serve as both a protective factor and a risk factor for suicidal ideation dependent on the particular sport (Gunn & Lester, 2014). Participation in team sports is associated with a protective effect whereas participating in a sport perceived to be outside of the gender norm (e.g., cheerleading for boys or wrestling for girls) is shown to act as a risk factor (Gunn & Lester, 2014).

Case Vignette 4.1

You are a mental health clinician in an outpatient child and adolescent psychiatric clinic. You are scheduled to do an intake with a new client who was referred for services following a visit to the local hospital's emergency department for an attempted suicide.

Your client, Robert, a 17-year-old high school junior, attempted suicide a week earlier by ingesting his mother's prescribed medication for arthritis. Upon intake, you learn that Robert has been experiencing a slow decline in functioning over the past 2 years since the divorce of his parents. Robert explained that the divorce did not come as a surprise because his parents never got along and always argued. He said he could not think of one time when the family was together without his parents verbally fighting.

Robert reacted strongly to their divorce. He mainly attributed his reaction to the fact that his older brother, Jonathan, chose to go and live with their father. He described Jonathan's moving away as a greater loss than his father's leaving the household. Jonathan was his idolized older brother, the person Robert turned to for advice and support, and he feared their relationship would change once Jonathan left home. Although Robert did not want to live with his father, he considered leaving his mother's house to be able to stay with his brother. Robert explained that when he mentioned the idea to his mother she looked so devastated that he did not have the heart to go through with it. He grew to feel responsible for his mother and guilty for contributing any further to her emotional pain.

Robert described feeling disconnected from and pressured by the people about whom he cared and, in response, he became increasingly withdrawn. A year prior to his suicide attempt, he had a discussion with his mother during which she asked him about being depressed. He reported feeling unable to tell her the truth because he was afraid that it would further hurt her. He attempted to talk to his father about his feelings; however, his father responded by saying that Robert's grandfather had suffered from depression and had attempted suicide. Consequently, his father reported that he "had no room in his life for any more sadness or stress." Feeling unsupported and alone, Robert withdrew from his friends, and his grades started slipping. He described feeling irritable and losing pleasure in most activities. Later, he spoke to his school guidance counselor about his depression and was subsequently referred to a mental health clinic; however, Robert never followed up on this referral. He reported feeling comfortable talking to the guidance counselor who knew him for years, but was worried that a stranger might think he "was crazy."

Robert explained that the week he attempted suicide he felt almost a "sense of relief" because he knew "it would all be over soon." Although his mother may be hurt by his suicide, she would no longer have to face constant disappointment and frustration with him. He hid a few of his mother's pills every day for 5 days until he had stored up what he believed to be enough pills to end his life. He stayed home from school feigning illness. After he kissed his mother goodbye and she left for work, he wrote letters to his mother, brother, and father, and then took all the pills. Fortunately, his mother left her briefcase at home and shortly returned to find him unconscious in his bed.

1. *What risk factors are present in the Case Vignette?*
2. *What other risk factors would you assess for?*
3. *What protective factors are present in the Case Vignette?*
4. *What other protective factors would you assess for?*
5. *What issues are important to focus on in establishing a treatment plan?*

ROLE-PLAY 4.1

Using Case Vignette 4.1, engage in a role-play in which you would assess for familial transmission of suicidal behavior. Have one person take the role of the clinician and another take the role of Robert.

MYTHS AND MISCONCEPTIONS

There are a number of myths and misconceptions that have developed and evolved in the field of suicidality in relation to children and adolescents. The following list is presented to highlight some of these key myths and misconceptions. The first six items are adapted from Moskos, Achilles, and Gray (2004).

1. *Suicide attempters and completers are similar.* According to research, males are four times more likely to die due to a suicide attempt, but females, more likely to attempt. The ratio between youth suicide attempters and youth suicide completers is estimated at 100–200:1. Attempting suicide is a recognized risk factor; however, the majority of suicide completers have no prior attempts.

2. *Current prevention programs work.* Adolescent prevention programs (school education programs, teen suicide hotlines, media campaigns, efforts to limit firearm access to teens) have not had a significant impact on lowering the teen suicide rate. Several reasons have been proposed as to why these programs have failed to effectively reduce teen suicide, including that they are not rigorously investigated, programs are used more by females than males, they have little impact on cluster suicides (suicides by unrelated groups of individuals), and they do not address access to means.

3. *Teenagers have the highest rate of suicide.* Statistically, senior adults, specifically older White males, are at the highest risk for suicide.

4. *Suicide is caused by family and social stress.* Research has found that adolescent completers may have experienced some social difficulty (disciplinary, shame, or amorous crisis event) prior to a suicide, but these events are not uncommon for adolescents, most of whom do not suicide. Research has clearly found that approximately 90% of teen completers have a psychiatric diagnosis.

5. *Suicidality is not inherited.* Genetics appear to have a strong association with mental health and suicide, including a risk of inheriting mental illnesses and/or increased impulsivity or aggression.

6. *Teen suicide represents treatment failure.* Research has found that few adolescent suicide completers were in treatment at the time of their deaths (1% were in public mental health treatment; 3% had detectable levels of psychotropic medications in the blood sample).

7. *Most suicides do not occur at home.* The majority of adolescent suicides occur in the home, with most households having at least one lethal means available at the time of the attempt (McManus et al., 1997). For example, research has identified that most of the guns used by adolescents who have completed suicide belong to their parents (Johnson, Barber, Azrael, Clark, & Hemenway, 2010). It is recommended that parents/caregivers of suicidal youths be provided with injury prevention education in emergency departments. However, many parents do not receive or do not act on injury prevention education, such as education regarding restricting access to lethal means of suicide (e.g., disposing or locking up of medications or guns) or monitoring/supervising the youths (Barber & Miller, 2014; Brent, Baugher, Birmaher, Kolko, & Bridge, 2000; McManus et al., 1997).

Case Vignette 4.2

You are completing an assessment of a 12-year-old male who presented with depression, social anxiety, and mild suicidal ideation. He is a polite child, but very quiet and reserved. You received some indication that he has been treated poorly by peers at school. You ask about bullying, and his mother forcefully interjects that her son does not get bullied.

1. *How would you work to engage the son in your assessment given the mother's forceful denial of any issues with peers?*
2. *How would you work to engage the mother in your assessment in a way that would create a safe space for her son to disclose any trouble he may be having with peers?*
3. *How would you proceed to assess the potential of bullying?*
4. *What questions would you use to assess for frequency, duration, and type?*
5. *It is important to assess for peer and adult response (e.g., perceptions, attitudes). How could this situation be used to support the child?*
6. *Reviewing locations or "hot spots" where bullying occurs is important. How may such questions assist parents and families to better understand the bullying experienced by this or other children?*
7. *What other assessment questions would you ask to better understand the potential risk factors and safety issues?*

ROLE-PLAY 4.2

Using Case Vignette 4.2, engage in a role-play in which you would assess for relevant risk factors for suicidal ideation. Have one person take the role of the clinician, another take the role of the 12-year-old boy, and another take the role of the mother.

ROLE-PLAY 4.3

Using the aforementioned role-play, change the type of bullying to cyberbullying. How might this role-play be different or the same if the child were experiencing cyberbullying?

CHILD AND ADOLESCENT DEVELOPMENT

Suicide is extremely rare before puberty (AACAP, 2001). As noted earlier, epidemiologically, suicide prior to 12 to 13 years of age is extraordinarily infrequent. There are many potential theories as to why children do not suicide, including lack of cognitive ability or formal operational thinking, low rates of substance use, lack of opportunity due to near constant parent/teacher/adult supervision, children's developmentally based reliance on parent/family support during stressful times or events, and fewer tumultuous social difficulties with peers.

Adolescence is a period of rapid developmental change that may exert increasing risk of suicide on youths as they transition from childhood. In addition, adolescents experience significant social, emotional, and cognitive transitions (Everall, Bostik, & Paulson, 2005). Research indicates that there are three major developmental processes that may influence adolescent suicidality: (a) cognitive development, (b) identity formation, and (c) the search for autonomy (Everall et al., 2005).

Cognitive development in adolescence is characterized by increased hypothetical and abstract reasoning abilities, viewing oneself as unique and different from others, and becoming more introspective and vulnerable to feelings of hopelessness. At the same time, adolescents experience limited decision-making skills, poor problem-solving abilities, and irrational decision making when stressed or experiencing strong affect or inescapable conflict (Everall et al., 2005).

Adolescence is a period of identity formation. According to Arnett (1999), during the process of developing their personal identities, adolescents will experience a range of difficulties, concerns, stresses, problems, and anxieties as they explore their individual thoughts, feelings, abilities, skills, and values (Arnett, 1999). Research has indicated that difficulties in developing an identity can result in maladaptive coping and ultimately become a suicide risk factor (Everall et al., 2005; Stillion & McDowell, 1991).

During adolescence, youths seek a balance between striving for autonomy and a renegotiated attachment with their parents (Allen, Aber, & Leadbeater, 1990; Allen & Land, 1999). This is a critical stage-salient task (Allen, Hauser, Bell, & O'Connor, 1994). Fundamental to successful development of this balance between autonomy and relatedness are skills to manage conflict, learning new coping and problem-solving strategies, and parents' abilities to provide security and negotiate their adolescent's increasing independence. Inadequate negotiation of autonomy and attachment systems may limit an adolescent's social and psychological well-being, resulting in increased suicide risk (Kaplan & Worth, 1993).

FAMILY SYSTEM

Current literature focusing on the *familial transmission* of suicide largely examines suicide attempters with a family history of suicide compared to nonattempters with a family history of suicide (Birmaher et al., 1996; Egeland & Sussex, 1985; Gould et al., 1996; Johnson, Brent, Bridge, & Connolly, 1998; Malone, Haas, Sweeny, & Mann, 1995; Powell, Geddes, Deeks, Goldacre, & Hawton, 2000; Roy, 2002a, 2002b, 2003; Runeson & Asberg, 2003; Sorenson & Rutter, 1991; Tsai, Kuo, Chen, & Lee, 2002; Tsuang, 1983). Additionally, several high risk studies have been conducted examining offspring of parents with and without a family history of suicide attempt (Brent et al., 2002, 2003; Fergusson, Beautrais, & Horwood, 2003).

Overall, this research has clearly established an association between family history of suicidal behavior and increased suicide attempt risk in study participants (Birmaher et al., 1996; Brent, Melhem, & Mann, 2015; Cheng, Chen, Chen, & Jenkins, 2000; Fu et al., 2002; Geulayov, Metcalfe, Heron, Kidger, & Gunnell, 2014; Glowinski et al., 2001; Gould et al., 1996; Hawton, Haw, Houston, & Townsend, 2002; Kuramoto, Brent, & Wilcox, 2009; Mann et al., 2005; Roy, 1993; Roy et al., 1995; Roy, Rylander, & Sarchiapone, 1997; Sorenson & Rutter, 1991). Suicidal behavior in family members has been associated with an increased risk for suicide attempt in other family members (Thompson & Light, 2011; Tong, Phillips, Duberstein, & Zhan, 2014). Brent et al. (2002) found that the risk of suicide attempt was six times greater among offspring of depressed suicide attempters as compared to offspring of depressed nonsuicide attempters. Others have found that as many as 24% of suicide attempters report a history of completed suicide among first- and second-degree relatives (Brodie & Leff, 1971; Linkowski, de Maertelaer, & Mendlewicz, 1985; Mann et al., 2005; Pitts & Winokur, 1964; Roy, 1983, 1985). Geulayov et al. (2014) found that children whose mother attempted suicide were more likely to report suicidal thoughts and plans; however, this same relationship was not found for children whose father attempted suicide. Further, among children of depressed mothers, higher levels of hopelessness and lower global self-worth are associated with increased risk of future suicidal ideation (Tsypes, 2016).

No one mechanism has been determined that fully accounts for the familial transmission of suicide risk. Rather, several mechanisms have been posited to explain the increased risk of suicidality among family members. The two areas that have gained the most support are (a) parental psychiatric illness as a moderator of suicide risk in offspring and (b) social learning models of suicide.

Parental Psychiatric Illness

Several studies indicate that parental psychiatric illness confers the risk of suicidal behavior in offspring, including completed suicide, attempted suicide, and suicidal ideation (Brent et al., 2002, 2004; Brent & Mann, 2005; Christiansen, Goldney, Beautrais, & Agerbo, 2011; Egeland, & Sussex, 1985; Fergusson et al., 2000; Garfinkel, Froese, & Hood, 1982; Linkowski, de Maertelaer, & Mendlewicz, 1985; Roy et al., 1991, 1995; Runeson, 1998; Sorenson & Rutter, 1991; Tsuang, 1983). It has clearly been established that parental psychiatric illness leads to an increased risk of psychiatric illness in offspring (Beardeslee, Versage, & Gladstone, 1998; DelBello & Geller, 2001; Downey & Coyne, 1990; Nomura, Warner, & Wickramaratne, 2001; Rutter & Quinton, 1984; Rutter, Silberg, O'Connor, & Simonoff, 1999). Furthermore, psychiatric illness is among the greatest risk factor for suicidality (Antikainen, Hintikka, Lehtonen, Koponen, & Arstila, 1995; Kaplan & Harrow, 1996; Mehlum, Friis, Vaglum, & Karterud, 1994; Sabo, Gunderson, Najavits, Chauncey, & Kisiel, 1995; Schneider, Philipp, & Muller, 2001; Scocco, Marietta, Tonietto, & Buono, 2000; Statham et al., 1998). Thus, offspring suicide risk may be moderated through the presence of psychiatric illness transmitted from parents to their offspring. Parental mood disorder (specifically depression and bipolar disorder), panic disorder, schizophrenia, and alcohol abuse are most often associated with increased risk for offspring suicide (Mann et al., 2005; Sorenson & Rutter, 1991).

For youths, mothers exert an identifiable influence on suicide risk. Maternal depression, in particular, is a significant risk factor for offspring suicide ideation and attempt (Hammerton et al., 2015; Hammerton, Zammit, Thapar, & Collishaw, 2016). One study has examined the contributing role of maternal suicide attempt, offspring psychiatric disorder, and parent–child relationship as mediating factors to explain this association. Results suggest that offspring of a depressed mother are at increased risk when the mother experiences severe symptomatology, when the mother has a history of attempting suicide, and when the offspring himself or herself has a psychiatric disorder. Results also found that poor parent–child relationship further contributed to offspring suicide attempt risk (Hammerton et al., 2016).

Research in this area, however, is inconclusive. While familial transmission of suicide may be partly accounted for by the transmission of psychiatric illness, several studies have also demonstrated that even after controlling for psychopathology, vulnerability toward suicidal behavior continues to appear to run in families (Agerbo, Nordentoft, & Mortenson, 2002; Brent, Bridge, Johnson, & Connolly, 1996; Bridge, Brent, Johnson, & Connolly, 1997; Cheng et al., 2000; Fu et al., 2002; Garfinkel, Froese, & Hood, 1982; Glowinski et al., 2001; Gould et al., 1996; Johnson et al., 1998; Linkowski, de Maertelaer, & Mendlewicz, 1985; Malone et al., 1995; Powell et al., 2000; Runeson & Asberg, 2003; Statham et al., 1998; Tsuang, 1983). Some researchers have associated the familial transmission of risk with a genetic inheritance or predisposition to suicidality; for example, twin studies have found a higher rate of suicide for monozyotic compared to dyzotic twins (Roy et al., 1991, 1997). However, further research is needed to understand the role and impact of parental psychiatric illness on offspring suicide risk.

Social Learning Model of Familial Suicide Risk

Another explanation for the high rate of suicidality among offspring of individuals who attempt and/or complete suicide is that parents model such behavior for their offspring (Runeson, 1998; Stack & Kposowa, 2008). According to social learning theory, when parents complete or attempt suicide, a message is sent to their offspring that such behavior is an acceptable means of coping with distress.

The social learning model of suicide extends beyond the micro level of family transmission and has been applied also to the societal level (Stack & Kposowa, 2008). It is suggested that the degree to which a community or society has positive attitudes toward suicide can have an impact on the overall societal suicide rate. Communities in which such behavior is condoned may represent a "subculture of suicide," and may have elevated suicide rates (Cutright & Fernquist, 2004; Stack & Kposowa, 2008). This has severe consequences. It has been suggested that exposure to elevated suicide rates increases the likelihood that individuals will develop more accepting attitudes toward suicidal behavior (Baller, Shin & Richardson, 2005). Agnew (1998) further suggests that when a community or society has a positive attitude toward suicide, individuals may not feel compelled to deter others from engaging in suicidal behaviors. Additionally, according to social learning theory, individuals who complete suicide in such communities serve as models for how to cope with problems (Stack & Kposowa, 2008), thereby potentially increasing suicide risk even further. Adolescents in these communities may have less respect for life and a lower aversion to death, which may make suicide a more acceptable option during times of heightened distress (Orbach, 1997).

Conversely, in communities with low suicide rates, individuals are more likely to have negative attitudes toward suicide. Given that fewer individuals are engaging in suicidal acts in these communities, there is less modeling of suicidal behavior as an acceptable option for dealing with stress. Individuals who do not engage in suicidal behavior serve as role models for alternative coping mechanisms, and further support the message that suicide is an unacceptable act (Stack & Kposowa, 2008). On a micro level, parents who cope with distress by seeking support from friends and family or by seeking psychosocial treatment serve as role models for positive coping mechanisms and model the unacceptability of suicide for their children. Although limited, the research that exists supports a social learning model of suicide (Agnew, 1998; Baller, Shin, & Richardson, 2005; Stack, 2002; Stack & Kposwoa, 2008).

INTERVENTIONS WITH CHILDREN AND ADOLESCENTS

Strikingly low rates of treatment utilization for suicidal ideation and behavior have been found among adolescents across all racial/ethnic groups (Nestor, Cheek, & Liu, 2016). Lower utilization rates in both inpatient and outpatient mental health services have also been found for adolescents from racial–ethnic minority groups (Wu, Hoven, Tief, Kovalenko, & Wicks, 2002). Among adolescents with any suicidal ideation and behavior, and suicide attempts specifically, non-Hispanic Blacks and Native Americans are less likely than Whites to receive outpatient treatment. Further, multiracial adolescents are less likely to be admitted to a psychiatric facility. Apart from Hispanics, racial–ethnic minorities are generally less likely to receive mental health care for suicidal ideation, particularly within psychiatric outpatient settings. A pattern exists regarding racial–ethnic differences in treatment utilization with rates being greatest among adolescents with the least severe suicidal ideation and behavior (Nestor et al., 2016). In a study examining 12-month suicidal symptoms and the use of services among adolescents, two-thirds of adolescents with suicidal ideation (67%) and half of those with a plan (54%) or attempt (57%) did not have any contact with a mental health specialist in the past year (Husky et al., 2012). A study examining service use among high school students with suicidality found that 72% of the at-risk students were not receiving any type of mental health service (Gould et al., 2009). However, of the students who were identified as being in need of services and subsequently referred to a mental health professional, nearly 70% followed through on this referral recommendation (Gould et al., 2009).

Another study reported that approximately half of the youths who have attempted suicide used mental health services in the preceding year (Wu et al., 2010). Wu and colleagues (2010) found that self-perceived poor health and residing in a single-parent family were associated with use of inpatient services, whereas female gender, higher family income, extracurricular involvement, and the presence of symptoms of anxiety or disruptive disorders were associated with use of outpatient services (Wu et al., 2010). Another study found that adolescents with thoughts of deliberate self-harm were more likely than youths without to seek help from friends, but less likely to seek help from parents (Goodwin, Mocarski, Marusic, & Beautrais, 2013). Also, adolescents with thoughts of deliberate self-harm were more likely to seek help from school officials, health professionals, or a counselor (Goodwin et al., 2013).

In terms of child and adolescent suicide completers, one study found that although 90% of suicide completers suffered from mental disorders, the majority were not receiving appropriate mental health care in the period preceding their suicide. More specifically, over two-thirds of suicide completers had no treatment contact within a month prior to the completion, and 55% of those who received treatment were considered poorly compliant or not compliant at all according to their medical/psychosocial records (Renaud et al., 2009). Results also demonstrated that female adolescent completers seemed to have more psychiatric and mental health service contacts in the past month than male adolescents, and that youths with depressive and anxiety disorders received more psychiatric and general mental health services in the past year (Renaud et al., 2009).

Youths at risk of self-harm and suicide are increasingly turning to the Internet to communicate, find information, and obtain support (Greidanus & Everall, 2010; Hardoff, 2013). Children and adolescents spend more than 6 hours each day with media (e.g., Internet, television, gaming), which is more time than in formal classroom instruction (O'Keeffe, Clarke-Pearson, & Council on Communications and Media, 2011). Research suggests that online and social media–based interventions may provide an opportunity for youths to enhance feelings of connectedness, a key protective factor against suicidal behavior (Rice et al., 2016; Robinson et al., 2014). In addition, research suggests that interventions using social media can be feasibly and safely conducted with youths at risk of suicide (Durkee, Hadlaczky, Westerlund, & Carli, 2011; Maniam et al., 2014; Rice et al., 2016). For example, Facebook has been used to alert parents and emergency personnel to adolescents who post suicidal intentions (Bennett et al., 2013). Research on tweets has found that Twitter may be a viable tool for real-time monitoring of suicide risk (Jashinsky et al., 2014). Internet Google searches have been suggested as a method of providing a faster way of monitoring possible trends in suicide (Gunn & Lester, 2014).

However, research in this area is not consistent. Findings suggest that although most children and adolescents use the Internet for constructive reasons (e.g., seeking support, coping strategies), for others, the Internet may exert a negative influence (e.g., normalizing self-harm, discouraging disclosure or engagement with professional mental health services; Daine et al., 2013; Singaravelu, Stewart, Adams, Simkin, & Hawton, 2014). A recent study investigating suicide and the Internet found that 54% of site hits contained information about new high-lethality methods (Biddle et al., 2015).

While many Internet sites and social media groups are potentially helpful, due to a lack of regulation many sites and groups can be unhelpful and even harmful (Townsend, Gearing, & Polyanskaya, 2012). Youths are turning to the Internet to receive information regarding how to suicide and/or self-harm. Some research has found that youths who visited websites containing information that supported suicide and/or self-harm were seven times more likely to say that they had thought about killing themselves and 11 times more likely to think about hurting themselves, even after adjusting for several known risk factors for self-harm and suicide ideations (Durkee et al., 2011; Mitchell, Wells, Priebe, & Ybarra, 2014).

The Internet may serve as a risk factor for adolescent suicide in other ways, as well. Research shows that adolescents who reported 5 hours or more of daily video games/Internet use had a significantly higher risk of sadness, suicidal ideation, and suicide planning, and that this relationship was consistent over time (Messias, Castro, Saini, Usman, & Peeples, 2011). Video game dependency, as compared to merely excessive use, has been found to be associated with increased levels of psychological and social stress, including lower school achievement, increased truancy, reduced sleep time, limited leisure activities, and increased thoughts of committing suicide (Rehbein, Kleimann, & Mössle, 2010). Further, problematic Internet usage is associated with increased emotional problems that may serve to further increase future pathological usage (Strittmatter et al., 2016). The relationship between problematic Internet use and conduct problems and hyperactivity/inattention has been found to be stronger among adolescent females, while the association between such use and symptoms of depression, anxiety, and peer relationship problems is stronger among adolescent males (Kaess et al., 2014). Some suggest this relationship may be due to the fact that excessive gaming/Internet use leads adolescents to engage in problem behaviors that impair the adolescent's functioning (Topor et al., 2011).

There are three general, but essential, intervention approaches for children and adolescents at risk of suicide: *crisis management, psychosocial evidence-based practices (EBP) interventions,* and *psychopharmacology.*

A child or adolescent who has attempted suicide, or is at risk of suicide and in need of crisis management, should be brought to a hospital emergency department for complete assessment. According to the American Academy of Child and Adolescent Psychiatry (AACAP) practice guidelines (2001), crisis staff and emergency room health professionals should attempt to establish a relationship and convey the importance of treatment to the youths and their families. If a youth remains at risk and either continues to express a desire to die or has an evident abnormal mental state, inpatient admission may be warranted.

Whether the youth is discharged home, is not admitted, or is at suicidal risk but does not require a hospital evaluation, research has found several EBPs to be effective in working with suicidal children and adolescents. The specific EBP treatment should meet the needs of the youths and their families. EBPs found to be effective in working with children and adolescents at risk of suicide are *cognitive-behavioral therapy (CBT), dialectical-behavioral therapy (DBT), interpersonal psychotherapy for adolescents (IPT-A), psychodynamic therapy,* and *family therapy* (AACAP, 2001). For further information on these EBP interventions, see Part II of this book.

Finally, psychopharmacology interventions may occur independently in conjunction with psychotherapeutic EBP treatments. Depending on the psychiatric presentation, symptoms, or disorder, several psychopharmacological treatments have been found to be effective in youths at risk of suicide.

A Closer Look: Adolescents and Antidepressants

An estimated 60% to 70% of acutely depressed individuals may experience suicidal ideation, with approximately 10% to 15% completing suicide (Licinio & Wong, 2005; Moller et al., 2003). Research has suggested that about 50% of adults and 75% of youths who commited suicide were experiencing depression or depressive symptomatology (Henriksson et al., 1993; Shafii et al., 1988). Antidepressants have been used to treat children and adolescents with depressive disorders, including youths experiencing suicidality. Research has demonstrated that using antidepressants to treat depression in youths has been effective in reducing depressive symptomatology and suicidality. Research has also found that increases in antidepressant prescriptions are associated with overall reductions in youth suicide (Bridge & Axelson, 2008).

In October 2004, the Federal Drug Administration (FDA) ordered that pharmaceutical companies add a "black box warning" on the use of antidepressant medication for the pediatric population, warning of the potential for a heightened risk of suicidal thoughts and behaviors (Friedman, 2014). Following that initial mandate, research indicated that an elevated risk of suicidal behavior exists in depressed individuals treated with antidepressants during the first 10 to 14 days of treatment, requiring careful monitoring (Wasserman et al., 2012). Thus, in 2007, the FDA updated the black box warning on antidepressants to include warnings about increased risks of suicidal thinking and behavior in young adults (aged 18–24) during initial treatment, generally during the first 1 to 2 months (Gibbons, Hur, Bhaumik, & Mann, 2006). At the present time, Fluoxetine (Prozac) is the only antidepressant medication approved by the FDA for the treatment of depression in children and adolescents (FDA, 2004, 2007; Kondro, 2004).

According to the FDA, there is a reported 2% to 4% increased risk of adverse events of suicidal ideation or suicide behaviors in children and adolescents treated with antidepressants (Bridge & Axelson, 2008). A follow-up meta-analysis of 27 clinical trials found a smaller risk (0.7% absolute risk increase) of suicidal thoughts and attempts (Bridge, Hanssens, & Santhanam, 2007). A more recent meta-analysis examined suicide and antidepressant use in children and adolescents since the 2004 black box warning, and found an increased risk of suicidal thoughts and behaviors of between 7 and 20 incidents per 1,000 of those treated with an antidepressant compared with placebo (Gordon & Melvin, 2013). Thus, the literature has identified a small but discernible risk of suicidal thoughts and behaviors in children and adolescents being treated with antidepressants, particularly early in treatment (Gordon & Melvin, 2013).

Before the black box warning issue in 2004, approximately two-thirds of adolescents diagnosed with a depressive disorder were treated with antidepressants. After the warning, the rate of antidepressant prescribing in the United States reportedly fell to 58%, lower than would have been expected from prewarning trends (Gordon & Melvin, 2013; Libby et al., 2007). Pediatric antidepressant prescriptions dropped 18.6% in the month following the FDA black box warning (Phend, 2007). According to the CDC, the actual number of suicides in youths increased by 18.2%; there were 1,487 more deaths by suicide between 2003 and 2004 (Bossarte & Caine, 2008; Bridge & Axelson, 2008). This significant increase in child and adolescent suicide was the first in a decade and the largest in the preceding 25 years (Bridge & Axelson, 2008). It has been argued that despite the established link between depression and suicide, clinicians may be undertreating depression in children and adolescents since the emergence of these concerns around the use of antidepressants (Menon, 2009).

Regardless of the identified benefits of antidepressants for many individuals with depression, both children and their parents or caregivers need to be informed of risks and warning signs. According to the Mayo Clinic, when a child is taking antidepressants, parents and caregivers should watch for any worsening of the child's condition or any signs that he or she may be at risk of self-harm (Mayo Clinic Staff, 2016). The following should be discussed right away with one's health care provider:

- Talk of suicide or dying
- Attempts to commit suicide
- Self-injury
- Agitation or restlessness
- New or worsening anxiety or panic attacks
- Irritability
- Increasing sadness or worsening of depression symptoms
- Impulsiveness
- Extreme increase in talking, energy, or activity
- Aggression, violence, or hostility
- Trouble sleeping or worsening insomnia
- Spending more time alone

It is important that a child or adolescent does not stop antidepressant treatment without the consultation and guidance of a provider, as flu-like symptoms, as well as other side effects, may result from suddenly stopping the medication (Mayo Clinic, 2016). Research encourages clinicians to carefully weigh risks and benefits before starting an antidepressant, and that youths and their parents should be informed and share in decision making (Gordon & Melvin, 2013; Wasserman et al., 2012).

SUMMARY

Completed suicide by children and adolescents is rare; however, attempts and ideation are more common. Across the life span, suicide risk increases with age. Developmentally, adolescents may be exposed to an increased risk of suicide. In youths, females are more likely to attempt, while males are more likely to complete suicide. Families can serve as a protective or risk factor for suicidality among children and adolescents. Identification and thorough assessment of risk and protective factors for suicide among youths are critical for suicide prevention and effective intervention.

KEY POINTS

1. The suicide risk of prepubertal children is very rare, but the risk grows with each year of adolescence.
2. Female youths report higher suicide ideation, and have more attempted suicide than males; however, adolescent males completed suicide four to six times more than females.
3. Although suicide in young children is rare it does occur.
4. Suicide in children is often related to a stressful home environment.
5. Adolescent suicide is often associated with mood disorders, substance abuse, and gender identity issues.
6. Offspring of parents who have a history of suicidal behavior are at increased risk for completed suicide, suicide attempt, and suicidal ideation.
7. Family transmission of suicide can be explained by genetic factors as well as social learning models.
8. It is important to separate fact from fiction, as there are a number of myths and misconceptions that surround children and adolescents at risk of suicide.
9. Three important developmental processes that may influence adolescent suicidality are cognitive development, identity formation, and autonomy.
10. The three intervention approaches in working with children and adolescents at risk of suicide are crisis management, psychosocial EBP interventions, and psychopharmacology.

ELECTRONIC RESOURCES

GENERAL

http://www.aacap.org/AACAP/Families_and_Youth/Facts_for_Families/Facts_for_Families_Pages/Teen_Suicide_10

https://www.nami.org/Search?searchtext=teen+suicide&searchmode=anyword

www.surgeongeneral.gov/library/mentalhealth/chapter3/sec5.html
www.teensuicide.us

SUPPORT FOR PARENTS

www.griefnet.org
www.kidsaid.com
www.bereavedparentsusa.org
www.childsuicide.homestead.com
www.psycom.net/depression.central.suicide.html

SUPPORT GROUPS AND OTHER RESOURCES FOR CHILDREN AND ADOLESCENTS

www.yellowribbon.org
www.kidsaid.com/k2k_support.html
www.dougy.org
www.supportline.org.uk
www.save.org
www.youth-suicide.com/gay-bisexual

KNOWLEDGE ACQUISITION TEST (KAT)

True or False

1. Children do not commit suicide.
2. There are no warning signs that children and adolescents may be considering suicide.
3. Suicide risk is familial.
4. Parental modeling of suicide is not a possible cause of offspring suicide.
5. Substance abuse is a risk factor for adolescent suicide.
6. Females attempt suicide more than males.
7. Males tend to use more lethal methods of suicide than females.
8. Children under 10 years have a higher suicide rate than children over 10 years of age.
9. Younger males (10–14 years) complete suicide more than older males (14–19 years).
10. Bullying is a risk factor for suicide attempt for male but not female adolescents.
11. Adverse childhood experiences have differential short-term and long-term consequences.

Short Answer

12. What are the main mechanisms presumed to explain family transmission of suicide?
13. Explain the social learning theory of family transmission of suicide.
14. What are the main risk factors against for suicide among adolescents?
15. What are some key theories that may explain why suicide completion is higher in males than females?
16. Why are younger prepubertal children less likely to complete suicide than older adolescents?
17. Describe the key developmental issues that may increase the risk of suicidality in adolescents?
18. Describe the ways in which the Internet can be both harmful and protective for youths at risk of suicide.
19. Describe how self-esteem can act as both a risk and a protective factor.

Multiple Choice

20. What age group is at the highest risk of suicide?
    A. 0 to 9 years
    B. 10 to 14 years
    C. 15 to 19 years
    D. All of the above are at equal risk
    E. None of the above
21. What item in the following list of myths or misconceptions related to suicidality and youth is untrue?
    A. Current prevention programs work
    B. Suicide is caused by family and social stress
    C. Most suicides occur at home
    D. All of the above
    E. None of the above
22. Which of the following is a protective factor against adolescent suicide?
    A. Family cohesion
    B. Musical ability

C. Employment
D. None of the above
E. All of the above

23. Which of the following parental psychiatric illnesses is associated with an increased risk of suicidality in offspring?
    A. Depression
    B. Bipolar disorder
    C. Panic disorder
    D. Schizophrenia
    E. None of the above
    F. All of the above

24. Which of the following is NOT a risk factor for child suicide?
    A. Parental divorce
    B. Depression
    C. Parental psychiatric illness
    D. Unsafe school environment
    E. None of the above
    F. All of the above

25. Which of the following is NOT a common method of suicide attempt among adolescents?
    A. Firearms
    B. Suffocation
    C. Poisoning
    D. Hanging
    E. None of the above
    F. All of the above

REFERENCES

Abdollahi, A., Carlbring, P., Khanbani, M., & Ghahfarokhi, S. A. (2016). Emotional intelligence moderates perceived stress and suicidal ideation among depressed adolescent inpatients. *Personality and Individual Differences, 102,* 223–228.

Abrutyn, S., & Mueller, A. S. (2014). Are suicidal behaviors contagious in adolescence? Using longitudinal data to examine suicide suggestion. *American Sociological Review, 79*(2), 211–227.

Adam, K. S., Bouckoms, A., & Streiner, D. (1982). Parental loss and family stability in attempted suicide. *Archives of General Psychiatry, 39,* 1081–1085.

Adams, D. M., Overholser, J. C., & Lehnert, K. L. (1994). Perceived family functioning and adolescent suicidal behavior. *Journal of the American Academy of Child & Adolescent Psychiatry, 33*(4), 498–507.

Agerbo, E., Nordentoft, M., & Mortenson, P. B. (2002). Familial, psychiatric, and socioeconomic risk factors for suicide in young people: Nested case-control study. *British Medical Journal, 325,* 74. doi:10.1136/bmj.325.7355.74

Agnew, R. (1998). The approval of suicide: A social psychological model. *Suicide and Life-Threatening Behavior, 28*(2), 205–225.

Ali, M. M., Dwyer, D. S., & Rizzo, J. A. (2011). The social contagion effect of suicidal behavior in adolescents: Does it really exist? *Journal of Mental Health Policy and Economics, 14*(1), 3–12.

Allen, J. P., Aber, J. L., & Leadbeater, B. J. (1990). Adolescent problem behaviors: The influence of attachment and autonomy. *Psychiatric Clinics of North America, 13*(3), 455–467.

Allen, J. P., Hauser, S. T., Bell, K. B., & O'Connor, T. G. (1994). Longitudinal assessment of autonomy and relatedness in adolescent-family interactions as predictors of adolescent ego development and self-esteem. *Child Development, 65,* 179–194.

Allen, J. P., & Land, D. (1999). Attachment in adolescents. In J. Cassidy & P. R. Shaver (Eds.), *Handbook of attachment: Theory, research, and clinical applications* (pp. 319–335). New York, NY: The Guilford Press.

American Academy of Child and Adolescent Psychiatry. (2001). Practice parameter for the assessment and treatment of children and adolescents with suicidal behavior. *Journal of the American Academy of Child & Adolescent Psychiatry, 40*(7), 24S–51S.

Amit, B. H., Krivoy, A., Mansbach-Kleinfeld, I., Zalsman, G., Ponizovsky, A. M., Hoshen, M., . . . Shoval, G. (2014). Religiosity is a protective factor against self-injurious thoughts and behaviors in Jewish adolescents: Findings from a nationally representative survey. *European Psychiatry, 29*(8), 509–513.

Anderson, H. D. (2011). Suicide ideation, depressive symptoms, and out-of-home placement among youth in the U.S. child welfare system. *Journal of Clinical Child & Adolescent Psychology, 40*(6), 790–796.

Anderson, R. N., & Smith, B. L. (2003). Deaths: Leading causes for 2001. *National Vital Statistics Report, 52*(9), 1–86.

Andrews, J. A., & Lewinsohn, P. M. (1992). Suicidal attempts among older adolescents: Prevalence and co-occurrence with psychiatric disorders. *Journal of the American Academy of Child & Adolescent Psychiatry, 31,* 655–662.

Antikainen, R., Hintikka, J., Lehtonen, J., Koponen, H., & Arstila, A. (1995). A prospective three-year follow-up study of borderline personality disorder inpatients. *Acta Psychiatrica Scandinavica, 92,* 327–335.

Araújo, R. M. F., & Lara, D. R. (2016). More than words: The association of childhood emotional abuse and suicidal behavior. *European Psychiatry, 37,* 14–21.

Armstrong, L. L., & Manion, I. G. (2006). Suicidal ideation in young males living in rural communities: Distance from school as a risk factor, youth engagement as a protective factor. *Vulnerable Children and Youth Studies, 1*(1), 102–113.

Arnett, J. J. (1999). Adolescent storm and stress, reconsidered. *American Psychologist, 54,* 317–326.

Asarnow, J. R., Carlson, G., & Mintz, J. (1988). Suicide attempts in preadolescent child psychiatry inpatients. *Suicide and Life-Threatening Behavior, 18,* 129–136.

Aseltine, R. H., Schilling, E. A., James, A., Glanovsky, J. L., & Jacobs, D. (2009). Age variability in the association between heavy episodic drinking and adolescent suicide attempts: Findings from a large-scale, school-based screening program. *Journal of the American Academy of Child & Adolescent Psychiatry, 48*(3), 262–270.

Babiss, L. A., & Gangwisch, J. E. (2009). Sports participation as a protective factor against depression and suicidal ideation in adolescents as mediated by self-esteem and social support. *Journal of Developmental and Behavioral Pediatrics, 30*(5), 376–384.

Bagley, C., & Tremblay, P. (2000). Elevated rates of suicidal behavior in gay, lesbian, and bisexual youth. *Crisis: The Journal of Crisis Intervention & Suicide Prevention, 21,* 111–117.

Baller, R. D., Shin, D. J., & Richardson, K. (2005). An extension and test of Sutherland's concept of differential social organization: The geographic clustering of Japanese suicide and homicide rates. *Suicide and Life-Threatening Behavior, 35*(3), 343–355.

Barber, C. W., & Miller, M. J. (2014). Reducing a suicidal person's access to lethal means of suicide: A research agenda. *American Journal of Preventive Medicine, 47*(3 Suppl. 2), S264–S272.

Beautrais, A. L., Joyce, P. R., & Mulder, R. T. (1998a). Psychiatric illness in a New Zealand sample of young people making serious suicide attempts. *New Zealand Medical Journal, 111*, 44–48.

Beautrais, A. L., Joyce, P. R., & Mulder, R. T. (1998b). Youth suicide attempts: A social and demographic profile. *Australian and New Zealand Journal of Psychiatry, 32*, 349–357.

Beautrais, A., Joyce, P., Mulder, R., Fergusson, D., Deavoll, B., & Nightingale, S. (1996). Prevalence and comorbidity of mental disorders in persons making serious suicide attempts: A case-control study. *American Journal of Psychiatry, 153*, 1009–1014.

Bennett, A., Pourmand, A., Shokoohi, H., Shesser, R., Sanchez, J., & Joyce J. (2013). Impacts of social networking sites on patient care in the emergency department. *Telemedicine and e-Health, 20*(1), 94–96.

Ben-Yehuda, A., Aviram, S., Govezensky, J., Nitzan, U., Levkovitz, Y., & Bloch, Y. (2012). Suicidal behavior in minors: Diagnostic differences between children and adolescents. *Journal of Developmental and Behavioral Pediatrics, 33*(7), 542–547.

Bernert, R. A., Kim, J. S., Iwata, N. G., & Perlis, M. L. (2015). Sleep disturbances as an evidence-based suicide risk factor. *Current Psychology Reports, 17*(3), 554. doi:10.1007/s11920-015-0554-4

Bernert, R. A., & Nadorff, M. R. (2015). Sleep disturbances and suicide risk. *Sleep Medicine Clinics, 10*(1), 35–39.

Birmaher, B., Ryan, N. D., Williamson, D. E., Brent, D. A., Kaufman, J., Dahl, R. E., . . . Nelson, B. (1996). Childhood and adolescent depression: A review of the past 10 years. Part I. *Journal of the American Academy of Child & Adolescent Psychiatry, 35*, 1427–1439.

Blank, M., Zhang, J., Lamers, F., Taylor, A. D., Hickie, I. B., & Merikangas, K. R. (2015). Health correlates of insomnia symptoms and comorbid mental disorders in a nationally representative sample of US adolescents. *Sleep, 38*(2), 197–204.

Boone, S. D., & Brausch, A. M. (2016). Physical activity, exercise motivations, depression, and nonsuicidal self-injury in youth. *Suicide and Life-Threatening Behavior, 46*(5), 625–633.

Bossarte, R. M., & Caine, E. D. (2008). Increase in US youth suicide rates 2004. *Injury Prevention, 14*(1), 2–3. doi:10.1136/ip.2007.017772

Borowsky, I. W., Ireland, M., & Resnick, M. D. (2001). Adolescent suicide attempts: Risks and protectors. *Pediatrics, 107*, 485–493.

Bostwick, W. B., Meyer, I., Aranda, F., Russell, S., Hughes, T., Birkett, M., & Mustanski, B. (2014). Mental health and suicidality among racially/ethnically diverse sexual minority youths. *American Journal of Public Health, 104*(6), 1129–1136.

Brausch, A. M., & Decker, K. M. (2014). Self-esteem and social support as moderators of depression, body image, and disordered eating for suicidal ideation in adolescents. *Journal of Abnormal Child Psychology, 42*(5), 779–789.

Brent, D. A., Baugher, M., Birmaher, B., Kolko, D. J., & Bridge, J. (2000). Compliance with recommendations to remove firearms in families participating in a clinical trial for adolescent depression. *Journal of the American Academy of Child & Adolescent Psychiatry, 39*(10), 1220–1226.

Brent, D. A., Bridge, J., Johnson, B. A., & Connolly, J. (1996). Suicidal behavior runs in families: A controlled family study of adolescent suicide victims. *Archives of General Psychiatry, 53*(12), 1145–1152.

Brent, D. A., & Mann, J. J. (2005). Family genetic studies, suicide, and suicidal behavior. *American Journal of Medical Genetics Part C: Seminars in Medical Genetics, 133C*(1), 13–24.

Brent, D. A., Melhem, N. M., & Mann, J. J. (2015). Pathways to offspring suicidal behavior may begin with maternal suicide attempt. *Journal of the American Academy of Child & Adolescent Psychiatry, 54*(10), 868.

Brent, D. A., Oquendo, M., Birmaher, B., Greenhill, L., Kolko, D., Stanley, B., . . . Mann, J. (2002). Familial pathways to early-onset suicide attempt: Risk for suicidal behavior in offspring of mood-disordered suicide attempters. *Archives of General Psychiatry, 59*, 801–807.

Brent, D. A., Oquendo, M., Birmaher, B., Greenhill, L., Kolko, D., Stanley, B., . . . Mann, J. (2003). Peripubertal suicide attempts in offspring of suicide attempters with siblings concordant for suicidal behavior. *American Journal of Psychiatry, 160*(8), 1486–1493.

Brent, D. A., Oquendo, M., Birmaher, B., Greenhill, L., Kolko, D., Stanley, B., . . . Mann, J. (2004). Familial transmission of mood disorders: Convergence and divergence with transmission of suicidal behavior. *Journal of the American Academy of Child & Adolescent Psychiatry, 43*(10), 1259–1266.

Brent, D. A., Perper, J., Goldstein, C., Kolko, D., Allan, M., Allman, C., & Zelenak, J. P. (1988). Risk factors for adolescent suicide: A comparison of adolescent suicide victims with suicidal inpatients. *Archives of General Psychiatry, 45,* 581–588.

Brent, D. A., Perper, J. A., & Moritz, G. (1993). Psychiatric sequelae to the loss of an adolescent peer to suicide. *Journal of the American Academy of Child & Adolescent Psychiatry, 32,* 509–517.

Breton, J. J., Labelle, R., Berthiaume, C., Royer, C., St. Georges, M., Ricard, D., . . . Guilé, J. M. (2015). Protective factors against depression and suicidal behaviour in adolescence. *Canadian Journal of Psychiatry, 60*(2 Suppl. 1), S5–S15.

Bridge, J. A., Asti, L., Horowitz, L. M., Greenhouse, J. B., Fontanella, C. A., Sheftall, A. H., . . . Campo, J. V. (2015). Suicide trends among elementary school aged children in the United States from 1993 to 2012. *Journal of American Medical Association Pediatrics, 169*(7), 673–677.

Bridge, J. A., & Axelson, D. A. (2008). The contribution of pharmacoepidemiology to the antidepressant-suicidality debate in children and adolescents. *International Review of Psychiatry, 20,* 209–214.

Bridge, J. A., Brent, D. A., Johnson, B. A., & Connolly, J. (1997). Familial aggregation of psychiatric disorders in a community sample of adolescents. *Journal of the American Academy of Child & Adolescent Psychiatry, 36,* 628–636.

Bridge, J. A., Reynolds, B., McBee-Strayer, S. M., Sheftall, A. H., Ackerman, J., Stevens, J., . . . Brent, D. A. (2015). Impulsive aggression, delay discounting, and adolescent suicide attempts: effects of current psychotropic medication use and family history of suicidal behavior. *Journal of Child and Adolescent Psychopharmacology, 25,* 114–123.

Bridge, S., Hanssens, L., & Santhanam, R. (2007). Dealing with suicidal thoughts in schools: information and education directed at secondary schools. *Austrailasian Psychiatry, 15*(1), S58–S62.

Brodie, H. K., & Leff, M. J. (1971). Bipolar depression: A comparative study of patient characteristics. *American Journal of Psychiatry, 127,* 1086–1090.

Brodsky, B. S., & Stanley, B. (2008). Adverse childhood experiences and suicidal behavior. *The Psychiatric Clinics of North America, 31,* 223–235.

Bucca, M., Ceppi, M., Pelosa, P., Archellaschi, M., Mussi, D., & Fele, P. (1994). Social variables and suicide in the population of Genoa, Italy. *Comprehensive Psychiatry, 35,* 64–69.

Bushe, C. J., & Savill, N. C. (2013). Suicide-related events and attention deficit hyperactivity disorder treatments in children and adolescents: A meta-analysis of atomoxetine and methylphenidate comparator clinical trials. *Child and Adolescent Psychiatry and Mental Health, 7,* 19. doi:10.1186/1753-2000-7-19

Button, D. M., O'Connell, D. J., & Gealt, R. (2012). Sexual minority youth victimization and social support: The intersection of sexuality, gender, race, and victimization. *Journal of Homosexuality, 59*(1), 18–43.

Canetto, S. S., & Sakinofsky, I. (1998). The gender paradox in suicide. *Suicide and Life-Threatening Behavior, 28*(1), 1–23.

Carubia, B., Becker, A., & Levine, B. H. (2016). Child psychiatric emergencies: Updates on trends, clinical care, and practice challenges. *Current Psychiatry Reports, 18*(4), 41. doi:10.1007/s11920-016-0670-9

Centers for Disease Control and Prevention. (2006). National Center for Injury Prevention and Control. Retrieved from https://www.cdc.gov/injury/index.html

Centers for Disease Control and Prevention. (2015). Suicide prevention: Youth suicide. Retrieved from https://www.cdc.gov/violenceprevention/suicide/index.html

Cha, C., & Nock, M. (2009). Emotional intelligence is a protective factor for suicidal behavior. *Journal of the American Academy of Child and Adolescent Psychiatry, 48,* 422–430. doi:0.1097/CHI.0b013e3181984f44

Chapple, A., Ziebland, S., McPherson, A., & Herxheimer, A. (2006). What people close to death say about euthanasia and assisted suicide: A qualitative study. *Journal of Medical Ethics, 32,* 706–710.

Cheng, A., Chen, T., Chen, C., & Jenkins, R. (2000). Psychosocial and psychiatric risk factors for suicide: Case-control psychological autopsy study. *British Journal of Psychiatry, 177,* 360–365.

Chioqueta, A. P., & Stiles, T. C. (2007). The relationship between psychological buffers, hopelessness, and suicidal ideation: Identification of protective factors. *Crisis, 28*(2), 67–73.

Christiansen, E., Goldney, R. D., Beautrais, A. L., & Agerbo, E. (2011). Youth suicide attempts and the dose-response relationship to parental risk factors: A population-based study. *Psychological Medicine, 41*(2), 313–319.

Chronis-Tuscano, A., Molina, B. S. G., Pelham, W. E., Applegate, B., Dahlke, A., Overmyer, M., & Lahey, B. B. (2010). Very early predictors of adolescent depression and suicide attempts in children with attention deficit/hyperactivity disorder. *Archives of General Psychiatry, 67*(10), 1044–1051.

Conner, K. R., Wyman, P., Goldston, D. B., Bossarte, R. M., Lu, N., Kaukeinen, K., . . . Hesselbrock, V. M. (2016). Two studies of connectedness to parents and suicidal thoughts and behavior in children and adolescents. *Journal of Clinical Child & Adolescent Psychology, 45*(2), 129–140.

Coohey, C., Dirks-Bihun, A., Renner, L. M., & Baller, R. (2014). Strain, depressed mood and suicidal thoughts among maltreated adolescents in the United States. *Child Abuse and Neglect, 38,* 1171–1179. doi:10.1016/j.chiabu.2014.04.008

Corney, R. H. (1998). A survey of professional help sought by patients for psychosocial problems. *The British Journal of General Practice, 40,* 365–368.

Cutright, P., & Fernquist, R. (2004). The culture of suicide through societal integration and regulation: 1996–1998 gender-specific suicide rates in 50 American states. *Archives of Suicide Research, 8,* 271–285.

Daine, K., Hawton, K., Singaravelu, V., Stewart, A., Simkin, S., & Montgomery, P. (2013). The power of the web: A systematic review of studies of the influence of the internet on self-harm and suicide in young people. *PLOS ONE, 8*(10), e77555. doi:10.1371/journal.pone.0077555

de Jong, M. L. (1992). Attachment, individuation and risk of suicide in late adolescence. *Journal of Youth and Adolescence, 21,* 357–373.

Dervic, K., Oquendo, M. A., Grunebaum, M. F., Ellis, S., Burke, A. K., & Mann, J. J. (2004). Religious affiliation and suicide attempt. *The American Journal of Psychiatry, 161,* 2303–2308. doi:10.1176/appi.ajp.161.12.2303

de Wilde, E. J., Kienhorst, I., Diekstra, R., & Waters, W. (1992). The relationship between adolescent suicidal behavior and life events in childhood and adolescence. *American Journal of Psychiatry, 149,* 45–51.

Diamond, G., Creed, T., Gillham, J., Gallop, R., & Hamilton, J. L. (2012). Sexual trauma history does not moderate treatment outcome in attachment-based family therapy (ABFT) for adolescents with suicide ideation. *Journal of Family Psychology, 26*(4), 595–605.

Dubow, E. F., Kausch, D. F., Blum, M. C., Reed, J., & Bush, E. (1989). Correlates of suicidal ideation and attempts in a community sample of junior high and high school students. *Journal of Clinical Child Psychology, 18,* 158–166.

Durkee, T., Hadlaczky, G., Westerlund, M., & Carli V. (2011). Internet pathways in suicidality: A review of the evidence. *International Journal of Environmental Research and Public Health, 8*(10), 3938–3952.

Egeland, J. A., & Sussex, J. N. (1985). Suicide and family loading for affective disorders. *Journal of the American Medical Association, 254,* 915–918.

Eisenberg, M. E., Ackard, D. M., & Resnick, M. D. (2007). Protective factors and suicide risk in adolescents with a history of sexual abuse. *Journal of Pediatrics, 151*(5), 482–487.

Eisenberg, M. E., & Resnick, M. D. (2006). Suicidality among gay, lesbian and bisexual youth: The role of protective factors. *Journal of Adolescent Health, 39*(5), 662–668.

El Asam, A., & Samara, M. (2016). Cyberbullying and the law: A review of psychological and legal challenges. *Computers in Human Behavior, 65,* 127–141.

Enns, M. W., Cox, B. J., Afifi, T. O., De Graaf, R., Ten Have, M., & Sareen, J. (2006). Childhood adversities and risk for suicidal ideation and attempts: A longitudinal population-based study. *Psychological Medicine, 36,* 1769–1778.

Evans, E., Hawton, K., Rodham, K., & Deeks, J. (2005). The prevalence of suicidal phenomena in adolescents: A systematic review of population-based studies. *Suicide and Life-Threatening Behavior, 35*(3), 239–250.

Everall, R. D., Bostik, K. E., & Paulson, B. L. (2005). I'm sick of being me: Developmental themes in a suicidal adolescent. *Adolescence, 40*(160), 693–708.

Fergusson, D. M., Beautrais, A. L., & Horwood, L. J. (2003). Vulnerability and resiliency to suicidal behaviours in young people. *Psychological Medicine, 33,* 61–73.

Fergusson, D. M., & Lynskey, M. T. (1995a). Childhood circumstances, adolescent adjustment, and suicide attempts in a New Zealand birth cohort. *Journal of the American Academy of Child & Adolescent Psychiatry, 34,* 612–622.

Fergusson, D. M., & Lynskey, M. T. (1995b). Suicide among female adolescents: Characteristics and comparison with males in the age group 13 to 22 years. *Journal of the American Academy of Child & Adolescent Psychiatry, 34*(10), 1297–1307.

Fergusson, D. M., Woodward, L. J., & Harwood, L. J. (2000). Risk factors and life processes associated with the onset of suicidal behaviour during adolescence and early adulthood. *Psychological Medicine, 30,* 23–39.

Fidan, T., Ceyhun, H., & Kirpinar, I. (2011). Coping strategies and family functionality in youths with or without suicide attempts. *Nöropsikiyatri Arşivi/Archives of Neuropsychiatry, 48*(3), 195–200.

Flannery, D. J., Todres, J., Bradshaw, C. P., Amar, A. F., Graham, S., Hatzenbuehler, M., . . . Rivara, F. (2016). Bullying prevention: A summary of the report of the national academies of sciences, engineering, and medicine. Committee on the biological and psychosocial effects of peer victimization: Lessons for bullying prevention. *Prevention Science, 17*(8), 1044–1053.

Fombonne, E. (1998). Suicidal behaviours in vulnerable adolescents. Time trends and their correlates. *British Journal of Psychiatry, 173,* 154–159.

Franić, T., Kralj, Z., Marčinko, D., Knez, R., & Kardum, G. (2014). Suicidal ideations and sleep-related problems in early adolescence. *Early Intervention in Psychiatry, 8*(2), 155–162.

Friedman, R. A. (2014). Antidepressants' black box warning—10 years later. *New England Journal of Medicine, 371*, 1666–1668. doi:10.1056/NEJMp1408480

Fu, Q., Heath, A. C., Bucholz, K. K., Nelson, E. C., Glowinski, A. L., Goldberg, J. F., . . . Eisen S. A. (2002). A twin study of genetic and environmental influences on suicidality in men. *Psychological Medicine, 32*(1), 11–24.

Fuller-Thomson, E., Baird, S. L., Dhrodia, R., & Brennenstuhl, S. (2016). The association between adverse childhood experiences (ACEs) and suicide attempts in a population-based study. *Child: Care, Health and Development, 42*(5), 725–734.

Galdas, P. M., Cheater, F., & Marshall, P. (2005). Men and health help-seeking behaviour: Literature review. *Journal of Advanced Nursing, 49*, 616–623.

Garfinkel, B. D., Froese, A., & Hood, J. (1982). Suicide attempts in children and adolescents. *American Journal of Psychiatry, 139*, 1257–1261.

Garrison, C. Z., Jackson, K. L., Addy, C. L., McKeown, R. E., & Waller, J. L. (1991). Suicidal behaviors in young adolescents. *American Journal of Epidemiology, 133*(10), 1005–1014.

Gart, R., & Kelly, S. (2015). How illegal drug use, alcohol use, tobacco use, and depressive symptoms affect adolescent suicidal ideation: A secondary analysis of the 2011 Youth Risk Behavior Survey. *Issues in Mental Health Nursing, 36*(8), 614–620.

Gascoigne, P., & Whitear, B. (1999). Making sense of testicular cancer symptoms: A qualitative study of the way in which men sought help from the health care services. *European Journal of Oncology Nursing, 3*, 62–69.

Geoffroy, M., Boivin, M., Arseneault, L., Turecki, G., Vitaro, F., Brendgen, M., . . . Côté, S. M. (2016). Associations between peer victimization and suicidal ideation and suicide attempt during adolescence: Results from a prospective population-based birth cohort. *Journal of the American Academy of Child & Adolescent Psychiatry, 55*(2), 99–105.

Geulayov, G., Metcalfe, C., Heron, J., Kidger, J., & Gunnell, D. (2014). Parental suicide attempt and offspring self-harm and suicidal thoughts: Results from the Avon Longitudinal Study of Parents and Children (ALSPAC) birth cohort. *Journal of the American Academy of Child & Adolescent Psychiatry, 53*(5), 509–517.

Gibbons, R. D., Hur, K., Bhaumik, D. K., & Mann, J. J. (2006). The relationship between antidepressant prescription rates and rate of early adolescent suicide. *American Journal of Psychiatry, 163*, 1898–1904.

Gilreath, T. D., Connell, C. M., & Leventhal, A. M. (2012). Tobacco use and suicidality: Latent patterns of co-occurrence among Black adolescents. *Nicotine & Tobacco Research, 14*(8), 970–976.

Gini, G., & Espelage, D. L. (2014). Peer victimization, cyberbullying, and suicide risk in children and adolescents. *Journal of the American Medical Association, 312*(5), 545–554.

Glowinski, A., Bucholz, K. K., Nelson, E. C., Fu, Q., Madden, P., Reich, W., & Heath, A. C. (2001). Suicide attempt in an adolescent female twin sample. *Journal of the American Academy of Child & Adolescent Psychiatry, 40*, 1300–1307.

Good, G. E., Dell, D. M., & Mintz, L. B. (1989). Male role and gender role conflict: Relations to help seeking in men. *Journal of Counseling Psychology, 36*, 295–300.

Good, G. E., & Mintz, L. B. (1990). Gender role conflict and depression in college men: Evidence for compounded risk. *Journal of Counseling and Development, 69*, 17–21.

Good, G. E., & Sherrod, N. B. (2001). Men's problems and effective treatments: Theory and empirical support. In G. E. Good & G. R. Brooks (Eds.), *The new handbook of counseling and psychotherapy with men* (Vol. 1, pp. 22–40). San Francisco, CA: Jossey-Bass.

Goodwin, R. D., Mocarski, M., Marusic, A., & Beautrais, A. (2013). Thoughts of self-harm and help-seeking behavior among youth in the community. *Suicide and Life-Threatening Behavior, 43*(3), 305–312.

Gordon, M., & Melvin, G. (2013). Selective serotonin re-uptake inhibitors: A review of the side effects in adolescents. *Australian Family Physician, 42*(9), 620–623.

Görzig, A. (2016). Adolescents' viewing of suicide-related web content and psychological problems: Differentiating the roles of cyberbullying involvement. *Cyberpsychology, Behavior, and Social Networking, 19*(8): 502–509. doi:10.1089/cyber.2015.0419

Gould, M. S., Fisher, P., Parides, M., Flory, M., & Shaffer, D. (1996). Psychosocial risk factors of child and adolescent completed suicides. *Archives of General Psychiatry, 53*, 1155–1162.

Gould, M. S., & Kramer, R. A. (2001). Youth suicide prevention. *Suicide and Life-Threatening Behavior, 31*(Suppl.), 6–31.

Gould, M. S., Marrocco, F. A., Hoagwood, K., Kleinman, M., Amakawa, L., & Altschuler, E. (2009). Service use by at-risk youths after school-based suicide screening. *Journal of the American Academy of Child & Adolescent Psychiatry, 48*(12), 1193–1201.

Greene-Palmer, F. N., Wagner, B. M., Neely, L. L., Cox, D. W., Kochanski, K. M., Perera, K. U., & Ghahramanlou-Holloway, M. (2015). How parental reactions change in response to adolescent suicide attempt. *Archives of Suicide Research, 19*(4), 414–421.

Greening, L., & Stoppelbein, L. (2002). Religiosity, attributional style, and social support as psychosocial buffers for African American and white adolescents' perceived risk for suicide. *Suicide and Life-Threatening Behavior, 32*, 404–417. doi:10.1521/suli.32.4.404.22333

Greger, H. K., Myhre, A. K., Lydersen, S., & Jozefiak, T. (2015). Previous maltreatment and present mental health in a high-risk adolescent population. *Child Abuse & Neglect, 45*, 122–134.

Greger, H. K., Myhre, A. K., Lydersen, S., & Jozefiak, T. (2016). Child maltreatment and quality of life: A study of adolescents in residential care. *Health and Quality of Life Outcomes, 14*, 74. doi:10.1186/s12955-016-0479-6

Greidanus, E., & Everall, R. D. (2010). Helper therapy in an online suicide prevention community. *British Journal of Guidance & Counselling, 38*(2), 191–204.

Gunn, J. F., & Lester, D. (2014). Sports participation and suicidal behaviour: Does sport type matter? *International Journal of Sport and Exercise Psychology, 12*(4), 333–338.

Hall-Lande, J. A., Eisenberg, M. E., Christenson, S. L., & Neumark-Sztainer, D. (2007). Social isolation, psychological health, and protective factors in adolescence. *Adolescence, 42*(166), 265–286.

Hammerton, G., Zammit, S., Mahedy, L., Pearson, R. M., Sellers, R., Thapar, A., & Collishaw, S. (2015). Pathways to suicide-related behavior in offspring of mothers with depression: The role of offspring psychopathology. *Journal of the American Academy of Child & Adolescent Psychiatry, 54*(5), 385–393.

Hammerton, G., Zammit, S., Thapar, A., & Collishaw, S. (2016). Explaining risk for suicidal ideation in adolescent offspring of mothers with depression. *Psychological Medicine, 46*(2), 265–275.

Hanley, A. J., & Gibb, B. E. (2011). Verbal victimization and changes in hopelessness among elementary school children. *Journal of Clinical Child & Adolescent Psychology, 40*(5), 772–776.

Hardoff, D. (2013). Health issues in adolescents' Internet use: Benefits and risks. *Georgian Med News, 222*, 99–103.

Harrington, R., Bredenkamp, D., Groothues, C., Rutter, M., Fudge, H., & Pickles, A. (1994). Adult outcomes of childhood and adolescent depression. III. Links with suicidal behaviours. *Journal of Child Psychology & Psychiatry, 35*(7), 1309–1319.

Hawton, K., Haw, C., Houston, K., & Townsend, E. (2002). Family history of suicidal behavior: Prevalence and significance in deliberate self-harm patients. *Acta Psychiatrica Scandinavica, 106*, 387–393.

Hawton, K., O'Grady, J., Osborn, M., & Cole, D. (1982). Adolescents who take overdoses: Their characteristics, problems and contacts with helping agencies. *British Journal of Psychiatry, 140*, 118–123.

He, A. S., Fulginiti, A., & Finno-Velasquez, M. (2015, April). Connectedness and suicidal ideation among adolescents involved with child welfare: A national survey. *Child Abuse & Neglect, 42*, 54–62.

Henriksson, M. M., Aro, H. M., Marttunen, M. J., Heikkinen, M. E., Isometsä, E. T., Kuoppasalmi, K. I., & Lönnqvist, J. K. (1993). Mental disorders and comorbidity in suicide. *American Journal of Psychiatry, 150*, 935–940.

Hickey, K., Rossetti, J., Strom, J., & Bryant, K. (2015). Issues most important to parents after their children's suicide attempt: A pilot Delphi study. *Journal of Child and Adolescent Psychiatric Nursing, 28*(4), 157–164.

Hilton, S. C., Fellingham, G. W., & Lyon, J. L. (2002). Suicide rates and religious commitment in young adult males in Utah. *Journal of Epidemiology and Community Health, 155*(5), 413–419.

Hirschtritt, M. E., Ordóñez, A. E., Rico, Y. C., & LeWinn, K. Z. (2015). Internal resilience, peer victimization, and suicidal ideation among adolescents. *International Journal of Adolescent Medicine and Health, 27*, 415–423.

Hoffman, S., & Marsiglia, F. F. (2014). The impact of religiosity on suicidal ideation among youth in central Mexico. *Journal of Religion and Health, 53*, 255–266. doi:10.1007/s10943-012-9654-1

Hollis, C. (1996). Depression, family environment, and adolescent suicidal behavior. *Journal of the American Academy of Child & Adolescent Psychiatry, 35*, 622–630.

Holt, M. K., Vivolo-Kantor, A. M., Polanin, J. R., Holland, K. M., DeGue, S., Matjasko, J. L., . . . Reid, G. (2015). Bullying and suicidal ideation and behaviors: A meta-analysis. *Pediatrics, 135*(2), e496–e509.

Hong, J. S., Kral, M. J., & Sterzing, P. R. (2015). Pathways from bullying perpetration, victimization, and bully victimization to suicidality among school-aged youth: A review of the potential mediators and a call for further investigation. *Trauma, Violence, & Abuse*, 16(4), 379–390. doi:10.1177/152483801 4537904

Husky, M. M., Olfson, M., He, J. P., Nock, M. K., Swanson, S. A., & Merikangas, K. R. (2012). Twelve-month suicidal symptoms and use of services among adolescents: Results from the National Comorbidity Survey. *Psychiatric Services*, 63(10), 989–996.

Jashinsky, J., Burton, S. H., Hanson, C. L., West, J., Giraud-Carrier, C., Barnes, M. D., & Argyle, T. (2014). Tracking suicide risk factors through Twitter in the US. *Crisis*, 35(1), 51–59.

Joe, S., Banks, A., & Belue, R. (2016). Suicide risk among urban children. *Children and Youth Services Review*, 68, 73–79.

Joffe, R. T., Offord, D. R., & Boyle, M. H. (1988). Ontario Child Health Study: Suicidal behaviour in youth age 12–16 years. *American Journal of Psychiatry*, 145, 1420–1423.

Johnson, B. A., Brent, D. A., Bridge, J., & Connolly, J. (1998). The familial aggregation of adolescent suicide attempts. *Acta Psychiatrica Scandinavica*, 97, 18–24.

Johnson, R. M., Barber, C., Azrael, D., Clark, D. E., & Hemenway, D. (2010). Who are the owners of firearms used in adolescent suicides? *Suicide and Life-Threatening Behavior*, 40(6), 609–611.

Jones, H. A., Bilge-Johnson, S., Rabinovitch, A. E., & Fishel, H. (2014). Self-reported peer victimization and suicidal ideation in adolescent psychiatric inpatients: The mediating role of negative self-esteem. *Clinical Child Psychology and Psychiatry*, 19(4), 606–616.

Kaess, M., Durkee, T., Brunner, R., Carli, V., Parzer, P., Wasserman, C., . . . Wasserman, D. (2014). Pathological Internet use among European adolescents: Psychopathology and self-destructive behaviours. *European Child & Adolescent Psychiatry*, 23(11), 1093–1102.

Kaplan, K. J., & Harrow, M. (1996). Positive and negative symptoms as risk factors for later suicidal activity in schizophrenics versus depressives. *Suicide and Life-Threatening Behavior*, 26(2), 105–120.

Kaplan, K. J., & Worth, S. A. (1993). Individuation-attachment and suicide trajectory: A developmental guide for the clinician. *Omega*, 27, 207–237.

Kaplan, S. G., Ali, S. K., Simpson, B., Britt, V., & McCall, W. V. (2014). Associations between sleep disturbance and suicidal ideation in adolescents admitted to an inpatient psychiatric unit. *International Journal of Adolescent Medicine and Health*, 26(3), 411–416.

Karaman, D., & Durukan, I. (2013). Suicide in children and adolescents. *Psikiyatride Güncel Yaklaşımlar*, 5(1), 30–47.

Katz, L. Y., Au, W., Singal, D., Brownell, M., Roos, N., Martens, P. J., . . . Sareen, J. (2011). Suicide and suicide attempts in children and adolescents in the child welfare system. *Canadian Medical Association Journal*, 183(17), 1977–1981.

Kelly, E. V., Newton, N. C., Stapinski, L. A., Slade, T., Barrett, E. L., Conrod, P. J., & Teesson, M. (2015). Suicidality, internalizing problems and externalizing problems among adolescent bullies, victims and bully-victims. *Preventive Medicine*, 73, 100–105.

Khurana A., & Romer, D. (2012). Modeling the distinct pathways of influence of coping strategies on youth suicidal ideation: A national longitudinal study. *Prevention Science*, 13(6), 644–654.

Kim, J., Park, E., Lee, S. G., & Yoo, K.-B. (2015). Associations between time in bed and suicidal thoughts, plans and attempts in Korean adolescents. *BMJ Open*, 5. doi: 10.1136bmjopen-2015-008766

King, C. A., Jiang, Q., Czyz, E. K., & Kerr, D. C. R. (2014). Suicidal ideation of psychiatrically hospitalized adolescents has one-year predictive validity for suicide attempts in girls only. *Journal of Abnormal Child Psychology*, 42(3), 467–477.

Kodish, T., Herres, J., Shearer, A., Atte, T., Fein, J., & Diamond, G. (2016). Bullying, depression, and suicide risk in a pediatric primary care sample. *Crisis: The Journal of Crisis Intervention and Suicide Prevention*, 37(3), 241–246.

Kõlves, K., & De Leo, D. (2014). Suicide rates in children aged 10–14 years worldwide: Changes in the past two decades. *The British Journal of Psychiatry*, 205(4), 283–285.

Kondro, W. (2004). FDA urges "black box" warning on pediatric antidepressants. *Canadian Medical Association Journal*, 171(8), 837–838. doi:10.1503/cmaj.1041507

Kosky, R. (1983). Childhood suicidal behavior. *Journal of Child Psychology & Psychiatry*, 24, 457–468.

Kosky, R., Silburn, S., & Zubrick, S. R. (1990). Are children and adolescents who have suicidal thoughts different from those who attempt suicide? *Journal of Nervous and Mental Disease*, 178, 38–43.

Kovacs, M., Goldston, D., & Catsonis, C. (1993). Suicidal behaviors and child and adolescent depressive disorders: A longitudinal investigation. *Journal of the American Academy of Child & Adolescent Psychiatry*, 32, 8–20.

Kuramoto, S. J., Brent, D. A., & Wilcox, H. C. (2009). The impact of parental suicide on child and adolescent offspring. *Suicide and Life-Threatening Behavior, 39*(2), 137–151.

Labouliere, C. D., Kleinman, M., & Gould, M. S. (2015). When self-reliance is not safe: Associations between reduced help-seeking and subsequent mental health symptoms in suicidal adolescents. *International Journal of Environmental Research and Public Health, 12*(4), 3741–3755.

Lee, J. L., Ma, W. F., Yen, W. J., Huang, X. Y., & Chiang, L. C. (2012). Predicting the likelihood of suicide attempts for rural outpatients with schizophrenia. *Journal of Clinical Nursing, 21*(19–20), 2896–2904.

Lesage, A. D., Boyer, R., Grunberg, F., Vanier, C., Morisette, R., Menard-Buteau, C., & Loyer, M. (1994). Suicide and mental disorders: A case-control study of young men. *American Journal of Psychiatry, 151*, 1063–1068.

Libby, A. M., Brent, D. A., Morrato, E. H., Orton, H. D., Allen, R., & Valuck, R. J. (2007). Decline in treatment of pediatric depression after FDA advisory on risk of suicidality with SSRIs. *American Journal of Psychiatry, 164*, 884–891.

Licinio, J., & Wong, M. L. (2005). Depression, antidepressants and suicidality: A critical appraisal. *Nature Reviews Drug Discovery, 4*(2), 165–171.

Lin, F., Lin, J., Hsieh, Y., & Chang, C. (2014). Quarrelsome family environment as an enhanced factor on child suicidal ideation. *Research in Developmental Disabilities, 35*(12), 3245–3253.

Linkowski, P., de Maertelaer, V., & Mendlewicz, J. (1985). Suicidal behaviour in major depressive illness. *Acta Psychiatrica Scandinavica, 72*(3), 233–238.

Lizardi, D., Currier, D., Galfalvy, H., Sher, L., Burke, A., Mann, J., & Oquendo, M. (2007). Perceived reasons for living at index hospitalization and future suicide attempt. *The Journal of Nervous and Mental Disease, 195*, 451–455.

Malik, S., Kanwar, A., Sim, L. A., Prokop, L. J., Wang, Z., Benkhadra, K., & Murad, M. H. (2014). The association between sleep disturbances and suicidal behaviors in patients with psychiatric diagnoses: A systematic review and meta-analysis. *Systematic Reviews, 3*, 18. doi:10.1186/2046-4053-3-18

Malone, K. M., Haas, G. L., Sweeny, J. A., & Mann, J. J. (1995). Major depression and the risk of attempted suicide. *Journal of Affective Disorders, 34*, 173–185.

Maniam, T., Marhani, M., Firdaus, M., Kadir, A. B., Mazni, M. J., Azizul, A., . . . Noor Ani, A. (2014). Risk factors for suicidal ideation, plans and attempts in Malaysia—results of an epidemiological survey. *Comprehensive Psychiatry, 55*, S121–S125.

Mann, J. J., Bortinger, J., Oquendo, M. A., Currier, D., Li, S., & Brent, D. A. (2005). Family history of suicidal behavior and mood disorders in probands with mood disorders. *American Journal of Psychiatry, 162*(9), 1672–1679.

Maris, R. W., Berman, A. L., & Silverman, M. M. (2000). *Comprehensive textbook of suicidology.* New York, NY: Guilford Press.

Martin, J. A., Kochanek, K. D., Strobino, D. M., Guyer, B., & MacDorman, M. F. (2005). Annual Summary of Vital Statistics—2003. *Pediatrics, 115*(3), 619–634.

Mayes, S. D., Calhoun, S. L., Baweja, R., Feldman, L., Syed, E., Gorman, A. A., . . . Siddiqui, F. (2015). Suicide ideation and attempts are associated with co-occurring oppositional defiant disorder and sadness in children and adolescents with ADHD. *Journal of Psychopathology and Behavioral Assessment, 37*(2), 274–282.

Mayo Clinic Staff. (2016, May 24). Antidepressants for children and teens. Retrieved from https://www.mayoclinic.org/diseases-conditions/teen-depression/in-depth/antidepressants/art-20047502

McKnight-Eily, L. R., Eaton, D. K., Lowry, R., Croft, J. B., Presley-Cantrell, L., & Perry, G. S. (2011). Relationships between hours of sleep and health-risk behaviors in US adolescent students. *Preventive Medicine, 53*(4–5), 271–273.

McMahon, E. M., Corcoran, P., McAuliffe, C., Keeley, H., Perry, I. J., & Arensman, E. (2013). Mediating effects of coping style on associations between mental health factors and self-harm among adolescents. *Crisis: The Journal of Crisis Intervention and Suicide Prevention, 34*(4), 242–250.

McManus, B. L., Kruesi, M. J., Dontes, A. E., Defazio, C. R., Piotrowski, J. T., & Woodward, P. J. (1997). Child and adolescent suicide attempts: An opportunity for emergency departments to provide injury prevention education. *The American Journal of Emergency Medicine, 15*(4), 357–360.

Mehlum, L., Friis, S., Vaglum, P., & Karterud, S. (1994). The longitudinal pattern of suicidal behaviour in borderline personality disorder: A prospective follow-up study. *Acta Psychiatrica Scandinavica, 90*(2), 124–130.

Menon, K. (2009). To prescribe or not to prescribe? *The British Journal of Psychiatry, 194*, 189. doi:10.1192/bjp.194.2.189a

Messias, E., Castro, J., Saini, A., Usman, M., & Peeples, D. (2011). Sadness, suicide, and their association with video game and internet overuse among teens: results from the youth risk behavior survey 2007 and 2009. *Suicide and Life-Threatening Behavior, 41*, 307–315.

Miller, A. B., Esposito-Smythers, C., & Leichtweis, R. N. (2015). Role of social support in adolescent suicidal ideation and suicide attempts. *Journal of Adolescent Health, 56*(3), 286–292.

Miller, A. B., Esposito-Smythers, C., Weismoore, J. T., & Renshaw, K. D. (2013). The relation between child maltreatment and adolescent suicidal behavior: A systematic review and critical examination of the literature. *Clinical Child and Family Psychology Review, 16*(2), 146–172.

Minor, T., Ali, M. M., & Rizzo, J. A. (2016). Body weight and suicidal behavior in adolescent females: The role of self-perceptions. *The Journal of Mental Health Policy and Economics, 19*(1), 21–31.

Miranda, R., Jaegere, E., Restifo, K., & Shaffer, D. (2014). Longitudinal follow-up study of adolescents who report a suicide attempt: Aspects of suicidal behavior that increase risk of a future attempt. *Depression and Anxiety, 31*(1), 19–26.

Mirsky, E. L., & Omar, H. A. (2015). Cyberbullying in adolescents: The prevalence of mental disorders and suicidal behavior. *International Journal of Child and Adolescent Health, 8*(1), 37–39.

Mitchell, K. J., Wells, M., Priebe, G., & Ybarra, M. L. (2014). Exposure to websites that encourage self-harm and suicide: Prevalence rates and association with actual thoughts of self-harm and thoughts of suicide in the United States. *Journal of Adolescence, 37*(8), 1335–1344.

Molnar, B. E., Berkman, L. F., & Buka, S. L. (2001). Psychopathology, childhood sexual abuse, and other childhood adversities: Relative links to subsequent suicidal behavior in the US. *Psychological Medicine, 31*, 965–977. doi:10.1017/S0033291701004329

Moscicki, E. K. (1994). Gender differences in completed and attempted suicides. *Annals of Epidemiology, 4*, 152–158.

Moscicki, E. K. (1995). Epidemiology of suicidal behavior. *Suicide and Life-Threatening Behavior, 25*(1), 22–35.

Moscicki, E. K. (2001). Epidemiology of completed and attempted suicide: Toward a framework for prevention. *Clinical Neuroscience Research, 1*, 310–323.

Moskos, M. A., Achilles, J., & Gray, D. (2004). Adolescent suicide myths in the United States. *Crisis, 25*(4), 176–182.

Möller-Leimkühler, A. M. (2002). Barriers to help-seeking by men: a review of sociocultural and clinical literature with particular reference to depression. *Journal of Affective Disorders, 71*(1–3), 1–9.

Mustanski, B., Andrews, R., Herrick, A., Stall, R., & Schnarrs, P. W. (2014). A syndemic of psychosocial health disparities and associations with risk for attempting suicide among young sexual minority men. *American Journal of Public Health, 104*(2), 287–294.

Nanayakkara, S., Misch, D., Chang, L., & Henry, D. (2013). Depression and exposure to suicide predict suicide attempt. *Depression and Anxiety, 30*(10), 991–996.

National Center for Health Statistics. (2000). *Death rates for 72 selected causes, by 5-year age groups, race, and sex: United States, 1979–1997.* Atlanta, GA: Centers for Disease Control and Prevention.

Nestor, B. A., Cheek, S. M., & Liu, R. T. (2016). Ethnic and racial differences in mental health service utilization for suicidal ideation and behavior in a nationally representative sample of adolescents. *Journal of Affective Disorders, 202*, 197–202.

NHS Executive. (1998). Retrieved from http://webarchive.nationalarchives.gov.uk/20120503231618/http://www.dh.gov.uk/prod_consum_dh/groups/dh_digitalassets/@dh/@en/documents/digitalasset/dh_4014469.pdf

Nomura, Y., Warner, U., & Wickramaratne, P. (2001). Parents concordant for major depressive disorder and the effect of psychopathology in offspring. *Psychological Medicine, 31*, 1211–1222.

O'Keeffe, G. S., Clarke-Pearson, K., & Council on Communications and Media. (2011). The impact of social media on children, adolescents, and families. *Pediatrics, 127*, 800–804. doi:10.1542/peds.2011-0054

Orbach, I. (1997). A taxonomy of factors related to suicidal behavior. *Clinical Psychology: Science and Practice, 4*, 208–224.

Patton, G. C., Harris, R., Carlin, J. B., Hibbert, M. E., Coffey, C., Schwartz, M., . . . Bowes, G. (1997). Adolescent suicidal behaviours: A population-based study of risk. *Psychological Medicine, 27*, 715–724.

Pelkonen, M., Marttunen, M., Pulkkinen, E., Laippala, P., & Aro, H. (1997). Characteristics of outpatient adolescents with suicidal tendencies. *Acta Psychiatrica Scandinavica, 95*, 100–107.

Perez, N. M., Jennings, W. G., Piquero, A. R., & Baglivio, M. T. (2016). Adverse childhood experiences and suicide attempts: The mediating influence of personality development and problem behaviors. *Journal of Youth and Adolescence, 45*(8), 1527–1545.

Peters, K. D., Kochanek, K. D., & Murphy, S. L. (1998). Deaths: Final data for 1996. *National Vital Statistics Reports, 47*(9), 1–100.

Pettit, J. W., Green, K. L., Grover, K. E., Schatte, D. J., & Morgan, S. T. (2011). Domains of chronic stress and suicidal behaviors among inpatient adolescents. *Journal of Clinical Child & Adolescent Psychology, 40*(3), 494–499.

Pfeffer, C. R. (1991). Suicide in Japan. *Journal of the American Academy of Child & Adolescent Psychiatry, 30*(5), 847–848.

Pfeffer, C. R., Klerman, G. L., Hurt, S. W., Kakuma, T., Peskin, J. R., & Siefker, C. A. (1993). Suicidal children grow up: Rates and psychosocial risk factors for suicide attempts during follow-up. *Journal of the American Academy of Child & Adolescent Psychiatry, 32*(1), 106–113.

Phend, C. (2007, April 7). Antidepressant black-box warnings alter pediatric prescribing. *MedPage Today.* Retrieved from https://www.medpagetoday.com/psychiatry/depression/5377

Pitts, F. N., & Winokur, G. (1964). Affective disorder, III: Diagnostic correlates and incidence of suicide. *Journal of Nervous & Mental Disease, 139*, 176–181.

Pleck, J. H. (1995). The gender role strain paradigm: An update. In R. Levant & W. S. Pollack (Eds.), *A new psychology of men* (pp. 11–32). New York, NY: Basic Books.

Powell, J. M., Geddes, J., Deeks, J., Goldacre, M., & Hawton, K. (2000). Suicide in psychiatric hospital in-patients: Risk factors and their predictive powers. *British Journal of Psychiatry, 176*, 266–272.

Rabinovitch, S. M., Kerr, D. C., Leve, L. D., & Chamberlain, P. (2015). Suicidal behavior outcomes of childhood sexual abuse: Longitudinal study of adjudicated girls. *Suicide and Life-Threatening Behavior, 45*(4), 431–447.

Randell, B. P., Wang, W., Herting, J. R., & Eggert, L. L. (2006). Family factors predicting categories of suicide risk. *Journal of Family and Child Studies, 15*(3), 255–270.

Rehbein, F., Kleimann, M., & Mössle, T. (2010). Prevalence and risk factors of video game dependency in adolescence: results of a German nationwide survey. *Cyberpsychology, Behavior and Social Networks, 13*(3), 269–277.

Renaud, J., Berlim, M. T., Séguin, M., McGirr, A.,Tousignant, M., & Turecki, G. (2009). Recent and lifetime utilization of health care services by children and adolescent suicide victims: A case-control study. *Journal of Affective Disorders, 117*(3), 168–173.

Resnick, M. D., Bearman, P. S., Blum, R. W., Bauman, K. E., Harris, K. M., Jones, J., . . . Udry, J. R. (1997). Protecting adolescents from harm findings from the National Longitudinal Study on Adolescent Health. *Journal of the American Medical Association, 278*, 823–832.

Riala, K., Hakko, H., & Räsänen, P. (2009). Nicotine dependence is associated with suicide attempts and self-mutilation among adolescent females. Study-70 Workgroup; *Comprehensive Psychiatry, 50*(4), 293–298.

Rice, S., Robinson, J., Bendall, S., Hetrick, S., Cox, G., Bailey, E., . . . Alvarez-Jimenez, M. (2016). Online and social media suicide prevention interventions for young people: A focus on implementation and moderation. *Journal of the Canadian Academy of Child and Adolescent Psychiatry/Journal de l'Académie canadienne de psychiatrie de l'enfant et de l'adolescent, 25*(2), 80–86.

Richardson, C. A., & Rabiee, F. (2001). A question of access: An exploration of the factors influencing the health of young males aged 15 to 19 living in Corby and their use of health care services. *Health Education Journal, 60*, 3–6.

Robinson, J., Hetrick, S., Cox, G., Bendall, S., Yung, A., Yuen, H. P., . . . Pirkis, J. (2014). The development of a randomised controlled trial testing the effects of an online intervention among school students at risk of suicide. *BioMed Central Psychiatry, 14*, 155. doi:10.1186/1471-244X-14-155

Roy, A. (1983). Family history of suicide. *Archives of General Psychiatry, 40*, 971–974.

Roy, A. (1985). Family history of suicide in manic-depressive patients. *Journal of Affect Disorders, 8*, 187–189.

Roy, A. (1993). Genetic and biological risk factors for suicide in depressive disorders. *Psychiatric Quarterly, 64*, 345–358.

Roy, A. (2002a). Characteristics of opiate-dependent patients who attempt suicide. *Journal of Clinical Psychiatry, 63*, 403–407.

Roy, A. (2002b). Family history of suicide and neuroticism: A preliminary study. *Psychiatry Research, 110*, 87–90.

Roy, A. (2003). Characteristics of drug addicts who attempt suicide. *Psychiatry Research, 121*, 99–103.

Roy, A., Rylander, G., & Sarchiapone, M. (1997). Genetics of suicides. Family studies and molecular genetics. *Annals of the New York Academy of Sciences, 836*, 135–157.

Roy, A., Segal, N. L., Centerwall, B. S., & Robinette, C. D. (1991). Suicide in twins. *Archives of General Psychiatry, 48*, 29–32.

Roy, A., Segal, N. L., & Sarchiapone, M. (1995). Attempted suicide among living co-twins of twin suicide victims. *American Journal of Psychiatry, 152*, 1075–1076.

Rubenstein, J. L., Halton, A., Kasten, L., Rubin, C., & Stechler, G. (1998). Suicidal behavior in adolescents: Stress and protection in different family contexts. *American Journal of Orthopsychiatry, 68*(2), 274–284.

Rubenstein, J. L., Heeren, T., Housman, D., Rubin, C., & Stechler, G. (1989). Suicidal behavior in "normal" adolescents: Risk and protective factors. *American Journal of Orthopsychiatry, 1*, 59–71.

Runeson, B., & Asberg, M. (2003). Family history of suicide among suicide victims. *American Journal of Psychiatry, 160*, 1525–1526.

Runeson, B. S. (1998). History of suicidal behaviour in the families of young suicides. *Acta Psychiatrica Scandinavica, 98*, 497–501.

Rutter, M., & Quinton, D. (1984). Parental psychiatric disorder: Effects on children. *Psychological Medicine, 14*, 853–880.

Rutter, M., Silberg, J., O'Connor, T., & Simonoff, E. (1999). Genetics and child psychiatry: 1. Advances in quantitative and molecular genetics. *Journal of Child Psychology and Psychiatry, 40*, 3–18.

Sabo, A. N., Gunderson, J. G., Najavits, L. M., Chauncey, D., & Kisiel, C. (1995). Changes in self-destructiveness of borderline patients in psychotherapy: A prospective follow-up. *Journal of Nervous and Mental Disease, 183*(6), 337–376.

Saewyc, E. M., Heinz, P. A., Bearinger, L. H., Blum, R. W., & Resnick, M. D. (1998). Gender differences in health and risky behaviors among bisexual and homosexual adolescents. *Journal of Adolescent Health, 23*, 181–188.

Salzinger, S., Rosario, M., Feldman, R. S., & Ng-Mak, D. S. (2007). Adolescent suicidal behavior: Associations with preadolescent physical abuse and selected risk and protective factors. *Journal of the American Academy of Child and Adolescent Psychiatry, 46*(7), 859–866.

Schmidtke, A., Bille-Brahe, U., DeLeo, D., & Kerkhof, A. (1996). Attempted suicide in Europe: Rates, trends and sociodemographic characteristics of suicide attempters during the period 1989–1992. *Acta Psychiatrica Scandinavica, 93*(5), 327–338.

Schneider, B., Philipp, M., & Muller, M. J. (2001). Psychopathological predictors of suicide in patients with major depression during a 5-year follow-up. *European Psychiatry, 16*, 283–288.

Scocco, P., Marietta, P., Tonietto, M., & Buono, M. D. (2000). The role of psychopathology and suicidal intention in predicting suicide risk: A longitudinal study. *Psychopathology, 33*, 143–150.

Serafini, G., Muzio, C., Piccinini, G., Flouri, E., Ferrigno, G., Pompili, M., . . . Amore, M. (2015). Life adversities and suicidal behavior in young individuals: A systematic review. *European Child & Adolescent Psychiatry, 24*(12), 1423–1446.

Shaffer, D., Gould, M., Fisher, P., Trautman, P., Moreau, D., & Kleinman, M. (1996). Psychiatric diagnosis in child and adolescent suicide. *Archives of General Psychiatry, 53*, 339–348.

Shafi, M., Steltz-Lenarsky, J., Derrick, A. M., Beckner, C., & Whittinghill, R. (1988). Comorbidity of mental disorders in the post-mortem diagnosis of completed suicide in children and adolescents. *Journal of Affective Disorders, 14*, 227–233.

Sharaf, A. Y., Thompson, E. A., & Walsh, E. (2009). Protective effects of self-esteem and family support on suicide risk behaviors among at-risk adolescents. *Journal of Child and Adolescent Psychiatric Nursing, 22*(3), 160–168.

Sharaf, A. Y., Thompson, E. A., & Walsh, E. (2010). 'Protective effects of self-esteem and family support on suicide risk behaviors among at-risk adolescents:' Corrigendum. *Journal of Child and Adolescent Psychiatric Nursing, 23*(1), 45.

Shaunessey, K., Cohen, J. L., Plummer, B., & Berman, A. (1993). Suicidality in hospitalized adolescents: Relationship to prior abuse. *American Journal of Orthopsychiatry, 63*, 113–119.

Shpiegel, Y., Klomek, A. B., & Apter, A. (2015). Bullying, cyberbullying, depression and suicide ideation among youth: Comparing online to paper-and-pencil questionnaires. *International Journal of Child and Adolescent Health, 8*(2), 161–167.

Sibold, J., Edwards, E., Murray-Close, D., & Hudziak, J. J. (2015). Physical activity, sadness, and suicidality in bullied US adolescents. *Journal of the American Academy of Child & Adolescent Psychiatry, 54*(10), 808–815.

Sinclair, K. O., Bauman, S., Poteat, V. P., Koenig, B., & Russell, S. T. (2012). Cyber and bias-based harassment: Associations with academic, substance use, and mental health problems. *Journal of Adolescent Health, 50*(5), 521–523.

Singaravelu, V., Stewart, A., Adams, J., Simkin, S., & Hawton, K. (2014). Information-seeking on the internet: An investigation of websites potentially accessed by distressed or suicidal adolescents. *Crisis: The Journal of Crisis Intervention and Suicide Prevention, 36*(3), 211–219.

Soole, R., & Kõlves, K. (2015). Suicide in children: A systematic review. *Archives of Suicide Research, 19*(3), 285–304.

Sorenson, S. B., & Rutter, C. M. (1991). Transgenerational patterns of suicide attempt. *Journal of Consulting & Clinical Psychology, 59*(6), 861–866.

Soylu, N., & Alpaslan, A. H. (2013). Suicidal behavior and associated factors in sexually abused adolescents. *Children and Youth Services Review, 35*(2), 253–257.

Stack, S. (1983). The effect of religious commitment on suicide: Across-national analysis. *Journal of Health and Social Behavior, 24*, 362–374. doi:10.2307/2136402

Stack, S. (2002). Opera subculture and suicide for honor. *Death Studies, 26*, 431–437.

Stack, S., & Kposowa, A. J. (2008). The association of suicide rates with individual-level suicide attitudes: A cross-national analysis. *Social Science Quarterly, 89*(1), 39–59.

Statham, D. J., Heath, A. C., Madden, P. A., Bucholz, K. K., Bierut, L., Dinwiddie, S. H., . . . Martin, N. J. (1998). Suicidal behaviour: An epidemiological and genetic study. *Psychological Medicine, 28*, 839–855.

Stein, B. D., & Dubowitz, T. (2015). Rx exercise: Physical activity is good medicine. *Journal of the American Academy of Child & Adolescent Psychiatry, 54*(10), 795–796.

Stewart, D. E., Vigod, S., & Riazantseva, E. (2016). New developments in intimate partner violence and management of its mental health sequelae. *Current Psychiatry Reports, 18*(1), 4. doi:10.1007/s11920-015-0644-3

Stewart, J. G., Kim, J. C., Esposito, E. C., Gold, J., Nock, M. K., & Auerbach, R. P. (2015). Predicting suicide attempts in depressed adolescents: Clarifying the role of disinhibition and childhood sexual abuse. *Journal of Affective Disorders, 187*, 25–34.

Stillion, J. M., & McDowell, E. E. (1991). Examining suicide from a life-span perspective. *Death Studies, 15*, 327–354.

Strittmatter, E., Parzer, P., Brunner, R., Fischer, G., Durkee, T., Carli, V., . . . Kaess, M. (2016). A 2-year longitudinal study of prospective predictors of pathological internet use in adolescents. *European Child & Adolescent Psychiatry, 25*(7), 725–734.

Stronski-Huwiler, S. M., & Remafedi, G. (1998). Adolescent homosexuality. *Advances in Pediatrics, 45*, 107–144.

Taliaferro, L. A., Eisenberg, M. E., Johnson, K. E., Nelson, T. F., & Neumark-Sztainer, D. (2011). Sport participation during adolescence and suicide ideation and attempts. *International Journal of Adolescent Medicine and Health, 23*(1), 3–10.

Taliaferro, L. A., & Muehlenkamp, J. J. (2014). Risk and protective factors that distinguish adolescents who attempt suicide from those who only consider suicide in the past year. *Suicide and Life-Threatening Behavior, 44*(1), 6–22.

Taussig, H. N., Harpin, S. B., & Maguire, S. A. (2014). Suicidality among preadolescent maltreated children in foster care. *Child Maltreatment, 19*(1), 17–26.

Taylor, E., & Stansfeld, S. (1984). Children who poison themselves: II. Prediction of attendance for treatment. *British Journal of Psychiatry, 145*, 132–135.

Thompson, M. P., Kuruwita, C., & Foster, E. M. (2009). Transitions in suicide risk in a nationally representative of adolescents. *Journal of Adolescent Health, 44*(5), 458–463.

Thompson, M. P., & Light, L. S. (2010). Examining gender differences in risk factors for suicide attempts made 1 and 7 years later in a nationally representative sample. *Journal of Adolescent Health, 48*(4), 391–397.

Thompson, M. P., & Light, L. S. (2011). Examining gender differences in risk factors for suicide attempts made 1 and 7 years later in a nationally representative sample. *Journal of Adolescent Health, 48*(4), 391–397.

Thompson, R., Proctor, L. J., English, D. J., Dubowitz, H., Narasimhan, S., & Everson, M. D. (2012). Suicidal ideation in adolescence: Examining the role of recent adverse experiences. *Journal of Adolescence, 35*(1), 175–186.

Tong, Y., Phillips, M. R., Duberstein, P., & Zhan, W. (2014). Suicidal behavior in relatives or associates moderates the strength of common risk factors for suicide. *Suicide and Life-Threatening Behavior, 45*(4), 505–517.

Topor, D. R., Swenson, L. P., Liguori, G. M., Spirito, A., Lowenhaupt, E. A., & Hunt, J. I. (2011). Problematic video game use scale: initial psychometric properties with psychiatrically hospitalized adolescents. *Journal of Clinical Psychiatry, 72*, 1611-5.

Tørmoen, A. J., Rossow, I., Mork, E., & Mehlum, L. (2014). Contact with child and adolescent psychiatric services among self-harming and suicidal adolescents in the general population: A cross sectional study. *Child and Adolescent Psychiatry and Mental Health, 8,* 13.

Townsend, L., Gearing, R. E., & Polyanskaya, O. (2012). Influence of health beliefs and stigma on choosing internet support groups over formal mental health services. *Psychiatric Services, 63,* 370–378. doi:10.1176/appi.ps.201100196

Tsai, S. -Y. M., Kuo, C. -J., Chen, C. -C., & Lee, H. -C. (2002). Risk factors for completed suicide in bipolar disorder. *Journal of Clinical Psychiatry, 63*(6), 469–476.

Tsuang, M. T. (1983). Risk of suicide in relatives of schizophrenics, manics, depressives, and controls. *Journal of Clinical Psychiatry, 44,* 396–400.

Tsypes, A., & Gibb, B. E. (2016). Cognitive vulnerabilities and development of suicidal thinking in children of depressed mothers: A longitudinal investigation. *Psychiatry Research, 239,* 99–104.

Unlu, G., & Cakaloz, B. (2016). Effects of perpetrator identify on suicidality and nonsuicidal self-injury in sexually victimized female adolescents. *Neuropsychiatric Disease and Treatment, 12,* 1489–1497.

Utter, J., Denny, S., Robinson, E., Fleming, T., Ameratunga, S., & Grant, S. (2013). Family meals and the well-being of adolescents. *Journal of Paediatrics and Child Health, 49*(11), 906–911.

van Heeringen, K. (2001). Understanding suicidal behavior: The suicidal process approach to research, treatment, and prevention. New York, NY: Wiley.

Wasserman C., Hoven, C. W., Wasserman, D., Carli, V., Sarchiapone, M., Al-Halabí, S., . . . Poštuvan, V. (2012). Suicide prevention for youth—a mental health awareness program: Lessons learned from the Saving and Empowering Young Lives in Europe (SEYLE) intervention study. *BioMed Central Public Health, 12,* 776–787.

Wherry, J. N., Baldwin, S., Junco, K., & Floyd, B. (2013). Suicidal thoughts/behaviors in sexually abused children. *Journal of Child Sexual Abuse: Research, Treatment, & Program Innovations for Victims, Survivors, & Offenders, 22*(5), 534–551.

Wilczynska-Kwiatek, A. (2011). Outcast youngsters: Psychosocial conditions of social exclusion risk. *International Journal on Disability and Human Development, 8*(2), 175–180. doi:10.1515/IJDHD.2009.8.2.175

Williams, K. R., & Guerra, N. G. (2007). Prevalence and predictors of internet bullying. *Journal of Adolescent Health, 41,* S14–S21. doi:10.1016/j.jadohealth.2007.08.018

Winsler, A., Deutsch, A., Vorona, R. D., Payne, P. A., & Szklo-Coxe, M. (2015). Sleepless in Fairfax: The difference one more hour of sleep can make for teen hopelessness, suicidal ideation, and substance use. *Journal of Youth and Adolescence, 44*(2), 362–378.

Wintersteen, M. B., Diamond, G. S., & Fein, J. A. (2007). Screening for suicide risk in the pediatric emergency and acute care setting. *Current Opinion in Pediatrics, 19*(4), 398–404.

Wisch, A. F., Mahalik, J. R., Hayes, J. A., & Nutt, E. A. (1995). The impact of gender role conflict and counseling technique on psychological help seeking in men. *Sex Roles, 33,* 77–88.

Wolff, J., Frazier, E. A., Esposito-Smythers, C., Burke, T., Sloan, E., & Spirito, A. (2013). Cognitive and social factors associated with NSSI and suicide attempts in psychiatrically hospitalized adolescents. *Journal of Abnormal Child Psychology, 41*(6), 1005–1013.

Wu, P., Hoven, C. W., Tiet, Q., Kovalenko, P., & Wicks, J. (2002). Factors associated with adolescent utilization of alcohol treatment services. *American Journal of Drug and Alcohol Abuse, 28*(2), 353–369.

Zakharov, S., Navratil, T., & Pelclova, D. (2013). Suicide attempts by deliberate self-poisoning in children and adolescents. *Psychiatry Research, 210*(1), 302–307.

Zalsman, G., & Mann, J. J. (2005). Editorial: The neurobiology of suicide in adolescents: An emerging field of research. *International Journal of Adolescent Medicine and Health, 17*(3), 195–196.

CHAPTER FIVE

ADULT SUICIDE

Although there has been an increase in federal spending on suicide prevention, the overall number of suicides in the United States has actually increased over the past several years. Despite ongoing treatment efforts and initiatives, there has been a lack of progress in the efforts to reduce and mitigate this persistent phenomenon. It is important to understand the epidemiological trends, prevalence, and incidence rates of adult suicidality to understand why our effectiveness at reducing adult suicide rates has been so limited. Further, in order to improve existing prevention and intervention efforts, identification of relevant risk and protective factors among adults is essential. These factors are highlighted in this chapter. In addition, this chapter deconstructs myths and misconceptions related to suicide among adults. An overview of empirically grounded strategies for effective assessment and treatment of this population is also provided.

GOALS AND OBJECTIVES

An understanding of:

- Relationship between progressing through the adult developmental phase and suicidality
- Influence of gender on adult suicidality
- Epidemiology of adult suicidality
- Adult rates of completed suicide and attempted suicide
- The dominant myths and misconceptions regarding adult suicidality
- Psychiatric risk and protective factors for adult suicide
- Sociodemographic risk and protective factors for adult suicide
- Differences between adult suicide attempters and completers
- Differences between adult single and multiple attempters
- Help-seeking behavior in relation to adult suicide
- Mental health service utilization and adult suicide
- Evidence-based interventions for working with this population

---

Suicide is a leading cause of death worldwide (National Institute of Mental Health, n.d.; Nock et al., 2008). Nearly 90 Americans complete suicide every day with hundreds more attempting. Although we often associate suicide with adolescents, the majority of these suicide attempts and completions are by adults (Shah & De, 1998; U.S. Department of Health and Human Services, 2015). Between 2001 and 2014, the suicide rates among adults in the United States, aged 45 to 64 years, increased 27% (U.S. Department of Health and Human Services, 2015).

Suicide at any age is a tragedy. A question that emerges is how does the age of a suicidal client impact the clinician? More specifically, does the age of the individual at risk of suicide impact our ability to engage, assess, and treat him or her? Is the suicide of a younger person a greater tragedy than that of an older individual? Should older individuals know better, be wiser, or more able to make decisions? As a mental health clinician, do you hold one age group as more vulnerable than another? How does the age of a client influence your practice? In clinical work with individuals experiencing suicidality, it is important to assess and treat every individual with professional rigor, ethics, and empathy. To assume that the age of a client does not impact you professionally may be a disservice to both you and your clients.

Individual Exercise 5.1

1. Would working with a suicidal client who is an adult, rather than an adolescent, be more problematic for you as a mental health clinician? Why or why not?
2. Would working with a suicidal client who is an adult, rather than an adolescent, be easier for you as a mental health clinician? Why or why not?
3. Describe the differences in working with a suicidal adult who is younger versus older than you? How might this impact your work with the client?
4. What lessons do you learn from this exercise?

Small Group Exercise 5.1

In small groups of two to three, please discuss, as you are comfortable, your responses to Individual Exercise 5.1. Remember, answers are personal and there are no correct or incorrect answers.

1. What were the response similarities in your group?
2. What were the response differences in your group?
3. Did you find any surprises in the group discussion? If so, what were they and in what way were you surprised?

STATISTICS, EPIDEMIOLOGY, AND TRENDS IN ADULT SUICIDE

In a cross-national study of 17 countries, Nock and colleagues (2008) estimated that among adults, the lifetime prevalence of suicidal ideation is 9.2%, plans 3.1%, and attempts 2.1% (Nock et al., 2008). In addition, an estimated 60% of ideators transition into planners or attempters within the first year of having suicidal ideation (Nock et al., 2008). Research has found that, on average, suicide rates increase with age (Shah & De, 1998). However, Shah's (2007) study using World Health Organization (WHO) suicide data from 62 countries found a significant increase in suicide rates with increasing age in many countries, but no significant increase in others (Shah, 2007). Findings suggest regional and cross-national variations influence the relationship between increased suicide rates and aging (Shah, 2007).

In the United States, more than 1.3 million adults over 18 years of age attempted suicide in 2012 (Han, Compton, Gfroerer, & McKeon, 2014; Substance Abuse and Mental Health Services Administration [SAMHSA], 2014), with 39,426 completing suicide (Centers for Disease Control and Prevention, 2013; Han et al., 2016). Approximately 3.8% of adults 18 years or older in the United States report having suicidal ideation in the past 12 months, and among past-year suicidal ideators, 13.2% attempted suicide in that 1-year time frame (Han et al., 2014). Among U.S. college-aged individuals, suicide is the third leading cause of death (Centers for Disease Control and Prevention, 2013). Across the United States, approximately 55% of college undergraduate students endorse lifetime suicide ideation, with 6% reporting experiencing suicide ideation in the past year (Bozzay, Karver, Verona, 2016; Drum, Brownson, Burton Denmark, & Smith, 2009).

Among middle-aged adults, an estimated 12% of individuals report experiencing suicide ideation at some point during college. Of those individuals, 25% had more than one episode of ideation while in college (Wilcox et al., 2010).

It is important, however, to recognize that trends do not account for gender, geographical, racial, or ethnic differences. For example, the highest U.S. suicide rates have consistently been among older White males (Keppel, Pearcy, & Wagener, 2002). However, the suicide risk for White females and Blacks in the United States tends to peak at midlife (Maris & Nisbet, 2000; Woodbury, Manton, & Blazer, 1988). With regard to attempted suicide, it is difficult to determine prevalence rates, as many suicide attempts remain unreported. However, Doshi, Boudreaux, Wang, Pelletier, and Camargo (2005) investigated U.S. emergency department (ED) visits from 1997 to 2001 for attempted suicide and self-inflicted injury. Their research found that the average age of patients presenting to an ED due to attempted suicide and self-inflicted injury was 31 years and that ED visits were more common in younger than older patients (Doshi, Boudreaux, Wang, Pelletier, & Camargo et al., 2005).

Research has also examined temporal trends in the occurrence of fatal and nonfatal suicidal behaviors. Both fatal and nonfatal suicidal behaviors have an excess occurrence on Mondays and Tuesdays and are less likely to occur on Saturdays. However, there is a significant gender difference in terms of days on which such behaviors occur. Specifically, males are more likely than females to act on Wednesdays and Saturdays. Nonfatal suicidal behaviors occur more often in April and May, while completed suicide rates peak during February and March and are at a low during November (Miller, Furr-Holden, Lawrence, & Weiss, 2012).

The method of suicide of adult completers has also received attention. Research has found that adult males are more likely to use hanging and poisoning, while females are more likely to use drowning and self-immolation. Within-group differences have also been found for gender based on age. Among adult females, younger adult females more often use hanging when compared to older females who more often use drowning as their method of suicide (Kanchan, Menon, & Menezes, 2009).

RISK AND PROTECTIVE FACTORS

Risk Factors for Suicide

Research has extensively examined risk factors for future suicide. The following section details many of the most examined and salient risk factors. Adult suicide attempters and completers embody unique risk factors differentiating between the two groups. For example, research has found that suicide completers are significantly more likely than attempters to use alcohol or drugs prior to their suicidal act and are more likely to leave a suicide note. Suicide completers are also significantly more likely to have encountered significant job stress and financial problems as compared to attempters (DeJong, Overholser, & Stockmeier, 2010).

Several factors have also been identified as associated with increased risk for both attempters and completers. A history of suicide attempts has been found to increase the likelihood of a future attempt as much as four times (Bille-Brahe et al., 1997; Bradvik & Berglund, 1993; Duggan, Sham, Lee, & Murray, 1991; Fawcett et al., 1990; Goldstein, Black, Nasrallah, & Winokur, 1991; Nordstrom, Asberg, Aber-Wistedt, & Nordin, 1995; Sidley, Calam, Wells, Hughes, & Whitaker, 1999; Schneider, Philipp, & Muller, 2001; Wasserman & Cullberg, 1989). The presence of a psychiatric disorder, such as depression, has also been shown to double the risk of future suicide attempt (Antikainen, Hintikka, Lehtonen, Koponen, & Arstila, 1995; Kaplan & Harrow, 1996; Mehlum, Friis, Vaglum, & Karterud, 1994; Sabo, Gunderson, Najavits, Chauncey, & Kisiel, 1995; Scocco, Marietta, Tonietto, & Buono, 2000; Schneider et al., 2001; Statham et al., 1998). A further description and discussion of the impact of psychiatric disorders on suicide can be found in Part IV of this text.

A relationship between loss or separation and suicidality has also been established (Borg & Stahl, 1982). Duggan et al. (1991) found that the experience of loss by either death or separation was more common among suicide attempters than nonattempters (59% vs. 37.5%). However, further analysis revealed that loss by separation, rather than loss by death, is associated with higher suicide risk. This finding has been replicated in more recent years, and additional studies have found that, particularly in younger males, separation appears to be more strongly associated with the risk of suicide as compared to older males or adult females of any age (Wyder, Ward, & De Leo, 2009).

Impulsivity and aggression have consistently been shown to be risk factors for suicide (Angst & Clayton, 1998; Brent et al., 2003; Goldney, Winefield, Saebel, Winefield, & Tiggeman, 1997; Kleiman, Riskind, Schaefer, & Weingarden, 2012; Lopez-Castroman et al., 2014; Malone, Haas, Sweeny, & Mann, 1995; Mann et al., 2005; May & Klonsky, 2016; Rawlings, Shevlin, Corcoran, Morriss, Taylor, 2015; Spokas, Wenzel, Brown, Beck, 2012). For example, one study found that nearly half of the individuals presenting to a psychiatric hospital after a suicide attempt reported that the period between the first current thought of suicide and the actual attempt had lasted 10 minutes or less (Deisenhammer et al., 2009). The study also found that impulsivity was not associated with the duration of the suicidal process. Kleiman and colleagues (2012) further found that social support moderates the relationship between impulsivity and suicidal risk.

A family history of suicidality is also associated with increased risk of suicidal behavior (Mann et al., 2005; Nakagawa, Grunebaum et al., 2009). Some research has found that men whose father or mother died by suicide had higher odds of completing suicide themselves than men whose father died of other causes. The same relationship was observed for women. The odds of suicide increased with decreasing age at death of parent. Results indicate that a mother dying by suicide increases risk more than a father dying by suicide, particularly if the mother died by suicide at a young age (Garssen, Deerenberg, Mackenbach, Kerkhof, & Kunst, 2011). Several studies comparing suicide attempters and nonattempters with a family history of suicidal behavior have found that impulsivity and aggression mediate the familial transmission of suicide (Brent, Bridge, Johnson, & Connolly, 1996; Carballo et al., 2008; Forman, Berk, Henriques, Brown, & Beck, 2004; Galfalvy et al., 2006; Garfinkel, Froese, & Hood, 1982; Hawton, Haw, Houston, & Townsend, 2002; Jeglic, Sharp, Chapman, Brown, & Beck, 2005; Linkowski, de Maertelaer, & Mendlewicz, 1985; Roy, 1993).

In addition to psychiatric and personality variables, numerous sociodemographic characteristics have been shown to increase suicide risk. Gender is a main risk factor for suicidality among adults. Females attempt suicide three to four times more often than males, and males complete suicide more often than females (Houle, Mishara, & Chagnon, 2008; Lefebvre, Lesage, Cyr, & Toupin, 1998; Moscicki et al., 1988; Pirkis, Burgess, & Dunt, 2000; Schmidtke et al., 1996; Suominen, Isometsa, Haukka, & Lonnqvist, 2004). Several explanations have been posited for this gender differential. For example, alcohol use disorders occur more frequently in males (Kessler et al., 1994; Robins & Regier, 1991) and such disorders are associated with increased suicide risk (see further discussion later in this chapter; Blair-West, Cantor, Mellsop, & Eyeson, 1999; Buckley, 2006; Mukamal,

Kawachi, Miller, & Rimm, 2007; Tidemalm, Elofsson, Stefansson, Waern, & Runeson, 2005). Additionally, males have easier access to lethal means of suicide, such as guns (Chuang & Huang, 2004; Fischer, Comstock, Monk, & Sencer, 1993; Helmkamp, 1996; Lester, 2000; Mahon, Tobin, Cusack, Kelleher, & Malone, 2005; Stark et al, 2006). Males are also more likely to employ highly lethal methods of suicide as compared to females (Denning, Conwell, King, & Cox, 2000; Gibb, Beautrais, & Fergusson, 2005; Klerman, 1987; Suokas & Lonnqvist, 1991).

Low education (Abel & Kruger, 2005) and low income have been demonstrated to be associated with increased suicide rates (Abel & Kruger, 2005; Chung et al., 2013; Magnusson & Makinen, 2010; Sareen, Afifi, McMillan, & Asmundson, 2001). However, some research indicates that not only are low income and education risk factors for suicidality, but that the risk of suicidal ideation (in particular) is further increased when there is a discrepancy between one's actual socioeconomic status and one's perceived social status (Kim, Park, & Yoo, 2015). According to Pompili and colleagues (2013), adults with higher educational achievement may be more prone to suicide risk when facing failures, public shame, and high premorbid functioning (Pompili et al., 2013).

Related to the idea of income as a stressor, the experience of being in debt and the specific type of debt have also been explored as risk factors for suicide. Number of debts, source of debt, and reasons for debt are associated with suicidal ideation. Specifically, individuals who are in debt are twice as likely to think about suicide after controlling for sociodemographic, economic, social, and lifestyle factors. Difficulty in making purchase or mail order repayments, paying off credit card debt, and housing-related debt (i.e., rent and mortgage payments) are strongly associated with increased suicidal thoughts (Meltzer et al., 2011). Research further suggests that personal debt and house repossessions may contribute to increased suicide rates in younger men, whereas for middle-aged men, job loss and long-term unemployment serve as greater risk factors (Coope et al, 2014).

Unemployment has also been shown to increase the risk of suicide attempt (Kposowa, 2001; Coope et al., 2015; Saurina, Bragulat, Saez, Lopez-Casasnovas, 2013; Yip et al., 2011; Zhang et al., 2015). This relationship is particularly strong among women (Kposowa, 2001). Further, research has found some increase in suicide attempts and completions during economic hard times and recessions (Elliot, Naphan, Kohlenberg, 2015; Luo, Florence, Quispe-Agnoli, Ouyang, & Crosby, 2011; Norström & Grönqvist, 2015).

Age is also a risk factor for suicide among adults. The suicide rate among elderly males is higher than that of any other age group (Joe, Baser, Breeden, Neighbors, & Jackson, 2006). This will be explored in detail in Chapter 11.

Interestingly, cigarette smoking has been found to be a strong indicator of suicide risk, as well (Donald, Dower, Correa-Velez, & Jones, 2006; Oquendo et al., 2007). This relationship between cigarette smoking and increased suicide risk has been found for both men and women (Oquendo et al., 2007).

Adverse childhood experiences, including childhood sexual abuse, childhood physical abuse, and parental domestic violence, have a long-term impact on development and are associated with an increased risk of adult suicidal ideation and attempts (Afifi et al., 2014; Daray et al., 2016; Fuller-Thomson, Baird, Dhrodia, & Brennenstuhl, 2016). Childhood sexual abuse has been shown to directly increase the odds of an adult suicide attempt (Daray et al., 2016) as has childhood physical abuse (Fuller-Thomson et al., 2016). Research has also shown that both childhood physical and sexual abuses are associated with increased odds of suicide planning (Afifi et al., 2014).

Intimate partner abuse has also been examined as a risk factor for suicidality among adults. For example, in a recent literature review, McLaughlin, O'Carroll, and O'Connor (2012) found that research has consistently identified intimate partner abuse, defined as any incident of threatening behavior, violence, or abuse (psychological, physical, sexual, financial, or emotional) between individuals who are or have been intimate partners, regardless of gender or sexuality (Centers for Disease Control and Prevention, n.d.), as a significant risk factor for suicidal thoughts and behaviors (McLaughlin et al., 2012). The review also identified a dose–response effect between intimate partner abuse severity and suicide risk, such that the more severe the abuse, the higher the risk of suicide.

Research has also identified an association between adult perceptions of poor health and suicide ideation and attempt (Goodwin & Marusic, 2011). Goodwin and Marusic (2011) examined a representative sample (n = 5,877) of adults 15 to 54 years of age in the United States and found that perceptions of poor health were significantly associated with an increased likelihood of suicidal ideation and suicide attempt.

Additionally, having a personal history of alcohol use disorders (both abuse and dependence) has been shown to be related to increased risk of completed suicide and suicide attempt risk (Boenisch et al., 2010; Flensborg-Madsen et al., 2009; Sher, 2006). The lifetime mortality due to suicide in alcohol dependence has been shown to be as high as 15% (Brady, 2006; Roy & Linnoila, 1986), and the prevalence of suicide attempt among individuals with alcohol dependence is as high as 25% (Chignon, Cortes, Martin, & Chabannes, 1998). Furthermore, individuals with alcohol dependence have between 60 and 120 times greater suicide risk than those in the general population (Pompili et al., 2010; Sher, 2006). Among both adult men and women, alcohol intoxication has been found to be associated with violent methods of suicide (Kaplan et al., 2013). Also, acute alcohol use may be a risk factor in suicide attempts (Bagge et al., 2013). A study found that a third of individuals who recently attempted suicide reported being drunk before the attempt, but most (73%) who used alcohol did not do so to facilitate the attempt (Bagge, Conner, Reed, Dawkins, Murray, 2015).

Among adults, research has demonstrated that sociodemographic risk factors differ between single and multiple attempters. Multiple attempters tend to be younger (Choi et al., 2013), not married (Choi et al., 2013), have more severe psychopathology (e.g., psychiatric disorder [Choi et al., 2013; Olie, Guillaume, Jaussent, Courtet, & Jollant, 2010], personality disorder, lower function, and suicide family history), more severe suicidality (e.g., repetitive/severe/continuous suicide ideation; Choi et al., 2013; Olie, 2010), and more dysfunctional interpersonal/intrapersonal resources (e.g., interpersonal stress/conflict, socially isolated, lower personal achievement, and lower ability to control emotion) than single attempters (Choi et al., 2013). Further, multiple attempters are significantly more likely to meet criteria for borderline personality disorder and to have higher impulsivity scores than single attempters (Boisseau et al., 2013). Repeat suicide attempters are also more likely to report impaired perceived parental bonding and more maladaptive early experiences than single or nonattempters (Dale, Power, Kane, Stewart, & Murray, 2010). Gender differences between single and multiple attempters have also been found. Male repeat attempters are characterized by substance use disorders whereas female re-attempters are more often characterized by posttraumatic stress disorder and more severe objective depression (Monnin et al., 2011).

Adult Risk Factors for Suicide

> History of suicide attempts
> History of psychiatric illness
> Impulsivity
> Aggression
> Loss and separation
> Family history of psychiatric illness

(continued)

> Family history of suicide attempts and/or completions
> Intimate partner abuse
> Adverse childhood experiences (child sexual abuse, child physical abuse)
> Gender
> Unemployment
> Fewer years of education
> Low income
> Personal debt
> Perception of poor physical health
> Cigarette smoking
> Alcohol abuse, dependence, and intoxication

Protective Factors Against Suicide

Protective factors against adult suicidal behavior have received less scientific scrutiny than risk factors for suicide. Reasons for living, as measured by the Reasons for Living Inventory (Linehan, Goodstein, Nielsen, & Chiles, 2008) are said to reflect adaptive beliefs and expectations that help individuals resist suicidal urges. Reasons for living are generally classified as belonging to one of six categories, including survival and coping beliefs, moral objections to suicide, fear of social disapproval, fear of suicide, child-related concerns, and responsibility to family (Linehan et al., 1983). Research has prospectively examined the role of reasons for living as protective factors against suicidality. This research indicates that reasons for living serve as a protective factor against suicide attempt for females yet not for males (Lizardi et al., 2007; Oquendo et al., 2007). Overall, research also shows that females most often endorse child-related concerns and fear of suicide as reasons for living. Among females, no differences in the categories of reasons for living endorsed have been found based on age. However, among males, age differences have been established. Specifically, older men more often endorse responsibility to family, fear of suicide, and moral objections as their main reasons for living as compared to younger men (McLaren, 2011). In general, having greater moral objections to suicide is associated with lower levels of suicidal ideation (Richardson-Vejlgaard, Sher, Oquendo, Lizardi, & Stanley, 2009). Lastly, among adults, Blacks report greater moral objections toward suicide as compared to Whites or Hispanics (Richardson-Vejlgaard et al., 2009).

Resiliency has consistently been identified in the research as a protective factor against suicide (Dhingra, Boduszek, & O'Connor, 2016; Kleiman & Beaver, 2013; Wisco, Marx, Wolf, & Miller, 2014). Suicide resilience is a relatively new concept that has emerged in the suicide literature and is defined as "the perceived ability, resources, or competence to regulate suicide-related thoughts, feelings, and attitudes" (Osman et al., 2004, p. 1351). Across age groups, low resilience has been shown to be associated with an increased risk of suicidality (Liu, Fairweather-Schmidt, Roberts, Burns, & Anstey, 2014). Further, a higher level of resilience has been found to be protective against moderate to severe suicide ideation among individuals with higher levels of depression and/or anxiety (Min, Lee, & Chae, 2015). Related to this, endorsing only the presence of meaning in life (rather than searching for the meaning of life) has been found to increase resiliency and reduce odds of a lifetime suicide attempt (Kleiman & Beaver, 2013). However, both the presence of and the search for meaning in life decrease the risk of suicide ideation (Kleiman & Beaver, 2013).

Social support and connectedness have consistently been shown to be protective factors against suicidality (Donald et al., 2006; Duberstein et al., 2004; Kleiman & Beaver, 2013; Park, Cho, & Moon, 2010). Marital status, in particular, is associated with suicide risk (Kposowa, 2000; Silventoinen, Moustgaarid, Peltonen, & Martikainen, 2013). Divorced and separated individuals are more likely to complete suicide than married individuals (Kposowa, 2000). The relationship between marital status and gender is especially strong. The suicide rate among divorced males is twice that of married males (Hawton, 2000; Kposowa, 2003; Moller-Leimkuhler, 2003). Among females, the protective effect of marriage seems to be mediated by the effect of being a parent (Agerbo, 2005; Oquendo et al., 2007). The protective nature of family support has been found to vary based on employment status and level of education of the individual. Individuals who are not working experience more protection against suicide from having family support than do working adults. Further, those adults with more education experience greater protection from having family support than those with less education (Denney, 2014).

Consistently, restricted access to firearms has been shown to be a protective factor against suicidality (Agerbo, Gunnell, Bonde, Mortensen, & Nordentoft, 2007; Dahlberg, Ikeda, & Kresnow, 2004; Ilgen, Zivin, McMannon, & Valenstein, 2008; Miller, Lippmann, Azrael, & Hemenway, 2007; Shenassa, Rogers, Spalding, & Roberts, 2004; U.S. Department of Health and Human Services, 2013). Limited access to firearms is associated with decreased suicide attempts and completions, and strong empirical evidence exists to support this relationship (Mann et al., 2005; Rodríguez Andrés & Hempstead, 2011). Rodríguez Andrés and Hempstead's (2011) examination of gun control and suicide in the United States found that gun control measures (e.g., permit and licensing requirements) have a negative effect on suicide rates among males. Despite this strong evidence, a study examining ED providers found that many ED doctors and nurses are skeptical about the preventability of suicide and the effectiveness of means restriction, resulting in most providers not assessing suicidal patients' firearm access except when a patient has a firearm suicide plan (Betz, Miller, et al., 2013; Betz, Sullivan, et al., 2013).

The protective effects of ethnicity and religion are discussed in detail in Chapters 2 and 3.

Adult Protective Factors Against Suicide

> Reasons for living

> Social support and connectedness

> Employment

> Limited access to firearms

> Marital status

> Ethnicity

> Religious affiliation

> Resiliency

Individual Exercise 5.2

You are a mental health clinician on an inpatient adult psychiatry unit. You are scheduled to do an intake with a new patient who was transferred from a medical unit where she was being treated for the past week for medical consequences due to an attempted suicide. The patient is known to the unit from two prior admissions, one for a major depressive episode and the other for an attempted suicide. Consider the following questions:

1. What risk factors will you assess for during your interview with the client?
2. What protective factors will you assess for during your interview with the client?
3. Are there certain risk or protective factors that are easier or harder to assess for? If so, why?
4. What factors need to be considered in order to establish an effective treatment plan?

ROLE-PLAY 5.1

Using the scenario from Individual Exercise 5.1, break into groups of three and assume the role of the mental health clinician and the new patient on the psychiatry unit. The third member will act as a recorder and can be called upon to consult and assist the mental health clinician. Engage in a role-play in which you would assess for risk and protective factors for a repeat suicide attempt.

MYTHS AND MISCONCEPTIONS ABOUT ADULT SUICIDE

A number of unfounded perceptions and beliefs exist among lay individuals and clinical professionals relating to adult suicide. While many of these accepted misconceptions or myths are ill-informed but harmless, some erroneous thoughts can negatively influence clinical assessments and treatment. The following are six commonly held fallacies related to suicide:

1. *Using the word "suicide" increases the likelihood that at-risk people may view suicide as an option.* A widespread, but unfounded, belief is that when assessing or talking to someone who is at risk for suicide, the use of the word "suicide" should be avoided, lest it provide the individual with a previously unconsidered option. There is no evidence that using the word "suicide" increases risk (Thobaben, 2000). Rather, it will frequently open a dialogue that can aid an individual in discussing a taboo topic, resulting in a fuller, more detailed assessment and an effective treatment plan.
2. *People who want to end their lives will not talk about their suicidal thoughts.* A common myth is that individuals intending to suicide do not talk about their suicidal thoughts or plans. The overwhelming majority of individuals who are seriously considering suicide have clearly described their thoughts on the issue or provided hints (Barrero, 2008).
3. *Suicide prevention or no-harm contracts work.* There has existed for some time a common practice of using suicide prevention or no-harm contracts in working with individuals who express suicidal ideation. There is no empirical support for the effectiveness of suicide prevention contracts in clinical practice (Rudd, Mandrusiak, & Joiner, 2006). Furthermore, the belief that such contracts can work may result in some clinicians substituting contracting for a thorough clinical assessment and treatment (Goin, 2003; Lee & Bartlett, 2005; Rudd et al., 2006).
4. *"Birthday blues" lead to an increase in suicide.* It is often believed that all people are more likely to commit suicide near or on their birthday. Reulbach, Biermann, Markovic, Kornhuber, and Bleich's (2007) population-based research study found

no evidence of a birthday blues effect on suicide (Reulbach et al., 2007). However, Williams and colleagues (2011) did find that birthdays are periods of increased risk among specific cohorts, notably men aged 35 years and older in the general population and for those receiving mental health care (Williams et al., 2011).

5. *Seasonal influence of suicide increases the risk in the late fall and early winter.* There does exist a distinct suicide seasonal pattern. There is a peak of suicides in spring and early summer and a decline in suicides during the late fall and early winter seasons (Jamison & Hawton, 2005; Mergl et al., 2010; Voracek, Tran, & Sonneck, 2007; Woo, Okusaga, & Postolache, 2012). However, people commonly believe the direct opposite. It is important for mental health clinicians to distinguish fact from fiction and to be aware of the documented seasonal influence of suicides in order to conduct an accurate assessment.

6. *Lunar phases influence suicide.* A commonly held unsubstantiated misconnection is that there is a relationship between lunar phases and suicide. Research has found no evidence to support this perceived association (Biermann et al., 2005; Gutierrez-Garcia & Tusell, 1997).

SERVICE UTILIZATION

Research has identified that approximately 20% to 50% of adults with past-year ideation, plans, or attempts reported contact with some type of mental health services in the past year (Encrenaz et al., 2012; Han, Compton, Gfroerer, McKeon, 2014; Stanley, Hom, Joiner, 2015). Research has found that compared to those who did not seek out treatment, help-seekers had significantly greater odds of using overdosing with medications as their method of attempting (Millner & DeLeo, 2010). Further, females (Encrenaz et al., 2012; Millner & DeLeo, 2010; Stanley et al., 2015), non-Hispanic Whites (Stanley et al., 2015), those over 30 years of age (Encrenaz et al., 2012), medically compromised individuals (Millner & DeLeo, 2010; Stanley et al., 2015), those with more serious psychopathology (Encrenaz et al., 2012; Millner & DeLeo, 2010; Stanley et al., 2015), and those who had disclosed their suicidal thoughts to friends and/or family (Encrenaz et al., 2012; Millner & DeLeo, 2010) were more likely to have connected with mental health services. A recent study examining individuals who attempted suicide within the past 12 months found that 56.3% received outpatient or inpatient mental health treatment at some point during the year prior to their attempt (Han et al., 2014). Specifically, nearly 40% received some outpatient mental health treatment over the past year, with just over 21% receiving more than five sessions. Additionally, 28.8% of individuals who attempted suicide received inpatient psychiatric treatment. Furthermore, approximately half of the individuals who attempted suicide and who received mental health treatment perceived residual unmet treatment needs, indicating that they might have received insufficient care (Han et al., 2014).

Research finds that between 11% and 50% of suicide attempters who present to emergency rooms refuse outpatient referrals or drop out of outpatient therapy very early on in treatment (Kurz & Moller, 1984) Some studies have noted rates of up to 60% of suicide attempters failing to attend outpatient psychosocial treatment 1 week postdischarge from the emergency room (O'Brien, Holton, Hurren, Wyatt, & Hassanyeh, 1987). Of those who do attend treatment, after 3 months postdischarge from a psychiatric hospitalization for a suicide attempt, 38% of attempters will not be attending outpatient treatment (Monti, Cedereke, & Ojehagen, 2003), and, after a year, 73% of attempters will no longer be in treatment (Krulee & Hales, 1988). This is particularly concerning given that the risk of repeat suicide attempt is highest within the first 3 months following an initial attempt (Appleby et al., 1999; Kerkhof et al., 1998).

Research examining characteristics associated with a lack of treatment engagement among suicide attempters has been inconclusive. Some studies have identified marital status (Cremniter, Payanb, Meidingera, Batistaa, & Fermanian, 2001; Jauregui, Martinez, Rubio, & Santo-Domingo, 1999), history of suicide attempts (Goethe, Dornelas, & Gruman, 1999), and previous psychiatric history (Cremniter et al., 2001; Goethe et al., 1999; Krulee & Hayes, 1988) as predictors of poor treatment engagement. Specifically, being married and having a history of previous suicide attempts and hospitalizations have been found to predict greater rates of treatment attendance. Yet, other studies have not been able to identify any sociodemographic or clinical characteristics that distinguish between those suicidal individuals who do and do not attend outpatient treatment (Cedereke, Monti, & Ojehagen, 2002).

Research indicates that among suicidal individuals, in addition to stigma regarding mental illness, the main barriers to service include limited awareness of mental disorders, limited understanding of the mental health system, lack of information, language barriers, and lack of insurance (Fiscella, Franks, Doescher, & Saver, 2002; Sadavoy, Meier, Ong, & Yuk, 2004; Snowden, Masland, & Guerrero, 2003; Strug & Mason, 2001; Vega & Rumbaut, 1999; Reynders, Kerkhof, Molenberghs, Van Audenhove, 2014, 2015; Wells, Golding, Hough, Burnam, & Karno, 1988). One study found that high suicide literacy and low suicide stigma were significantly associated with more positive help-seeking attitudes (Calear, Batterham, & Christensen, 2014). Furthermore, when help is sought by suicide attempters, research demonstrates that it is generally done so at the recommendation of friends and family (Barnes, Ikeda, & Kresnow, 2001; Owens, Lambert, Donovan, & Lloyd, 2005). This may factor into the protective role that having a strong support network plays against suicidal behavior.

HELP-SEEKING BEHAVIOR

Research indicates that females are more willing to seek help than males (Corney, 1990; Gijsbers van Wijk, van Vliet, Kolk, & Everaerd, 1991; Hibbard & Pope, 1993).

Individual Exercise 5.3

1. List the main reasons for which you believe women seek help.
2. List the main reasons for which you believe men seek help.
3. Was this exercise more difficult or less difficult than you anticipated? Explain your rationale.

Research demonstrates that females and males seek help for problems that are seen as gender related; for example, women are more likely to seek help for depression (Jorm et al., 2000), whereas men are more likely to seek help for alcohol problems (Bennett, Jones, & Smith, 2014). Women more often seek consultation for psychosocial distress and emotional difficulties (Galdas, Cheater, & Marshall, 2005; Möller-Leimkühler, 2002). Men more often seek treatment when physical symptoms are present (Corney, 1990; Galdas et al., 2005; Möller-Leimkühler, 2002; NHS Executive, 1998), and have more difficulty expressing emotions (Good & Sherrod, 2001; Taylor, Ryan, & Bagby, 1985). In a study by Shand and colleagues (2015), men with recent suicide attempts reported the most commonly endorsed barriers to accessing help were not wanting to burden others and self-isolation. Men surveyed reported that "the perceived consequences for my suicide on my family" as the factor that stopped a suicide attempt (Shand et al., 2015). Also, men reportedly wanted others to notice changes in their behavior and to approach them without judgment (Shand et al., 2015).

It is important to note that the differences seen in help-seeking behavior are not merely the result of men needing help less often, but rather are due to differences in how help is sought and in the perception of need for treatment. For example, it has been suggested that the higher rate of depression in women (nearly two times the rate of men) actually reflects underreporting of depressive symptoms by males rather than a lower rate of depression among males (Sharaf, Thompson, & Walks, 2009; Cochran, 2001). Furthermore, research indicates that men do not consider mental health treatment as a solution for problems and tend to rationalize any pain experienced (Sanden Larsson, & Eriksson, 2000; Sharpe & Arnold, 1998).

Small Group Exercise 5.2

In small groups of two to three, please discuss, as you are comfortable, your responses to the Individual Exercise 5.3. Remember, answers are personal and there are no correct or incorrect answers.

1. What were the response similarities in your group?
2. What were the response differences in your group?
3. Did you find any surprises in the group discussion? If so, what were they and how were you surprised?
4. What lessons did you learn from this exercise?

INTERVENTIONS WITH ADULT SUICIDAL CLIENTS

In working with individuals with suicidal ideation, intention, plans, or after a suicide attempt has been made, a number of interventions have been developed. The three most common approaches include *crisis management, psychosocial evidence-based practice (EBP) interventions*, and *psychopharmacology*. These approaches are reviewed in Part II of this book.

As with children, any adult who is at risk of suicide, has attempted suicide, or is in need of crisis management should be brought to a hospital ED for complete psychiatric assessment. According to the American Psychiatric Association (APA) practice guidelines (2003) after an assessment, management of an at-risk individual requires establishing and maintaining a therapeutic alliance, attending to the patient's safety, determining a treatment setting, developing a plan of treatment, and coordinating care and collaborating with other clinicians (APA, 2003).

Research has found several EBPs to be effective in treating adults experiencing suicidality. The specific EBP treatment should meet the needs of the client, with the input of the client's family whenever possible or advisable. EBPs found to be effective in working with adults at risk of suicide are *cognitive behavioral therapy (CBT), dialectical behavioral therapy (DBT), interpersonal psychotherapy for adolescents (IPT)*, and *motivational interviewing (MI)*. For detailed information on these interventions see Part II of this book. These treatments are often combined with psychopharmacology.

Overall, research provides contradictory evidence on antidepressant use and risk of suicide, with some studies indicating that the use of selective serotonin reuptake inhibitors (SSRIs) is associated with an elevated risk of suicide, notably early in treatment, while other studies did not find this association (Cheung et al., 2015). For example, Cheung and colleagues (2015) investigated this association in a population-based cohort and did not find an increase in the risk of suicide after starting treatment with SSRIs. Conversely, Valuck, Orton, and Libby (2009) found that the highest risk period associated with antidepressants was during the initiation of treatment, closely followed by periods of dosing changes and discontinuation (Valuck et al., 2009). Although there is inconclusive evidence that antidepressants lower suicide rates, they are effective in treating anxiety and depression that may contribute to an individual's higher risk of suicide (APA, 2003).

SUMMARY

Generally, aging increases suicide risk in individuals. As clinicians, we cannot assume that an individual is not at risk without conducting a comprehensive assessment. Although the presence of a diagnosable mental disorder, specifically depression, raises an adult's risk potential, many adults without a diagnosis may be suicidal. Consequently, it is critical to be aware of current research when working with at-risk adults to effectively assess for past attempts, suicidal ideation, and plans. Sociodemographic and psychiatric risk and protective factors should be assessed to aid in determining suicide risk to fully assess and plan treatment.

KEY POINTS

1. The suicide risk generally increases with age.
2. Differences exist between adult suicide attempters and completers as well as between single and multiple adult attempters.
3. Talk openly and directly about suicide when working with clients at risk.
4. Suicide contracts do not work and do not replace rigorous assessment or effective evidence-based treatments.
5. There is no empirical support to the belief that lunar phases or birthdays increase suicidal risk.
6. A history of suicide attempt is the strongest known predictor of a future suicide risk.
7. Social connectedness is a major protective factor against suicide.
8. The majority of suicide attempters do not engage in outpatient psychosocial treatment.
9. Differences seen in help-seeking behavior are not explained by men needing help less often, but rather, by differences in how help is sought and in the perception of need for treatment.
10. Social support, including family and friends, is very influential regarding the decision to seek help.

ELECTRONIC RESOURCES

APA GUIDELINES

General: www.psychiatryonline.com/pracGuide/pracGuideHome.aspx

MYTHS AND MISCONCEPTIONS ABOUT SUICIDE

www.annals-general-psychiatry.com/content/7/1/1
www.wordworx.co.nz/myths.html
www.familyresource.com/health/mental-health/suicide-myth-versus-reality

SUPPORT

www.samaritans.org
www.ulifeline.org
www.afsp.org
www.nami.org

EDUCATION AND RESOURCES

www.mentalhealth.org
www.sprc.org
www.mhaofnyc.org
www.nmh.org
www.spanusa.org
www.afsp.org

KNOWLEDGE ACQUISITION TEST (KAT)

True or False

1. Generally, age increases suicide risk.
2. A woman's suicide risk continues to increase with age.
3. Suicide contracts are effective at reducing suicidal risk.
4. Individuals who complete suicide talked about suicide before their attempt.
5. Research has comprehensively found that antidepressants lower suicide rates.
6. The majority of suicide attempters seek treatment.
7. Males and females do not seek professional help for the same reasons.
8. Being divorced is a greater risk factor for suicide for males than for females.
9. Impulsivity is associated with decreased risk for suicide attempt.
10. Perceived health status is associated with increased risk of suicidal behavior.
11. Alcohol use does not increase the risk of suicidal behavior.

Short Answer

12. Discuss how age is a risk factor for suicidal behavior for all adults, but impacts gender and race differently?
13. What does research inform us about suicide contracts? As a mental health clinician, why can such contracts be a concern?
14. How does using the word "suicide" generally impact clients?
15. Explain two possible reasons for the differences in help-seeking behavior among males and females as they relate to suicidal behavior.
16. List the main barriers to service utilization among suicidal individuals.
17. Describe the gender difference in the protective role of marital status against suicidal behavior.
18. Describe the differences between single and multiple suicide attempters.
19. Describe the temporal patterns of suicidal behavior for men and women.

Multiple Choice

20. What group is at the highest risk of suicide?
    A. White adult males
    B. White adult females
    C. Black adult males
    D. Black adult females
    E. All of the above are at equal risk
    F. None of the above
21. What item in the following list of myths or misconceptions related to suicidality and adults is untrue?
    A. Suicide contracts do not work.
    B. Adults who complete suicide talked about suicide before attempting.
    C. Most suicides occur in winter.
    D. An approaching birthday does not increase the risk of suicide.
    E. All of the above.
    F. None of the above.
22. Which of the following is NOT a risk factor for suicide among adults?
    A. Prior suicide attempt
    B. Gender
    C. Cigarette smoking

    D. Age

    E. Height

23. Which of the following is NOT a protective factor for males?

    A. Social support

    B. Marriage

    C. Restricted access to firearms

    D. Reasons for living

    E. All of the above

    F. None of the above

24. Which of the following is a barrier to accessing mental health treatment?

    A. Perceived stigma

    B. Lack of insurance

    C. Limited understanding of the mental health system

    D. Language barriers

    E. All of the above

    F. None of the above

25. Birthdays are associated with increased risk of suicide for:

    A. Females aged 35 years and older

    B. Individuals who are receiving mental health care

    C. Males between the ages of 18 and 25 years

    D. Individuals who are not receiving treatment

    E. All of the above

    F. None of the above

REFERENCES

Abel, E. L., & Kruger, M. L. (2005). Educational attainment and suicide rates in the United States. *Psychological Reports, 91*(1), 25–28.

Afifi, T. O., MacMillan, H. L., Boyle, M., Taillieu, T., Cheung, K., & Sareen, J. (2014). Child abuse and mental disorders in Canada. *CMAJ : Canadian Medical Association Journal, 186*(9), 324–332.

Agerbo, E. (2005). Midlife suicide risk, partner's psychiatric illness, spouse and child bereavement by suicide or other modes of death: A gender-specific study. *Journal of Epidemiology and Community Health, 59*(5), 407–412.

Agerbo, E., Gunnell, D., Bonde, J., Mortensen, P., & Nordentoft, M. (2007). Suicide and occupation: The impact of socio-economic, demographic and psychiatric differences. *Psychological Medicine, 37*(8), 1131–1140.

American Psychiatric Association. (2003). Assessing and treating suicidal behaviors: A quick reference guide. Retrieved from http://www.psychiatryonline.com/pracGuide/loadPracQuickRefPdf.aspx?file=Suibehavs_QRG

Angst, J. L., & Clayton, P. J. (1998). Personality, smoking and suicide: A prospective study. *Journal of Affective Disorders, 51*, 55–62.

Antikainen, R., Hintikka, J., Lehtonen, J., Koponen, H., & Arstila, A. (1995). A prospective three-year follow-up study of borderline personality disorder inpatients. *Acta Psychiatrica Scandinavica, 92*, 327–335.

Appleby, L., Shaw, A., Amos, T., McDonnell, R., Harris, C., McCann, K., . . . Parsons, R. (1999). Suicide within 12 months of contact with mental health services: National clinical survey. *British Medical Journal, 318*(7193), 1235–1239.

Bagge, C. L., Conner, K. R., Reed, L., Dawkins, M., & Murray, K. (2015). Alcohol use to facilitate a suicide attempt: An event-based examination. *Journal of Studies on Alcohol and Drugs, 76*(3), 474–481.

Bagge, C. L., Lee, H., Schumacher, J. A., Gratz, K. L., Krull, J. L., & Holloman, G. (2013). Alcohol as an acute risk factor for recent suicide attempts: A case-crossover analysis. *Journal of Studies on Alcohol and Drugs, 74*(4), 552–558.

Barnes, L. S., Ikeda, R. M., & Kresnow, M. J. (2001). Help-seeking behavior prior to nearly lethal suicide attempts. *Suicide and Life-Threatening Behavior, 32*(Suppl. 1), 68–75.

Barrero, S. A. P. (2008). Preventing suicide: A resource for the family. *Annals of General Psychiatry, 7*(1), e1–e8.

Bennett, C., Jones, R. B., & Smith, D. (2014). Prevention strategies for adolescent depression. *Advances in Psychiatric Treatment, 20*, 116–124. doi: 10.1192/apt.bp.112.010314

Betz, M. E., Miller, M., Barber, C., Miller, I., Sullivan, A. F., Camargo, C. A., Boudreaux, E. D., & ED-SAFE Investigators. (2013). Lethal means restriction for suicide prevention: Beliefs and behaviors of emergency department providers. *Depression and Anxiety, 30*(10), 1013–1020.

Betz, M. E., Sullivan, A. F., Manton, A. P., Espinola, J. A., Miller, I., Camargo, C. A., Boudreaux, E. D., & ED-SAFE Investigators. (2013). Knowledge, attitudes, and practices of emergency department providers in the care of suicidal patients. *Depression and Anxiety, 30*(10), 1005–1012.

Biermann, T., Estel, D., Sperling, W., Bleich, S., Kornhuber, J., & Reulbach, U. (2005). Influence of lunar phases on suicide: The end of a myth? A population-based study. *Chronobiology International, 22*(6), 1137–1143.

Bille-Brahe, U., Kerkhof, A., DeLeo, D., Schmidke, A., Crepet, P., Lonngvist, J., . . . Jensen, B. (1997). A repetition-prediction study on European parasuicide populations: A summary of the first report from Part II of the WHO/EURO Multicentre Study on Parasuicide in co-operation with the EC Concerted Action on Attempted Suicide. *Acta Psychiatrica Scandinavica, Supplementum, 95*, 81–86.

Blair-West, G. W., Cantor, C. H., Mellsop, G. W., & Eyeson, M. L. (1999). Lifetime suicide risk in major depression: Sex and age determinants. *Journal of Affective Disorders, 55*(3), 171–178.

Boenisch, S., Bramesfeld, A., Mergl, R., Havers, I., Althaus, D., . . . Hegerl, U. (2010). The role of alcohol use disorder and alcohol consumption in suicide attempts: A secondary analysis of 1921 suicide attempts. *European Psychiatry, 25*(7), 414–420.

Boisseau, C., Yen, S., Markowitz, J., Grilo, C., Sanislow, C., Shea, M., . . . McGlashan, T. (2013). Individuals with single versus multiple suicide attempts over 10 years of prospective follow-up. *Comprehensive Psychiatry, 54*(3), 238–242.

Borg, S. E., & Stahl, M. (1982). A prospective study of suicides and controls among psychiatric patients. *Acta Psychiatrica Scandinavica, 65*, 221–232.

Bozzay, M. L., Karver, M. S., & Verona, E. (2016). Linking insomnia and suicide ideation in college females: The role of socio-cognitive variables and depressive symptoms in suicide risk. *Journal of Affective Disorders, 199*, 106–113.

Bradvik, L., & Berglund, M. (1993). Risk factors for suicide in melancholia: A case-record evaluation of 89 suicides and their controls. *Acta Psychiatrics Scandinavica, 87*, 306–311.

Brady, J. (2006). The association between alcohol misuse and suicidal behaviour. *Alcohol and Alcoholism, 41*(5), 473–478.

Brent, D., Bridge, J., Johnson, B. A., & Connolly, J. (1996). Suicidal behavior runs in families: A controlled family study of adolescent suicide victims. *Archives of General Psychiatry, 53*(12), 1145–1152.

Brent, D., Oquendo, M., Birmaher, B., Greenhill, L., Kolko, D., Stanley, B., . . . Mann, J. J. (2003). Peripubertal suicide attempts in offspring of suicide attempters with siblings concordant for suicidal behavior. *American Journal of Psychiatry, 160*(8), 1486–1493.

Buckley, P. F. (2006). Prevalence and consequences of the dual diagnosis of substance abuse and severe mental illness. *Journal of Clinical Psychiatry, 67* (Suppl. 7), 5–9.

Calear, A. L., Batterham, P. J., & Christensen, H. (2014). Predictors of help-seeking for suicidal ideation in the community: Risks and opportunities for public suicide prevention campaigns. *Psychiatry Research, 219*(3), 525–530.

Carballo, J. J., Harkavy-Friedman, J., Burke, A. K., Sher, L., Baca-Garcia, E., Sullivan, G. M., . . . Oquendo, M. A. (2008). Family history of suicidal behavior and early traumatic experiences: Additive effect on suicidality and course of bipolar illness? *Journal of Affective Disorders, 109*(1), 57–63.

Cedereke, M., Monti, K., & Ojehagen, A. (2002). Telephone contact with patients in the year after a suicide attempt: Does it affect treatment attendance and outcome? A randomized controlled study. *European Psychiatry, 17*, 82–91.

Centers for Disease Control and Prevention. (n.d.). Injury prevention. Retrieved from https://www.cdc .gov/violenceprevention/nisvs/summaryreports.html

Centers for Disease Control and Prevention. (2013). Web-based Injury Statistics Query and Reporting System (WISQARS). National Center for Injury Prevention and Control, CDC (producer). Retrieved from http://www.cdc.gov/injury/ wisqars/index.html

Cheung, K., Aarts, N., Noordam, R., van Blijderveen, J. C., Sturkenboom, M. C., Ruiter, R., . . . Stricker, B. H. (2015). Antidepressant use and the risk of suicide: A population-based cohort study. *Journal of Affective Disorders, 174*, 479–484.

Chignon, J. M., Cortes, M. J., Martin, P., & Chabannes, J. P. (1998). Attempted suicide and alcohol dependence: results of an epidemiologic survey. *L'Encéphale, 24*(4), 347–354.

Choi, K., Wang, S., Yeon, B., Suh, S., Oh, Y., Lee, H., . . . Lee, K. (2013). Risk and protective factors predicting multiple suicide attempts. *Psychiatry Research, 210*(3), 957–961.

Chuang, H. L., & Huang, W. C. (2004). A multinomial logit analysis of methods used by persons who. completed suicide. *Suicide and Life-Threatening Behavior, 34*, 298–310.

Chung, C. H., Pai, L., Kao, S., Lee, MS., Yang, T., & Chien, WC. (2013). The interaction effect between low income and severe illness on the risk of death by suicide after self-harm. *The Journal of Crisis Intervention and Suicide Prevention, 34*(6), 398–405.

Cochran, S. (2001). *Assessing and treating depression in men* (Vols. 1 & 2). San Francisco, CA: Jossey-Bass.

Coope, C., Donovan, J., Wilson, C., Barnes, M., Metcalfe, C., Hollingworth, W., . . . Gunnell, D. (2015). Characteristics of people dying by suicide after job loss, financial difficulties and other economic stressors during a period of recession (2010–2011): A review of coroners' records. *Journal of Affective Disorders, 183*, 98–105.

Coope, C., Gunnell, D., Hollingworth, W., Hawton, K., Kapur, N., Fearn, V., . . . Metcalfe, C. (2014). Suicide and the 2008 economic recession: Who is most at risk? Trends in suicide rates in England and Wales 2001–2011. *Social Science & Medicine, 117*, 76–85.

Corney, R. (1990). Sex differences in general practice attendance and help seeking for minor illness. *Journal of Psychosomatic Research, 34*(5), 525–534.

Cremniter, D., Payanb, C., Meidingera, A., Batistaa, G., & Fermanian, J. (2001). Predictors of short-term deterioration and compliance in psychiatric emergency room patients: A prospective study of 457 patients referred to the emergency room of a general hospital. *Psychiatry Research, 104*(1), 49–59.

Dahlberg, L. L., Ikeda, R. M., & Kresnow, M. J. (2004). Guns in the home and risk of a violent death in the home: Findings from a national study. *American Journal of Epidemiology, 160*(10), 929–936.

Dale, R., Power, K., Kane, S., Stewart, A. M., & Murray, L. (2010). The role of parental bonding and early maladaptive schemas in the risk of suicidal behavior repetition. *Archives of Suicide Research, 14*(4), 311–328.

Daray, F. M., Rojas, S. M., Bridges, A. J., Badour, C. L., Grendas, L., Rodante, D., . . . Rebok, F. (2016). The independent effects of child sexual abuse and impulsivity on lifetime suicide attempts among female patients. *Child Abuse & Neglect, 58*, 91–98.

Deisenhammer, E. A., Ing, C., Strauss, R., Kemmler, G., Hinterhuber, H., & Weiss, E. M. (2009). The duration of the suicidal process: How much time is left for intervention between consideration and accomplishment of a suicide attempt? *The Journal of Clinical Psychiatry, 70*(1), 19–24.

DeJong, T. M., Overholser, J. C., & Stockmeier, C. A. (2010). Apples to oranges? A direct comparison between suicide attempters and suicide completers. *Journal of Affective Disorders, 124*(1–2), 90–97.

Denney, J. T. (2014). Families, resources, and suicide: Combined effects on mortality. *Journal of Marriage and Family, 76*(1), 218–231.

Denning, D., Conwell, Y., King, D., & Cox, C. (2000). Method choice, intent, and gender in completed suicide. *Suicide and Life-Threatening Behavior, 30*(3), 282–288.

Dhingra, K., Boduszek, D., & O'Connor, R. C. (2016). Motivational-volitional model of suicidal behavior. *Psychiatry Research, 239*, 169–178.

Donald, M., Dower, J., Correa-Velez, I., & Jones, M. (2006). Risk and protective factors for medically serious suicide attempts: A comparison of hospital-based with population-based samples of young adults. *The Australian and New Zealand Journal of Psychiatry, 40*(1), 87–96.

Doshi, A., Boudreaux, E. D., Wang, N., Pelletier, A. J., & Camargo, C. A. J. (2005). National study of US emergency department visits for attempted suicide and self-inflicted injury, 1997–2001. *Annals of Emergency Medicine, 46*(4), 369–375.

Drum, D. J., Brownson, C., Burton Denmark, A., & Smith, S. E. (2009). New data on the nature of suicidal crises in college students: Shifting the paradigm. *Professional Psychology: Research and Practice, 40*(3), 213–222. doi:10.1037/a0014465

Duberstein, P. R., Conwell, Y., Conner, K. R., Eberly, S., Evinger, J. S., & Caine, E. D. (2004). Poor social integration and suicide: Fact or artifact? A case-control study. *Psychological Medicine, 34*, 1331–1337.

Duggan, C. F., Sham, P., Lee, A. S., & Murray, R. M. (1991). Can future suicidal behaviour in depressed patients be predicted? *Journal of Affective Disorders, 22*, 111–118.

Elliot, M., Naphan, D. E., & Kohlenberg, B. L. (2015). Suicidal behavior during economic hard times. *International Journal of Social Psychiatry, 61*(5), 492–497.

Encrenaz, G., Kovess-Masfety, V., Gilbert, F., Galera, C., Lagarde, E., Mishara, B., & Messiah, A. (2012). Lifetime risk of suicidal behaviors and communication to a health professional about suicidal ideation: Results from a large survey of the French adult population. *The Journal of Crisis Intervention and Suicide Prevention, 33*(3), 127–136.

Fawcett, J., Scheftner, W. A., Fogg, L., Clark, D. C., Young, M. A., Hedeker, D., & Gibbons, R. (1990). Time-related predictors of suicide in major affective disorder. *American Journal of Psychiatry, 147*, 1189–1194.

Fiscella, K., Franks, P., Doescher, M., & Saver, B. (2002). Disparities in health care by race, ethnicity, and language among the insured: Findings from a national sample. *Medical Care, 40*, 52–59.

Fischer, E. P., Comstock, G. W., Monk, M. A., & Sencer, D. J. (1993). Characteristics of completed suicides: Implications of differences among methods. *Suicide and Life-Threatening Behavior, 23*(2), 91–100.

Flensborg-Madsen, T., Knop, J., Mortensen, E. L., Becker, U., Sher, L., & Grønbæk, M. (2009). Alcohol use disorders increase the risk of completed suicide—irrespective of other psychiatric disorders: A longitudinal cohort study. *Psychiatry Research, 167*(1–2), 123–130.

Forman, E. M., Berk, M. S., Henriques, G. R., Brown, G. K., & Beck, A. T. (2004). History of multiple suicide attempts as a behavioral marker of severe psychopathology. *American Journal of Psychiatry, 161*(3), 437–443.

Fuller-Thomson, E., Baird, S. L., Dhrodia, R., & Brennenstuhl, S. (2016). The association between adverse childhood experiences (ACEs) and suicide attempts in a population-based study. *Child: Care, Health, and Development, 42*(5):725–734.

Galdas, P., Cheater, F., & Marshall, P. (2005). Men and health help-seeking behaviour: Literature review. *Journal of Advanced Nursing, 49*(6), 616–623.

Galfalvy, H., Oquendo, M. A., Carballo, J. J., Sher, L., Grunebaum, M. F., Burke, A., & Mann, J. J. (2006). Clinical predictors of suicidal acts after major depression in bipolar disorder: A prospective study. *Bipolar Disorders, 8*(5 Pt 2), 586–595.

Garfinkel, B. D., Froese, A., & Hood, J. (1982). Suicide attempts in children and adolescents. *American Journal of Psychiatry, 139*, 1257–1261.

Garssen, J., Deerenberg, I., Mackenbach, J. P., Kerkhof, A., & Kunst, A. E. (2011). Familial risk of early suicide: Variations by age and sex of children and parents. *Suicide and Life-Threatening Behavior, 41*(6), 585–593.

Gibb, S. J., Beautrais, A. L., & Fergusson, D. M. (2005). Mortality and further suicidal behaviour after an index suicide attempt: A 10-year study. *Australian & New Zealand Journal of Psychiatry, 39*(1–2), 95–100.

Gijsbers van Wijk, C. M. T., van Vliet, K. P., Kolk, A. M., & Everaerd, W. T. (1991). Symptom sensitivity and sex differences in physical morbidity: A review of health surveys in the United States and The Netherlands. *Women & Health, 17,* 91–124.

Goethe, J., Dornelas, E., & Gruman, C. (1999). Predicting service utilization after psychiatric hospitalization. *Comprehensive Psychiatry, 40*(3), 192–197.

Goin, M. (2003). The "Suicide-Prevention Contract": A dangerous myth. *Psychiatric News, 38*(14), 3–38.

Goldney, R., Winefield, A., Saebel, J., Winefield, H., & Tiggeman, M. (1997). Anger, suicidal ideation, and attempted suicide: a prospective study. *Comprehenive Psychiatry, 38*(5), 264–268.

Goldstein, R. B., Black, D. W., Nasrallah, A., & Winokur, G. (1991). The prediction of suicide: Sensitivity, specificity, and predictive value of a multivariate model applied to suicide among 1,906 patients with affective disorders. *Archives of General Psychiatry, 48,* 418–422.

Good, G., & Sherrod, N. (2001). *Men's problems and effective treatments: Theory and empirical support* (Vols. 1 & 2.). San Francisco, CA: Jossey-Bass.

Goodwin, R. D., & Marusic, A. (2011). Perception of health, suicidal ideation, and suicide attempt among adults in the community. *Crisis, 32*(6), 346–351.

Gutierrez-Garcia, J. M., & Tusell, F. (1997). Suicides and the lunar cycle. *Psychological Reports, 80*(1), 243–250.

Han, B., Compton, W. M., Gfroerer, J., & McKeon, R. (2014). Mental health treatment patterns among adults with recent suicide attempts in the United States. *American Journal of Public Health, 104*(12), 2359–2368.

Hawton, K. (2000). Sex and suicide. Gender differences in suicidal behaviour. *British Journal of Psychiatry, 177,* 484–485.

Hawton, K., Haw, C., Houston, K., & Townsend, E. (2002). Family history of suicidal behavior: Prevalence and significance in deliberate self-harm patients. *Acta Psychiatrica Scandinavica, 106,* 387–393.

Helmkamp, J. C. (1996). Occupation and suicide among males in the US Armed Forces. *Annals of Epidemiology, 6*(1), 83–88.

Hibbard, J., & Pope, C. (1983). Gender roles, illness orientation and use of medical services. *Social Science & Medicine, 17*(3), 129–137.

Houle, J., Mishara, B. L., & Chagnon, F. (2008). An empirical test of a mediation model of the impact of the traditional male gender role on suicidal behavior in men. *Journal of Affective Disorders, 107*(1–3), 37–43.

Ilgen, M. A., Zivin, M. A., McMannon, R. J., & Valenstein, M. (2008). Mental illness, previous suicidality, and access to guns in the United States. *Psychiatric Services, 59*(2), 198–200.

Jamison, K. R., & Hawton, K. (2005). The burden of suicide and clinical suggestions for prevention. In K. Hawton (Ed.), *Prevention and treatment of suicidal behaviour: From science to practice* (pp. 183–196). Oxford, UK: Oxford University Press.

Jauregui, J., Martinez, M., Rubio, G., & Santo-Domingo, J. (1999). Patients who attended suicide and failed to attend mental health centres. *European Psychiatry, 14*(4), 205–209.

Jeglic, E. L., Sharp, I. R., Chapman, J. E., Brown, G. K., & Beck, A. T. (2005). History of family suicide behaviors and negative problem solving in multiple suicide attempters. *Archives of Suicide Research, 9*(2), 135–146.

Joe, S., Baser, R. E., Breeden, G., Neighbors, H. W., & Jackson, J. S. (2006). Prevalence of and risk factors for lifetime suicide attempts among Blacks in the United States. *Journal of the American Medical Academy, 296,* 2112–2123.

Jorm, A. F., Christensen, H., Medway, J., Korten, A. E., Jacomb, P. A., & Rodgers, B. (2000). Public belief systems about the helpfulness of interventions for depression: Associations with history of depression and professional help-seeking. *Social Psychiatry and Psychiatric Epidemiology, 35,* 211–219.

Kanchan, T., Menon, A., & Menezes, R. G. (2009). Methods of choice in completed suicides: Gender differences and review of literature. *Journal of Forensic Sciences, 54*(4), 938–942.

Kaplan, K. J., & Harrow, M. (1996). Positive and negative symptoms as risk factors for later suicidal activity in schizophrenics versus depressives. *Suicide and Life-Threatening Behavior, 26*(2), 105–120.

Kaplan, M., McFarland, B. H., Huguet, N., Conner, K., Caetano, R., Giesbrecht, N., & Nolte, K. B. (2013). Acute alcohol intoxication and suicide: A gender-stratified analysis of the National Violent Death Reporting System. *Injury Prevention, 19*(1), 38–43.

Keppel, K., Pearcy, J., & Wagener, D. (2002). Trends in racial and ethnic-specific rates for the health status indicators: United States, 1990–1998. *Healthy People 2000 Stat Notes, 23*, 1–16.

Kessler, R. C., McGonagle, K. A., Zhao, S., Nelson, C. B., Hughes, M., Eshleman, S., . . . Kendler, K. S. (1994). Lifetime and 12-month prevalence of DSM-III-R psychiatric disorders in the United States. Results from the National Comorbidity Survey. *Archives of General Psychiatry, 51*, 8–19.

Kim, J., Park, E., & Yoo, K. (2015). Effects of the gap between socioeconomic status and perceived social class on suicidal ideation: Unique perspectives using a longitudinal analysis. *Archives of Gerontology and Geriatrics, 61*(3), 384–391.

Kleiman, E. M., & Beaver, J. K. (2013). A meaningful life is worth living: Meaning in life as a suicide resiliency factor. *Psychiatry Research, 210*(3), 934–939.

Kleiman, E. M., Riskind, J. H., Schaefer, K. E., & Weingarden, H. (2012). The moderating role of social support on the relationship between impulsivity and suicide risk. *Crisis: The Journal of Crisis Intervention and Suicide Prevention, 33*(5), 273–279.

Klerman, G. L. (1987). Clinical epidemiology of suicide. *Journal of Clinical Psychiatry, 48*(Suppl.), 33–38.

Kposowa, A. J. (2000). Marital status and suicide in the National Longitudinal Mortality Study. *Journal of Epidemiology and Community Health, 54*(4), 254–261.

Kposowa, A. J. (2001). Unemployment and suicide: A cohort analysis of social factors predicting suicide in the U.S. National Longitudinal Mortality Study. *Psychological Medicine, 31*, 127–138.

Kposowa, A. J. (2003). Divorce and suicide risk. *Journal of Epidemiology and Public Health, 57*, 993–995.

Krulee, D., & Hayes, R. (1988). Compliance with psychiatric referrals from a General Hospital Psychiatry Outpatient Clinic. *General Hospital Psychiatry, 10*, 339–345.

Kurz, A., & Moller, H. (1984). Help-seeking behavior and compliance of suicidal patients. *Psychiatrische Praxis, 11*, 6–13.

Lee, J. B., & Bartlett, M. L. (2005). Suicide prevention: Critical elements for managing suicidal clients and counselor liability without the use of a no-suicide contract. *Death Studies, 29*(9), 847–865.

Lefebvre, F., Lesage, A., Cyr, M., & Toupin, J. (1998). Factors related to utilization of services for mental health reasons in Montreal, Canada. *Social Psychiatry & Psychiatric Epidemiology, 33*, 291–298.

Lester, D. (2000). *Why people kill themselves* (4th. ed.). Springfield, IL: Charles Thomas.

Linehan, M. M., Goodstein, J. L., Nielsen, S. L., & Chiles, J. A. (1983). Reasons for staying alive when you are thinking of killing yourself: The reasons for living inventory. *Journal of Consulting & Clinical Psychology, 51*, 276–286.

Linkowski, P., de Maertelaer, V., & Mendlewicz, J. (1985). Suicidal behaviour in major depressive illness. *Acta Psychiatrica Scandinavica, 72*(3), 233–238.

Liu, D., Fairweather-Schmidt, A. K., Roberts, R. M., Burns, R., & Anstey, K. J. (2014). Does resilience predict suicidality? A lifespan analysis. *Archives of Suicide Research, 18*(4), 453–464.

Lizardi, D., Currier, D., Galfalvy, H., Sher, L., Burke, A., Mann, J., & Oquendo, M. (2007). Perceived reasons for living at index hospitalization and future suicide attempt. *The Journal of Nervous and Mental Disease, 195*(5), 451–455. doi:10.1097/NMD.0b013e3180522661

Lopez-Castroman, J., Jaussent, I., Beziat, S., Guillaume, S., Baca-Garcia, E., Genty, C., . . . Courtet, P. (2014). Increased severity of suicidal behavior in impulsive aggressive patients exposed to familial adversities. *Psychological Medicine, 44*(14), 3059–3068.

Luo, F., Florence, C. S., Quispe-Agnoli, M., Ouyang, L., & Crosby, A. E. (2011). Impact of business cycles on US suicide rates, 1928–2007. *American Journal of Public Health, 101*(6), 1139–1146.

Magnusson, S., & Makinen, I. H. (2010). Sweden: Income and suicide. *Psychological Reports, 107*(1), 157–162.

Mahon, M. J., Tobin, J. P., Cusack, D. A., Kelleher, C., & Malone, K. M. (2005). Suicide among regular-duty military personnel: A retrospective case-control study of occupation-specific risk factors for workplace suicide. *American Journal of Psychiatry, 162*(9), 1688–1696.

Malone, K. M., Haas, G. L., Sweeny, J. A., & Mann, J. J. (1995). Major depression and the risk of attempted suicide. *Journal of Affective Disorders, 34*, 173–185.

Mann, J. J., Bortinger, J., Oquendo, M. A., Currier, D., Li, S., & Brent, D. A. (2005). Family history of suicidal behavior and mood disorders in probands with mood disorders. *American Journal of Psychiatry, 162*(9), 1672–1679.

Maris, R. W., & Nisbet, P. (2000). Age and the lifespan. In R. W. Maris, A. L. Berman, & M. M. Silverman (Eds.), *Comprehensive Textbook of Suicidology* (pp. 127–144). New York, NY: The Guilford Press.

May, A. M., & Klonsky, E., D. (2016). 'Impulsive' suicide attempts: What do we really mean? *Personality Disorders: Theory, Research and Treatment, 7*(3), 293–302.

McLaren, S. (2011). Age, gender, and reasons for living among Australian adults. *Suicide and Life-Threatening Behavior, 41*(6), 650–660.

McLaughlin, J., O'Carroll, R. E., & O'Connor, R. C. (2012). Intimate partner abuse and suicidality: A systematic review. *Clinical Psychology Review, 32*(8), 677–689.

Mehlum, L., Friis, S., Vaglum, P., & Karterud, S. (1994). The longitudinal pattern of suicidal behaviour in borderline personality disorder: A prospective follow-up study. *Acta Psychiatrica Scandinavica, 90*(2), 124–130.

Meltzer, H., Bebbington, P., Brugha, T., Jenkins, R., McManus, S., & Dennis, M. S. (2011). Personal debt and suicidal ideation. *Psychological Medicine, 41*(4), 771–778.

Mergl, R., Havers I., Althaus D., Rihmer Z., Schmidtke A., Lehfeld H., Niklewski G., & Hegerl U. (2010). Seasonality of suicide attempts: Association with gender. *European Archives of Psychiatry and Clinical Neuroscience, 260*, 393–400.

Miller, M., Lippmann, S. J., Azrael, D., & Hemenway, D. (2007). Household firearm ownership and rates of suicide across the 50 United States. *The Journal of Trauma, 62*(4), 1034–1035.

Miller, T. R., Furr-Holden, C. D., Lawrence, B. A., & Weiss, H. B. (2012). Suicide deaths and nonfatal hospital admissions for deliberate self-harm in the United States: Temporality by day of week and month of year. *Crisis: The Journal of Crisis Intervention and Suicide Prevention, 33*(3), 169–177.

Millner, A., & DeLeo, D. (2010). Who seeks treatment where? Suicidal behaviors and health care: Evidence from a community survey. *Journal of Nervous Mental Disorder, 198*(6), 412–419.

Min, J., Lee, C., & Chae, J. (2015). Resilience moderates the risk of depression and anxiety symptoms on suicidal ideation in patients with depression and/or anxiety disorders. *Comprehensive Psychiatry, 56*, 103–111.

Möller-Leimkühler, A. M. (2002). Barriers to help-seeking by men: A review of sociocultural and clinical literature with particular reference to depression. *Journal of Affective Disorders, 71*, 1–9.

Monnin, J., Thiemard, E., Vandel, P., Nicolier, M., Tio, G., Courtet, P., . . . Haffen, E. (2011). Sociodemographic and psychopathological risk factors in repeated suicide attempts: Gender differences in a prospective study. *Journal of Affective Disorders, 136*(1–2), 35–43.

Moscicki, E. K., O'Carroll, P., Rae, D. S., Locke, B. Z., Roy, A., & Regier, D. A. (1988). Suicide attempts in the Epidemiologic Catchment Area Study. *Yale Journal of Biology and Medicine, 61*, 259–268.

Mukamal, K. J., Kawachi, I., Miller, M., & Rimm, E. B. (2007). Drinking frequency and quantity and risk of suicide among men. *Social Psychiatry & Psychiatric Epidemiology, 42*(2), 153–160.

Nakagawa, A., Grunebaum, M. F., Oquendo, M. A., Burke, A. K., Kashima, H., & Mann, J. J. (2009). Clinical correlates of planned, more lethal suicide attempts in major depressive disorder. *Journal of Affective Disorders, 112*(1–3), 237–242.

National Health Service Executive. (1998). *National survey of NHS patients, general practice.* London, UK: TSO.

National Institute of Mental Health. (n.d.). Suicide. Retrieved from https://www.nimh.nih.gov/health/statistics/suicide/index.shtml#part_153199

Nock, M. K., Borges, G., Bromet, E. J., Alonso, J., Angermeyer, M., Beautrais, A., . . . William, D. (2008). Cross-national prevalence and risk factors for suicidal ideation, plans and attempts. *British Journal of Psychiatry, 192*(2), 98–105.

Nordstrom, P., Asberg, M., Aber-Wistedt, A., & Nordin, C. (1995). Attempted suicide predicts suicide risk in mood disorders. *Acta Psychiatrica Scandinavica, 92*, 345–350.

Norström, T., & Grönqvist, H. (2015). The Great Recession, unemployment and suicide. *Journal of Epidemiology and Community Health, 69*(2), 110–116.

O'Brien, G., Holton, A., Hurren, K., Wyatt, L., & Hassanyeh, F. (1987). Deliberate self-harm and predictors of outpatient attendance. *British Journal of Psychiatry, 150*, 246–247.

Olie, E., Guillaume, S., Jaussent, I., Courtet, P., & Jollant, F. (2010). Higher psychological pain during a major depressive episode may be a factor of vulnerability to suicidal ideation and act. *Journal of Affective Disorders, 120*(1–3), 226–230.

Oquendo, M. A., Bongiovi-Garcia, M. E., Galfalvy, H., Goldberg, P. H., Grunebaum, M. F., Burke, A. K., & Mann, J. J. (2007). Sex differences in clinical predictors of suicidal acts after major depression: A prospective study. *American Journal of Psychiatry, 164*(1), 134–141.

Osman, A., Gutierrez, P. M., Muehlenkamp, J. J., Dix-Richardson, F., Barrios, F. X., & Kopper, B. A. (2004). Suicide Resilience Inventory-25: Development and preliminary psychometric properties. *Psychological Reports., 94*, 1349–1360.

Owens, C., Lambert, H., Donovan, J., & lloyd, K. R. (2005). A qualitative study of help-seeking and primary care consultation prior to suicide. *The British Journal of General Practice: The Journal of the Royal College of General Practitioners, 55*(516), 503–509.

Park, S., Cho, S., & Moon, S. (2010). Factors associated with suicidal ideation: Role of emotional and instrumental support. *Journal of Psychosomatic Research, 69*(4), 389–397.

Pirkis, J., Burgess, P., & Dunt, D. (2000). Suicidal ideation and suicide attempts among Australian adults. *Crisis: The Journal of Crisis Intervention and Suicide Prevention, 21*(1), 16–25.

Pompili, M., Serafini, G., Innamorati, M., Dominici, G., Ferracuti, S., Kotzalidis, G. D., . . . Lester, D. (2010). Suicidal behavior and alcohol abuse. *International Journal of Environmental Research and Public Health, 7*(4), 1392–1431.

Pompili, M., Vichi, M., Qin, P., Innamorati, M., De Leo, D., & Girardi, P. (2013). Does the level of education influence completed suicide? A nationwide register study. *Journal of Affective Disorders, 147*(1–3), 437–440.

Rawlings, J., Shevlin, M., Corcoran, R., Morriss, R., & Taylor, P. J. (2015). Out of the blue: Untangling the association between impulsivity and planning in self-harm. *Journal of Affective Disorders, 184*, 29–35.

Reulbach, U., Biermann, T., Markovic, K., Kornhuber, J., & Bleich, S. (2007). The myth of the birthday blues: A population-based study about the association between birthday and suicide. *Comprehensive Psychiatry, 48*(6), 554–557.

Reynders, A., Kerkhof, A. J. F. M., Molenberghs, G., & Van Audenhove, C. (2014). Attitudes and stigma in relation to help-seeking intentions for psychological problems in low and high suicide rate regions. *Social Psychiatry & Psychiatric Epidemiology, 49*(2), 231–239.

Reynders, A., Kerkhof, A. J. F. M., Molenberghs, G., & Van Audenhove, C. (2015). Help-seeking, stigma and attitudes of people with and without a suicidal past. A comparison between a low and a high suicidal rate country. *Journal of Affective Disorders, 178*, 5–11.

Richardson-Vejlgaard, R., Sher, L., Oquendo, M. A., Lizardi, D., & Stanley, B. (2009). Moral objections to suicide and suicidal ideation among mood-disordered Whites, Blacks, and Hispanics. *Journal of Psychiatric Research, 43*(4), 360–365.

Robins, L. N., & Regier D. A. (Eds). (1991). *Psychiatric disorders in America: The epidemiologic catchment area study.* New York, NY: The Free Press.

Rodríguez Andrés, A., & Hempstead, K. (2011). Gun control and suicide: The impact of state firearm regulations in the United States, 1995–2004. *Health Policy, 101*(1): 95–103.

Roy, A. (1993). Genetic and biological risk factors for suicide in depressive disorders. *Psychiatric Quarterly, 64*, 345–358.

Roy, A., & Linnoila, M. (1986). Alcoholism and suicide. *Suicide and Life-Threatening Behavior, 16*(2), 244–273.

Rudd, M. D., Mandrusiak, M., & Joiner, T. E. (2006). The case against no-suicide contracts: The commitment to treatment statement as a practice alternative. *Journal of Clinical Psychology, 62*(2), 243–251.

Sabo, A. N., Gunderson, J. G., Najavits, L. M., Chauncey, D., & Kisiel, C. (1995). Changes in self-destructiveness of borderline patients in psychotherapy. A prospective follow-up. *Journal of Nervous and Mental Disease, 183*(6), 337–376.

Sadavoy, J., Meier, R., Ong, A., & Yuk, M. (2004). Barriers to access to mental health services for ethnic seniors: The Toronto Study. *Canadian Journal of Psychiatry, 49*(3), 192–199.

Sanden, I., Larsson, U. S., & Eriksson, C. (2000). An interview study of men discovering testicular cancer. *Cancer Nursing, 23*(4), 304–309.

Sareen, J., Afifi, T. O., McMillan, K. A., & Asmundson, G. J. (2001). Relationship between household income and mental disorders: Findings from a population-based longitudinal study. *Archives of General Psychiatry, 68*(4), 419–426.

Saurina, C., Bragulat, B., Saez, M., & Lopez-Casasnovas, G. (2013). A conditional model for estimating the increase in suicides associated with the 2008–2010 economic recession in England. *Journal of Epidemiology and Community Health, 67*(9), 779–787.

Schmidtke, A., Bille-Brahe, U., DeLeo, D., Kerkhof, A., Bjerke, T., Crepet, P., . . . Sampaio-Faria, J. G. (1996). Attempted suicide in Europe: rates, trends and sociodemographic characteristics of suicide attempters during the period 1989–1992. Results of the WHO/EURO Multicentre Study on Parasuicide. *Acta Psychiatrica Scandinavica, 93*(5), 327–338.

Schneider, B., Philipp, M., & Muller, M. J. (2001). Psychopathological predictors of suicide in patients with major depression during a 5-year follow-up. *European Psychiatry, 16*, 283–288.

Scocco, P., Marietta, P., Tonietto, M., & Buono, M. D. (2000). The role of psychopathology and suicidal intention in predicting suicide risk: A longitudinal study. *Psychopathology, 33,* 143–150.

Shah, A. (2007). The relationship between suicide rates and age: An analysis of multinational data from the World Health Organization. *International Psychogeriatrics, 19*(6), 1141–1152.

Shah, A. J., & De, T. (1998). Suicide and the elderly. *International Journal of Psychiatry in Clinical Practice, 2,* 3–17.

Shand, F. L., Proudfoot, J., Player, M. J., Fogarty, A., Whittle, E., Wilhelm, K., . . . Christensen, H. (2015). What might interrupt men's suicide? Results from an online survey of men. *British Medical Journal Open, 5,* e008172. doi:10.1136

Sharaf, A., Thompson, E. A., Walsh, E. (2009). Protective effects of self-esteem and family support on suicide risk behaviors among at-risk adolescents. *Journal of Child and Adolescent Psychiatric Nursing, 22*(3), 160–168.

Sharpe, S., & Arnold, S. (1998). Men, lifestyle and health: A study of health beliefs and practices. Swindon, UK: Economic and Social Research Council.

Shenassa, E. D., Rogers, M. L., Spalding, K. L., & Roberts, M. B. (2004). Safer storage of firearms at home and risk of suicide: A study of protective factors in a nationally representative sample. *Journal of Epidemiology and Community Health, 58*(10), 841–848. doi:10.1136/jech.2003.017343

Sher, L. (2006). Alcoholism and suicidal behavior: A clinical overview. *Acta Psychiatrica Scandinavica, 113,* 13–22.

Sidley, G. L., Calam, R., Wells, A., Hughes, T., & Whitaker, K. (1999). The prediction of parasuicide repetition in a high-risk group. *British Journal of Clinical Psychology, 38,* 375–386.

Silventoinen, K., Moustgaarid, H., Peltonen, R., & Martikainen, P. (2013). Changing associations between partnership history and risk of accidents, violence and suicides. *Journal of Epidemiology and Community Health, 67*(3), 265–270.

Snowden, L., Masland, M., & Guerrero, R. (2003). *Ethnic access to public mental health services in California.* Berkeley: University of California, California Policy Research Center: Program on Access to Care.

Spokas, M., Wenzel, A., Brown, G. K., & Beck, A. T. (2012). Characteristics of individuals who make impulsive suicide attempts. *Journal of Affective Disorders, 136*(3), 1121–1125.

Stanley, I. H., Hom, M. A., & Joiner, T. E. (2015). Mental health service use among adults with suicide ideation, plans, or attempts: Results from a National Survey. *Psychiatric Services, 66*(12), 1296–1302.

Stark, C., Belbin, A., Hopkins, P., Gibbs, D., Hay, A., & Gunnell, D. (2006). Male suicide and occupation in Scotland. *Health Statistics Quarterly, 29,* 26–29.

Statham, D. J., Heath, A. C., Madden, P. A., Bucholz, K. K., Bierut, L., Dinwiddie, S. H., . . . Martin, N. G. (1998). Suicidal behaviour: An epidemiological and genetic study. *Psychological Medicine, 28,* 839–855.

Strug, D., & Mason, S. (2001). Social service needs of Hispanic immigrants: An exploratory study of the Washington Heights community. *Journal of Ethnic & Cultural Diversity in Social Work, 10*(3), 69–88.

Substance Abuse and Mental Health Services Administration. (2014). Results from the 2013 National Survey on Drug Use and Health: Mental Health Findings, NSDUH Series H-49, HHS Publication No. (SMA) 14–4887. Rockville, MD: Author.

Suokas, J., & Lonnqvist, J. (1991). Outcome of attempted suicide and psychiatric consultation: Risk factors and suicide mortality during a five-year follow-up. *Acta Psychiatrica Scandinavica, 84*(6), 545–549.

Suominen, K., Isometsa, E., Haukka, J., & Lonnqvist, J. (2004). Substance use and male gender as risk factors for deaths and suicide: A 5-year follow-up study after deliberate self-harm. *Social Psychiatry & Psychiatric Epidemiology, 39*(9), 720–724.

Taylor, G. J., Ryan, D., & Bagby, R. M. (1985). Toward the development of a new self-report alexithymia scale. *Psychotherapy and Psychosomatics, 44,* 191–199.

Thobaben, M. (2000). Myths & facts . . . about suicide. *Nursing, 30*(10), 73.

Tidemalm, D., Elofsson, S., Stefansson, C., Waern, M., & Runeson, B. (2005). Predictors of suicide in a community-based cohort of individuals with severe mental disorder. *Social Psychiatry & Psychiatric Epidemiology, 40*(8), 595–600.

U.S. Department of Health and Human Services. (2013). National Center for Health Statistics. Health, United States, 2012: With special feature on emergency care. Hyattsville, MD. Retrieved from https://www.cdc.gov/nchs/data/hus/hus12.pdf

Valuck, R. J., Orton, H. D., & Libby, A. M. (2009). Antidepressant discontinuation and risk of suicide attempt: A retrospective, nested case-control study. *The Journal of Clinical Psychiatry, 70*(8), 1069–1077.

Vega, W., & Rumbaut, R. G. (1991). Ethnic minorities and mental health. *Annual Review of Sociology, 17*, 351–383.

Voracek, M., Tran, U. S., & Sonneck, G. (2007). Facts and myths about seasonal variation in suicide. *Psychological Reports, 100*(3, Pt. 1), 810–814.

Wasserman, D., & Cullberg, J. (1989). Early separation and suicidal behaviors in the parental homes of 40 consecutive suicide attempters. *Acta Psychiatrica Scandinavica, 79*, 296–302.

Wells, K. B., Golding, J. M., Hough, R. L., Burnam, M. A., & Karno, M. (1988). Factors affecting the probability of use of general and medical health and social/community services for Mexican Americans and non-Hispanic Whites. *Medical Care, 26*, 441–452.

Wilcox, H. C., Arria, A. M., Caldeira, K. M., Vincent, K. B., Pinchevsky, G. M., & O'Grady, K. E. (2010). Prevalence and predictors of persistent suicide ideation, plans, and attempts during college. *Journal of Affective Disorders, 127*(1–3), 287–294.

Williams, A., While, D., Windfuhr, K., Bickley, H., Hunt, I. M., Shaw, J., . . . Kapur, N. (2011). Birthday blues: Examining the association between birthday and suicide in a national sample. *Crisis, 32*(3):134–142.

Wisco, B. E., Marx, B. P., Wolf, E. J., & Miller, M. W. (2014). Posttraumatic stress disorder in the US veteran population: Results from the National Health and Resilience in Veterans Study. *The Journal of Clinical Psychiatry, 75*(12), 1338–1346.

Woo, J. M., Okusaga, O., & Postolache, T. T. (2012). Seasonality of suicidal behavior. *International Journal of Environmental Research and Public Health, 9*(2), 531–547.

Woodbury, M. A., Manton, K. G., & Blazer, D. (1988). Trends in US suicide mortality rates 1968 to 1982: Race and sex differences in age, period and cohort components. *International Journal of Epidemiology, 17*(2), 356–362.

Wyder, M., Ward, P., & De Leo, D. (2009). Separation as a suicide risk factor. *Journal of Affective Disorder, 116*(3), 208–213.

Yip, P. S., Hawton, K., Liu, K., Liu, K. S., Ng, P. W., Kam, P. M., . . . Wong, T. W. (2011). A study of deliberate self-harm and its repetition among patients presenting to an emergency department. *Crisis, 32*(4), 217–224.

Zhang, Y., Yip, P. S. F., Chang, S.-S., Wong, P. W. C., & Law, F. Y. W. (2015). Association between changes in risk factor status and suicidal ideation incidence and recovery. *The Journal of Crisis Intervention and Suicide Prevention, 36*(6), 390–398.

CHAPTER SIX

OLDER ADULT SUICIDE

Because older adults (65 years and older), often referred to as "seniors" or "the elderly," have the highest rate of suicide in the United States, it is important to understand the epidemiological trends, prevalence, and incidence rates of older adult suicidality. In order to improve the existing prevention and intervention efforts, identification of risk and protective factors unique to the aging population is essential. These factors are highlighted in this chapter. In addition, this chapter deconstructs myths and misconceptions related to suicide among older adults. A brief overview of empirically grounded strategies for effective assessment and treatment of this population is also provided.

GOALS AND OBJECTIVES

An understanding of:

- Older adult suicide risk
- Epidemiology of older adult suicidality
- Older adult rates of completed suicide and attempted suicide
- dominant myths and misconceptions of older adult suicidality
- Professional bias in working with older adults
- Psychiatric risk factors for older adult suicide
- Sociodemographic risk factors for older adult suicide
- Psychiatric protective factors for older adult suicide
- Sociodemographic protective factors for older adult suicide
- Relationship between physical health and suicide among the aging

---

In a pattern found across the globe, rates of suicide for men and women consistently increase with age, reaching their highest peaks in the 85-year and older age group (Szanto et al., 2013). In the United States, older adults account for 13% of the population, yet 18% of suicides (Arias, Anderson, Kung, Murphy, & Kochanek, 2003). Of all age groups, older adults are the most likely to die from a suicide attempt (Pearson & Conwell, 1995). Older adults have a higher rate of suicide most probably because life circumstances such as living alone and poor health status lead to more fatal outcomes (Szanto et al., 2002). Additionally, attempts among older adults are well planned and generally involve highly lethal methods leading to a high rate of success (Szanto et al., 2002). Suicide in later life remains a major public health problem in the United States, with more than 6,000 older adults taking their own lives each year (Conwell, 2014).

Despite the high success rate and high lethality associated with suicide among older adults, 40% to 70% of adults aged 65 years and older communicated a wish to die to a health professional in the year prior to suicide (Conwell & Duberstein, 2001; Juurlink, Herrmann, Szalai, Kopp, & Redelmeier, 2004; Krach, 1998; Luoma & Pearson, 2002; Waern, Beskow, Runeson, & Skoog, 1999) and approximately 75% communicated suicidal ideation to a family member or acquaintance in the year prior to death (Waern et al., 1999). One study found that reactions, mostly from family members, to older adult suicide warnings, centered around four main themes: "not taken seriously," "helplessness," "exhaustion," and "acceptance" (Kjølseth & Ekeberg, 2012). Another study found that only 8% of older adults denied suicidal ideation when asked (Waern et al., 1999).

It is alarming that even though the majority of older adults who are considering suicide express such ideation, the completion rate of suicide among older adults remains the highest of all age groups. What accounts for this discrepancy? Are older adult individuals not taken seriously when they express such ideation? Some have noted that thoughts of death are expected of older adults and, therefore, expressions of such thoughts are inaccurately characterized as "typical of an old person" rather than as suicidal ideation. It is essential to be aware of the biases, stereotypes, and misconceptions one may hold that may interfere with the accurate identification of an older adult at risk for suicidal behavior.

Individual Exercise 6.1

1. Do you believe that thoughts of death are common among older adults? Why or why not?
2. Is it a natural part of the aging process to contemplate one's own death? In what way?
3. How may your responses to questions 1 and 2 impact your ability to accurately identify the risk of suicide in older adult clients with whom you may work?

Small Group Exercise 6.1

In small groups of two to three, please discuss, as you are comfortable, your responses to Individual Exercise 6.1. Remember, answers are personal and there are no correct or incorrect answers.

1. What were the response similarities in your group?
2. What were the response differences in your group?
3. Did you find any surprises in the group discussion? If so, what were they and how were you surprised?

STATISTICS, EPIDEMIOLOGY, AND TRENDS IN OLDER ADULT SUICIDE

Approximately every 90 minutes, an older adult (anyone 65 years of age and older) completes suicide (Hart-Hester, 2003). In general, for every 12 suicide attempts made, one is completed; however, in those 75 years and older, for every four suicide attempts made, one is completed (LaBode & Sher, 2011). The highest at-risk group for suicide is older adults. Suicide rates in the United States are 10.9 per 100,000 people (Centers for Disease Control and Prevention [CDC], 2006, 2013]. Suicide rates for older adults have been declining in the past 15 years, from a peak in 1987 of 21.7 per 100,000 to 15.6 per 1,000,000 in 2002 (McKeown, Cuffe, & Schulz, 2006). Despite a slight closing in the gap across age groups, older adults have consistently recorded the highest suicide rate. As noted earlier, adults over the age of 65 years comprised 13% of the U.S. population in 1998, but accounted for 18% of all suicide deaths (Arias et al., 2003; Substance Abuse and Mental Health Services Administration [SAMHSA], 2015). Research examining suicide rates after 60 years of age found that for men, suicide rates continued to increase for each of the seven 5-year age-bands from 60 to 64 years to 90 to 94 years, and then declined slightly for the 95- to 99-year age-band, whereas for women, suicide rates continued to increase for each of the six 5-year age-bands from 60 to 64 years to 85 to 89 years, and then declined slightly for the 90- to 94-year and 95- to 99-year age-bands (Shah, Bhat, Zarate-Escudero, DeLeo, & Erlangsen, 2016).

Older males, more than older females, and older Whites, more than older Blacks, are at higher risk. White male suicide risk continues to rise with age; however, female and Black adult suicide risk peaks around midlife and gradually lessens in older age. In addition, persons over the age of 85 years have a higher suicide risk than those 65 to 85 years of age (CDC, 2013; Holkup, 2003; McKeown et al., 2006). A recent study estimated the lifetime prevalence of suicidal ideation and attempts among older Blacks in the United States was 6.1% and 2.1%, respectively, with male ideation and attempts higher than that of females (Joe, Ford, Taylor, & Chatters, 2014). Research has also identified that the incidence of suicide in nursing homes (14.16 per 100,000) was lower than that in the community (15.66 per 100,000; Mezuk, Lohman, Leslie, & Powell, 2015).

In contrast to the higher suicide completion rates in older adults, suicide attempts are lower in comparison to other demographic age groups. Rates of suicide attempts decline with age, and older adults have the lowest rates of attempted suicide (CDC, 2013; Doshi, Boudreaux, Wang, Pelletier, & Camargo, 2005) and nonfatal injuries (Hempstead, 2006).

In older adults, violent methods are the most prevalent form of suicide (CDC, 2013; Conwell, Rotenberg, & Caine, 1990; Ojima, Nakamura, & Detels, 2004). Although methods of suicide vary depending on the country and culture, in the United States, firearms are most common for both older males and females (Ojima et al., 2004), followed by suicide by hanging for males (Ojima et al., 2004).

RISK AND PROTECTIVE FACTORS AMONG OLDER ADULTS

Risk Factors for Suicide

Assessing for suicide risk among the older adult population is complicated by several factors:

1. Communications of possible suicidal intent or ideation are often unheard or misunderstood. It is assumed that older adults are preoccupied with death and dying so that statements of passive suicidal ideation, such as "I have nothing to look forward to," are often not interpreted as suicidal statements (Conwell et al., 1998).
2. Older adults have greater intent and are more likely to take precautions against discovery (Conwell et al., 1998).
3. It is difficult to detect depression in this age group because vegetative symptoms of depression may overlap with many physical illnesses prevalent among older adults and because older adults tend to make somatic complaints and minimize their psychological distress (Conwell et al., 1998).

Research with individuals over 70 years of age has identified a number of factors associated with attempted suicide, including being unmarried, living alone, low education level, history of psychiatric treatment, and previous suicide attempt (Wiktorsson, Runeson, Skoog, Ostling, & Waern, 2010). Also, suicide ideation in first onset cases was found to be triggered by illness and physical discomfort, conflicts with family members or friends, illness of family members, death of family members/friends, and loneliness (Lee, Tsai, Chen, & Huang, 2014). Although a history of suicide attempts is the strongest predictor of suicidality among adults, it is noteworthy that only 20% of older adults who commit suicide have a prior history of suicide attempts (Rubenowtiz, Waern, Wilhelmmson, & Allebeck, 2001). This indicates that 80% of older adults will not meet the criteria for suicide risk based on the strongest known risk factor for adults. Furthermore, it is estimated that, on average, 85% of older adult suicide completers have at least one diagnosed mental disorder, most frequently depression (Beautrais, 2002; Conwell, 1996; Harwood, Hawton, Hope, & Jacoby, 2001; Quan, Arboleda-Florez, Fick, Stuart, & Love, 2002; SAMHSA, 2015; Suominen, Isometsa, & Lonnqvist, 2004; Waern, Runeson, et al., 2002). At the same time, the oldest age group has the lowest percentage of antidepressant use, with only 17% of suicide victims aged 85 years and older taking antidepressants (Abrams et al., 2009). Despite lower rates of antidepressant use compared to other age ranges, older adults exhibited the largest increase in antidepressant usage and biggest declines in suicide rates between 1998 and 2007(Phillips & Nugent, 2013). Another study found that fewer persons aged 80 years and older who completed suicide had received antidepressant prescriptions during the past months of life than younger individuals who committed suicide (Erlangsen & Conwell, 2014). However, it is important to note that concerns exist around prescribing antidepressants to older adults, because there are changes in physiology associated with advancing age that produce clinically significant differences in drug metabolism. Additionally, older adults tend to take multiple prescription medications at any given time that may lead to adverse interactions with antidepressants (Spina & Scordo, 2002). Alcohol use disorders have also been demonstrated to be associated with increased risk of suicide among older adults (Morin et al., 2013). This indicates that approximately 15% of suicide completers in this age group have no diagnosable disorder. Therefore, it is imperative to consider the other factors that play a role in conferring suicide risk in this age group.

The presence of suicidal ideation is another strong predictor of suicide in older adults (Oquendo et al., 2007; Sirey et al., 2008). Suicidal ideation is frequently associated with depression (Sirey et al., 2008); however, such ideation is not always present when an older adult is depressed and may be present when an older adult is not depressed. Research suggests that perceived burdensomeness mediates the relationship between suicidal ideation and depression among older adults (Cukrowicz, Cheavens, Van Orden, Ragain, & Cook, 2011; Guidry & Cukrowicz, 2016; Jahn, Cukrowicz, Linton, & Prabhu, 2011), even after controlling for severity of depression, level of hopelessness, functional impairment, and gender (Cukrowicz et al., 2011; Fässberg et al., 2016). Perceived burdensomeness includes the perception that one is a burden on others, even if they do not report feeling burdened, and may also involve a sense of self-hate (Cukrowicz et al., 2011; Van Orden et al., 2010). The perception of being a burden on one's spouse has been found to increase suicide risk as compared to the perception of being a burden on other caregivers (Van Orden et al., 2013). The concept of perceived burdensomeness is particularly relevant for older adults who, as they age and lose functional impairment, become more dependent on others to complete activities of daily living and, often, to provide physical care and financial assistance.

Bereavement is a major risk factor for suicide among older adults (Carney, Rich, Burke, & Fowler, 1994; Conwell et al., 1990; Isometsa et al., 1995). Within that group, the subgroup with the highest rate of suicide is bereaved men. The suicide risk is highest within the first-year post loss but remains elevated for as long as 5 years. Furthermore, the risk is higher among those experiencing complicated or traumatic grief (Szanto et al., 2002).

Other risk factors for suicide among older adults include difficulty adjusting to physical, emotional, and social changes (Clark, 1995a). Financial and legal difficulties, as well as changes in employment status, also confer risk (Beautrais, 2002; Carney et al., 1994; Isometsa et al., 1995; Kim, 2016; Rubenowtiz et al., 2001). Research posits that low socioeconomic status (SES) is associated with an increased risk of suicidal ideation among older adults (Ju et al., 2016).

Social isolation has been demonstrated to be a risk factor for suicide among older adults. Social isolation in this case refers to more than just living alone but also includes having limited contact with extended family members and peers (Barraclough, 1971; Beautrais, 2002; Duberstein, Conwell, Conner, Eberly, & Caine, 2004; Draper, 2014; Miller, 1978; Rubenowtiz et al. 2001; Szanto et al., 2012; Turvey et al., 2002; Wiktorsson et al., 2010). Older adults who report a lack of social connectedness are more likely to employ more lethal methods and have a higher risk of repeat attempts than older adults who report a strong sense of belongingness (Van Orden et al., 2015). Degenerative and chronic diseases increase the risk of suicide in older adults (Minayo & Cavalcante, 2015). Suicide risk increases when such health issues result in physical dependence. Functional impairment in regard to ability to complete activities of daily living is associated with increased suicide risk (Conwell et al., 2000, 2010; Rubenowtiz et al., 2001; Fässberg et al. 2016). Additionally, recent research indicates an association between insomnia in older adults and increased risk of suicide, even after controlling for interpersonal difficulties, executive functioning, benzodiazepine use, or the presence of posttraumatic stress disorder (Kay et al., 2016). Others have found that other forms of sleep problems are also significantly associated with the wish to die in older adults (Lapierre et al., 2012). Further, daytime dysfunction due to sleep problems is also associated among older adults with the wish to die (Lapierre et al., 2012).

Several sociodemographic characteristics are associated with increased suicide risk among older adults. Male gender, Caucasian ethnicity, being a widow/widower (Conwell, 2001; Wiktorsson, Marlow, Runeson, Skoog, & Waern, 2011), and low education (Ngamini, Vasiliadis, & Preville, 2015; Wiktorsson et al., 2011) are the strongest known sociodemographic risk factors.

Others have taken a qualitative approach to understanding the cognitive perspective of older adults that may serve as a risk factor for suicidal ideation and/or behavior. Such research indicates that among older adults, often their daily experiences are in conflict with their expectations of what life should or would be like and with their idea of who they are. As this disconnection becomes stronger (due to, e.g., functional impairment limiting the ability to care for self and engage in activities), the desire to end one's life also increases. The suicidal desire is further strengthened by (a) a sense of deep loneliness, (b) the pain of not being important, (c) the inability to express oneself, (d) multidimensional tiredness, and (f) a sense of aversion toward feared dependence (Fiske & O'Riley, 2016; van Wijngaarden, Leget, & Goossensen, 2015). An overall sense of loss of control over one's life and lack of a sense of purpose are consistent themes reported by older adults who have engaged in suicidal behavior (Bonnewyn, 2014; Fiske & O'Riley, 2016). This suggests several areas that can be targeted in clinical treatment to reduce suicide risks including, but not limited to, modifying the patients' expectations, enhancing and restoring their self-image, modifying and enhancing their sense of independence and autonomy.

Older Adult Risk Factors for Suicide

> Difficulty adjusting to health status
> Recent emotional and/or social change
> Financial difficulties/Low SES
> Legal difficulties

(continued)

> ❯ Change in employment status
> ❯ Social isolation
> ❯ Functional impairment
> ❯ Insomnia
> ❯ Bereavement
> ❯ Complicated or traumatic grief
> ❯ Male gender
> ❯ Older age
> ❯ Caucasian ethnicity

Protective Factors Against Suicide

Several protective factors against suicidal behavior among older adults have been identified. Being more extroverted and open to new experiences (Kelly et al., 1998) are among the leading protective factors against suicide. Higher levels of self-care functioning are also associated with decreased suicide risk (Ross, Bernstein, Trent, Henderson, & Paganini-Hill, 1990).

Having children (Lee et al., 2014; Rubenowtiz et al., 2001; Waern, Runeson, et al., 2002) and positive social support networks are other strong protective factors against suicide (Lee et al., 2014; Turvey et al., 2002; Van Orden et al., 2015). Research has found that family connectedness moderates the association between living alone and suicide ideation in older adults (Purcell et al., 2012). Social connection has also been found to decrease suicide risk, specifically in males (Fässberg et al., 2012). Older adults who are engaged in social participation and activities such as hobbies, friendship networks, religious involvement, and/or social organizations are at decreased risk for suicidal behavior (Ra & Cho, 2013; Rubenowtiz et al., 2001; Waern, Runeson, et al., 2002). Overall, perceived meaning in life, life satisfaction, adaptive coping, and a lack of hopelessness have been identified as protective factors against elderly suicide(Heisel & Flett, 2016).

Lastly, the degree of religious commitment appears to protect against suicide in the elderly (Heisel, 2006) as does female gender and a non-Caucasian ethnicity (Conwell, 2001). See Chapters 2 and 3 for an in-depth review of the relationship between religion, culture, and suicide.

Elderly Protective Factors Against Suicide

> ❯ Being extroverted and open to new experiences
> ❯ Self–health care
> ❯ Having children
> ❯ Positive social support networks
> ❯ Family connection
> ❯ Engagement in activities (hobbies, organizations)
> ❯ Religious commitment

(continued)

> > Gender
> > Perceived meaning in life
> > Life satisfaction
> > Adaptive coping
> > Lack of hopelessness

Individual Exercise 6.2

You are a mental health clinician in a family practice clinic. Your next client has been referred by one of the medical doctors in the clinic. Henry is a 73-year-old man who presented to the MD with complaints of body aches, exhaustion, and "just not feeling like he used to." After a brief screening, the MD concluded that a mental health evaluation to assess for depression may be appropriate. During your meeting, you learn that Henry has recently been widowed. His wife of 52 years was his best friend. She died after a complicated medical illness. Consider the following questions:

1. Is this man at risk of engaging in suicidal behavior? On what do you base your answer?
2. What risk factors will you assess for during your interview with the client?
3. What protective factors will you assess for during your interview with the client?
4. What factors need to be considered in order to establish an effective treatment plan?

ROLE-PLAY 6.1

Using the scenario from Individual Exercise 6.2, break into pairs and assume the role of the mental health clinician and the client. Engage in a role-play in which you would assess for risk and protective factors for suicide.

MYTHS AND MISCONCEPTIONS ABOUT OLDER ADULT SUICIDE

As with other age groups, there are a number of myths and misconceptions associated with older adults and suicidality. Unfortunately, misconceptions held by mental health professionals may exert unfortunate clinical implications in assessing and treating individuals within this demographic population. Five myths and misconceptions related to older adults and suicide are presented in the following:

1. *Older adults rarely complete suicide.* Although many individuals may believe that older adults are not as likely to complete suicide as younger demographic groups, the reality is that older adults are statistically at the highest risk of completing suicide (McKeown et al., 2006). Individuals over 65 years of age have the highest suicide rate.

2. *Deliberate self-harm is as common in older adults as in younger adults.* Research has found that older adults are less likely to attempt suicide than other age groups (Doshi, Boudreaux, Wang, Pelletier, & Camargo, 2005). In addition, rates of nonfatal injury decline with age (Hempstead, 2006). Although attempts and self-harm rates are lower, suicidal intent is often high (Hawton, 2005). Consequently, mental health professionals need to be extra vigilant regarding assessing for and treating suicidality in older adults who present following a self-harming episode.

3. *Suicide and depression are harder to recognize in older patients resulting in less treatment.* In a study that investigated detection of suicide and depression in adults versus elderly adults, physicians overwhelmingly were able to detect both the depression and suicidal ideation (Uncapher & Arean, 2000). However, findings indicated that primary care physicians were willing to treat geriatric suicidal ideation but not to the extent that they were willing to treat suicide ideation in younger adults (Uncapher & Arean, 2000). It has been suggested that health care professionals may be more likely to accept suicidal thoughts, ideations, and ideas in older adults than in other age groups, and therefore be less likely to promote treatment of underlying problems (Barnow & Linden, 2000). This is especially concerning given that research indicates that older adults are most likely to have seen a medical physician versus a mental health professional in the year prior to their completed suicide (Cheung, Hatters Friedman, Sundram, 2016).

4. *Health care and mental health professionals cannot help older adults who are suicidal.* A common belief is that older adults do not access health care and mental health professionals. However, it is estimated that between 40% and 70% of elderly people who complete suicide have seen a health professional in the month before their suicide (Conwell & Duberstein, 2001; Juurlink et al., 2004; Krach, 1998; Luoma & Pearson, 2002; Waern et al., 1999).

5. *Older adults are as likely to receive health and mental health care as everyone else.* There appears to be a recognized bias among health care and mental health professionals in treating older individuals. Older patients are less likely than younger patients to be referred for psychiatric consultation, and past psychiatric history and suicidal ideation are assessed less often in the elderly (Grant, 1996; Harwood, Hawton, Hope, & Jacoby, 2000; Hillerbrand & Shaw, 1990). In addition, mental health clinicians reportedly hold negative views toward working with older patients, feeling that it may be a waste of time, energy, and money (Lagana & Shanks, 2002).

6. *Thoughts of death are normative among older adults.* Expressions of suicidal thoughts by older adults are often overlooked or misclassified as "normal" expressions of death. However, there is a distinction between the awareness that one is closer to death and/or recognition that one's life is in the end stage versus experiencing an active desire to end one's own life (Monette, 2012). Some studies have demonstrated that recent death ideation does not typically occur in older adults in the absence of other risk factors for suicide; rather, individuals reporting recent death ideation also report either recent high levels of depression and anxiety or a history of serious suicidal ideation, both of which increase the risk of eventual suicide (Van Orden et al., 2013).

ILLNESS AND SUICIDE AMONG OLDER ADULTS

General medical illnesses and chronic pain increase suicide risk among older adults (Fässberg et al., 2016). Since the majority of suicide completers have visited their primary care physician in the year before suicide, primary care is an ideal setting to assess for suicidal behavior (Raue, Ghesquiere, & Bruce, 2014). However, research also indicates that up to 25% of elderly patients are considered "lost to follow-up" (Li, Proctor, & Morrow-Howell, 2005). This is especially concerning as suicides of patients with general medical illness typically occur early in the course of treatment (Szanto et al., 2013). It may be that primary care physicians underestimate the mental health needs of their patients and fail to inquire about potential suicidal ideation or, in the event that a patient discloses suicidal ideation, may not know how to respond (Szanto, 2016). Further, one study found that even when primary care physicians recognize and implicitly acknowledge suicide risk in their older patients, they tend to go no further than assessment, without developing any treatment plans (Vannoy, Tai-Seale, Duberstein, Eaton, & Cook, 2011). To compound the problem, other research has found that many older adults expressed distrust of health services once their functional decline began. They reported a fear of losing their autonomy should they become dependent on help, resulting in a refusal to accept health services. In addition, older adults reported that as they became more dependent on medical care, they were not given the kind of help and/or care they desired, resulting in distrust in their physicians and a failure in communication (Kjølseth, Ekeberg, & Steihaug, 2010). Clearly, opportunities for primary care physicians exist during the periods of illness detection, initial diagnosis, early treatment, and formal care transitions to improve not only suicide risk recognition but also the quality and nature of doctor–patient communication, support the older adult patient's autonomy and dignity, develop effective treatment plans, and connect older adults to treatment services (Kjølseth et al., 2010; Szanto, 2016).

Cognitive Impairment, Alzheimer's, and Dementia

Cognitive impairment has been associated with suicidal behavior in older adults (Gujral et al., 2016). A review found that research in this area is mixed, with some studies finding increased suicide risks in individuals with mild dementia or Huntington's disease, and overall, the risk of suicide in dementia appearing similar to aged-matched general population (Haw, Harwood, & Hawton, 2009). However, research does identify an increased suicide risk in individuals with dementia soon after their diagnosis (Haw et al., 2009).

Alzheimer's disease has been reported to be a potential predictor for suicidal behavior. Yet, again, results are inconsistent. Some have found that suicide occurs in Alzheimer's disease even many years following the initial diagnosis of dementia (Serafini et al., 2016). Others have found no relationship between receiving a diagnosis of Alzheimer's disease and an increased risk of suicide attempt (Mormont, Jamart, & Jacques, 2014). However, a recent systematic review on Alzheimer's disease and suicidal behavior found that Alzheimer's disease is associated with a moderate risk of suicide, and recommends that clinicians working with clients with Alzheimer's disease should conduct assessment of their suicidal risk (Serafini et al., 2016).

Physical Illness

In considering physical illness as a risk factor for suicide, research indicates that visual impairment, seizure disorders, cancer (specifically, lung cancer, gastrointestinal cancer, breast cancer, genital cancer, bladder cancer, and lymph node cancer), arthritis, chronic pulmonary disease, and moderate-to-severe pain have consistently been shown to increase suicide risk among older adults (Cole, Bowling, Patetta, & Blazer, 2014; Erlangsen, Stenager, & Conwell, 2015; Juurlink et al., 2004; Kim, 2016; Parpa, Tsilika, Gennimata, & Mystakidou, 2015; Quan et al., 2002; Waern, Runeson, et al., 2002). Research has found that older adults diagnosed with some form of cancer and reporting suicidal ideation are more likely to meet the criteria for posttraumatic stress disorder and panic disorder to experience more physical distress and to report feeling unsupported (Spencer, Ray, Pirl, & Prigerson, 2012). They also report a lack of religious affiliation, spirituality, and sense of self-efficacy (Spencer et al., 2012). Additionally, research has indicated an increased risk for suicide in older adults diagnosed with cerebrovascular diseases, cataract, heart diseases, gastrointestinal disease, liver disease, osteoporosis, prostate disorders, male genital disorders, and spinal fracture when compared to older adults who present without these illnesses (Erlangsen et al., 2015). Waern, Rubenowitz, et al. (2002) examined the association between suicidality in later life and physical illness and found that suicide risk among physically ill older adults was elevated only among men, yet not among women.

In addition to the actual physical health status, perceived physical health is a major risk factor for suicide among older adults (Duberstein et al., 2004; Turvey et al., 2002). Further, among older adults, depression and comorbid medical conditions are highly associated (Alexopoulos, Bruce, Hull, Sirey, & Kakuma, 1999; Conner, Duberstein, Conwell, Seidlitz, & Caine, 2001; Conwell, Duberstein, & Caine, 2002; Miles, 1977; Pearson & Brown, 2000; Turvey et al., 2002; Valiengo, Stella, & Forlenza, 2016). Conwell et al. (2000) found that once depression was controlled, the effect of physical illness burden and functional impairment on suicide risk among older adults was dramatically reduced. Research examining cardiovascular disease and comorbid depression found that individuals with these conditions were more likely to have past attempts, and males were more likely to complete suicide (Hawkins et al., 2016).

However, it is important to appreciate that most older adults who commit suicide are not terminally ill at the time of death (Barraclough, 1971; Clark, 1995b; Filiberti et al., 2001). In fact, studies have found that serious medical illness is present in rates as low as 2% to 4% of older adult suicides (Szanto et al., 2002).

INTERVENTIONS WITH OLDER ADULTS

Research and clinical practice have demonstrated effective methods in intervening successfully with older adults. Age should not be a criterion for a mental health clinician's willingness to effectively assess and treat an individual presenting with suicidality. Like other age groups, older adults manage a number of risk factors that can increase the risk of suicide. Each individual, especially in this most at-risk group, requires the same professionalism and dedication to mental health care.

Any older adult who is at risk of suicide, has attempted suicide, or is in need of crisis management should be brought to a hospital emergency department for complete psychiatric assessment. For all at-risk adults, effective assessment and management requires mental health clinicians to establish and maintain a therapeutic alliance, attend to the individual's safety, determine a treatment setting, develop a plan of treatment, and coordinate care and collaborate with other professionals (American Psychiatric Association, 2003). The most common approaches to intervention in working with older adults include *crisis management, psychosocial evidence-based practice (EBP) interventions, cognitive-behavioral therapy (CBT), dialectical-behavioral therapy (DBT), interpersonal psychotherapy (IPT),* and *psychopharmacology.* These approaches are reviewed in Part II of this book.

The percentage of older adults residing in assisted living or nursing homes has risen over the past 30 years (Mezuk, Rock, Lohman, & Choi, 2014). The World Health Organization (WHO) recommends the training of gatekeepers as part of a suicide prevention program (WHO, 2012). Gatekeeper programs offer nursing home or adult home staff members, who have regular contact with residents at high risk of suicide, a 2-day training focusing on the epidemiology of suicide in older adults, suicidal crisis and periods of stress, identification of suicide risk factors, and risk assessment (Chauliac et al., 2016). The Gatekeeper prevention program found improved skills of those who had been trained, an increased number of measures for managing suicidal residents, and an increase in the number of institution-level actions for preventing suicide within their institutions (Chauliac et al., 2016). Research has also identified that providing increased training on suicide risk and barriers to suicide is warranted in community-based caregivers, such as geriatric case managers (Slovak, Pope, & Brewer, 2016) or home care providers (Salvatore, 2015).

SUMMARY

Although suicide risk increases with age, it is not uncommon for professionals to provide a lower standard of care and service to older individuals. If prevention of suicide is a goal of mental health clinical work, then the age of the client should not influence the clinician's effectiveness. Like children, adolescents, or adults, older adults at risk require evidence-based interventions that have been proven effective to address their suicidality. It is critical to be aware of the factors that contribute to suicide in this group in order to design effective suicide prevention and intervention programs and to effectively assess for suicide risk in older adults. It is equally important to be aware of the factors that protect against suicide in this group in order to support and enhance these qualities in an effort to reduce suicide rates.

KEY POINTS

1. Older adults are at highest suicide risk of any age group.
2. Male gender, Caucasian ethnicity, and being a widower are the strongest known sociodemographic risk factors for suicide in later life.
3. Professionals tend to be less willing to treat older adults, even when effectively assessing for risk.
4. Older adults are less likely to attempt suicide than other age groups.
5. Generally, older adults do not have the same access to and do not receive the same level of mental health care.
6. Of all age groups, older adults are the most likely to die from a suicide attempt.
7. Having positive social support networks is a protective factor against suicide in later life.
8. Older adults who are engaged in activities such as hobbies and/or social organizations are at decreased risk for suicidal behavior.
9. Bereavement can be a major risk factor for suicide among older adults.
10. Having a sense of control over one's life is a protective factor against suicide in later life.

ELECTRONIC RESOURCES

www.suicide.org
www.afsp.org
www.samaritans.org
www.ulifeline.org
www.nami.org

KNOWLEDGE ACQUISITION TEST (KAT)

True or False

1. Generally, the risk of suicide for older adults decreases after age 65 years.
2. Older adults receive more access to mental health care than younger populations.
3. There appears to be a recognized bias in health care and mental health professionals in treating older individuals.
4. The majority of older adults experiencing suicidality do not seek out professional help.
5. The percentage of older adult suicides is lower than their population percentage.
6. Suicide attempt is a leading risk factor for suicide among the elderly.
7. Being male is a risk factor for suicidal behavior later in life.
8. Most elderly who commit suicide are seriously medically ill at the time of death.
9. More often than not, the elderly communicate suicidal ideations.
10. Older adults exhibited the smallest increase in antidepressant usage between 1998 and 2007.
11. Dementia is always a suicide risk factor in older adults.

Short Answer

12. What are the clinical implications of the differences between higher rates of completed suicide and lower rates of suicide attempts for older adults?
13. Describe the common bias of health and mental health professionals in working with older adults?
14. Why is assessing for suicide risk among the elderly difficult?
15. What is the main difference in risk factors for suicide between adults and the elderly?
16. What are the main protective factors against suicidality among the elderly?
17. Describe the relationship between physical illness, depression, and suicide among the elderly.
18. Describe the role that perceived burdensomeness plays in older adult suicide risk.
19. Describe the myth that exists regarding thoughts of death as "normal" among older adults.

Multiple Choice

20. Every _____ hours an older adult (65+ years of age) completes suicide.
    A. 24 hours
    B. 18 hours
    C. 12 hours
    D. 6 hours
    E. 1.5 hours
    F. None of the above
21. Common method(s) of suicide for older adults include:
    A. Firearms
    B. Hanging
    C. Overdose
    D. All of the above
    E. None of the above

22. When seeing older adults, health and mental health professionals are:
    A. More likely to offer treatment
    B. More willing to treat geriatric suicidal ideation
    C. More likely to accept suicidal thoughts, ideations, and ideas in older adults than in other age groups
    D. All of the above
    E. None of the above

23. Which of the following is a major risk factor for late-life suicide?
    A. Social isolation
    B. Functional impairment
    C. Recent social changes
    D. Bereavement
    E. All of the above
    F. None of the above

24. Which of the following is not a protective factor against suicide among the elderly?
    A. Having children
    B. Having an extroverted personality
    C. Being engaged in hobbies
    D. High levels of education
    E. All of the above
    F. None of the above

25. Which of the following trends for suicide rates in older adults is incorrect?
    A. For men, suicide rates continued to increase for each of the seven 5-year age-bands from 60 to 64 years to 90 to 94 years.
    B. For men, there is a slight decline in suicide rates after age 95 years.
    C. For men, suicide rates are at their highest after age 95 years.
    D. For women, suicide rates continued to increase for each of the six 5-year age-bands from 60 to 64 years to 85 to 89 years.
    E. For women, there is a slight decline in suicide rates after age 90 years.

REFERENCES

Abrams, R. C., Leon, A. C., Tardiff, K., Marzuk, P. M., Li, C., & Galea, S. (2009). Antidepressant use in elderly suicide victims in New York City: An analysis of 255 cases. *The Journal of Clinical Psychiatry, 70*(3), 312–317.

Alexopoulos, G. S., Bruce, M. L., Hull, J., Sirey, J. A., & Kakuma, T. (1999). Clinical determinants of suicidal ideation and behavior in geriatric depression. *Archives of General Psychiatry, 56*(11), 1048–1053.

American Psychiatric Association. (2003). Assessing and treating suicidal behaviors: A quick reference guide. Retrieved from http://www.psychiatryonline.com/pracGuide/loadPracQuickRefPdf.aspx ?file=Suibehavs_QRG

Arias, E., Anderson, R. N., Kung, H. C., Murphy, S. L., & Kochanek, K. D. (2003). Deaths: Final data for 2001. *National Vital Statistics Reports, 52*(3), 1–115.

Barnow, S., & Linden, M. (2000). Epidemiology and psychiatric morbidity of suicidal ideation among the elderly. *The Journal of Crisis Intervention and Suicide Prevention, 21*(4), 171–180.

Barraclough, B. M. (1971). Suicide in the elderly: Recent developments in psychogeriatrics. *British Journal of Psychiatry,* (Suppl. 6), 87–97.

Beautrais, A. (2002). A case control study of suicide and attempted suicide in older adults. *Suicide and Life-Threatening Behavior, 32,* 1–9.

Bonnewyn, A., Shah, A., Bruffaerts, R., Schoevaerts, K., Robert, P., Van Parys, H., & Demyttenaere, K. (2014). Reflections of older adults on the process preceding their suicide attempt: A qualitative approach. *Death Studies, 38*(6–10), 612–618.

Carney, S. S., Rich, C. L., Burke, P. A., & Fowler, R. C. (1994). Suicide over 60: The San Diego study. *Journal of Geriatric Psychiatry, 3,* 251–261.

Centers for Disease Control and Prevention. (2006). National Center for Injury Prevention and Control. Retrieved from http://www.cdc.gov/ncipc/wisqars

Centers for Disease Control and Prevention. (2013).Web-based Injury Statistics Query and Reporting System (WISQARS) [Online]. National Center for Injury Prevention and Control, CDC. Retrieved from https://www.cdc.gov/injury/wisqars/index.html

Chauliac, N., Brochard, N., Payet, C., Duclos, A., Terra, J. L., & EGEE (Etude Gatekeepers en EHPAD) study group. (2016). How does gatekeeper training improve suicide prevention for elderly people in nursing homes? A controlled study in 24 centres. *European Psychiatry: The Journal of the Association of European Psychiatrists, 37,* 56–62.

Cheung, G., Hatters Friedman, S., & Sundram, F. (2016). Late-life homicide-suicide: A national case series in New Zealand. *Psychogeriatrics: The Official Journal of the Japanese Psychogeriatric Society, 16*(1), 76–81.

Clark, S. (1995a). *After suicide: Help for the bereaved.* Melbourne, AU: Hill of Content Publishing.

Clark, S. (1995b). Grief reactions and recovery in a support group for people bereaved by suicide. *Crisis: The Journal of Crisis Intervention & Suicide Prevention, 16*(1), 27–33.

Cole, T. B., Bowling, J. M., Patetta, M. J., & Blazer, D. G. (2014). Risk factors for suicide among older adults with cancer. *Aging and Mental Health, 18*(7), 854–860.

Conner, K. R., Duberstein, P. R., Conwell, Y., Seidlitz, L., & Caine, E. D. (2001). Psychological vulnerability to completed suicide: A review of empirical studies. *Suicide and Life-Threatening Behavior, 31,* 367–385.

Conwell, Y. (1996). *Diagnosis and treatment of depression in late life.* Washington, DC: American Psychiatric Press.

Conwell, Y. (2001). Suicide in later life: A review and recommendations for prevention. *Suicide and Life-Threatening Behavior, 31*(Suppl.), 32–47.

Conwell, Y. (2014). Suicide later in life: challenges and priorities for prevention. *American Journal of Preventive Medicine, 47*(3 Suppl. 2), S244–S250.

Conwell, Y., & Duberstein, P. R. (2001). Suicide in elders. In H. Hendin & J. J. Mann (Eds.), *The clinical science of suicide prevention* (pp. 132–150). New York, NY: New York Academy of Sciences.

Conwell, Y., Duberstein, P. R., & Caine, E. D. (2002). Risk factors for suicide in later life. *Biological Psychiatry, 52,* 193–204.

Conwell, Y., Duberstein, P. R., Cox, C., Hermann, J. M., Forbes, N., & Caine, E. D. (1998). Age differences in behaviors leading to completed suicide. *American Journal of Geriatric Psychiatry, 6*(2), 122–126.

Conwell, Y., Duberstein, P. R., Hirsch, J. K., Conner, K. R., Eberly, S., & Caine, E. D. (2010). Health status and suicide in the second half of life. *International Journal of Geriatric Psychiatry, 25*(4), 371–379.

Conwell, Y., Lyness, J. M., Duberstein, P., Cox, C., Seidlitz, L., DiGiorgio, A., & Caine, E. D. (2000). Completed suicide among older patients in primary care practices: A controlled study. *Journal of the American Geriatrics Society, 48,* 23–29.

Conwell, Y., Rotenberg, M., & Caine, E. D. (1990). Completed suicide at age 50 and over. *Journal of the American Geriatric Society, 38*(6), 640–644.

Cukrowicz, K. C., Cheavens, J. S., Van Orden, K. A., Ragain, R. M., & Cook, R. L. (2011). Perceived burdensomeness and suicide ideation in older adults. *Psychology and Aging, 26*(2), 331–338.

Doshi, A., Boudreaux, E. D., Wang, N., Pelletier, A. J., & Camargo, C. A. J. (2005). National study of US emergency department visits for attempted suicide and self-inflicted injury, 1997–2001. *Annals of Emergency Medicine, 46*(4), 369–375.

Draper, B. M. (2014). Suicidal behaviour and suicide prevention in later life. *Maturitas, 79*(2), 179–183.

Duberstein, P. R., Conwell, Y., Conner, K. R., Eberly, S., & Caine, E. D. (2004). Suicide at 50 years of age and older: Perceived physical illness, family discord and financial strain. *Psychological Medicine, 34*(1), 137–146.

Erlangsen, A., & Conwell, Y. (2014). Age-related response to redeemed antidepressants measured by completed suicide in older adults: A nationwide cohort study. *The American Journal of Geriatric Psychiatry: Official Journal of the American Association for Geriatric Psychiatry, 22*(1), 25–33.

Erlangsen, A., Stenager, E., & Conwell, Y. (2015). Physical diseases as predictors of suicide in older adults: A nationwide, register-based cohort study. *Social Psychiatry and Psychiatric Epidemiology, 50*(9), 1427–1439.

Fässberg, M. M., Cheung, G., Canetto, S., Erlangsen, A., Gallo, J., Lapierre, S., . . . Wærn, M. (2016). A systematic review of physical illness, functional disability, and suicidal behaviour among older adults. *Aging and Mental Health, 20*(2), 166–194.

Fässberg, M. M., van Orden, K. A., Duberstein, P., Erlangsen, A., Lapierre, S., Bodner, E., . . . Waern, M. (2012). A systematic review of social factors and suicidal behavior in older adulthood. *International Journal of Environmental Research and Public Health, 9*(3), 722–745.

Filiberti, A., Ripamonti, C., Totis, A., Ventafridda, V., De Conno, F., Contiero, P., & Tamburini, M. (2001). Characteristics of terminal cancer patients who committed suicide during a home palliative care program. *Journal of Pain & Symptom Management, 22*(1), 544–553.

Fiske, A., & O'Riley, A. A. (2016). Toward an understanding of late life suicidal behavior: the role of lifespan developmental theory. *Aging & Mental Health, 20*(2), 123–130.

Grant, L. D. (1996). Effects of ageism on individual and health care providers' responses to healthy aging. *Health & Social Work, 21*(1), 9–15.

Guidry, E. T., & Cukrowicz, K. C. (2016). Death ideation in older adults: Psychological symptoms of depression, thwarted belongingness, and perceived burdensomeness. *Aging and Mental Health, 20*(8), 823–830.

Gujral, S., Ogbagaber, S., Dombrovski, A. Y., Butters, M. A., Karp, J. F., & Szanto, K. (2016). Course of cognitive impairment following attempted suicide in older adults. *International Journal of Geriatric Psychiatry, 31*(6), 592–600.

Hart-Hester, S. (2003). Elderly suicides: A need for prevention. *Journal of the Mississippi State Medical Association, 44*(6), 167–172.

Harwood, D. M., Hawton, K., Hope, T., & Jacoby, R. (2000). Suicide in older people: Mode of death, demographic factors, and medical contact before death. *International Journal of Geriatric Psychiatry, 15*(8), 736–743.

Harwood, D. M., Hawton, K., Hope, T., & Jacoby, R. (2001). Psychiatric disorder and personality factors associated with suicide in older people. *International Journal of Geriatric Psychiatry, 16*(2), 155–165.

Haw, C., Harwood, D., & Hawton, K. (2009). Dementia and suicidal behavior: A review of the literature. *International Psychogeriatrics/IPA, 21*(3), 440–453.

Hawkins, M., Schaffer, A., Reis, C., Sinyor, M., Herrmann, N., & Lanctot, K. L. (2016). Suicide in males and females with cardiovascular disease and comorbid depression. *Affective Disorders, 197,* 88–93.

Hawton, K. (2005). Psychosocial treatments following attempted suicide: Evidence to inform clinical practice. In K. Hawton (Ed.), *Prevention and Treatment of Suicidal Behaviour* (pp. 197–220). Oxford, UK: Oxford University Press.

Heisel, M. J. (2006). Suicide and its prevention among older adults. *Canadian Journal of Psychiatry—Revue Canadienne de Psychiatrie, 51*(3), 143–154.

Heisel, M. J., & Flett, G. L. (2016). Investigating the psychometric properties of the Geriatric Suicide Ideation Scale (GSIS) among community-residing older adults. *Aging and Mental Health, 20*(2), 208–221.

Hempstead, K. (2006). The geography of self-injury: Spatial patterns in attempted and completed suicide. *Social Science & Medicine, 62*(12), 3186–3196.

Hillerbrand, E. T., & Shaw, D. (1990). Age bias in a general hospital: Is there ageism in psychiatric consultation? *Clinical Gerontologist, 2*(2), 3–13.

Holkup, P. A. (2003). Evidence-based protocol elderly suicide: Secondary prevention. *Journal of Gerontological Nursing, 29*(6), 6–17.

Isometsa, E., Henrikksson, M., Marttunen, M., Heikkinen, M., Aro, H., Kuoppasalmi, K., & Lönnqvist, J. (1995). Mental disorders in young and middle aged men who commit suicide. *British Medical Journal, 310*, 1366–1367.

Jahn, D. R., Cukrowicz, K. C., Linton, K., & Prabhu, F. (2011). The mediating effect of perceived burdensomeness on the relation between depressive symptoms and suicide ideation in a community sample of older adults. *Aging and Mental Health, 15*(2), 214–220.

Joe, S., Ford, B. C., Taylor, R. J., & Chatters, L. M. (2014). Prevalence of suicide ideation and attempts among Black Americans in later life. *Transcultural Psychiatry, 51*(2), 190–208.

Ju, Y. J., Park, E. C., Han, K. T., Choi, J. W., Kim, J. L., Cho, K. H., & Park, S. (2016). Low socioeconomic status and suicidal ideation among elderly individuals. *International Psychogeriatrics/IPA, 26*, 1–12.

Juurlink, D. N., Herrmann, N., Szalai, J. P., Kopp, A., & Redelmeier, D. A. (2004). Medical illness and the risk of suicide in the elderly. *Archives of Internal Medicine, 164*(11), 1179–1184.

Kay, D. B., Dombrovski, A. Y., Buysse, D. J., Reynolds, C. F., Begley, A., & Szanto, K. (2016). Insomnia is associated with suicide attempt in middle-aged and older adults with depression. *International Psychogeriatrics/IPA, 28*(4), 613–619.

Kelly, B., Raphael, B., Judd, F., Perdices, M., Kernutt, G., Burnett, P., Burrows, G. (1998). Suicidal ideation, suicide attempts, and HIV infection. *Psychosomatics, 39*(5), 405–415.

Kim, S. H. (2016). Suicidal ideation and suicide attempts in older adults: Influences of chronic illness, functional limitations, and pain. *Geriatric Nursing, 37*(1), 9–12.

Kjølseth, I., & Ekeberg, Ø. (2012). When elderly people give warning of suicide. *International Psychogeriatrics, 24*(9), 1393–1401.

Kjølseth, I., Ekeberg, Ø., & Steihaug, S. (2010). Elderly people who committed suicide—their contact with the health service. What did they expect, and what did they get? *Aging and Mental Health, 14*(8), 938–946.

Krach, P. (1998). Myths & facts . . . about suicide in the elderly. *Nursing, 28*(5), 17.

LaBode, V., & Sher, L. (2011). Suicide prevention in older males: Do medical professionals know enough? *Australian and New Zealand Journal of Psychiatry, 45*, 1094.

Lagana, L., & Shanks, S. (2002). Mutual biases underlying the problematic relationship between older adults and mental health providers: Any solution in sight? *International Journal of Aging & Human Development, 55*(3), 271–295.

Lapierre, S., Boyer, R., Desjardins, S., Dube, M., Lorraine, D., Preville, M., & Brassard, J. (2012). Daily hassles, physical illness, and sleep problems in older adults with wishes to die. *International Psychogeriatrics/IPA, 24*(2), 243–252.

Lee, S. H., Tsai, Y. F., Chen, C. Y., & Huang, L. B. (2014). Triggers of suicide ideation and protective factors of actually executing suicide among first onset cases in older psychiatric outpatients: A qualitative study. *BioMed Central Psychiatry, 14*, 269. doi:10.1186/s12888-014-0269-9

Li, H., Proctor, E., & Morrow-Howell, N. (2005). Outpatient mental health service use by older adults after acute psychiatric hospitalization. *Journal of Behavioral Health Services and Research, 32*, 74–84.

Luoma, J. B., & Pearson, J. L. (2002). Suicide and marital status in the United States, 1991–1996: Is widowhood a risk factor? *American Journal of Public Health, 92*, 1518–1522.

McKeown, R. E., Cuffe, S. P., & Schulz, R. M. (2006). US suicide rates by age group, 1970–2002: An examination of recent trends. *American Journal of Public Health, 96*(10), 1744–1751.

Mezuk, B., Lohman, M., Leslie, M., & Powell, V. (2015). Suicide risk in nursing homes and assisted living facilities: 2003–2011. *American Journal of Public Health, 105*(7), 1495–1502.

Mezuk, B., Rock, A., Lohman, M. C., & Choi, M. (2014). Suicide risk in long-term care facilities: A systematic review. *International Journal of Geriatric Psychiatry, 29*(12), 1198–1211.

Miles, C. P. (1977). Conditions predisposing to suicide: A review. *Journal of Nervous and Mental Disease, 164*(4), 231–246.

Miller, M. (1978). Geriatric suicide: The Arizona study. *Gerontologist, 18*(5 Pt. 1), 488–495.

Minayo, M. C., & Cavalcante, F. G. (2015). Suicide attempts among the elderly: A review of the literature. *Ciencia & Saude Coletiva, 20*(6), 1751–1762.

Monette, M. (2012). Senior suicide: An overlooked problem. *CMAJ : Canadian Medical Association Journal, 184*(17), E885–E886. doi:10.1503/cmaj.109-4287

Morin, J., Wiktorsson, S., Marlow, T., Olesen, P. J., Skoog, I., & Waern, M. (2013). Alcohol use disorder in elderly suicide attempters: A comparison study. *The American Journal of Geriatric Psychiatry: Official Journal of the American Association for Geriatric Psychiatry, 21*(2), 196–203.

Mormont, E., Jamart, J., & Jacques, D. (2014). Symptoms of depression and anxiety after the disclosure of the diagnosis of Alzheimer's disease. *Journal of Geriatric Psychiatry and Neurology, 27*(4), 281–286.

Ngamini, N. A., Vasiliadis, H. M., & Preville, M. (2015). Individual and area-level factors correlated with death by suicide in older adults. *Preventive Medicine, 75,* 44–48.

Ojima, T., Nakamura, Y., & Detels, R. (2004). Comparative study about methods of suicide between Japan and the United States. *Journal of Epidemiology, 14*(6), 187–192.

Oquendo, M. A., Bongiovi-Garcia, M. E., Galfalvy, H., Goldberg, P. H., Grunebaum, M. F., Burke, A. K., & Mann, J. J. (2007). Sex differences in clinical predictors of suicidal acts after major depression: a prospective study. *American Journal of Psychiatry, 164*(1), 134–141.

Parpa, E., Tsilika, E., Gennimata, V., & Mystakidou, K. (2015). Elderly cancer patients' psychopathology: A systematic review: Aging and mental health. *Archives of Gerontology and Geriatrics, 60*(1), 9–15.

Pearson, J. L., & Brown, G. K. (2000). Suicide prevention in late life: Directions for science and practice. *Clinical Psychology Review, 20*(6), 685–705.

Pearson, J. L., & Conwell, Y. (1995). Suicide in late life: Challenges and opportunities for research. Introduction. *International Psychogeriatrics, 7*(2), 131–136.

Phillips, J. A., & Nugent, C. N. (2013). Antidepressant use and method of suicide in the United States: Variation by age and sex, 1998–2007. *Archives of Suicide Research: Official Journal of the International Academy for Suicide Research, 17*(4), 360–372.

Purcell, B., Heisel, M. J., Speice, J., Franus, N., Conwell, Y., & Duberstein, P. R. (2012). Family connectedness moderates the association between living alone and suicide ideation in a clinical sample of adults 50 years and older. *The American Journal of Geriatric Psychiatry: Official Journal of the American Association for Geriatric Psychiatry, 20*(8), 717–723.

Quan, H., Arboleda-Florez, J., Fick, G. H., Stuart, H. L., & Love, E. J. (2002). Association between physical illness and suicide among the elderly. *Social Psychiatry & Psychiatric Epidemiology, 37*(4), 190–197.

Ra, C. K., & Cho, Y. (2013). Differentiated effects of social participation components on suicidal ideation across age groups in South Korea. *BioMed Central Public Health, 25*(13), 890. doi:10.1186/1471-2458-13-890

Raue, P. J., Ghesquiere, A. R., & Bruce, M. L. (2014). Suicide risk in primary care: Identification and management in older adults. *Current Psychiatry Reports, 16*(9), 466. doi:10.1007/s11920-014-0466-8

Ross, R. K., Bernstein, L., Trent, L., Henderson, B. E., & Paganini-Hill, A. (1990). A prospective study of risk factors for traumatic death in the retirement community. *Preventive Medicine, 19*(3), 323–334.

Rubenowtiz, E., Waern, M., Wilhelmmson, K., & Allebeck, P. (2001). Life events and psychosocial factors in elderly suicides: A case control study. *Psychological Medicine, 31,* 1193–1202.

Salvatore, T. (2015). Suicide risk in homebound elderly individuals: What home care clinicians need to know. *Home Healthcare Now, 33*(9), 476–481.

Serafini, G., Calcagno, P., Lester, D., Girardi, P., Amore, M., & Pompili, M. (2016). Suicide risk in Alzheimer's disease: A systematic review. *Current Alzheimer Research, 13*(10), 1083–1099.

Shah, A., Bhat, R., Zarate-Escudero, S., DeLeo, D., & Erlangsen, A. (2016). Suicide rates in five-year age-bands after the age of 60 years: The international landscape. *Aging and Mental Health, 20*(2), 131–138.

Sirey, J. A., Bruce, M. L., Carpenter, M., Booker, D., Reid, M. C., Newell, K., & Alexopoulos, G. S. (2008). Depressive symptoms and suicidal ideation among older adults receiving home delivered meals. *International Journal of Geriatric Psychiatry, 23*(12), 1306–1311.

Slovak, K., Pope, N. D., & Brewer, T. W. (2016). Geriatric case managers' perspectives on suicide among community-dwelling older adults. *Journal of Gerontological Social Work, 59*(1), 3–15.

Spencer, R. J., Ray, A., Pirl, W. F., & Prigerson, H. G. (2012). Clinical correlates of suicidal thoughts in patients with advanced cancer. *The American Journal of Geriatric Psychiatry, 20*(4), 327–336. doi:10.1097/JGP.0b013e318233171a

Spina, P., & Scordo, M. G. (2002). Clinically significant drug interactions with antidepressants in the elderly. *Drugs & Aging, 19*(4), 299–320.

Substance Abuse and Mental Health Services Administration. (2015). Suicidal thoughts and behavior among adults: Results from the 2015 National Survey on Drug Use and Health. Retrieved from https://www.samhsa.gov/data/sites/default/files/NSDUH-DR-FFR3-2015/NSDUH-DR-FFR3-2015.htm

Suominen, K., Isometsa, E., & Lonnqvist, J. (2004). Elderly suicide attempters with depression are often diagnosed only after the attempt. *International Journal of Geriatric Psychiatry, 19*(1), 35–40.

Szanto, K., Dombrovski, A. Y., Sahakian, B. J., Mulsant, B. H., Houck, P. R., Reynolds, C. F. 3rd, & Clark, L. (2012). Social emotion recognition, social functioning, and attempted suicide in late-life depression. *The American Journal of Geriatric Psychiatry, 20*, 257–265.

Szanto, K., Gildengerrs, A., Mulsant, B. H., Brown, G., Alexopoulos, G. S., & Reynolds, C. F. (2002). Identification of suicide ideation and prevention of suicidal behaviour in the elderly. *Drugs & Aging, 19*(1), 11–24.

Szanto, K., Lenze, E. J., Waern, M., Duberstein, P., Bruce, M. L., Epstein-Lubow, G., & Conwell, Y. (2013). Research to reduce the suicide rate among older adults: Methodology roadblocks and promising paradigms. *Psychiatric Services, 64*(6), 586–589.

Turvey, C. L., Conwell, Y., Jones, M. P., Phillips, C., Simonsick, E., Pearson, J. L., & Wallace, R. (2002). Risk factors for late-life suicide: A prospective, community based study. *American Journal of Geriatric Psychiatry, 10*, 398–406.

Uncapher, H., & Arean, P. A. (2000). Physicians are less willing to treat suicidal ideation in older patients. *Journal of the American Geriatrics Society, 48*(2), 188–192.

Valiengo Lda, C., Stella, F., & Forlenza, O. V. (2016). Mood disorders in the elderly: Prevalence, functional impact, and management challenges. *Neuropsychiatric Disease and Treatment, 24*(12), 2105–2114.

Vannoy, S. D., Tai-Seale, M., Duberstein, P., Eaton, L. J., & Cook, M. A. (2011). Now what should I do? Primary care physicians' responses to older adults expressing thoughts of suicide. *Journal of General Internal Medicine, 26*(9), 1005–1011.

Van Orden, K. A., O'Riley, A. A., Simning, A., Podgorski, C., Richardson, T. M., & Conwell, Y. (2015). Passive suicide ideation: An indicator of risk among older adults seeking aging services? *The Gerontologist, 55*(6), 972–980.

Van Orden, K. A., Stone, D. M., Rowe, J., McIntosh, W. L., Podgorski, C., & Conwell, Y. (2013). The senior connection: Design and rationale of a randomized trial of peer companionship to reduce suicide risk in later life. *Contemporary Clinical Trials, 35*(1), 117–126.

Van Orden, K. A., Witte, T. K., Cukrowicz, K. C., Braithwaite, S. R., Selby, E. A., & Joiner, J. E. (2010). The interpersonal theory of suicide. *Psychological Review, 117*(2), 575–600.

van Wijngaarden, E. J., Leget, C. J., & Goossensen, A. (2015). Till death do us part: The lived experience of an elderly couple who chose to end their lives by spousal self-euthanasia. *The Gerontologist, 56*(6), 1062–1071.

Waern, M., Beskow, J., Runeson, B., & Skoog, I. (1999). Suicidal feelings in the last year of life in elderly people who commit suicide. *Lancet, 354*(9182), 917–918.

Waern, M., Rubenowitz, E., Runeson, B., Skoog, I., Wilhelmson, K., & Allebeck, P. (2002). Burden of illness and suicide in elderly people: Case-control study. *British Medical Journal, 324*(7350), 1355–1357.

Waern, M., Runeson, B. S., Allebeck, P., Beskow, J., Rubenowitz, E., Skoog, I., & Wilhelmsson, K. (2002). Mental disorder in elderly suicides: A case-control study. *American Journal of Psychiatry, 159*, 450–455.

Wiktorsson, S., Marlow, T., Runeson, B., Skoog, I., & Waern, M. (2011). Prospective cohort study of suicide attempters aged 70 and above: One-year outcomes. *Journal of Affective Disorders, 134*(1–3), 333–340.

Wiktorsson, S., Runeson, B., Skoog, I., Ostling, S., & Waern, M. (2010). Attempted suicide in the elderly: Characteristics of suicide attempters 70 years and older and a general population comparison group. *The American Journal of Geriatric Psychiatry: Official Journal of the American Association for Geriatric Psychiatry, 18*(1), 57–67.

World Health Organization. (2012). Public health action for the prevention of suicide. Retrieved from http://apps.who.int/iris/bitstream/10665/75166/1/9789241503570_eng.pdf

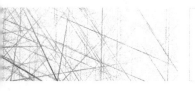

PART III

Suicide and Mental Illness

CHAPTER SEVEN

DEPRESSIVE AND BIPOLAR DISORDERS AND SUICIDE

Depressive disorders, particularly major depressive disorder (MDD), are the most common psychiatric disorders associated with suicide. Despite the increased availability of empirically supported medicines and evidence-based psychosocial interventions, there has been little change in the past 25 years in the annual prevalence of depression rates (Kessler & Üstün, 2008; Patten et al., 2015, 2016). In 2015, an estimated 6.7% of all U.S. adults (16.1 million individuals) had at least one major depressive episode in the past year (National Institute of Mental Health [NIMH], 2016). Research demonstrates that while more than 90% of individuals who suicide fulfill the criteria for one or more psychiatric disorders (American Psychiatric Association [APA], 2010), 60% of all suicides occur in persons with a depressive disorder (Malone & Lartey, 2004). It is estimated that the mortality risk for suicide among individuals with depression is more than 20-fold greater than in the general population (Lépine & Briley, 2011). More specifically, depressed adult males are 21 times more likely and depressed females are 27 times more likely to complete suicide than the general population (Lépine & Briley, 2011). Bipolar disorder is also associated with an elevated risk of completed suicide and suicide attempts. Bipolar disorder affects approximately 5.7 million adult Americans, or about 2.6% of the U.S. population over age 18 years. Between 25% and 50% of individuals with bipolar disorder report attempting suicide at least once (Jamison, 2000), and as many as one in five individuals with bipolar disorder completes suicide (U.S. Department of Health and Human Services, 2015). This chapter examines the relationship between depressive and bipolar disorders and suicidality.

GOALS AND OBJECTIVES

An understanding of:

- *Diagnostic and Statistical Manual* (*DSM-5*) criteria for depressive disorder and bipolar disorder
- Etiology and epidemiology of depression and bipolar disorder
- Relationship between depression and suicide
- Relationship between bipolar disorders and suicide
- Risk and protective factors for suicide unique to individuals with depression
- Risk and protective factors for suicide unique to individuals with bipolar disorder
- Evidence-based practices for addressing suicidality within the context of depression and bipolar disorders

Managing a depressive disorder or depressive symptoms is an all too common human experience. The most common psychiatric disorders impacting millions of individuals, their families, and the larger society are depressive disorders. Depressive disorders are the most common psychiatric conditions associated with suicide attempts and completed suicide (Bostwick & Pankratz, 2000; Lépine & Briley, 2011). Depressive disorders are characterized by irritability or depressed mood; loss of interest or pleasure; changes in appetite, weight, and/or sleep; loss of energy; feelings of hopelessness, worthlessness, inappropriate guilt; difficulty making decisions; and mania (APA, 2013).

The number of supported evidence-based practices (e.g., cognitive behavioral therapy [CBT], interpersonal psychotherapy [IPT], motivational interviewing, and psychopharmacology) that have been found to successfully treat depression and bipolar disorder have increased over the past few decades. However, unsupported stereotypes can become barriers to treatments. Mood disorders, including major depression disorder and bipolar disorders, are biological conditions that are not caused by individual values, laziness, lack of motivation, poor work ethic, improper principles, and so forth. Individuals suffering from these conditions need efficacious treatment and cannot simply "pull themselves up by their bootstraps" or "just snap out of it." It is essential for clinicians working with individuals managing depressive and/or bipolar disorders to become aware of not only the beliefs of others, but also their personal and professional values and assumptions regarding depression and mania. Lacking professional and personal awareness may pose a barrier to effectively engage and treat individuals with depressive and bipolar disorders, despite using an effective treatment.

Individual Exercise 7.1

1. Do you approach the assessment and treatment of an individual diagnosed with major depression as you would a client with leukemia or diabetes? Describe the differences or similarities.
2. Do you approach the assessment and treatment of an individual diagnosed with a bipolar disorder as you would a client with major depression? Describe the differences or similarities.
3. When you hear the word "depression," what are the first words or thoughts that come to your mind?
4. Are your listed words or thoughts generally positive or negative? Did they surprise you in any way? If so, how?
5. When you hear the word "mania," what are the first words or thoughts that come to your mind?
6. Are your listed words or thoughts generally positive or negative? Did they surprise you in any way? If so, how?
7. What personal *and* professional considerations and assumptions may make it hard for you to work with a depressed client? A manic client?
8. What personal *and* professional considerations may make it easy for you to work with a depressed client? A manic client?

DSM-5 DIAGNOSIS

Depressive Disorders

A diagnosis of depression can be complicated by comorbid illnesses or medications that mimic depressive symptoms. MDD, or major depression, is generally diagnosed via psychiatric assessment using the *DSM-5* (5th ed.; American Psychiatric Association [APA], 2013). According to the *DSM-5*, a major depressive episode is diagnosed when five or more of the following symptoms of depression are present during the same 2-week period and represent a change from previous functioning. In addition, at least one of the symptoms must be either (a) depressed mood or (b) loss of interest or pleasure in activities (APA, 2013).

- Depressed or irritable mood
- Loss of interest or pleasure in activities (e.g., hobbies, work, sex, or being with friends)
- Sudden change in weight (weight loss without dieting, gaining more than 5% of body weight in 1 month) or a change in appetite
- Inability to sleep or sleeping too much
- Agitation or restlessness (observed by others)
- Constant fatigue or loss of energy
- Frequent feelings of worthlessness or inappropriate guilt
- Difficulty concentrating or making decisions
- Frequent thoughts of death or suicide (or a suicide attempt or plan)

These symptoms must cause significant distress to the individual or significant impairment in the individual's ability to function, and cannot be attributable to the physiological effects of a substance (e.g., drug abuse, a medication) or a general medical condition (e.g., hypothyroidism). A difference in the *DSM-5* compared to earlier versions of the *DSM* is that depression symptoms resulting from bereavement (i.e., after the loss of a loved one) are no longer excluded. Thus, under the *DSM-5*, an individual with a major depressive episode will be diagnosed with an MDD if he or she meets the criteria.

Related depressive conditions include persistent depressive disorder (formerly called "dysthymia"), which features similar, albeit fewer, symptoms than major depression disorder and is a chronic illness lasting at least 2 years in adults or 1 year in adolescents; double-depression (persistent depressive disorder with a current major depressive episode); and two recently added, yet long studied, disorders: disruptive mood dysregulation disorder (low mood characterized by lasting 12 months or longer with three or more weekly episodes of verbal or physical temper outbursts) and premenstrual dysphoric disorder (five or more mood symptoms associated with most menstrual cycles in the preceding year; APA, 2013).

Bipolar and Related Disorders

A diagnosis of a bipolar or related disorder is a serious mental condition that can exert a number of associated health and mental health implications for the individual. A bipolar diagnosis is associated with an increased risk for suicidality. Bipolar disorders include a number of specific conditions, including bipolar I, bipolar II, and cyclothymic disorders, diagnosed through a psychiatric assessment using the *DSM-5* (APA, 2013).

A bipolar I disorder diagnosis requires the presence of a full manic episode, which may be preceded or followed by a depressive episode (APA, 2013). According to the *DSM-5*, a manic episode requires both (a) a noticeable period of persistently increased goal-directed activity or energy and (b) an elevated, expansive, or irritable mood most of the day nearly every day for 1 week or requiring hospitalization (APA, 2013). During the period of mood disturbances, three (four, if mood is irritable) of the following seven symptoms are evident and a change from previous presentation (APA, 2013):

- Increased self-esteem or grandiosity
- Decreased need for sleep
- More talkativeness

- Flight of ideas or racing thoughts
- Distractibility
- Increased goal-directed activity or psychomotor agitation
- Excessive involvement in activities (with risk of painful consequences)

These symptoms must cause significant distress to the individual or significant impairment in the individual's ability to function, and cannot be attributable to the physiological effects of a substance (e.g., drug abuse, a medication) or a general medical condition. One episode of mania is sufficient for a bipolar I diagnosis.

Major related bipolar conditions include bipolar II and cyclothymic disorders. Bipolar II disorder is very similar but requires the presence of at least one major depressive episode and a hypomanic episode (APA, 2013). A hypomanic is similar to a manic episode with identical symptoms, but in a condensed time period of 4 to 6 days and does not require hospitalization. Cyclothymic disorder requires an extended period of time (2 years in adults and 1 year in youths) characterized by times of depression and mania-like symptoms, without fully meeting the criteria of a major depressive episode, manic episode, or hypomanic episode (APA, 2013).

EPIDEMIOLOGY AND PROGNOSIS OF DEPRESSION

Depression is considered the most common psychiatric illness (Lehtinen & Joukamaa, 1994), with an estimated annual rate of any depressive disorder nearing 7% (Kessler, Chiu, Demler, Merikangas, & Walters, 2005) and a lifetime prevalence rate of 15% in the United States (Lépine & Briley, 2011). Studies have indicated that racial–ethnic differences may vary with research finding approximately 7% of Whites, 4.5% of Blacks, and 5% of Hispanics having a lifetime prevalence rate of depression (Oquendo , Lizardi, Greenwald, Weissman, & Mann, 2004). In addition, MDDs were estimated to be the leading cause of disability in the United States (Ustun, Ayuso-Mateos, Chatterji, Mathers, & Murray, 2004). The annual economic consequences of depression in the United States have risen over the years with an estimated annual cost of $83 billion in 1994 (Coyne, Fechner-Bates, & Schwenk, 1994) to $210 billion per year in 2015 (Greenberg, 2015).

At any given time, 4% of men and 8% of women suffer from a clinically significant depressive disorder, and depressive symptoms are even more common (Lehtinen & Joukamaa, 1994). More specifically, the lifetime rate for a major depression among women was nearly 12% and for men almost 6% (Ford & Erlinger, 2004). Females have a lifetime rate of major depression 1.7 to 2.7 times greater than that for men (Burt & Stein, 2002). In terms of the general youth population, 3% of preschoolers and 2% of school-aged children suffer from depression (Birmaher & Brent, 1998; Wolraich, Felice, & Drotar, 1996). In 2015, approximately 3 million youths (between 12 and 17 years of age) or 12.5% of this population in the United States experienced one or more major depressive episodes in the past year (Center for Behavioral Health Statistics and Quality, 2016).

In terms of the course of illness, up to 50% of individuals who have a major depressive episode experience a reoccurrence in the year following an index episode (Dawson, Lavori, Coryell, Endicott, & Keller, 1998; Kessler & Bromet, 2013). Twenty percent will develop chronic depression. Fifteen percent to 20% suffer from lingering symptoms, considered partial remission. Ten percent to 15% experience the "bipolarization" of an illness, meaning their major depressive episode is followed by a manic episode and a shift in diagnosis to bipolar disorder (Dawson, Lavori, Coryell, Endicott, & Keller, 1998).

The following factors are associated with an increased risk of depression:

- Family history of depression (Ivanova & Israel, 2005; Kendler, Gardner, & Prescott, 1999; Magnil, Janmarker, Gunnarsson, & Björkelund, 2013; Peters, Shankman, Deckersbach, & West, 2015)

- Early childhood trauma (i.e., loss of a parent before adolescence; child neglect; physical, emotional, or sexual abuse; and parental divorce; Mandelli, Petrelli, & Serretti, 2015; O'Mahen, Karl, Moberly, & Fedock, 2015)
- Poor emotion regulation skills (Berking, Wirtz, Svaldi, & Hofmann, 2014; Berking & Wupperman, 2012; Ehring, Tuschen-Caffier, Schnuelle, Fischer, & Gross, 2010)
- Comorbid psychiatric illness (Magnil et al., 2013; Peters et al., 2015)
- Low socioeconomic status (Culpin, Stapinski, Miles, Araya, & Joinson, 2015; Mossakowski, 2015; Patten et al., 2014; van der Waerden Hoefnagels, Hosman, & Jansen, 2014)
- Marital status (being unmarried; Hiyoshi, Fall, Netuveli, & Montgomery, 2015; Ivanova & Israel, 2005; Musick & Bumpass, 2012; Ohayon, 2007; Yan, Huang, Huang, Wu, & Qin, 2011)
- Work status (i.e., being unemployed; Ivanova & Israel, 2005; Ohayon, 2007; Richards, 2011; Richards & Sanabria, 2014)
- Lower levels of education (Ohayon, 2007; Peters et al., 2015)
- Physical illness (Magnil et al., 2013)
- Female gender (Costello, Swendsen, Rose, & Dierker, 2008; Ivanova & Israel, 2005; Ohayon, 2007; Peters et al., 2015; Yaroslavsky, Pettit, Lewinsohn, Seeley, & Roberts 2013)
- Cigarette smoking (Bares, 2014; Ohayon, 2007; Weinstein & Mermelstein, 2013)

The following are considered protective factors reducing the risk of depression:

- Spiritual well-being (Ivanova & Israel, 2005)
- A sense of personal value in society (Ivanova & Israel, 2005)
- Social support (Ivanova & Israel, 2005; Taylor, Chae, Lincoln, & Chatters, 2015)
- Family stability (Ivanova & Israel, 2005; Taylor et al., 2015)

DEPRESSION AND SUICIDE

Over 90% of individuals who successfully suicide have a psychiatric disorder (APA, 2003; Isometsä et al., 1995; Kaplan & Harrow, 1996; Strakowski et al., 1996). Depressive disorders are the most common psychiatric conditions associated with suicide or serious suicide attempt. Approximately 60% of all suicides occur in persons with a depressive disorder (Bostwick et al., 2000). Lifetime rate of mortality secondary to suicide has been estimated to be 2% to 15% for individuals with depressive disorders and 15% to 20% for those psychiatric patients who have a history of one hospitalization for their disorder. Estimates of the rate of completed suicide among individuals with bipolar disorder are approximately 15%, and it is estimated that between 25% and 50% attempt suicide at least once (Bostwick et al., 2000).

There is a vast difference in the lifetime risk of suicide in depression among males and females. Where risk for males is estimated at 7%, it is estimated at only 1% for females (Blair-West, Cantor, Mellsop, & Eyeson, 1999). The risk of suicide among those depressed individuals not receiving antidepressants is 1.8 times higher than the risk of suicide among those treated with antidepressants. However, only approximately one out of every five depressed individuals is treated with antidepressants (Isacssona, Bergamn, & Rich, 1996).

Risk Factors

There are a number of established risk factors for suicidal acts among individuals with major depression. These include:

- Previous suicide attempts (Bradley et al., 2015; Beghi, Rosenbaum, Cerri, & Cornaggia, 2013; Chesin & Jeglic, 2016; Deisenhammer et al., 2009; Hawton, Comabella,

Casañas, Haw, & Saunders, 2103; Malone et al., 2000; Rihmer, 2007; Sachs-Ericsson et al., 2014)

- Suicidal ideation (Malone et al., 2000)
- Nonsuicidal self-harm (Burke, Hamilton, Cohen, Stange, & Alloy, 2016; Knorr et al., 2016; Ward-Ciesielski, Schumacher, & Bagge, 2016)
- Family history of psychiatric illness (Hawton et al., 2013; Husain et al., 2009; Korten, Comijs, Lamers, & Penninx, 2012; Kulkarni, Rao, & Begum, 2013; McGirr, Diaconu, Berlim, & Turecki, 2011)
- Family history of suicidal behavior (Brent et al., 2002; Chaudhury et al., 2016; Kendler, Gardner, & Prescott, 1999; Malone et al., 2000; Melhem et al., 2007; Rihmer et al., 2013)
- Impulsive behavior (Boisseau et al., 2013; Chachamovich, Stefanello, Botega, & Turecki, 2009; Chaudhury et al., 2016; Dombrovski, Szanto, Clark, Reynolds, & Siegle, 2013; Melhem et al., 2007; Oquendo et al., 2000; Rawlings, Shevlin, Corcoran, Morriss, & Taylor, 2015)
- Aggressive behavior (Antypa, Van der Does, & Penninx, 2010; Brent, Melhem, & Mann, 2015; Brent, Melhem, Oquendo, et al., 2015; Dalca, McGirr, Renaud, & Turecki, 2013; Malone et al., 2000; Melhem et al., 2007; Santana et al., 2015; Thompson, Connelly, Thomas-Jones, & Eggert, 2013)
- Insomnia (Hom et al., 2016; Kay et al., 2016)
- Loss or separation (Berg, Rostila, & Hjern, 2016; Kim et al., 2013; Malone et al., 2000)
- Poor social support (Cáceda, Strassnig, & Nemeroff, 2012; Holma et al., 2010; O'Riley et al., 2014; Tuisku et al., 2014)
- Hopelessness (Bozzay, Karver, & Verona, 2016; Fisher, Overholser, Ridley, Braden, & Rosoff, 2015; Hawton et al., 2013; Horesh, Levi, & Apter, 2012; Malone et al., 2000; O'Connor, Smyth, & Williams, 2015; Valtonen et al., 2007)
- Severity of depression (Holma et al., 2010; Malone et al., 2000; Rihmer, 2007)
- Comorbidity with anxiety (Arditte, Morabito, Shaw, & Timpano, 2016; Bolton, Pagura, Enns, Grant, & Sareen, 2010; Hawton et al., 2013; Rihmer, 2007)
- Comorbidity with alcohol/substance abuse (Bolton, 2010; Cheek, Nestor, & Liu, 2016)

Protective Factors

Conversely, several protective factors have been identified among depressed individuals that serve to reduce the risk of suicide. These include:

- Reasons for living, including having greater feelings of responsibility toward family, more fear of social disapproval, more moral objections to suicide, and greater fear of suicide (Bagge, Lamis, Nadorff, & Osman, 2014; Christensen, Batterham, Mackinnon, Donker, & Soubelet, 2014; Heisel, Neufeld, & Flett, 2016; Flowers, Walker, Thompson, & Kaslow, 2014; Lamis & Lester, 2013; Lizardi et al., 2009; Segal, Gottschling, Marty, Meyer, & Coolidge, 2015).
- Increased survival and coping skills (Bagge et al., 2014; Christensen, 2014; Heisel, 2016; Flowers et al, 2014; Lamis & Lester, 2013; Lee, 2014; Lizardi et al., 2009; Malone et al., 2000; Segal et al., 2015).
- Optimism (Bryan, Ray-Sannerud, Morrow, & Etienne, 2013; Chang et al., 2013; Chin & Holden, 2013; Huffman et al., 2016)
- Endorsing a higher degree of religiosity (Davidson, Wingate, Grant, Judah, & Mills, 2011; Hovey, Hurtado, Morales, & Seligman, 2014; Mosqueiro, da Rocha, & de Almeida Fleck, 2015; Rushing, Corsentino, Hames, Sachs-Ericsson, & Steffens, 2013).

EPIDEMIOLOGY AND PROGNOSIS
OF BIPOLAR DISORDERS

The estimated lifetime prevalence rates across the bipolar spectrum disorders range from 2.8% to 6.5% (Bauer & Pfennig, 2005; Benazzi, 2007), with an estimated 12-month prevalence of 2.6% in the U.S. adult population (Murray et al., 2012). The average age of symptom onset for bipolar I is 18 years, and 22 years for bipolar II; however, detection and diagnosis often occur around 25 years of age (Kessler et al., 2005). In the United States, bipolar disorders are the sixth most common cause of disability (Altman et al., 2006).

Evidence does not support any strong association across ethnicity, race, or gender (Kessler et al., 2005). Research has identified that having a parent diagnosed with a bipolar disorder increases the risk that the offspring will have the disorder from a 2% (not having a parent diagnosed with a bipolar disorder) to a 15% risk (Barnett & Smoller, 2009).

Individuals diagnosed with a bipolar disorder deal with a lifetime risk for mood variations, frequently with challenging, and at times devastating, consequences (Leahy, 2007), including suicide (Baldessarini, Pompili, & Tondo, 2006). A bipolar disorder is considered a serious mental illness (SMI) and typically has a cyclical and recurring course marked with episodes of depression, mania, and/or hypomania. Bipolar disorders are commonly chronic in nature and associated with significant interpersonal, social, academic, and occupational dysfunction (Goodwin & Jamison, 2007).

The following are some core factors associated with an increased risk of bipolar disorder:

- Genetics: A first-degree relative with a bipolar disorder (e.g., parent, sibling)
- Brain structure and biological differences (physical changes in them, such as dysfunction of certain neurotransmitters)
- Family history of bipolar illness
- Periods of high stress (e.g., trauma, death of a loved one)
- Drug or alcohol abuse
- Poor sleep hygiene (disrupted circadian rhythm sleep)

BIPOLAR DISORDERS AND SUICIDE

Suicide is among the leading causes of death of individuals with bipolar disorder (Lan et al., 2015; Nilsson, 2016; Schaffer et al., 2015). Research indicates that the lifetime rates for attempted suicide among individuals with bipolar disorder are much higher than those in the general or community population (1 to 3 vs. 1 to 30; Baldessarini et al., 2006). The rate of completed suicide is also significantly higher and is estimated to be 60 times that of the general population (Baldessarini et al., 2006; Fountoulakis, Gonda, Siamouli, & Rihmer, 2009). Schaffer et al. (2015) recently conducted a systematic literature review of studies examining bipolar disorder and suicide risk published from January 1, 1980, to May 30, 2014. The review specifically focused on all studies of factors putatively associated with suicide attempts or suicide deaths in bipolar disorder samples. They categorized the factors into four domains: (a) sociodemographics, (b) clinical characteristics of bipolar disorder, (c) comorbidities, and (d) other clinical variables. A total of 141 studies were included that examined 20 different factors for their association with suicide risk. Results indicated that at least one study identified an association between the following characteristics and increased risk of suicide among individuals with bipolar disorder: sex, age, race, marital status, religious affiliation, age of illness onset, duration of illness, bipolar disorder subtype, polarity of first episode, polarity of current/recent episode, predominant polarity, mood episode characteristics, psychosis, psychiatric comorbidity, personality characteristics, sexual dysfunction, first-degree family history of suicide or mood disorders, past suicide attempts, early life trauma, and psychosocial precipitants (Schaffer et al., 2015).

Another systematic review of 101 studies across 22 countries of attempted suicide risk of individuals with bipolar disorder found that suicide risk and incidence rates are similar across bipolar I and II disorders (Tondo, Pompili, Forte, & Baldessarini, 2016). Within bipolar I and II disorders, suicide risk increases with proximity to onset of illness (Tondo, Isacsson, & Baldessarini, 2003), mixed episodes, and depressed episodes (Oquendo et al., 2000; Tondo, Isacsson, & Baldessarini, 2003). Interestingly, neither objective severity of depression nor quantity of recent life events has been found to differentiate between depressed suicide attempters and nonattempters (Malone et al., 2000).

Risk Factors

There are a number of established risk factors for suicidal acts among individuals with bipolar disorders. These include:

- Social isolation (Nilsson, 2016)
- Having negative social interactions (Owen, Gooding, Dempsey, & Jones, 2015)
- Suicidal ideation (Ballard et al., 2016)
- History of suicide attempt (Schaffer, Sinyor, Reis, Goldstein, & Levitt, 2014)
- Loss of interest (Ballard et al., 2016)
- Anxiety (Ballard et al., 2016)
- Depressive episodes (Saunders & Hawton, 2015; Schaffer et al., 2015)
- Psychomotor agitation (Ballard et al., 2016)
- Engaging in high-risk behavior (Ballard et al., 2016)
- Comorbid attention-deficit/hyperactive disorder (ADHD; Lan et al., 2015)
- Comorbid alcohol or substance use disorders (Carrà, Bartoli, Crocamo, Brady, & Clerici, 2014; Carrà, Bartoli, Crocamo, Brady, & Clerici, 2015)
- Comorbid borderline personality disorder (Zimmerman et al., 2014)
- Childhood trauma, specifically emotional neglect (Cakir, Durak, Ozyildirim, Ince, & Sar, 2015)
- Younger age (da Silva Costa et al., 2015; Schaffer et al., 2014; Song et al., 2012)
- Female (Schaffer et al., 2014)
- Not being acknowledged or feeling misunderstood (Owen et al., 2015)
- Having a negative self-image (Owen et al., 2015)
- Perceived incompetence (Nilsson, 2016)

Protective Factors

Although significantly fewer, a small number of protective factors have been identified among individuals with bipolar disorder that serve to reduce the risk of suicide. These include:

- Recognizing the impact that suicide would have on loved ones (Owen et al., 2015)
- Remembering positive social interactions (Owen et al., 2015)
- Receiving lithium treatment (Oquendo et al., 2011; Shulman, 2010)
- Endorsing moral and/or religious objections to suicide (Dervic et al., 2011)

Case Vignette 7.1

Adam is a 19-year-old single White, Jewish male. He is a high school graduate and completed 1 year of college. He was raised in an upper-middle-class family where academic and career success was extremely important, as was their Orthodox faith. Adam was the last of five children. Seven years apart from the next youngest of his siblings, Adam was an unplanned child. He was a good student but had to work hard to earn his grades. He had several friends and dated occasionally throughout high school but never had a serious girlfriend or a best friend.

After graduation from high school, Adam went away to college. He did well in his first semester and passed all of his classes with above-average grades, but the adjustment to living away from home and college life was not easy. By the spring semester, Adam began to become increasingly despondent. He became more withdrawn and isolated from the people he befriended in fall semester. When he came home for the summer after his first year, his parents noted that he did not engage with his old friends and spent most time watching TV or in his room. Adam frequently was up very late at nights and took naps during the day. His appetite dropped off as did his general hygiene. His mother started to recognize that he was often wearing the same clothes and had very little laundry at the end of each week. When his father encouraged Adam to wake up early and go fishing with him, an old pastime they had engaged in for years, Adam responded with "why bother."

Adam returned to school that fall but was unable to concentrate in class and began to experience increased isolation, deterioration in personal hygiene, and after only a few weeks he just stopped attending classes. During the winter break he returned home and did not go back to school for the spring semester. Over the next year, Adam continued to hang around the house and isolate himself socially. Rarely would he go out with any of his friends from high school or his family members and eventually stopped speaking to anyone on the phone. One day his mother overheard Adam state "I wish I had a gun; that's a way to end it all," while he was watching a police TV show in which a police officer suicided. His parents finally insisted that he see a psychiatrist.

On mental status examination, Adam is alert and oriented x3; although he kept his head down and rarely made eye contact. His clothes are unclean and mismatched. He is unshaven and had noticeable body odor. He displays limited range of affect and frequently answers in monosyllabic monotones. Adam denies that he hears voices. In the past few months, Adam had lost 23 pounds and described a very minimal appetite. He cannot recall the last time he laughed and is not concerned by his inability to smile. He sees life as a never-ending burden. He admits long-standing suicide ideation. Although he denies any prior suicide attempts, he noted collecting pills.

Case Vignette 7.2

Using the same Case Vignette 7.1, change the following:

Diagnosis: From major depression to bipolar I
Gender: From Adam (male) to Anne (female)
Religion: From Judaism to Christianity

Case Vignette 7.3

Using the same Case Vignette 7.1, change the following:

Diagnosis: From major depression to bipolar II
Sexual orientation: From heterosexual to homosexual
Religion: From Judaism to Muslim

Case Vignette 7.4

Using the same Case Vignette 7.1, change the following:

Immigration status: From born in the United States to immigrated from Algeria
Family history: Mother has a long history of MDD

ROLE-PLAY 7.1

Using Case Vignettes 7.1 and 7.2, in groups of three (clinician, client, and observer), engage the client and conduct an assessment for depression and suicide risk. What specific risk and protective factors should you consider? Be aware of your personal and professional attitudes in working with this client. What other information would you need to know? How do the changes in the vignette impact your answers to the above questions?

ROLE-PLAY 7.2

Using Case Vignettes 7.1 and 7.2, in groups of three (clinician, client, and observer), engage the client and conduct an assessment for bipolar disorder and suicide risk. What specific risk and protective factors should you consider? Be aware of your personal and professional attitudes in working with this client. What other information would you need to know? How do the changes in the vignette impact your answers to the above questions?

CURRENT PRACTICE GUIDELINES AND EVIDENCE-BASED PRACTICE FOR DEPRESSIVE DISORDERS

Several treatment approaches have been shown to be effective for the treatment of depression. Specifically, CBT, interpersonal therapy (IPT) for depression (Jackson & Lurie, 2006), and psychopharmacological approaches (Chang & Fava, 2010; Frank et al., 1990; Grunze, 2005; Klerman & Weissman, 1993; Klerman, Weissman, Rounsaville, & Chevron, 1984; Thase, 1996, 2008; Thase et al., 2007; Young & Hammond, 2007) have gained wide support through randomized control trials as effective treatments for depression across age groups, gender, and ethnicity. Although these practice approaches are described in depth in Chapters 20 to 23, a brief review of their specific application to depression follows.

CBT focuses on the nature of an individual's dysfunctional beliefs (i.e., cognitive distortions based on catastrophizing, jumping to false conclusions, maladaptive views of oneself, others, and the world; Beck, Rush, Shaw, & Emery, 1979; Thase, 1996). CBT, when aimed at reducing depression, focuses on (a) identifying symptoms and diagnosis of depression, (b) assessing for the presence of dysfunctional beliefs and behaviors, (c) identifying context and life events that might be triggering dysfunctional responses, (d) looking for developmental, family antecedents of automatic thoughts and beliefs, and learned behaviors, (e) linking changes in mood to the occurrence of self-disparaging or other negative beliefs, possibly related to early learning, and (6) targeting treatment toward changing dysfunctional beliefs, thoughts, and behaviors (Beck et al., 1979; Thase, 1996). CBT has repeatedly been shown to be as effective as medication in the treatment of depression (Appleby, Warner, Whitton, & Faragher, 1997; Thase, 2008; Thase et al., 2007).

IPT views depression as having a dynamic relationship with interpersonal problems. Depression leads to interpersonal problems, and interpersonal problems lead to depressed mood. Interpersonal problems are categorized into four areas: (a) grief, (b) role transition, (c) interpersonal disputes, and (d) interpersonal deficits. According to IPT, the improvement or resolution of the interpersonal problem(s) linked to the onset of depression can bring about the improvement or remission of depressive symptoms (Frank et al., 1990; Klerman & Weissman, 1993; Klerman et al., 1984).

Monoamines and neurotransmitters have been identified as biological markers of depression, specifically, monoamine oxidase, serotonin, norepinephrine, and dopamine (Preston & Johnson, 2016). Medications targeting these areas such as selective serotonin reuptake inhibitors and tricyclic antidepressants have been shown to be effective for treating depression. However, despite their efficacy, most types of antidepressants, especially selective serotonin reuptake inhibitors (SSRIs), do lead to negative side-effects (Preston & Johnson, 2016; Rosse, Fanous, Gaskins, & Deutsch, 2007). Previous research has reported rates of discontinuation of antidepressant medication ranging from 33% to 53% with adverse side effects cited as the main reason for discontinuations in up to 36% of cases (Crawford et al., 2014; Demyttenaere et al., 2001). The most common side-effects experienced when first beginning antidepressant treatment include sleep disturbance, headaches, and nausea (Fergusson, 2001; Fergusson et al., 2005; Kostev, Rex, Eith, & Heilmaier, 2014). Two of the most commonly reported long-term side effects are sexual side effects and weight gain (Crawford et al., 2014; Fergusson, 2001; Fergusson et al., 2005; Kostev et al., 2014). Additionally, some research has established a link between antidepressant use and increased risk of suicidal ideation. For an in-depth discussion please refer to the "A Closer Look: Antidepressants" section in Chapter 4. In addition, practice guidelines recommend community intervention following a suicide, efforts to reduce suicide contagion, and training of primary care physicians and mental health professionals in recognizing suicide risk and making appropriate referrals (Shaffer & Pfeffer, 2001).

Practice guidelines have long been established for working with individuals diagnosed with depression. Commonly established guidelines include (a) establishing an effective therapeutic relationship, (b) completing a full psychiatric assessment, (c) evaluating the safety of the client, (d) determining the appropriate treatment setting, (e) evaluating the client's level of functional impairment and his or her quality of life, (f) coordinating the client's care with other treating clinicians, (g) ongoing monitoring of the client's psychiatric status, (h) integrating measurements into the client's treatment, (i) enhancing treatment adherence, and (j) providing the client and significant others with psychoeducation regarding the illness, the rationale for treatment, the likelihood of a positive response, and the expected time frame (APA, 2010; RANZCP, 2004).

Treatment recommendations for those diagnosed with moderately severe depression include antidepressants, CBT, and IPT, recognizing that evidence suggests that they are all equally effective. Clinicians should, of course, consider treatment benefits as well as negatives, such as side-effects and toxicity. In severe depression, antidepressant treatment is recommended above and beyond psychosocial therapy as a frontline treatment. For depression with psychosis, electroconvulsive therapy (ECT) or a tricyclic combined with an antipsychotic are recommended and considered equally effective (APA, 2010; RANZCP, 2004).

The American Psychiatric Association (2010) further recommends that when treating depressed clients expressing suicidality, clinicians should consider a more intense type of treatment, including hospitalization and/or a combined treatment of pharmacotherapy and psychotherapy. It also suggests that the specific factors to consider in determining the nature and intensity of treatment should include among other things (a) the nature of the doctor–client alliance, (b) the availability and adequacy of social supports,

(c) access to and lethality of suicide means, (d) the presence of a co-occurring substance use disorder, and (e) past and family history of suicidal behavior.

CURRENT PRACTICE GUIDELINES AND EVIDENCE-BASED PRACTICE FOR BIPOLAR DISORDERS

Psychopharmacological treatments including mood stabilizers, anticonvulsants, and antipsychotics are the frontline treatment for bipolar disorders. These medications target symptoms associated with both depressive episodes and manic episodes. In addition to mood stabilizers, antipsychotics are commonly used in the treatment of patients with acute mania and as maintenance treatment (Sachs, Printz, Kahn, Carpenter, & Docherty, 2000; Tohen et al., 2002).

Although the primary approach for treating bipolar disorder is psychopharmacological (Frank, Swartz, & Boland, 2007), research suggests that for individuals with bipolar disorder, interpersonal, cognitive, and behavioral techniques may be effective for controlling mood shifts, increasing compliance with pharmacotherapy, and maintaining morale and motivation in the face of slow or poor therapeutic response (Fountoulakis, 2009).

In addition to the evidence-based practices used for treating major depression and suicide (i.e., cognitive behavior therapy [CBT], dialectical behavior therapy [DBT]; see Chapters 17–20), interpersonal and social rhythm therapy (IPSRT; Frank, 2005; Frank et al., 2007) has a growing body of literature supporting its effectiveness for addressing some of the common difficulties associated with bipolar disorder (Frank et al., 2007; Goldstein et al., 2014; Malkoff-Schwartz et al., 2000; Miklowitz, 2006; Shen, Alloy, Abramson, & Sylvia, 2008; Zaretsky, Rizvi, & Parikh, 2007). IPSRT is based on the belief that disruptions of our circadian rhythms and sleep deprivation may trigger or exacerbate the symptoms commonly associated with bipolar disorder (Frank et al., 2007). Specifically, IPSRT is geared toward stabilizing patients' routines while at the same time improving the quality of their interpersonal relationships and their performance of key social roles. Overall, IPSRT aims to improve patients' current mood and level of functioning and to provide them with the skills necessary to protect them from new affective episodes.

Evidence suggests that IPSRT can be effective at helping individuals with bipolar disorder to improve their lifestyle routines, reduce both manic and depressive symptoms, and increase days of maintaining a consistent, regular mood (Frank et al., 2007; Golstein, 2014; Malkoff-Schwartz et al., 2000; Shen et al., 2008; Zaretsky et al., 2007).

The British Association for Psychopharmacology (Goodwin et al., 2016) suggests a number of practice guidelines for clinicians treating individuals with bipolar disorder. The most recent version is based directly on available evidence and is intended to aid clinical decision making for practitioners and to serve as a source of information for individuals with the disorder and their caregivers. The recommendations were developed via a consensus meeting in which experts in bipolar disorder and its treatment reviewed key areas and considered the strength of evidence and clinical implications. Additionally, the best evidence from randomized controlled trials and observational studies using quasi-experimental designs were used to evaluate treatment options (Goodwin et al., 2016).

The primary recommendations resulting from the guidelines are (a) to achieve a personalized choice of medicine that is both effective and well tolerated, (b) to receive informed adherence and an understanding of illness course from both the patient and those involved in their care, and (c) to establish the aforementioned as early as possible in the course of treatment. In order to achieve this, several factors are critical including (a) having an accurate diagnosis according to the *DSM-5*, (b) providing access to specialized care, (c) establishing and maintaining a therapeutic alliance, (d) providing psychoeducation regarding the disorder, (e) supporting treatment adherence, (f) promoting trigger recognition and identification of signs of relapse, (g) promoting symptom management, (h) considering physical health, alcohol/substance use, and risk of self-harm in the management of the client, and (i) recognizing the need to include additional support to female clients of child-bearing age in terms of managing the postpartum period and providing guidance regarding breast-feeding while taking medication, and so forth (Goodwin et al., 2016).

SUMMARY

Although a significant number of individuals diagnosed with a mood disorder attempt and complete suicide, a majority do not. However, those with a depressive and bipolar disorder remain at an elevated risk for both suicide attempt and completion. To engage, develop a therapeutic alliance, and effectively assess and treat individuals with depression and bipolar disorder at risk of suicide, clinicians need to become informed of not only the risk and protective factors but also their own personal and professional beliefs. A lack of awareness may minimize clinicians' abilities to recognize, assess, and treat, as well as potentially limit clients' abilities to openly access and work with them. Individuals with mood disorders may have an elevated risk of suicidality, but they also have a number of strengths and abilities that can effectively be supported and drawn upon in their treatment.

KEY POINTS

1. Depressive disorders are characterized by depressed mood or loss of interest/pleasure in activities that impairs functioning and causes significant distress.
2. Approximately 60% of all suicides occur in persons with a depressive disorder.
3. Lifetime prevalence of depression is estimated at 5% to 12% in males and 12% to 20% in females.
4. For individuals managing an MDD, approximately one-third to one-half of lifetime cases have recurrent episodes.
5. Lifetime rate of mortality secondary to suicide has been estimated to be 2% to 15% for individuals with depressive disorders.
6. Key predictors of suicide for individuals diagnosed with a depressive disorder include previous suicide attempt, family history of depression, family history of suicide, aggressive behavior, impulsivity, loss, separation, comorbid anxiety, and substance use.
7. In the United States, bipolar disorder is the sixth most common cause of disability.
8. A diagnosis of bipolar disorder is characterized by the presence of both a depressive episode and either a manic or hypomanic episode.
9. Research indicates that among individuals with bipolar disorder, the lifetime rates for attempted suicide are much higher than those in the general or community population (1 to 3 vs. 1 to 30), and the rate of completed suicide is estimated to be 60 times that of the general population.
10. Key predictors of increased risk of suicide among individuals with bipolar disorder include sex, age, race, marital status, religious affiliation, age of illness onset, duration of illness, bipolar disorder subtype, polarity of first episode, polarity of current/recent episode, predominant polarity, mood episode characteristics, psychosis, psychiatric comorbidity, personality characteristics, sexual dysfunction, first-degree family history of suicide or mood disorders, past suicide attempts, early life trauma, and psychosocial precipitants.

ELECTRONIC RESOURCES

NATIONAL INSTITUTE OF MENTAL HEALTH

www.nimh.nih.gov/health/topics/bipolar-disorder/index.shtml

NATIONAL ALLIANCE ON MENTAL ILLNESS

www.nami.org/Learn-More/Mental-Health-Conditions/Bipolar-Disorder

AMERICAN FOUNDATION FOR SUICIDE PREVENTION

www.afsp.org

EDUCATIONAL AND INFORMATIVE SITES

www.allaboutdepression.com/gen_04.html
www.psycom.net/depression.central.suicide.html
www.suicide.org/depression-and-suicide.html
www.surgeongeneral.gov/library/mentalhealth/chapter3/sec5.html

KNOWLEDGE ACQUISITION TEST (KAT)

TRUE OR FALSE

1. Depression affects less than 2% of the population.
2. Depressed males are more likely to attempt suicide than depressed females.
3. Depressed males are more likely to complete suicide than depressed females.
4. An episode of depression is not required for a diagnosis of bipolar disorder.
5. Psychopharmacological treatments are more effective than psychosocial interventions for reducing risk of suicide in individuals with bipolar disorder.
6. Fewer than 10% of individuals with a major depressive disorder (MDD) will have a recurrent episode.
7. If someone is experiencing bereavement, which may be contributing to meeting the criteria for an MDD, he or she will nonetheless receive the MDD diagnosis.
8. Psychopharmacological treatments are more effective than psychosocial interventions for reducing risk of suicide in individuals with depression.

Short Answer

9. List the key risk factors for suicide among individuals with depression.
10. List the key risk factors for suicide among individuals with bipolar disorder.
11. Describe the recommended practice guidelines for treatment of individuals with depression.
12. Describe the recommended practice guidelines for treatment of individuals with bipolar disorder.

Multiple Choice

13. Which item in the following list is not a *DSM-5* criterion for depression?
    A. Sleep disturbances
    B. Suicidal ideation
    C. Loss of appetite
    D. Loss of interest
    E. All of the above
    F. None of the above
14. Which of the following is not a mood diagnosis?
    A. Major depressive disorder
    B. Bipolar II disorder
    C. Premenstrual dysphoric disorder
    D. Bereavement
    E. All of the above
    F. None of the above
15. When a client presents with a depressive or bipolar disorder, a health care clinician should:
    A. Assess only for suicidality if risk factors are described or presented
    B. Assess only after a client has endorsed some aspect of suicidality
    C. Assess only after consulting with a supervisor on the need and rationale for an assessment
    D. Not assess, but refer to an expert on mental health or the nearest Emergency Department
    E. Always assess for suicidality
    F. Rely on his or her clinical experience to determine whether a suicide assessment is required

REFERENCES

Altman, S., Haeri, S., Cohen, L. J., Ten, A., Barron, E., Galynker, I. I., & Duhamel, K. N. (2006). Predictors of relapse in bipolar disorder: A review. *Journal of Psychiatric Practice, 12*(5), 269–282.

American Psychiatric Association. (2010). Practice guideline for the treatment of patients with major depressive disorder (3rd ed.). Retrieved from https://psychiatryonline.org/pb/assets/raw/sitewide/practice_guidelines/guidelines/mdd.pdf

American Psychiatric Association. (2013). *Diagnostic and statistical manual of mental disorders*, text revision (5th ed.). Arlington, VA: American Psychiatric Publishing.

American Psychological Association. (2003). Teen suicide is preventable. Retrieved from http://www.apa.org/research/action/suicide.aspx

Antypa, N., Van der Does, A. J. W., & Penninx, B. W. (2010). Cognitive reactivity: Investigation of a potentially treatable marker of suicide risk in depression. *Journal of Affective Disorders, 122*(1–2), 46–52.

Appleby, L., Warner, R., Whitton, A., & Faragher, B. (1997). A controlled study of fluoxetine and cognitive-behavioural counselling in the treatment of postnatal depression. *British Medical Journal, 314*(7085), 932–936.

Arditte, K. A., Morabito, D. M., Shaw, A. M., & Timpano, K. R. (2016). Interpersonal risk for suicide in social anxiety: The roles of shame and depression. *Psychiatry Research, 239*, 139–144.

Bagge, C. L., Lamis, D. A., Nadorff, M., & Osman, A. (2014). Relations between hopelessness, depressive symptoms and suicidality: Mediation by reasons for living. *Journal of Clinical Psychology, 70*(1), 18–31.

Baldessarini, R. J., Pompili, M., & Tondo, L. (2006). Suicide in bipolar disorder: Risks and management. *CNS Spectrums, 11*(6), 465–471.

Ballard, E. D., Vande Voort, J. L., Luckenbaugh, D. A., Machado-Vieira R., Tohen M., & Zarate, C. A. (2016). Acute risk factors for suicide attempts and death: Prospective findings from the STEP-BD study. *Bipolar Disorders, 18*, 363–372. doi:10.1111/bdi.12397

Bares, C. B. (2014). Gender, depressive symptoms, and daily cigarette use. *Journal of Dual Diagnosis, 10*(4), 187–196.

Barnett, J. H., & Smoller, J. W. (2009). The genetics of bipolar disorder. *Neuroscience, 164*, 331–343.

Bauer, M., & Pfennig, A. (2005). Epidemiology of bipolar disorders. *Epilepsia, 46*(Suppl. 4), 8–13.

Beck, A. T., Rush, A. J., Shaw, B. F., & Emery, G. (1979). *Interview with a depressed suicidal patient*. New York, NY: The Guilford Press.

Beghi, M., Rosenbaum, J. F., Cerri, C., & Cornaggia, C. M. (2013). Risk factors for fatal and nonfatal repetition of suicide attempts: A literature review. *Neuropsychiatric Disease and Treatment, 9*, 1725–1736.

Benazzi, F. (2007). Bipolar II disorder: Epidemiology, diagnosis and management. *CNS Drugs, 21*(9), 727–740.

Berg, L., Rostila, M., & Hjern, A. (2016). Parental death during childhood and depression in young adults: A national cohort study. *Journal of Child Psychology and Psychiatry, 57*(9), 1092–1098.

Berking, M., Wirtz, C. M., Svaldi, J., Hofmann, S. G. (2014). Emotion regulation predicts symptoms of depression over five years. *Behaviour Research and Therapy, 57*, 13–20.

Berking, M., & Wupperman, P. (2012). Emotion regulation and health: State of the art. *Current Opinion in Psychiatry, 25*, 128–134.

Birmaher, B., & Brent, D. (1998). Practice parameters for the assessment and treatment of children and adolescents with depressive disorders. *Journal of the American Academy of Child & Adolescent Psychiatry, 37*(Suppl. 10), 63S–82S.

Blair-West, G. W., Cantor, C. H., Mellsop, G. W., & Eyeson, M. L. (1999). Lifetime suicide risk in major depression: Sex and age determinants. *Journal of Affective Disorders, 55*(3), 171–178.

Boisseau, C. L., Yen, S., Markowitz, J. C., Grilo, C. M., Sanislow, C. A., Shea, M. T., . . . Morey, L. C. (2013). Individuals with single versus multiple suicide attempts over 10 days of prospective follow-up. *Comprehensive Psychiatry, 54*(3), 238–242.

Bolton, J. M., Pagura, J., Enns, M. W., Grant, B., & Sareen, J. (2010). A population-based longitudinal study of risk factors for suicide attempts in major depressive disorder. *Journal of Psychiatric Research, 44*, 817–826.

Bostwick, J. M., & Pankratz, V. S. (2000). Affective disorders and suicide risk: A reexamination. *American Journal of Psychiatry, 157*(12), 1925–1932.

Bozzay, M. L., Karver, M. S., & Verona, E. (2016). Linking insomnia and suicide ideation in college females: The role of socio-cognitive variables and depressive symptoms in suicide risk. *Journal of Affective Disorders, 199*, 106–113.

Bradley, K. A., Case, J. A. C., Khan, O., Ricart, T., Hanna, A., Alonso, C. M., & Gabbay, V. (2015). The role of the kynurenine pathway in suicidality in adolescent major depressive disorder. *Psychiatry Research, 227*(2–3), 206–212.

Brent, D. A., Melhem, N. M., Oquendo, M., Burke, A., Birmaher, B., Stanley, B., . . . Mann, J. (2015). Familial pathways to early-onset suicide attempt: A 5.6-year prospective study. *JAMA Psychiatry, 72*(2), 160–168.

Brent, D. A., Melhem, N. M., & Mann, J. (2015). Pathways to offspring suicidal behavior may begin with maternal suicide attempt. *Journal of the American Academy of Child & Adolescent Psychiatry, 54*(10), 868.

Brent, D. A., Oquendo, M., Birmaher, B., Greenhill, L., Kolko, D., Stanley, B., . . . Mann, J. J. (2002). Familial pathways to early-onset suicide attempt: Risk for suicidal behavior in offspring of mood-disordered suicide attempters. *Archives of General Psychiatry, 59*, 801–807.

Bryan, C. J., Ray-Sannerud, B. N., Morrow, C. E., & Etienne, N. (2013). Optimism reduces suicidal ideation and weakens the effect of hopelessness among military personnel. *Cognitive Therapy and Research, 37*(5), 996–1003.

Burke, T. A., Hamilton, J. L., Cohen, J. N., Stange, J. P., & Alloy, L. B. (2016). Identifying a physical indicator of suicide risk: Non-suicidal self-injury scars predict suicidal ideation and suicide attempts. *Comprehensive Psychiatry, 65*, 79–87.

Burt, V. K., & Stein, K. (2002). Epidemiology of depression throughout the female life cycle. *Journal of Clinical Psychiatry, 63*(Suppl. 7), 9–15.

Cáceda, R., Strassnig, M. T., & Nemeroff, C. B. (2012). Advances in the neuropsychology of suicide. *Psichiatrica, 53*(1), 61–78.

Cakir, S., Durak, R. T., Ozyildirim, I., Ince, E., & Sar, V. (2016). Childhood trauma and treatment outcome in bipolar disorder. *Journal of Trauma & Dissociation, 17*(4), 397–409.

Carrà, G., Bartoli, F., Crocamo, C., Brady, K. T., & Clerici, M. (2014). Attempted suicide in people with co-occurring bipolar and substance use disorders: Systematic review and meta-analysis. *Journal of Affective Disorders, 167*, 125–135.

Carrà, G., Bartoli, F., Crocamo, C., Brady, K. T., & Clerici, M. (2015). Cannabis use disorder as a correlate of suicide attempts among people with bipolar disorder. *Academic Journal Bipolar Disorders, 17*(1), 113–114.

Center for Behavioral Health Statistics and Quality. (2016). Major depression among adolescents. Retrieved from https://www.nimh.nih.gov/health/statistics/prevalence/major-depression-among-adolescents.shtml

Chachamovich, E., Stefanello, S., Botega, N., & Turecki, G. (2009). Which are the recent clinical findings regarding the association between depression and suicide? *Revista Brasileira de Psiquiatria, 31*(Suppl. 1), S18–S25.

Chang, E. C., Yu, E. A., Lee, J. Y., Hirsch, J. K., Kupfermann, Y., & Kahle, E. R. (2013). An examination of optimism/pessimism and suicide risk in primary care patients: Does belief in a changeable future make a difference? *Cognitive Therapy and Research, 37*(4), 796–804.

Chang, T., & Fava, M. (2010). The future of psychopharmacology of depression. *The Journal of Clinical Psychiatry, 71*(8), 971–975.

Chaudhury, S. R., Singh, T., Burke, A., Stanley, B., Mann, J. J., Grunebaum, M., . . . Oquendo, M. A. (2016). Clinical correlates of planned and unplanned suicide attempts. *Journal of Nervous and Mental Disease, 204*(11), 806–811.

Cheek, S. M., Nestor, B. A., & Liu, R. T. (2016). Substance use and suicidality: Specificity of substance use by injection to suicide attempts in a nationally representative sample of adults with major depression. *Depression and Anxiety, 33*(6), 541–548. doi:10.1002/da.22407

Chesin, M. S., & Jeglic, E. L. (2016). Factors associated with recurrent suicidal ideation among racially and ethnically diverse college students with a history of suicide attempt: The role of mindfulness. *Archives of Suicide Research, 20*(1), 29–44.

Chin, J., & Holden, R. R. (2013). Multidimensional future time perspective as moderators of the relationships between suicide motivation, preparation, and its predictors. *Suicide and Life Threatening Behavior, 43*, 395–405. doi:10.1111/sltb.12025

Christensen, H., Batterham, P. J., Mackinnon, A. J., Donker, T., & Soubelet, A. (2014). Predictors of the risk factors for suicide identified by the interpersonal-psychological theory of suicidal behavior. *Psychiatry Research, 219*(2), 290–297.

Costello, D. M., Swendsen, J., Rose, J. S., & Dierker, L. C. (2008). Risk and protective factors associated with trajectories of depressed mood from adolescence to early adulthood. *Journal of Consulting and Clinical Psychology, 76*(2), 173–183. doi:10.1037/0022-006X.76.2.173

Coyne, J. C., Fechner-Bates, S., & Schwenk, T. L. (1994). Prevalence, nature, and comorbidity of depressive disorders in primary care. *General Hospital Psychiatry, 16*(4), 267–276.

Crawford, A., Lewis, S., Nutt, D., Peters, T. J., Cowen, P., O'Donovan, M. C., . . . Lewis, G. (2014). Adverse effects from antidepressant treatment: Randomised controlled trial of 601 depressed individuals. *Psychopharmacology, 231*(15), 2921–2931.

Culpin, I., Stapinski, L., Miles, O. B., Araya, R., & Joinson, C. (2015). Exposure to socioeconomic adversity in early life and risk of depression at 18 years: The mediating role of locus of control. *Journal of Affective Disorders, 183*, 269–278.

Dalca, I. M., McGirr, A., Renaud, J., & Turecki, G. (2013). Gender-specific suicide risk factors: a case-control study of individuals with major depressive disorder. *The Journal of Clinical Psychiatry, 74*(12), 1209–1216.

da Silva Costa, L., Alencar, Á. P., Neto, P. J. N., dos Santos, M. S. V., da Silva, C. G. L., Pinheiro, S. F. L., & Neto, M. L. R. (2015). Risk factors for suicide in bipolar disorder: A systematic review. *Journal of Affective Disorders, 170*, 237–254.

Davidson, C. L., Wingate, L. R., Grant, D. M., Judah, M. R., & Mills, A. C. (2011). Interpersonal suicide risk and ideation: The influence of depression and social anxiety. *Journal of Social and Clinical Psychology, 30*(8), 842–855.

Dawson, R., Lavori, P. W., Coryell, W. H., Endicott, J., & Keller, M. B. (1998). Maintenance strategies for unipolar depression: An observational study of levels of treatment and recurrence. *Journal of Affective Disorders, 49*, 31–44.

Demyttenaere, K., Enzlin, P., Dewe, W., Boulanger, B., De Bie, J., De Troyer, W., & Mesters, P. (2001). Compliance with antidepressants in a primary care setting, 1: Beyond lack of efficacy and adverse events. *Journal of Clinical Psychiatry, 62*, 30–33. doi:10.4088/JCP.v62n0107

Deisenhammer, E. A., Ing, C. M., Strauss, R., Kemmler, G., Hinterhuber, H., & Weiss, E. M. (2009). The duration of the suicidal process: How much time is left for intervention between consideration and accomplishment of a suicide attempt? *The Journal of Clinical Psychiatry, 70*(1), 19–24.

Dervic, K., Carballo, J. J., Baca-Garcia, E., Galfalvy, H. C., Mann, J. J., Brent, D. A., & Oquendo, M. A. (2011). Moral or religious objections to suicide may protect against suicidal behavior in bipolar disorder. *Journal of Clinical Psychiatry, 72*(10), 1390–1396.

Dombrovski, A. Y., Szanto, K., Clark, L., Reynolds, C. F., & Siegle, G. J. (2013). Reward signals, attempted suicide, and impulsivity in late-life depression. *Journal of American Medical Association Psychiatry, 70*(10), 1020–1030.

Ehring, T., Tuschen-Caffier, B., Schnuelle, J., Fischer, S., & Gross, J. J. (2010). Emotion regulation and vulnerability to depression: Spontaneous versus instructed use of emotion suppression and reappraisal. *Emotion, 10*, 563–572.

Fergusson, D., Doucette, S., Glass, K. C., Shapiro, S., Healy, D., Hebert, P., & Hutton, B. (2005). Association between suicide attempts and selective serotonin reuptake inhibitors: Systematic review of randomized controlled trials. *British Medical Journal, 330*, 396–399.

Fergusson, J. M. (2001). SSRI antidepressant medications: Adverse effects and tolerability. *Primary Care Companion to the Journal of Clinical Psychiatry, 3*(1), 22–27.

Fisher, L. B., Overholser, J. C., Ridley, J., Braden, A., & Rosoff, C. (2015). From the outside looking in: Sense of belonging, depression, and suicide risk. *Psychiatry, 78*, 29–41. doi:10.1080/00332747.2015.1015867

Flowers, K. C., Walker, R. L., Thompson, M. P., & Kaslow, N. J. (2014). Associations between reasons for living and diminished suicide intent among African American female suicide attempters. *Journal of Nervous and Mental Disease, 202*(8), 569–575.

Ford, D. E., & Erlinger, T. P. (2004). Depression and C-reactive protein in US adults: Data from the third National Health and Nutrition Survey. *Archives of Internal Medicine, 164*, 1010–1014.

Fountoulakis, K. N., Gonda, X., Siamouli, M., & Rihmer, Z. (2009). Psychotherapeutic intervention and suicide risk reduction in bipolar disorder: A review of the evidence. *Journal of Affective Disorders, 113*(1–2), 21–29.

Frank, E. (2005). *Treating bipolar disorder: A clinician's guide to interpersonal and social rhythm therapy.* New York, NY: Guilford.

Frank, E., Kupfer, D., Perel, J. M., Cornes, C., Jarrett, D. B., Mallinger, A. G., . . . Grochocinski, V. J. (1990). Three-year outcomes for maintenance therapies in recurrent depression. *Archives of General Psychiatry, 47*(12), 1093–1099.

Frank, E., Swartz, H. A., & Boland, E. (2007). Interpersonal and social rhythm therapy: An intervention addressing rhythm dysregulation in bipolar disorder. *Dialogues in Clinical Neuroscience, 9*(3), 325–332.

Goldstein, T. R., Fersch-Podrat, R., Axelson, D. A., Gilbert, A., Hlastala, S. A., Birmaher, B., & Frank, E. (2014). Early intervention for adolescents at high risk for the development of bipolar disorder: Pilot study of Interpersonal and Social Rhythm Therapy (IPSRT). *Psychotherapy, 51*(1), 180–189.

Goodwin, F., & Jamison, K. (2007). *Manic-depressive illness.* New York, NY: Oxford University Press.

Goodwin, G. M., Haddad, P. M., Ferrier, I. N., Aronson, J. K., Barnes, A., Cipriani, D. R., . . . Young, A. H. (2016). Evidence-based guidelines for treating bipolar disorder: Revised third edition recommendations from the British Association for Psychopharmacology. *Journal of Psychopharmacology, 30*(6), 495–553.

Greenberg, P. E. (2015). The growing economic burden of depression in the U.S. *Scientific American.* Retrieved from https://blogs.scientificamerican.com/mind-guest-blog/the-growing-economic -burden-of-depression-in-the-u-s

Grunze, H. (2005). Reevaluating therapies for bipolar depression. *Journal of Clinical Psychiatry, 66*(Suppl. 5), 17–25.

Hawton, K., Comabella, C., Casañas, I., Haw, C., & Saunders, K. (2013). Risk factors for suicide in individuals with depression: A systematic review. *Journal of Affective Disorders, 147*(1–3), 17–28.

Heisel, M. J., Neufeld, E., & Flett, G. L. (2016). Reasons for living, meaning in life, and suicide ideation: Investigating the roles of key positive psychological factors in reducing suicide risk in community-residing older adults. *Aging & Mental Health, 20*(2), 195–207.

Hiyoshi, A., Fall, K., Netuveli, G., & Montgomery, S. (2015). Remarriage after divorce and depression risk. *Social Science & Medicine, 141*, 109–114.

Holma, K. M., Melartin, T. K., Haukka, J., Holma, I. A., Sokero, T. P., & Isometsa, E. T. (2010). Incidence and predictors of suicide attempts in *DSM-IV* major depressive disorder: A five-year prospective study. *American Journal of Psychiatry, 167*, 801–808.

Hom, M. A., Lim, I. C., Stanley, I. H., Chiurliza, B., Podlogar, M. C., Michaels, M. S., . . . Joiner, T. E. (2016). Insomnia brings soldiers into mental health treatment, predicts treatment engagement and outperforms other suicide-related symptoms as a predictor of major depressive episodes. *Journal of Psychiatric Research, 79*, 108–115.

Horesh, N., Levi, Y., & Apter, A. (2012). Medically serious versus non-serious suicide attempts: Relationships of lethality and intent to clinical and interpersonal characteristics. *Journal of Affective Disorders, 136*(3), 286–293.

Hovey, J. D., Hurtado, G., Morales, L. R. A., & Seligman, L. D. (2014). Religion-based emotional social support mediates the relationship between intrinsic religiosity and mental health. *Archives of Suicide Research, 18*(4), 376–391.

Huffman, J. C., Boehm, J. K., Beach, S. R., Beale, E. E., DuBois, C. M., & Healy, B. C. (2016). Relationship of optimism and suicidal ideation in three groups of patients at varying levels of suicide risk. *Journal of Psychiatric Research, 77*, 76–84.

Husain, M. M., Rush, A. J., Wisniewski, S. R., McClintock, S. M., Fava, M., Nierenberg, A. A., & Trivedi, M. H. (2009). Family history of depression and therapeutic outcome: Findings from STARD. *The Journal of Clinical Psychiatry, 70*(2), 185–195.

Isacssona, G., Bergamn, U., & Rich, C. L. (1996). Epidemiological data suggest antidepressants reduce suicide risk among depressives. *Journal of Affective Disorders, 41*(1), 1–8.

Isometsä, E., Henriksson, M., Marttunen, M., Heikkinen, M., Aro, H., Kuoppasalmi, K., & Lönnqvist, J. (1995). Mental disorders in young and middle aged men who commit suicide. *British Medical Journal, 310*, 1366–1367.

Ivanova, M. Y., & Israel, A. C. (2005). Family stability as a protective factor against the influences of pessimistic attributional style on depression. *Cognitive Therapy and Research, 29*(2), 243–251.

Jackson, B., & Lurie, S. (2006). Adolescent depression: Challenges and opportunities: A review and current recommendations for clinical practice. *Advances in Pediatrics, 53*, 111–163.

Jamison, K. R. (2000). Suicide and bipolar disorder. *Journal of Clinical Psychiatry, 61*(Suppl 9), 47–51.

Kaplan, K. J., & Harrow, M. (1996). Positive and negative symptoms as risk factors for later suicidal activity in schizophrenics versus depressives. *Suicide and Life-Threatening Behavior, 26*, 105–121.

Kay, D. B., Dombrovski, A. Y., Buysse, D. J., Reynolds, C. F., Begley, A., & Szanto, K. (2016). Insomnia is associated with suicide attempt in middle-aged and older adults with depression. *International Psychogeriatrics, 28*(4), 613–619.

Kendler, K. S., Gardner, C. O., & Prescott, C. A. (1999). Clinical characteristics of major depression that predict risk of depression in relatives. *Archives of General Psychiatry, 56*(4), 322–327.

Kessler, R. C., & Bromet, E. J. (2013). The epidemiology of depression across cultures. *Annual Review of Public Health, 34,* 119–138.

Kessler, R. C., Chiu, W. T., Demler, O., Merikangas, K. R., & Walters, E. E. (2005). Prevalence, severity, and comorbidity of 12-month *DSM-IV* disorders in the National Comorbidity Survey Replication. *Archives of General Psychiatry, 62,* 617–627.

Kessler, R. C., & Üstün, T. B. (2008). *The WHO World Mental Health Surveys: Global perspectives on the epidemiology of mental disorders.* New York, NY: Cambridge University Press.

Kim, S.-W., Kang, H.-J., Kim, S.-Y., Kim, J.-M., Yoon, J.-S., Jung, S.-W., & Jun, T.-Y. (2013). Impact of childhood adversity on the course and suicidality of depressive disorders: The CRESCEND study. *Depression and Anxiety, 30*(10), 965–974.

Klerman, G., & Weissman, M. M. (1993). *New applications in interpersonal psychotherapy.* Washington, DC: American Psychiatric Press.

Klerman, G., Weissman, M. M., Rounsaville, B., & Chevron, E. (1984). *Interpersonal psychotherapy of depression.* New York, NY: Basic Books.

Knorr, A. C., Tull, M. T., Anestis, M. D., Dixon-Gordon, K. L., Bennett, M. F., & Gratz, K. L. (2016). The interactive effect of major depression and nonsuicidal self-injury on current suicide risk and lifetime suicide attempts. *Archives of Suicide Research, 20*(4), 539–552.

Korten, N. C. M., Comijs, H. C., Lamers, F., & Penninx, B. W. J. H. (2012). Early and late onset depression in young and middle aged adults: Differential symptomatology, characteristics and risk factors? *Journal of Affective Disorders, 138*(3), 259–267.

Kostev, K., Rex, J., Eith, T., & Heilmaier, C. (2014). Which adverse effects influence the dropout rate in selective serotonin reuptake inhibitor (SSRI) treatment? Results for 50,824 patients. *German Medical Science, 12,* 15. doi:10.3205/000200

Kulkarni, R. R., Rao, K. N., & Begum, S. (2013). Comorbidity of psychiatric and personality disorders in first suicide attempters: A case-control study. *Asian Journal of Psychiatry, 6*(5), 410–416.

Lamis, D. A., & Lester, D. (2013). Gender differences in risk and protective factors for suicidal ideation among college students. *Journal of College Student Psychotherapy, 27*(1), 62–77.

Lan, W. H., Bai, Y. M., Hsu, J. W., Huang, K. L., Su, T. P., Li, C. T., . . . Chen, M. H. (2015). Comorbidity of ADHD and suicide attempts among adolescents and young adults with bipolar disorder: A nationwide longitudinal study. *Journal of Affective Disorders, 176,* 171–175.

Leahy, R. L. (2007). Bipolar disorder: Causes, contexts, and treatments. *Journal of Clinical Psychology, 63*(5), 417–424.

Lehtinen, V., & Joukamaa, M. (1994). Epidemiology of depression: Prevalence, risk factors and treatment situation. *Acta Psychiatrica Scandinavica, 377,* 7–10.

Lépine, J. P., & Briley, M. (2011). The increasing burden of depression. *Neuropsychiatric Disease and Treatment, 7*(Suppl. 1), 3–7. doi:10.2147/NDT.S19617

Lizardi, D., Sher, L., Sullivan, G. M., Stanley, B., Burke, A., & Oquendo, M. A. (2009). Association between familial suicidal behavior and frequency of attempts among depressed suicide attempters. *Acta Psychiatrica Scandinavica, 119*(5), 406–410.

Magnil, M., Janmarker, L., Gunnarsson, R., & Björkelund, C. (2013). Course, risk factors, and prognostic factors in elderly primary care patients with mild depression: A two-year observational study. *Scandinavian Journal of Primary Health Care, 31*(1), 20–25.

Malkoff-Schwartz, S., Frank, E., Anderson, B. P., Hlastala, S. A., Luther, J. F., Sherrill, J. T., & Kupfer, D. J. (2000). Social rhythm disruption and stressful life events in the onset of bipolar and unipolar episodes. *Psychological Medicine, 30*(5), 1005–1016.

Malone, D. A., & Lartey, P. (2004). *Depression and suicide: Recognition and early intervention* (2nd ed.). American Medical Association. Washington, DC.

Malone, K. M., Oquendo, M. A., Haas, G. L., Ellis, S. P., Li, S., & Mann, J. J. (2000). Protective factors against suicidal acts in major depression: Reasons for living. *American Journal of Psychiatry, 157,* 1084–1088.

Mandelli, L., Petrelli, C., & Serretti, A. (2015). The role of specific early trauma in adult depression: A meta-analysis of published literature. Childhood trauma and adult depression. *European Psychiatry, 30*(6), 665–680.

McGirr, A., Diaconu, G., Berlim, M. T., & Turecki, G. (2011). Personal and family history of suicidal behaviour is associated with lower peripheral cortisol in depressed outpatients. *Journal of Affective Disorders, 131*(1–3), 368–373.

Melhem, N. M., Brent, D. A., Ziegler, M., Lyengar, S., Kolko, D., Oquendo, M., . . . Mann, J. J. (2007). Familial pathways to early-onset suicidal behavior: Familial and individual antecedents of suicidal behavior. *American Journal of Psychiatry, 164*(9), 1304–1306.

Miklowitz, D. J. (2006). A review of evidence-based psychosocial interventions for bipolar disorder. *Journal of Clinical Psychiatry, 67,* 28.

Mosqueiro, B. P., da Rocha, N. S., & de Almeida Fleck, M. P. (2015). Intrinsic religiosity, resilience, quality of life, and suicide risk in depressed inpatients. *Journal of Affective Disorders, 179,* 128–133.

Mossakowski, K. N. (2015). Disadvantaged family background and depression among young adults in the United States: The roles of chronic stress and self-esteem. *Stress and Health: Journal of the International Society for the Investigation of Stress, 31*(1), 52–62.

Murray, C. J., Vos, T., Lozano R, Naghavi, M., Flaxman, A. D., Michaud, C., . . . Memish, Z. A. (2012). Disability-adjusted life years (DALYs) for 291 diseases and injuries in 21 regions, 1990–2010: A systematic analysis for the Global Burden of Disease Study 2010. *Lancet, 380,* 2197–2223.

Musick, K., & Bumpass, L. (2012). Re-examining the case for marriage: Union formation and changes in well-being. *Journal of Marriage and Family, 74,* 1–18.

Nilsson, K. K. (2016). Early maladaptive schemas in bipolar disorder patients with and without suicide attempts. *Journal of Nervous and Mental Disease, 204*(3), 236–239.

O'Connor, R. C., Smyth, R., & Williams, J. M. G. (2015). Intrapersonal positive future thinking predicts repeat suicide attempts in hospital-treated suicide attempters. *Journal of Consulting and Clinical Psychology, 83*(1), 169–176.

Ohayon, M. M. (2007). Epidemiology of depression and its treatment in the general population. *Journal of Psychiatric Research, 41*(3–4), 207–213.

O'Mahen, H. A., Karl, A., Moberly, N., & Fedock, G. (2015). The association between childhood maltreatment and emotion regulation: Two different mechanisms contributing to depression? *Journal of Affective Disorders, 174,* 287–295.

Oquendo, M. A., Galfalvy, H. C., Currier, D., Grunebaum, M. F., Sher, L., Sullivan, G. M., . . . Mann, J. J. (2011). Treatment of suicide attempters with bipolar disorder: A randomized clinical trial comparing lithium and valproate in the prevention of suicidal behavior. *The American Journal of Psychiatry, 169*(2), 223.

Oquendo, M. A., Lizardi, D., Greenwald, S., Weissman, M. M., & Mann, J. J. (2004). Rates of lifetime suicide attempt and rates of lifetime major depression in different ethnic groups in the United States. *Acta Psychiatrica Scandinavica, 110,* 446–451.

Oquendo, M. A., Waternaux, C., Brodsky, B., Parsons, B., Haas, G. L., Malone, K. M., & Mann, J. J. (2000). Suicidal behavior in bipolar mood disorder: Clinical characteristics of attempters and non-attempters. *Journal of Affective Disorders, 59,* 107–117.

O'Riley, A. A., Van Orden, K. A., He, H., Richardson, T. M., Podgorski, C., & Conwell, Y. (2014). Suicide and death ideation in older adults obtaining aging services. *American Journal of Geriatric Psychiatry, 22*(6), 614–622.

Owen, R., Gooding, P., Dempsey, R., & Jones, S. (2015). A qualitative investigation into the relationships between social factors and suicidal thoughts and acts experienced by people with a bipolar disorder diagnosis. *Journal of Affective Disorders, 176,* 133–140.

Patten, S. B., Wilkes, T. C. R., Williams, J. V. A., Lavorato, D. H., El-Guebaly, N., Schopflocher, D., Wild, C., Colman, I., Bulloch, A. G. (2014). Retrospective and prospectively assessed childhood adversity in association with major depression, alcohol consumption and painful conditions. *Epidemiology and Psychiatric Sciences, 24*(2), 158–165.

Patten, S. B., Williams, J. V., Lavorato, D. H., Fiest, K. M., Bulloch, A. G., & Wang, J. (2015). The prevalence of major depression is not changing. *Canadian Journal of Psychiatry, 60,* 31–34.

Patten, S. B., Williams, J. V. A., Lavorato, D. H., Bulloch, A. G. M., Wiens, K., & Wang, J. (2016). Why is major depression prevalence not changing? *Journal of Affective Disorders, 190,* 93–97.

Peters, A. T., Shankman, S. A., Deckersbach, T., & West, A. E. (2015). Predictors of first-episode unipolar major depression in individuals with and without sub-threshold depressive symptoms: A prospective, population-based study. *Psychiatry Research, 230*(2), 150–156.

Preston, J., & Johnson, J. (2016). *Clinical psychopharmacology made ridiculously simple* (8th ed). Miami, FL: MedMaster.

Royal Australian and New Zealand College of Psychiatrists Clinical Practice Guidelines Team for Depression. (2004). Australian and New Zealand Clinical Practice Guidelines for the treatment of depression. *Australian and New Zealand Journal of Psychiatry, 38*(6), 389–407.

Rawlings, J., Shevlin, M., Corcoran, R., Morriss, R., & Taylor, P. J. (2015). Out of the blue: Untangling the association between impulsivity and planning in self-harm. *Journal of Affective Disorders, 184,* 29–35.

Richards, D. (2011). Prevalence and clinical course of depression: A review. *Clinical Psychology Review, 31*(7), 1117–1125.

Richards, D., & Sanabria, A. S. (2014). Point-prevalence of depression and associated risk factors. *The Journal of Psychology: Interdisciplinary and Applied, 148*(3), 305–326.

Rihmer, Z. (2007). Suicide risk in mood disorders. *Current Opinions in Psychiatry, 20*(1), 17–22.

Rihmer, Z., Gonda, X., Torzsa, P., Kalabay, L., Akiskal, H. S., & Eory, A. (2013). Affective temperament, history of suicide attempt and family history of suicide in general practice patients. *Journal of Affective Disorders, 149*(1–3), 350–354.

Rosse, R. B., Fanous, A., Gaskins, B. L., & Deutsch, S. I. (2007). Side effects in the modern psychopharmacology of depression. *Primary Psychiatry, 14*(7), 50–58.

Rushing, N. C., Corsentino, E., Hames, J. L., Sachs-Ericsson, N., & Steffens, D. C. (2013). The relationship of religious involvement indicators and social support to current and past suicidality among depressed older adults. *Aging & Mental Health, 17*(3), 366–374.

Sachs, G. S., Printz, D. J., Kahn, D. A., Carpenter, D., & Docherty, J. P. (2000, April). The expert consensus guideline series: Medication treatment of bipolar disorder. *Postgraduate Medicine,* 1–104.

Sachs-Ericsson, N., Hames, J. L., Joiner, T. E., Corsentino, E., Rushing, N. C., Palmer, E., . . . Steffens, D. C. (2014). Differences between suicide attempters and nonattempters in depressed older patients: Depression severity, white-matter lesions, and cognitive functioning. *The American Journal of Geriatric Psychiatry, 22*(1), 75–85.

Santana, G. L., Coelho, B. M., Borges, G., Viana, M. C., Wang, Y. P., & Andrade, L. H. (2015). The influence of parental psychopathology on offspring suicidal behavior across the lifespan. *PLoS ONE, 10*(7), e0134970.

Saunders, K. E. A., & Hawton, K. (2015). Suicidal behaviour in bipolar disorder: Understanding the role of affective states. *Bipolar Disorders, 17*(1), 24–26.

Schaffer, A., Isometsä, E. T., Azorin, J., Cassidy, F., Goldstein, T., Rihmer, Z., . . . Yatham, L. (2015). A review of factors associated with greater likelihood of suicide attempts and suicide deaths in bipolar disorder: Part II of a report of the International Society for Bipolar Disorders Task Force on Suicide in Bipolar Disoder. *Australian and New Zealand Journal of Psychiatry, 49*(11), 1006–1020.

Schaffer, A., Sinyor, M., Reis, C., Goldstein, B. I., & Levitt, A. J. (2014). Suicide in bipolar disorder: Characteristics and subgroups. *Bipolar Disorders, 16*(7), 732–740.

Segal, D. L., Gottschling, J., Marty, M., Meyer, W. J., & Coolidge, F. L. (2015). Relationships among depressive, passive-aggressive, sadistic and self-defeating personality disorder features with suicidal ideation and reasons for living among older adults. *Aging & Mental Health, 19*(12), 1071–1077.

Shaffer, D., & Pfeffer, C. R. (2001). Practice parameter for the assessment and treatment of children and adolescents with suicidal behavior. *Journal of the American Academy of Child & Adolescent Psychiatry, 40*(Suppl. 7), 24S–51S.

Shen, G. H., Alloy, L. B., Abramson, L. Y., & Sylvia, L. G. (2008). Social rhythm regularity and the onset of affective episodes in bipolar spectrum individuals. *Bipolar Disorders, 10*(4), 520–529.

Shulman, K. I. (2010). Lithium for older adults with bipolar disorder: Should it still be considered a first-line agent? *Drugs & Aging, 27*(8), 607–615.

Song, J. Y., Yu, H. Y., Kim, S. H., Hwang, S. S. H., Cho, H. S., Kim, Y. S., . . . Ang, Y. M. (2012). Assessment of risk factors related to suicide attempts in patients with bipolar disorder. *Journal of Nervous and Mental Disease, 200*(11), 978–984.

Strakowski, S. M., McElroy, S. L., Keck, P. E. Jr., & West, S. A. (1996). Suicidality among patients with mixed and manic bipolar disorder. *American Journal of Psychiatry, 153,* 674–676.

Taylor, R. J., Chae, D. H., Lincoln, K. D., & Chatters, L. M. (2015). Extended family and friendship support networks are both protective and risk factors for major depressive disorder and depressive symptoms among African Americans and Black Caribbeans. *Journal of Nervous and Mental Disease, 203*(2), 132–140.

Thase, M. E. (1996). *Cognitive behavioral therapy manual for treatment of depressed inpatients.* New York, NY: Plenum.

Thase, M. E. (2008). Citalopram-resistant depression: Cognitive therapy and medication similarly effective as second line treatments. *Evidence-Based Mental Health, 11,* 48.

Thase, M. E., Friedman, E. S., Biggs, M. M., Wisniewski, S. R., Trivedi, M. H., Luther, J. F., . . . Rush, A. J. (2007). Cognitive therapy versus medication in augmentation and switch strategies as second-step treatments: A STAR*D report. *American Journal of Psychiatry, 164*(5), 739–752.

Thompson, E. A., Connelly, C. D., Thomas-Jones, D., & Eggert, L. L. (2013). School difficulties and co-occurring health risk factors: Substance use, aggression, depression, and suicidal behaviors. *Journal of Child and Adolescent Psychiatric Nursing, 26*(1), 74–84.

Tohen, M., Chengappa, K. R., Suppes, T., Zarate, C. A., Calabrese, J. R., Bowden, C. L., & Keeter, E. L. (2002). Efficacy of olanzapine in combination with valproate or lithium in the treatment of mania in patients partially nonresponsive to valproate or lithium monotherapy. *Archives of General Psychiatry, 59*(1), 62–69.

Tondo, L., Isacsson, G., & Baldessarini, R. J. (2003). Suicidal behaviour in bipolar disorder: Risk and prevention. *CNS Drugs, 17*(7), 491–511.

Tondo, L., Pompili, M., Forte, A., & Baldessarini, R. J. (2016). Suicide attempts in bipolar disorders: Comprehensive review of 101 reports. *Acta Psychiatrica Scandinavica, 133*(3), 174–186.

Tuisku, V., Kiviruusu, O., Pelkonen, M., Karlsson, L., Strandholm, T., & Marttunen, M. (2014). Depressed adolescents as young adults: Predictors of suicide attempt and non-suicidal self-injury during an 8-year follow-up. *Journal of Affective Disorders, 152–154*, 313–319.

U.S. Department of Health and Human Services, National Institutes of Health, National Institute of Mental Health. (2015). NIMH Strategic Plan for Research (NIH Publication No. 02-2650). Retrieved from http://www.nimh.nih.gov/about/strategic-planning-reports/index.shtml

Ustun, T. B., Ayuso-Mateos, J. L., Chatterji, S., Mathers, C., & Murray, C. J. (2004). Global burden of depressive disorders in the year 2000. *British Journal of Psychiatry, 184*, 386–392.

Valtonen, H. M., Suominen, K., Mantere, O., Leppamaki, S., Arvilommi, P., & Isometsa, E. (2007). Suicidal behaviour during different phases of bipolar disorder. *Journal of Affective Disorders, 97*(1–3), 101–107.

van der Waerden, J. E. B., Hoefnagels, C., Hosman, C. M. H., & Jansen, M. W. J. (2014). Defining subgroups of low socioeconomic status women at risk for depressive symptoms: The importance of perceived stress and cumulative risks. *International Journal of Social Psychiatry, 60*(8), 772–778.

Ward-Ciesielski, E. F., Schumacher, J. A., & Bagge, C. L. (2016). Relations between nonsuicidal self-injury and suicide attempt characteristics in a sample of recent suicide attempters. *Crisis: The Journal of Crisis Intervention and Suicide Prevention, 37*(4), 310–313.

Weinstein, S. M., & Mermelstein, R. J. (2013). Influences of mood variability, negative moods, and depression on adolescent cigarette smoking. *Psychology of Addictive Behaviors, 27*(4), 1068–1078.

Wolraich, M., Felice, M. E., & Drotar, D. (1996). *The classification of child and adolescent mental diagnoses in primary care: Diagnostic and statistical manual for primary care (DSM-PC) child and adolescent version.* Elk Grove Village, IL: American Academy of Pediatrics.

Yan, X.-Y., Huang, S.-M., Huang, C.-Q., Wu, W.-H., & Qin, Y. (2011). Marital status and risk for late life depression: A meta-analysis of the published literature. *Journal of International Medical Research, 39*, 1142–1154.

Yaroslavskya, I., Pettit, J. W., Lewinsohn, P. M., Seeley, J. R., & Roberts, R. E. (2013). Heterogeneous trajectories of depressive symptoms: Adolescent predictors and adult outcomes. *Journal of Affective Disorders, 148*, 391–399. doi:10.1016/j.jad.2012.06.028

Young, A. H., & Hammond, J. M. (2007). Lithium in mood disorders: Increasing evidence base, declining use? *British Journal of Psychiatry, 191*, 474–476.

Zaretsky, A. E., Rizvi, S., & Parikh, S. V. (2007). How well do psychosocial interventions work in bipolar disorder? *The Canadian Journal of Psychiatry, 52*(1), 14–21.

Zimmerman, M., Martinez, J., Young, D., Chelminski, I., Morgan, T. A., & Dalrymple, K. (2014). Comorbid bipolar disorder and borderline personality disorder and history of suicide attempts. *Journal of Personality Disorders, 28*(3), 358–364.

CHAPTER EIGHT

SCHIZOPHRENIA AND SUICIDE

In this chapter, a focused review of the suicide risk associated with schizophrenia is provided. Special attention to suicide within schizophrenia is critical as the rate of suicide among individuals with schizophrenia is among the highest of all psychiatric illness, with 10% to 15% of individuals with schizophrenia dying by suicide (Cohen, Test, & Brown, 1990; Hor & Taylor, 2010; Siris, 2001), a rate 20 to 50 times higher than that in the general population (Pinikahana, Happell, & Keks, 2003; Sinyor & Remington, 2012; Tiihonen et al., 2006). Furthermore, the rate of suicide with schizophrenia is increasing (Hor & Taylor, 2010; Maris, Berman, & Silverman, 2000).

GOALS AND OBJECTIVES

An understanding of:

- *Diagnostic and Statistical Manual of Mental Disorders (DSM-5)* criteria for schizophrenia
- Course of illness of schizophrenia
- Etiology and epidemiology of schizophrenia
- Relationship between schizophrenia and suicide
- Risk factors for suicide unique to individuals with schizophrenia
- Protective factors for suicide unique to individuals with schizophrenia
- Evidence-based practices for schizophrenia

Schizophrenia is a major public health issue that has devastating consequences for individuals, families, and society (Alberdi-Sudupe et al., 2011; Altamura, Fagiolini, Galderisi, Rocca, & Rossi, 2014; Buchanan & Carpenter, 2000; Dyck, Hendryx, Short, Voss, & McFarlane, 2002; Foldemo, Gullberg, Ek, & Bogren, 2005; Fuller-Thompson & Hollister, 2016; Kasckow, Golshan, & Zisook, 2014; Wu et al., 2005). Characterized by grossly impaired reality testing, which may manifest as delusions, hallucinations, negative symptoms, highly disorganized behavior or disorganized speech, and impaired interpersonal relationships, schizophrenia has an approximate lifetime risk of 1% (Altamura et al., 2014; Nylander & Gillberg, 2001). The onset of illness is earlier for males than for females, and approximately 90% of all individuals with schizophrenia are between the ages of 15 and 55 years (Gogtay, Vyas, Testa, Wood, & Pantelis, 2011; McGrath, Saha, Chant, & Welham, 2008; Vyas, Kumra, & Puri, 2010; Welham, Thomis, & McGrath, 2004). Schizophrenics represent about 16% of all psychiatric patients who receive treatment; however, the median untreated rate, or treatment gap, for schizophrenia including other nonaffective psychoses was 32.2% as compared to 56.3% for major depression, 50.2% for bipolar disorder, and

55.9% for panic disorder (Kohn, Saxena, Levav, & Saraceno, 2004; Lora et al., 2012). In a study examining treatment availability and utilization for schizophrenia across countries, significantly higher rates of nonutilization were found, with 89% in low-income countries and 69% and 63% for lower-middle-income and upper-middle-income countries, respectively (Lora et al., 2012). The study also found that among individuals with schizophrenia, 80% were treated in outpatient facilities and that the availability of psychiatrists and nurses in mental health facilities was a significant predictor of service accessibility and treatment nonutilization. Unfortunately, the probability of relapse of psychotic episodes is quite high in schizophrenia with some finding rates as high as 41% (Robinson, Woerner, Alvir, Bilder et al., 1999) and others finding rates of only 17% within the first year, 35% after 18 months, and 74% after 5 years (Robinson, Woerner, Alvir, Geisler et al., 1999). Others have found that the average length of untreated psychosis lasts 38 weeks, with a median of 12 weeks, and that long duration of untreated psychosis is predicted by poor insight, social isolation, and preserved coping skills and predicts poorer outcomes such as increased severity of symptoms and poorer treatment response when treatment is finally received (Drake, Clifford, Shahid, & Lewis, 2000). Interestingly, there is no current evidence that length of untreated psychosis is related to relapse rates (Norman & Malla, 2001).

Stereotypes regarding individuals with schizophrenia pervade our society. Individuals with schizophrenia are often and unfairly portrayed as violent, scary, and dangerous. Research traditionally indicated that individuals with serious mental illnesses, such as schizophrenia, are no more likely to become violent than individuals in the general community who are not abusing alcohol or substances (Angermeyer, 2002). More recent research has established that individuals with schizophrenia are significantly more likely to be violent than members of the general population; however, the proportion of societal violence attributable to these individuals with schizophrenia is rather small. The proportion of violent crime in society attributable to schizophrenia has been shown to consistently fall below 10% (Walsh, Buchanan, & Fahy, 2002). Other research has found that individuals with schizophrenia are thought to be at an increased risk of committing violent crime four to six times the level of individuals without this disorder (Fazel, Långström, Hjern, Grann, & Lichtenstein, 2009). There remains extreme stigma associated with the diagnosis of schizophrenia. Clinicians need to become aware of their personal and professional beliefs and assumptions regarding schizophrenia. Without such awareness, it will be impossible to engage in a positive, effective therapeutic relationship with individuals with schizophrenia.

Individual Exercise 8.1

1. When you hear the word "schizophrenia," what are the first words or thoughts that come to your mind? Write them down.
2. Are your listed words or thoughts generally positive or negative? Did they surprise you in any way? If so, how?
3. What personal *and* professional considerations and assumptions may make it hard for you to work with this population?
4. What personal *and* professional considerations may make it easy for you to work with this population?

DSM-5 DIAGNOSIS

No physical or lab tests exist today that can diagnose schizophrenia. However, physical testing can rule out other conditions that may have some overlapping symptomatology

(i. e., seizure disorders, metabolic disorders, thyroid disease, brain tumors, lupus, drug abuse) as a means of narrowing down potential diagnoses. Diagnosis is generally established via psychiatric assessment using the *Diagnostic and Statistical Manual of Mental Disorders* (5th ed.; *DSM-5*; American Psychiatric Association [APA], 2013).

Schizophrenia and other psychotic disorders are a serious mental illness (SMI). These conditions comprise a number of specific criteria or psychotic symptoms, across a fixed time frame, which are not accountable for other reasons. Psychotic symptoms are clustered as positive symptoms (e.g., hallucinations, delusions, disorganized speech) or negative symptoms (e.g., affective flattening, avolition, or lack of motivation). According to the *DSM-5*, the diagnostic criteria for schizophrenia include two or more of the following five core symptoms (APA, 2013):

- Delusions
- Hallucinations
- Disorganized speech
- Grossly disorganized or catatonic behavior
- Negative symptoms

In addition, these symptoms need to have led to social and/or occupational dysfunction in one or more areas of functioning (e.g., work, interpersonal relations, self-care). Signs of disturbance must be present for a minimum of 6 months, with at least 1 month of active symptoms. Finally, these symptoms or disturbances must not be a result of a schizoaffective or a depressive disorder diagnosis, substance induced, or due to another medical condition (APA, 2013). There are two notable differences in the *DSM-5* to prior versions of the *DSM*. One, the *DSM-5* encourages clinicians to rate the severity of a client's presentation on the five main symptoms on a 0 (not present) to 4 (present and severe) scale. Two, the *DSM-5* no longer includes subtypes of the illness that were present in the prior *DSM* versions, such as paranoid or disorganized subtypes.

Related conditions include *schizophreniform disorder* (which is very similar to schizophrenia except that its duration is under 6 months and it may result in less impairment in social/occupational functioning) and *brief psychotic disorder* (symptoms include positive psychotic symptoms with a duration under 1 month). Other psychotic conditions are *schizoaffective disorder* (similar symptoms as schizophrenia, plus either a major depressive episode, or manic episode during the same period of time), *delusional disorder* (nonbizarre fixed false beliefs, without any of the main diagnostic criteria for schizophrenia), *substance/medication-induced psychotic disorder* (predominant hallucinations or delusions resulting from the use of substances), *psychotic disorder due to another condition* (includes psychotic symptoms, but lacks adequate information to make a specific diagnosis), and *catatonia*, which may be related to several disorders (characterized by decreased psychomotor disturbances).

EPIDEMIOLOGY AND PROGNOSIS

The average age of onset for schizophrenia is between 15 and 25 years for males, and 25 and 35 years for females (Gogtay, 2011; Hafner et al., 1994; McGrath et al., 2008; Vyas et al., 2010; Welham, 2004). Research has generally categorized three age-specific groups in schizophrenia: adult onset (AOS), more than the age of 19 years; early onset (EOS), between 14 and 18 years of age; and childhood onset (COS), up to 13 years of age. A systematic review on the prevalence and incidence rates associated with schizophrenia found, across 188 and 158 studies, respectively, that the median prevalence rates per 1,000 persons for lifetime risk was 4.6 (0.46%; McGrath et al, 2008). This study also identified that the core incidence median estimate was 15.2 per 100,000 people. These findings are in line with the *DSM* lifetime prevalence of schizophrenia for adults more than 18 years of age, which is

0.3% to 0.7% (APA, 2013) and the annual incidence is 5 to 50 per 100,000 (APA, 2000). Although onset of psychotic conditions can emerge in youth, their presence in children is noticeably rarer. Schizophrenia in children younger than 15 years of age is less than 0.14 per 1,000 (Beitchman, 1985), with some general population studies estimating the prevalence in onset before age 15 years to be between 1.6 and 1.9 per 100,000 (Burd & Kerbeshian, 1987; Gillberg, 1984; Gillberg & Steffenburg, 1987; Nylander & Gillberg, 2001). However, the prevalence rates increase in adolescents, from 0.23% in 15- to 18-year-olds (Nylander & Gillberg, 2001) to approximately 1% of the general population by the age of 18 years (Regier et al., 1993).

Although the nature of schizophrenia and other psychotic conditions is episodic, these disorders are generally chronic due to frequent episodic symptom relapses, readmission to hospital, and impaired social functioning (Eaton et al., 1992; Lay, Blanz, Hartmann, & Schmidt, 2000; Schmidt, Blanz, Dippe, Koppe, & Lay, 1995).

The relapse rate for individuals with psychotic disorders ranges from 34% in 6 months to over 80% within 5 years (Geddes et al., 1994; Leucht et al., 2012; Robinson,Woerner, Alvir, Bilder et al., 1999; Zipurskya, Menezesa, & Streinera, 2013), and is a major challenge in the care and prognosis of patients (Geller et al., 2002; Leucht et al., 2012; Robinson, Woerner, Alvir, Geisler et al., 1999; Rosenfarb et al., 2001; Zipurskya et al., 2013). Consequently, individuals managing these conditions experience poor prognostic outcomes throughout their lives (Fleischhaker et al., 2005; Gillberg, Hellgren, & Gillberg, 1993; Remschmidt, Schulz, Martin, Warnke, & Trott, 1994; Ropcke & Eggers, 2005; Werry, McClellan, & Chard, 1991).

Prognosis is complicated by poor adherence to treatment recommendations (medication and psychosocial interventions), substance use, and negative family environment. Nonadherence rates among individuals diagnosed with schizophrenia range widely from 33% to 60% (Bergen, Hunt, Armitage, & Bashir, 1998; Gearing et al., 2009; Gerlach & Larsen, 1999; Hamann, Lipp, Christ-Zapp, Spellmann, & Kissling, 2014; King et al., 2014; Lacro, Dunn, Dolder, Leckband, & Jeste, 2002; Perkins, 2002; Svedberg, Mesterton, & Cullberg, 2001). In terms of psychopharmacological treatment, research demonstrates medication discontinuation rates of between 75% and 90% within 12 to 24 months of hospital discharge, while others have found that 74% of patients discontinue medication within 18 months (Wade Tai, Awenat, & Haddock, 2017). A review by Lacro et al. (2002) found nonadherence rates to antipsychotic medication ranging from 4% to 72% with a mean of 41%. Nonadherence to medications in individuals with psychosis may result in greater symptom relapses with a six-time increase in hospital readmission (Ascher-Svanum et al., 2006; Bodén, Brandt, Kieler, Andersen, & Reutfors, 2011; Dassa et al. 2010; Higashi et al., 2013; Knapp, King, Pugner, & Lapuerta, 2004; Law, Soumerai, Ross-Degnan, & Adams, 2008; Novick et al., 2010; Verdoux et al., 2000; Verdoux, Liraud, Assens, Abalan, & van Os, 2002; Wade et al., 2017; Zipurskya et al., 2013). Use or abuse of substances can further result in poor adherence or trigger another psychotic episode (Bergen et al., 1998; King et al., 2014; Olfson et al., 2000; Perkins et al., 2008; Sullivan, Wells, Morgenstern, & Leake, 1995). Also, family support has been generally associated with improved treatment compliance (Hamann et al., 2014; Olfson et al., 2000; Prentice-Dunn, Wilson, & Lyman, 1981; Ran, Leff, Hou, Xiang, & Chan, 2003), and negative family environment, characterized by expressed emotion (EE; emotional over involvement and/or criticism and dissatisfaction), has been associated with relapse (Amaresha & Venkatasubramanian, 2012; Doane & Becker, 1993; Giron & Gomez-Beneyto, 1995; Lenior, Dingemans, Schene, Hart, & Linszen, 2002; Vasconcelos e Sa, Wearden, Hartley, Emsley, & Barrowclough, 2016).

Expressed emotion embodies family attitudes, usually negative, toward the illness and/or the individual (Lenior et al., 2002) and is generally operationalized as emotional overinvolvement and/or criticism and dissatisfaction (Amaresha & Venkatasubramanian, 2012; Lenior et al. 2002; Vasconcelos e Sa et al., 2016). This variable has been frequently attributed as a predictor of poor outcomes (Amaresha & Venkatasubramanian, 2012; Bebbington & Kuipers, 1994; Birchwood, Todd, & Jackson, 1998; Heinrichs, Bertram, Kuschel, &

Hahlweg, 2005; Jackson, Smith, & McGorry, 1990; Lenior et al., 2002; Loebel et al., 1992; Vasconcelos e Sa et al., 2016; Wyatt, Damiani, & Henter, 1998) and is associated with relapse (Doane & Becker, 1993; Giron & Gomez-Beneyto, 1995) Parents, partners, and families are impacted by the illness, which, in turn, affects their interaction with the individual, thereby influencing outcomes positively or negatively. Consequently, to be effective, interventions need to strengthen positive family support and minimize negative family interaction.

SCHIZOPHRENIA AND SUICIDE

On average, individuals with schizophrenia and psychotic disorders are two to three times as likely to die prematurely (Auquier, Lançon, Rouillon, & Lader, 2007; Bushe, Taylor, & Haukka, 2010; Fazel, Wolf, Palm, & Lichtenstein, 2014; Henderson, Vincenzi, Andrea, Ulloa, & Copeland, 2015; Martin et al., 2014; Saha, Chant, & McGrath, 2007). Suicide accounts for an excessive percentage of these deaths as compared to those in the general population. On examining, the suicide mortality of patients with schizophrenia is associated with a reduced life span, with over 15% lifetime risk for suicide and a 50% prevalence of suicide attempts (Harvey & Bowie, 2013). One notable study found that over 50% of deaths that occur in the first year of illness and 30% within 10 years are due to suicide (Limosin, Loze, Philippe, Casadebaig, & Rouillon, 2007). Study results also found a 16 times higher rate of suicide among individuals with schizophrenia compared to the general population (Limosin et al., 2007). One national study found that among individuals discharged from the hospital post first episode of psychosis within schizophrenia who are not taking any regular antipsychotic medication have a 37-fold increase in death by suicide (Tiihonen et al., 2006). Another seminal meta-analysis found that one in every 20 individuals with schizophrenia will commit suicide (Palmer, Pankratz, & Bostwick, 2005). Overall, research has reported that approximately 10% of all individuals diagnosed with schizophrenia will complete suicide (Sinyor & Remington, 2012; Caldwell & Gottesman, 1990). However, other research suggests the rates may not be as high. These studies have found the lifetime suicide rate for individuals with schizophrenia to be nearer to 5% (Hor & Taylor, 2010; Palmer et al., 2005). Research has also indicated a heightened risk of attempted suicide, with studies reporting a rate of suicide attempt as high as an estimated 20% to 40% (Clarke et al., 2006; Fuller-Thompson & Hollister 2016; Pompili et al., 2007; Siris et al., 2001; Suokas et al., 2010; Yildiz, Yazici, & Böke, 2010). Other research has found that the lifetime prevalence of suicide attempts among individuals with schizophrenia was 39.2% versus 2.8% of those without the disorder. After controlling for sociodemographic characteristics, childhood adverse experiences, substance use disorders, depression/anxiety, and chronic pain, individuals with schizophrenia had six times the likelihood of attempting suicide (Fuller-Thompson & Hollister, 2016).

Risk Factors

A number of key predictors of suicide for individuals diagnosed with a psychotic condition include:

- Male gender (Foster, 2013; Hor & Taylor, 2010)
- Younger individuals (Foster, 2013; Hor & Taylor, 2010; Popovic et al., 2014)
- Drug use/abuse (Bani-Fatemi et al., 2013; Hor & Taylor, 2010; McLean, Gladman, & Mowry, 2012; Melle & Barrett, 2012; Popovic et al., 2014)
- Prior attempts (Bani-Fatemi et al., 2013; Fleischhacker et al., 2014; Foster, 2013; Hor & Taylor, 2010; Kao & Liu, 2011; Melle & Barrett, 2012; Popovic et al., 2014; Sanchez-Gistau et al., 2013)

- Family history of suicide/suicide attempt (Abel et al., 2014; Foster, 2013; Hor & Taylor, 2010; Mauri, Paletta, Maffini, Moliterno, & Altamura, 2013)
- Comorbid disorders (especially mood disorders; Bani-Fatemi et al., 2013; Fleischhacker et al., 2014; Hor & Taylor, 2010; Kao & Liu, 2011; Melle & Barrett, 2012; Popovic et al., 2014; Sanchez-Gistau et al., 2013; Togay, Noyan, Tasdelen, & Ucok, 2015)
- Presence of hallucinations (Bani-Fatemi et al., 2013; DeVylder & Hilimire, 2015; Hor & Taylor, 2010; Kjelby et al., 2015; Lui, 2009)
- Impulsivity (Doihara et al., 2012; Melle & Barrett, 2012; Nanda et al., 2016; also shown to be a risk factor for suicidal ideation; Iancu et al., 2010)
- Greater insight into illness (Hor & Taylor, 2010; Kao & Liu, 2011; Lysaker, Buck, Salvatore, Popolo, & Dimaggio, 2009; Melle & Barrett, 2012), potentially mediated by depression and/or hopelessness (López-Moríñigo, Ramos-Ríos, David, & Dutta, 2012)
- Poor adherence to treatment (Gut-Fayand et al., 2001; Hawton, Sutton, Haw, Sinclair, & Deeks, 2005; Hor & Taylor, 2010; Limosin et al., 2007; Montross, Zisook, & Kasckow, 2005; Moran et al., 2003; Radomsky, Haas, Mann, & Sweeney, 1999; Sinclair, Mullee, King, & Baldwin, 2004; Togay et al., 2015)
- Poor social functioning (Jahn, DeVylder, Drapalski, Medoff, & Dixon, 2016)
- Negative, poor, or minimal family support and family stigma (Beiser, Erickson, Fleming, & Iacono, 1993; Birchwood, Todd, & Jackson, 1998; Janssen et al., 2004; Johnstone, Macmillan, Frith, Benn, & Crow, 1990; Kavanagh, 1992; Linszen et al., 1994; Ran et al., 2003; Wyatt et al., 1998), especially within the context of sibling relationship (Bowman, Alvarez-Jimenez, Howie, McGorry, & Wade, 2015)
- Negative religious coping (Rosmarin, Bigda-Peyton, Öngur, Pargament, & Björgvinsson, 2013)
- Early stage of illness (Ayesa-Arriola et al., 2015; Fleischhacker et al., 2014; Foster, 2013; Mauri, 2013; Palmer et al., 2005; Popovic et al., 2014)
- Negative recent life events (Foster, 2013)
- History of childhood maltreatment (Conus, Cotton, Schimmelmann, McGorry, & Lambert, 2010; Faravelli et al., 2014; Hassan, Stuart, & De Luca, 2016; Larsson et al., 2013)
- History of hospitalization (Popovic et al., 2014; Qin & Nordentoft, 2005) with an increased risk of suicide within the first week of admission and the first week after discharge (Qin & Nordentoft, 2005)
- Number of hospital admissions (Popovic et al., 2014)

Protective Factors

Conversely, though fewer, protective factors have been identified among individuals with psychotic disorders that serve to reduce the risk of suicide. These include:

- Supportive family environments, which have been linked to positive outcomes including reduced relapse rates (Beiser et al., 1993; Birchwood, Todd, & Jackson, 1998; Janssen et al., 2004; Johnstone et al., 1990; Kavanagh, 1992; Linszen et al., 1994; Machell, Rallis, & Esposito-Smythers, 2016; Ran et al., 2003; Wyatt et al., 1998)
- Lower IQ (Webb, Långström, Runeson, Lichtenstein, & Fazel, 2011)
- Adherence to treatment (Hor & Taylor, 2010; Lui, 2009)
- Positive self-appraisal (Johnson et al., 2010)
- Personal sense of recovery (protective factor against suicide ideation; Jahn et al., 2016)
- Personal characteristics (greater self-directedness and cooperativeness; Albayrak, Ekinci, & Çayköylü, 2012; Margetić et al., 2012)

Case Vignette 8.1

Adam is a 19-year-old single White, Jewish male. He is a high school graduate and has completed 1 year of college. He was raised in an upper-middle-class family where academic and career success was extremely important, as was their Orthodox faith. Adam was the last of five children. Seven years apart from the next youngest of his siblings, Adam was an unplanned child. He was a good student but had to work hard to earn his grades. He had several friends and dated occasionally throughout high school, but never had a serious girlfriend or a best friend.

After graduation from high school, Adam went away to college. He did well in his first semester and passed all of his classes with above-average grades, but the adjustment to living away from home and college life was not easy. During the spring semester, Adam began to act in bizarre ways. He became more withdrawn and suspicious of the people he befriended in the fall semester. When he came home for the summer after his first year, his parents noted that he talked to himself all the time. When they asked him about it, he indicated that he might be hearing voices. Confused and afraid, his parents agreed they would "wait and see if he got any worse" before they "jumped to any conclusions that Adam was crazy and needed help." Adam returned to school that fall but was unable to concentrate in class and began to experience increased paranoia toward his classmates, and after only a few weeks dropped out and returned home. Over the next year, Adam continued to isolate himself socially. He would not go out with any of his friends or family members and eventually refused to even speak on the phone to anyone. When Adam refused to leave his house for over 3 weeks, insisting that someone was "waiting to take (him)," his parents finally insisted that he see a psychiatrist.

On mental status examination, Adam is alert and oriented x3. His clothes are appropriate. He has a full range of affect although often it is inappropriate (laughing while discussing his beliefs that the world is ending and that he is being followed by the Central Itelligence Agency (CIA) who wants to kill him for this secret knowledge he has). He denies feeling depressed although he reports feeling saddened by the idea that he will die so young. He reports feeling as though "people can tell what I am thinking" and that he "knows that I am being watched because the CIA wants to keep me from telling everyone what I know." Adam does not deny that he hears voices that "warn me about the CIA outside of his house" and feels as though the voices are telling him the truth and he must do as they say. Sometimes the voices tell him to kill himself before the CIA gets to him. He has a plan of how he will "do it just in case the CIA is able to infiltrate his home."

ROLE-PLAY 8.1

Using Case Vignette 8.1, in groups of three (clinician, client, and observer), engage the client and conduct an assessment for schizophrenia and suicide risk. What specific risk and protective factors should you consider? Be aware of your personal and professional attitudes in working with this client. What other information would you need to know?

CURRENT PRACTICE GUIDELINES AND EVIDENCE-BASED PRACTICE

Research into the treatment of schizophrenia has highlighted the efficacy of psychopharmacological treatment, specifically atypical antipsychotic medications. There is a substantial and growing body of empirical evidence that supports their effectiveness as a necessary treatment for positive symptoms (e.g., hallucinations, delusions, thought disorder) and to a lesser extent for negative symptoms (e.g., withdrawal, apathy; Chapman & Large, 2015; Gearing, Mian, & Charach, 2008; Kiviniemi et al., 2013; Reutfors et al., 2013; Robinson, Woerner, Delman, & Kane, 2005; Thomas, Jiang, & McCombs, 2015; Wasserman et al., 2012). Specific psychopharmacological treatments, such as clozapine, have demonstrated effectiveness in reducing the risk of suicide in individuals with schizophrenia (Foster, 2013; Meltzer, 2005; Meltzer et al., 2003; Novakovic & Sher, 2012; Wasserman et al., 2012). At present, clozapine is the only medication approved by the U.S. Food and Drug Administration for preventing suicide in patients with schizophrenia (Kasckow, Felmet, & Zisook, 2011).

The APA in 2004 and the American Academy of Child and Adolescent Psychiatry (AACAP) in 2013 released practice parameters that recommend a comprehensive multimodal treatment approach to reduce symptoms, morbidity, and relapse rates while aiming to maintain the individual at home and in the community (McClellan, 2013; McClellan, & Stock, 2013). Specifically, the first-line treatments include atypical antipsychotics or traditional antipsychotic medications in conjunction with a number of adjunctive psychosocial and psychoeducational interventions including information about the illness, treatment options, social skills training, relapse prevention, life skills training, and coping and problem-solving strategies. In working with individuals with schizophrenia, a limited number of evidence-based practice (EBP) interventions have been developed. EBPs found to be effective in working with adults with schizophrenia at risk of suicide include cognitive behavioral therapy (CBT; Kuller, Ott, Goisman, Wainwright, & Rabin, 2010; Rathod, Phiri, & Kingdon, 2010; Tai & Turkington, 2009; Wasserman et al., 2012), and psychoeducational family treatment (Lincoln, Wilhelm, & Nestoriuc, 2007; Pilling et al., 2002; Pitschel-Walz, Leucht, Baumi, Kissling, & Engel, 2015; Pharoah, Mari, Rathbone, & Wong, 2010). See Part II of this book for more on effective treatments.

SUMMARY

The majority of individuals diagnosed with a psychotic disorder do not complete suicide. However, those with a psychotic disorder diagnosed are at an elevated risk for suicide ideation, attempts, and completions. It is important to recognize the unique risk and protective factors associated with suicide among those with schizophrenia or psychotic disorders. It is also important to be vigilant regarding the potential impact of personal assumptions and bias in working with this population. Individuals managing these serious mental illnesses have a wide range of strengths and abilities that can effectively be supported and enhanced.

KEY POINTS

1. Schizophrenia is characterized by the presence of positive and negative symptoms that can lead to grossly impaired functioning.
2. The average age of onset for schizophrenia is between 15 and 25 years for males, and 25 and 35 years for females.
3. Prognosis is complicated by poor adherence to treatment recommendations (medication and psychosocial interventions), substance use, and family environment.

(continued)

> ### KEY POINTS (*continued*)
>
> 4. On average, individuals with schizophrenia and psychotic disorders are two to three times as likely to die prematurely.
> 5. Approximately 10% (range 5%–15%) of individuals with schizophrenia will die by suicide.
> 6. The rate of suicide among individuals diagnosed with schizophrenia is approximately 15 to 20 times higher than among the general population.
> 7. Key predictors of suicide for individuals diagnosed with a psychotic condition include male gender, drug use/abuse, prior attempts, shorter duration of illness, comorbid disorders (e.g., depressive disorders, personality disorders), social isolation, and poor adherence to treatment.
> 8. Practice parameters recommend a comprehensive multimodal treatment approach.

ELECTRONIC RESOURCES

NATIONAL ALLIANCE FOR THE MENTALLY ILL

www.nami.org

NATIONAL SCHIZOPHRENIA FOUNDATION

www.NSFoundation.org

NATIONAL INSTITUTE OF MENTAL HEALTH

www.nimh.nih.gov/health/topics/schizophrenia/index.shtml

KNOWLEDGE ACQUISITION TEST (KAT)

True or False

1. Males with schizophrenia have a better prognosis than females.
2. Females have a later age of onset of schizophrenia than males.
3. The rate of suicide among individuals with schizophrenia is the same as that of the general population.
4. Substance abuse is not a risk factor for suicide among individuals with schizophrenia.
5. Expressed emotion reduces the risk of suicide among individuals with schizophrenia.
6. Individuals with schizophrenia and psychotic disorders are two to three times as likely to die prematurely.
7. Personal characteristics such as increased self-directedness and cooperativeness are protective factors for individuals with schizophrenia.
8. The rate of relapse among individuals with schizophrenia is less than 50% after 5 years of follow-up.

Short Answer

9. What are the three age-specific onset categories often used with individuals diagnosed with schizophrenia?
10. List the key risk factors for suicide among individuals with schizophrenia.
11. List the key protective factors for suicide among individuals with schizophrenia.
12. Describe the recommended practice guidelines for treatment of individuals with schizophrenia.

Multiple Choice

13. Which item in the following list is not a *DSM-5* criterion for schizophrenia?
    A. Auditory hallucinations
    B. Disorganized speech
    C. Loss of appetite
    D. Delusions
    E. All of the above
    F. None of the above
14. Which of the following is not a psychotic spectrum diagnosis?
    A. Schizophrenia
    B. Schizophreniform
    C. Schizoaffective
    D. Brief psychotic
    E. All of the above
    F. None of the above
15. Which of the following items is a risk factor among individuals with schizophrenia?
    A. Delusions
    B. Comorbid depression
    C. Hallucinations
    D. Confused thinking
    E. All of the above
    F. None of the above

REFERENCES

Abel, K. M., Heuvelman, H. P., Jörgensen, L., Magnusson, C., Wicks, S., Susser, E., . . . Dalman, C. (2014). Severe bereavement stress during the prenatal and childhood periods and risk of psychosis in later life: Population based cohort study. *British Medical Journal, 348*, f7679.

Albayrak, Y., Ekinci, O., & Çayköylü, A. (2012). Temperament and character personality profile relation to suicide attempts in patients with schizophrenia. *Comprehensive Psychiatry, 53*(8), 1130–1136.

Alberdi-Sudupe, J., Pita-Fernández, S., Gómez-Pardiñas, S. M., Iglesias-Gil-de-Bernabé, F., García-Fernández, J., Martínez-Sande, G., . . . Pértega-Díaz, S. (2011). Suicide attempts and related factors in patients admitted to a general hospital: A ten-year cross-sectional study (1997–2007). *BioMed Central Psychiatry, 11*(1), 51–60.

Altamura, C., Fagiolini, A., Galderisi, Rocca, P., & Rossi, A. (2014). Schizophrenia today: Epidemiology, diagnosis, course and models of care. *Journal of Psychopathology/Giornale di Psicopatologia, 20*(3), 223–243.

Amaresha, A. C., & Venkatasubramanian, G. (2012). Expressed emotion in schizophrenia: An overview. *Indian Journal of Psychological Medicine, 34*(1), 12–20.

American Academy of Child and Adolescent Psychiatry. (2013). Summary of the practice parameters for the assessment and treatment of children and adolescents with schizophrenia. *Journal of the American Academy of Child & Adolescent Psychiatry, 39*(12), 1580–1582.

American Psychiatric Association. (2013). *Diagnostic and statistical manual of mental disorders, text revision* (5th ed.). Arlington, VA: American Psychiatric Publishing.

Angermeyer, M. C. (2002). Schizophrenia and violence. *Acta Psychiatrica Scandinavica, 102*(407), 63–67.

Ascher-Svanum, H., Faries, D. E., Zhu, B., Ernst, F. R., Swartz, M. S., & Swanson, J. W. (2006). Medication adherence and long-term functional outcomes in the treatment of schizophrenia in usual care. *Journal of Clinical Psychiatry, 67*(3), 453–460.

Auquier, P., Lançon, C., Rouillon, F., & Lader, M. (2007). Mortality in schizophrenia. *Pharmacoepidemiology and Drug Safety, 16*(12), 1308–1312.

Ayesa-Arriola, R., Alcaraz, E. G., Hernández, B. V., Pérez-Iglesias, R., López Moríñigo, J. D., Duta, R., . . . Crespo-Facorro, B. (2015). Suicidal behaviour in first-episode non-affective psychosis: Specific risk periods and stage-related factors. *European Neuropsychopharmacology, 25*(12), 2278–2288.

Bani-Fatemi, A., Gonçalves, V. F., Zai, C., de Souza, R., Le Foll, B., Kennedy, J. L., . . . De Luca, V. (2013). Analysis of CpG SNPs in 34 genes: Association test with suicide attempt in schizophrenia. *Schizophrenia Research, 147*(2–3), 262–268.

Bebbington, P., & Kuipers, L. (1994). The predictive utility of expressed emotion in schizophrenia: An aggregate analysis. [erratum appears in *Psychological Medicine* 1995; 25(1): 215]. *Psychological Medicine, 24*(3), 707–718.

Beiser, M., Erickson, D., Fleming, J. A., & Iacono, W. G. (1993). Establishing the onset of psychotic illness. *American Journal of Psychiatry, 150*(9), 1349–1354.

Beitchman, J. H. (1985). Childhood schizophrenia: A review and comparison with adult-onset schizophrenia. *Psychiatric Clinics of North America, 8*(4), 793–814.

Bergen, J., Hunt, G., Armitage, P., & Bashir, M. (1998). Six-month outcome following a relapse of schizophrenia. *Australian and New Zealand Journal of Psychiatry, 32*(6), 815–822.

Birchwood, M., Todd, P., & Jackson, C. (1998). Early intervention in psychosis: The critical period hypothesis. *British Journal of Psychiatry—Supplementum, 172*(33), 53–59.

Bodén, R., Brandt, L., Kieler, H., Andersen, M., & Reutfors, J. (2011). Early non-adherence to medication and other risk factors for rehospitalization in schizophrenia and schizoaffective disorder. *Schizophrenia Research, 133*(1–3), 36–41.

Bowman, S., Alvarez-Jimenez, M., Howie, L., McGorry, P., & Wade, D. (2015). The impact of first-episode psychosis on the sibling relationship. *Psychiatry: Interpersonal and Biological Processes, 78*(2), 141–155.

Buchanan, R. W., & Carpenter, W. T. (2000). Schizophrenia. In B. J. Saddock & V. A. Saddock (Eds.), *Comprehensive textbook of psychiatry* (7th ed., pp. 1096–1110). Philadelphia, PA: Lippincott, Williams & Wilkins.

Burd, L., & Kerbeshian, J. (1987). A North Dakota prevalence study of schizophrenia presenting in childhood. *Journal of the American Academy of Child & Adolescent Psychiatry, 26*(3), 347–350.

Bushe, C. J., Taylor, M., & Haukka, J. (2010). Review: Mortality in schizophrenia: A measurable clinical endpoint. *Journal of Psychopharmacology, 24*(11 Suppl. 4), 17–25.

Caldwell, C. B., & Gottesman, I. (1990). Schizophrenics kill themselves too: A review of risk factors for suicide. *Schizophrenia Bulletin, 16*, 571–589.

Chapman, C. L., & Large, M. M. (2015). Should clozapine be available to people with early schizophrenia and suicidal ideation? *Australian and New Zealand Journal of Psychiatry, 49*(4), 393.

Clarke, M., Whitty, P., Browne, S., McTigue, O., Kinsella, A., Waddington, J. L., . . . Callaghan, E. O. (2006). Suicidality in first episode psychosis. *Schizophrenia Research, 86*(1–3), 221–225.

Cohen, L. J., Test, M. A., & Brown, R. L. (1990). Suicide and schizophrenia: Data from a prospective community treatment study. *American Journal of Psychiatry, 147*, 602–607.

Conus, P., Cotton, S., Schimmelmann, B. G., McGorry, P. D., & Lambert, M. (2010). Pretreatment and outcome correlates of sexual and physical trauma in an epidemiological cohort of first-episode psychosis patients. *Schizophrenia Bulletin, 36*(6), 1105–1114.

Dassa, D., Boyer, L., Benoit, M., Bourcet, S., Raymondet, P., & Bottai, T. (2010). Factors associated with medication non-adherence in patients suffering from schizophrenia: A cross-sectional study in a universal coverage health-care system. *Australian and New Zealand Journal of Psychiatry, 44*(10), 921–928.

DeVylder, J. E., & Hilimire, M. R. (2015). Suicide risk, stress sensitivity, and self-esteem among young adults reporting auditory hallucinations. *Health & Social Work, 40*(3), 175–181.

Doane, J. A., & Becker, D. F. (1993). Changes in family emotional climate and course of psychiatric illness in hospitalized young adults and adolescents. *New Trends in Experimental & Clinical Psychiatry, 9*(3), 63–77.

Doihara, C., Kawanishi, C., Ohyama, N., Yamada, T., Nakagawa, M., Iwamoto, Y., . . . Hirayasu, Y. (2012). Trait impulsivity in suicide attempters: Preliminary study. *Psychiatry and Clinical Neurosciences, 66*(6), 529–532.

Drake, R. J., Clifford, J. H., Shahid, A., & Lewis, S. W. (2000). Causes and consequences of duration of untreated psychosis in schizophrenia. *The British Journal of Psychiatry, 177*(6), 511–515.

Dyck, D. G., Hendryx, M. S., Short, R. A., Voss, W. D., & McFarlane, W. R. (2002). Service use among patients with schizophrenia in psychoeducational multiple-family group treatment. *Psychiatric Services, 53*(6), 749–754.

Eaton, W. W., Mortensen, P. B., Herrman, H., Freeman, H., Bilker, W., Burgess, P., . . . Wooff, K. (1992). Long-term course of hospitalization for schizophrenia: Part I. Risk for rehospitalization. *Schizophrenia Bulletin, 18*(2), 217–228.

Faravelli, C., Castellini, G., Fioravanti, G., Sauro, C. L., Pietrini, F., Lelli, L., . . . Ricca, V. (2014). Different childhood adversities are associated with different symptom patterns in adulthood. *Psychotherapy and Psychosomatics, 83*(5), 320–321.

Fazel, S., Långström, N., Hjern, A., Grann, M., & Lichtenstein, P. (2009). Schizophrenia, substance abuse, and violent crime. *Journal of American Medical Association, 301*(19), 2016–2023.

Fazel, S., Wolf, A., Palm, C., & Lichtenstein, P. (2014). Violent crime, suicide, and premature mortality in patients with schizophrenia and related disorders: A 38-year total population study in Sweden. *The Lancet Psychiatry, 1*(1), 44–54.

Fleischhacker, W. W., Kane, J. M., Geier, J., Karayal, O., Kolluri, S., Eng, S. M., . . . Strom, B. L. (2014). Completed and attempted suicides among 18,154 subjects with schizophrenia included in a large simple trial. *The Journal of Clinical Psychiatry, 75*(3), e184–e190.

Fleischhaker, C., Schulz, E., Tepper, K., Martin, M., Hennighausen, K., & Remschmidt, H. (2005). Long-term course of adolescent schizophrenia. *Schizophrenia Bulletin, 31*(3), 769–780.

Foldemo, A., Gullberg, M., Ek, A. C., & Bogren, L. (2005). Quality of life and burden in parents of outpatients with schizophrenia. *Social Psychiatry & Psychiatric Epidemiology, 40*(2), 133–138.

Foster, T. J. (2013). Suicide prevention as a prerequisite for recovery from severe mental illness. *International Journal of Psychiatry in Medicine, 46*(1), 15–25.

Fuller-Thomson, E. & Hollister, B. (2016). Schizophrenia and suicide attempts: Findings from a representative community-based Canadian sample. *Schizophrenia Research and Treatment*, 1–15.

Gearing, R. E., & Mian, I. A. (2005). An approach to maximizing treatment adherence of children and adolescents with psychotic disorders and major mood disorders. *The Canadian Child and Adolescent Psychiatry Review, 14*(4), 106–113.

Gearing, R. E., Mian, I., & Charach, A. (2008). Promoting adherence with children and adolescents with psychosis. *Child and Adolescent Psychopharmacology News, 13*(5–11).

Gearing, R. E., Mian, I. A., Sholonsky, A., Barber, J., Nicholas, D., Lewis, R., . . . Ickowicz, A. (2009). Developing a risk-model of time to first-relapse for children and adolescents diagnosed with psychotic disorders or mood disorders with psychotic features. *Journal of Nervous and Mental Disease, 197*, 6–14.

Geddes, J., Mercer, G., Frith, C. D., MacMillan, F., Owens, D. G., & Johnstone, E. C. (1994). Prediction of outcome following a first episode of schizophrenia. A follow-up study of Northwick Park first episode study subjects. *British Journal of Psychiatry, 165*(5), 664–668.

Geller, B., Craney, J. L., Bolhofner, K., Nickelsburg, M. J., Williams, M., & Zimerman, B. (2002). Two-year prospective follow-up of children with a prepubertal and early adolescent bipolar disorder phenotype. *American Journal of Psychiatry, 159*(6), 927–933.

Gerlach, J., & Larsen, E. B. (1999). Subjective experience and mental side-effects of antipsychotic treatment. *Acta Psychiatrica Scandinavica, Supplementum, 395*, 113–117.

Gillberg, C. (1984). Infantile autism and other childhood psychoses in a Swedish urban region: Epidemiological aspects. *Journal of Child Psychology and Psychiatry, 25*(1), 35–43.

Gillberg, C., Hellgren, L., & Gillberg, C. (1993). Psychotic disorders diagnosed in adolescence: Outcome at age 30 years. *Journal of Child Psychology and Psychiatry and Allied Disciplines, 34*, 1173–1185.

Gillberg, C., & Steffenburg, S. (1987). Outcome and prognostic factors in infantile autism and similar conditions: A population-based study of 46 cases followed through puberty. *Journal of Autism and Developmental Disorders, 17*(2), 273–287.

Giron, M., & Gomez-Beneyto, M. (1995). Relationship between family attitudes measured by the semantic differential and relapse in schizophrenia: A 2-year follow-up prospective study. *Psychological Medicine, 25*(2), 365–371.

Gogtay, N., Vyas, N. S., Testa, R., Wood, S. J., & Pantelis, C. (2011). Age of onset of schizophrenia: Perspectives from structural neuroimaging studies. *Schizophrenia Bulletin, 37*(3), 504–513.

Gut-Fayand, A., Dervaux, A., Olie, J. P., Loo, H., Poirier, M. F., & Krebs, M. O. (2001). Substance abuse and suicidality in schizophrenia: A common risk factor linked to impulsivity. *Psychiatry Research, 102*(1), 65–72.

Hafner, H., Maurer, K., Loffler, W., Fatkenheuer, B., van der Heiden, W., Riecher-Rossler, A., . . . Gattaz, W. F. (1994). The epidemiology of early schizophrenia: Influence of age and gender on onset and early course. *British Journal of Psychiatry—Supplementum, 23*, 29–38.

Hamann, J., Lipp, M. L., Christ-Zapp, S., Spellmann, I., & Kissling, W. (2014). Psychiatrist and patient responses to suspected medication **nonadherence** in **schizophrenia** spectrum disorders. *Services, 65*(7), 881–887.

Harvey, P. D., & Bowie, C. R. (2013). Schizophrenia spectrum conditions. In G. Stricker, T. A. Widiger, & I. B. Weiner (Eds.), *Handbook of psychology: Clinical psychology* (2nd ed., Vol. 8, pp. 240–261). Hoboken, NJ: John Wiley.

Hassan, A. N., Stuart, E. A., & De Luca, V. (2016). Childhood maltreatment increases the risk of suicide attempt in schizophrenia. *Schizophrenia Research, 176*(2–3), 572–577.

Hawton, K., Sutton, L., Haw, C., Sinclair, J., & Deeks, J. J. (2005). Schizophrenia and suicide: Systematic review of risk factors. *British Journal of Psychiatry, 187*, 9–20.

Heinrichs, N., Bertram, H., Kuschel, A., & Hahlweg, K. (2005). Parent recruitment and retention in a universal prevention program for child behavior and emotional problems: Barriers to research and program participation. *Prevention Science, 6*(4), 275–286.

Henderson, D. C., Vincenzi, B., Andrea, N. V., Ulloa, M., & Copeland, P. M. (2015). Pathophysiological mechanisms of increased cardiometabolic risk in people with schizophrenia and other severe mental illnesses. *The Lancet Psychiatry, 2*(5), 452–464.

Higashi, K., Medic, G., Littlewood, K. L., Diez, T., Granström, O., & De Hert, M. (2013). Medication adherence in schizophrenia: Factors influencing adherence and consequences of nonadherence: A systematic literature review. *Therapeutic Advances in Psychopharmacology, 3*(4), 200–218.

Hor, K., & Taylor, M. (2010). Suicide and schizophrenia: A systematic review of rates and risk factors. *Journal of Psychopharmacology, 24*(11 Suppl. 4), 81–90.

Iancu, I., Bodner, E., Roitman, S., Piccone Sapir, A., Poreh, A., & Kotler, M. (2010). Impulsivity, aggression and suicide risk among male schizophrenia patients. *Psychopathology, 43*(4), 223–229.

Jackson, H. J., Smith, N., & McGorry, P. (1990). Relationship between expressed emotion and family burden in psychotic disorders: An exploratory study. *Acta Psychiatrica Scandinavica, 82*(3), 243–249.

Jahn, D. R., DeVylder, J. E., Drapalski, A. L., Medoff, D., & Dixon, L. B. (2016). Personal recovery as a protective factor against suicide ideation in individuals with schizophrenia. *Journal of Nervous and Mental Disease, 204*(11), 827–831.

Janssen, I., Krabbendam, L., Bak, M., Hanssen, M., Vollebergh, W., de Graaf, R., & van Os, J. (2004). Childhood abuse as a risk factor for psychotic experiences. *Acta Psychiatrica Scandinavica, 109*(1), 38–45.

Johnson, J., Gooding, P. A., Wood, A. M., Taylor, P. J., Pratt, D., & Tarrier, N. (2010). Resilience to suicidal ideation in psychosis: Positive self-appraisals buffer the impact of hopelessness. *Behaviour Research and Therapy*, *48*(9), 883–889.

Johnstone, E. C., Macmillan, J. F., Frith, C. D., Benn, D. K., & Crow, T. J. (1990). Further investigation of the predictors of outcome following first schizophrenic episodes. *British Journal of Psychiatry*, *157*, 182–189.

Kao, Y., & Liu, Y. (2011). Suicidal behavior and insight into illness among patients with schizophrenia spectrum disorders. *Psychiatric Quarterly*, *82*(3), 207–220.

Kasckow, J., Felmet, K., & Zisook, S. (2011). Managing suicide risk in patients with schizophrenia. *CNS Drugs*, *25*(2), 129–143.

Kasckow, J., Golshan, S., & Zisook, S. (2014). Does age moderate the relationship between depressive symptoms and suicidal ideation in middle-aged and older patients with schizophrenia and sub-threshold depression? *The American Journal of Geriatric Psychiatry*, *22*(5), 437–441.

Kavanagh, D. J. (1992). Recent developments in expressed emotion and schizophrenia. *British Journal of Psychiatry*, *160*, 601–620.

King, D., Knapp, M., Patel, A., Amaddeo, F., Tansella, M., Schene, A., . . . Becker, T. (2014). The impact of nonadherence to medication in patients with schizophrenia on health, social care and societal costs. Analysis of the QUATRO Study. *Epidemiology and Psychiatric Sciences*, *23*(1), 61–70. ProQuest, Web. 11 Jan. 2017.

Kiviniemi, M., Suvisaari, J., Koivumaa-Honkanen, H., Häkkinen, U., Isohanni, M., & Hakko, H. (2013). Antipsychotics and mortality in first-onset schizophrenia: Prospective Finnish register study with 5-year follow-up. *Schizophrenia Research*, *150*(1), 274–280.

Kjelby, E., Sinkeviciute, I., Gjestad, R., Kroken, R. A., Løberg, E. M., Jørgensen, H. A., . . . Johnsen, E. (2015). Suicidality in schizophrenia spectrum disorders: The relationship to hallucinations and persecutory delusions. *European Psychiatry*, *30*(7), 830–836.

Knapp, M., King, D., Pugner, K., & Lapuerta, P. (2004). Non-adherence to antipsychotic medication regimens: Associations with resource use and costs. *British Journal of Psychiatry*, *184*, 509–516.

Kohn, R., Saxena, S., Levav, I., & Saraceno, B. (2004). The treatment gap in mental health care. *Bulletin of the World Health Organization*, *82*(11), 858–866.

Kuller, A. M., Ott, B. D., Goisman, R. M., Wainwright, L. D., & Rabin, R. J. (2010). Cognitive behavioral therapy and schizophrenia: A survey of clinical practices and views on efficacy in the United States and United Kingdom. *Community Mental Health Journal*, *46*(1), 2–9.

Lacro, J. P., Dunn, L. B., Dolder, C. R., Leckband, S. G., & Jeste, D. V. (2002). Prevalence of and risk factors for medication nonadherence in patients with schizophrenia: A comprehensive review of recent literature. *Journal of Clinical Psychiatry*, *63*(10), 892–909.

Larsson, S., Andreassen, O. A., Aas, M., Røssberg, J. I., Mork, E., Steen, N. E., . . . Lorentzen, S. (2013). High prevalence of childhood trauma in patients with schizophrenia spectrum and affective disorder. *Comprehensive Psychiatry*, *54*(2), 123–127.

Law, M. R., Soumerai, S. B., Ross-Degnan, D., & Adams, A. S. (2008). A longitudinal study of medication nonadherence and hospitalization risk in schizophrenia. *Journal of Clinical Psychiatry*, *69*(1), 47–53.

Lay, B., Blanz, B., Hartmann, M., & Schmidt, M. H. (2000). The psychosocial outcome of adolescent-onset schizophrenia: A 12-year follow-up. *Schizophrenia Bulletin*, *26*(4), 801–816.

Lenior, M. E., Dingemans, P. M., Schene, A. H., Hart, A. A., & Linszen, D. H. (2002). The course of parental expressed emotion and psychotic episodes after family intervention in recent-onset schizophrenia: A longitudinal study. *Schizophrenia Research*, *57*(2–3), 183–190.

Leucht, S., Tardy, M., Komossa, K., Heres, S., Kissling, W., Salanti, G., & Davis, J. M. (2012). Antipsychotic drugs versus placebo for relapse prevention in schizophrenia: A systematic review and meta-analysis. *Lancet*, *379*(9831), 2063–2071. doi:10.1016/S0140-6736(12)60239-6

Limosin, F., Loze, J. Y., Philippe, A., Casadebaig, F., & Rouillon, F. (2007). Ten-year prospective follow-up study of the mortality by suicide in schizophrenic patients. *Schizophrenia Research*, *94*(1–3), 23–28.

Lincoln, T. M., Wilhelm, K., & Nestoriuc, Y. (2007). Effectiveness of psychoeducation for relapse, symptoms, knowledge, adherence and functioning in psychotic disorders: A meta-analysis. *Schizophrenia Research*, *96*(1), 232–245.

Linszen, D. H., Dingemans, P. M., Lenior, M. E., Nugter, M., Scholte, W. F., & Van der Does, A. J. (1994). Relapse criteria in schizophrenic disorders: Different perspectives. *Psychiatry Research*, *54*(3), 273–281.

Loebel, A. D., Lieberman, J. A., Alvir, J. M., Mayerhoff, D. I., Geisler, S. H., & Szymanski, S. R. (1992). Duration of psychosis and outcome in first-episode schizophrenia. *American Journal of Psychiatry, 149*(9), 1183–1188.

López-Moríñigo, J. D., Ramos-Ríos, R., David, A. S., & Dutta, R. (2012). Insight in schizophrenia and risk of suicide: A systematic update. *Comprehensive Psychiatry, 53*(4), 313–322.

Lora, A., Kohn, R., Levav, I., McBain, R., Morris, J., & Saxena, S. (2012). Service availability and utilization and treatment gap for schizophrenic disorders: A survey in 50 low- and middle-income countries. *Bulletin of the World Health Organization, 90*(1), 47–54.

Lui, S. (2009). Risk factors for deliberate self-harm and completed suicide in young Chinese people with schizophrenia. *Australian and New Zealand Journal of Psychiatry, 43*(3), 252–259.

Lysaker, P. H., Buck, K. D., Salvatore, G., Popolo, R., & Dimaggio, G. (2009). Lack of awareness of illness in schizophrenia: Conceptualizations, correlates and treatment approaches. *Expert Review of Neurotherapeutics, 9*(7), 1035–1043.

Machell, K. A., Rallis, B. A., & Esposito-Smythers, C. (2016). Family environment as a moderator of the association between anxiety and suicidal ideation. *Journal of Anxiety Disorders, 40*, 1–7.

Margetić, B. A., Jakovljević, M., Ivanec, D., Marčinko, D., Margetić, B., & Jakšić, N. (2012). Current suicidality and previous suicidal attempts in patients with schizophrenia are associated with different dimensions of temperament and character. *Psychiatry Research, 200*(2–3), 120–125.

Maris, R. W., Berman, A. L., & Silverman, M. (2000). *Comprehensive textbook of suicidology.* New York, NY: Guilford Press.

Martin, J. L., McLean, G., Park, J., Martin, D. J., Connolly, M., Mercer, S. W., & Smith, D. J. (2014). Impact of socioeconomic deprivation on rate and cause of death in severe mental illness. *BioMed Central Psychiatry, 14*, 261.

Mauri, M. C., Paletta, S., Maffini, M., Moliterno, D., & Altamura, A. C. (2013). Suicide attempts in schizophrenic patients: Clinical variables. *Asian Journal of Psychiatry, 6*(5), 421–427.

McClellan, J. (2013). Practice parameter for the assessment and treatment of children and adolescents with schizophrenia. *Journal of the American Academy of Child & Adolescent Psychiatry, 52*(9), 976–990.

McClellan, J., & Stock, S. (2013). American Academy of Child and Adolescent Psychiatry Committee on Quality Issues. Practice parameter for the assessment and treatment of children and adolescents with schizophrenia. *Journal of American Academy of Child & Adolescent Psychiatry, 52*(9), 976–990.

McGrath, J., Saha, S., Chant, D., & Welham, J. (2008). Schizophrenia: A concise overview of incidence, prevalence, and mortality. *Epidemiologic Reviews, 30*, 67–76.

McLean, D., Gladman, B., & Mowry, B. (2012). Significant relationship between lifetime alcohol use disorders and suicide attempts in an Australian schizophrenia sample. *Australian and New Zealand Journal of Psychiatry, 46*(2), 132–140.

Melle, I., & Barrett, E. A. (2012). Insight and suicidal behavior in first-episode schizophrenia. *Expert Review of Neurotherapeutics, 12*(3), 353–359.

Meltzer, H. (2005). Suicide in schizophrenia, clozapine, and adoption of evidence-based medicine. *Journal of Clinical Psychiatry, 66*(4), 530–533.

Meltzer, H., Alphs, L., Green, A. I., Altamura, A. C., Anand, R., Bertoldi, A., . . . International Suicide Prevention Trial Study Group. (2003). Clozapine treatment for suicide in schizophrenia. *Archives of General Psychiatry, 60*(1), 82–91.

Montross, L. P., Zisook, S., & Kasckow, J. (2005). Suicide among patients with schizophrenia: A consideration of risk and protective factors. *Annals of Clinical Psychiatry, 17*(3), 173–182.

Moran, P., Walsh, E., Tyrer, P., Burns, T., Creed, F., & Fahy, T. (2003). Does co-morbid personality disorder increase the risk of suicidal behaviour in psychosis? *Acta Psychiatrica Scandinavica, 107*(6), 441–448.

Nanda, P., Tandon, N., Mathew, I. T., Padmanabhan, J. L., Clementz, B. A., Pearlson, G. D., . . . Keshavan, M. S. (2016). Impulsivity across the psychosis spectrum: Correlates of cortical volume, suicidal history, and social and global function. *Schizophrenia Research, 170*(1), 80–86.

Norman, R. M. G., & Malla, A. K. (2001). Duration of untreated psychosis: A critical examination of the concept and its importance. *Psychological Medicine, 31*(3), 381–400.

Novakovic, V., & Sher, L. (2012, March). The use of clozapine for the treatment of schizophrenia and implications for suicide prevention. *International Journal on Disability and Human Development, 11*(1), 5–8.

Novick, D., Haro, J. M., Suarez, D., Perez, P., Dittmann, R. W., & Haddad, P. M. (2010). Predictors and clinical consequences of non-adherence with antipsychotic medication in the outpatient treatment of schizophrenia. *Psychiatry Research, 176*(2–3), 109–113.

Nylander, L., & Gillberg, C. (2001). Screening for autism spectrum disorders in adult psychiatric out-patients: A preliminary report. *Acta Psychiatrica Scandinavica, 103*(6), 428–434.

Olfson, M., Mechanic, D., Hansell, S., Boyer, C. A., Walkup, J., & Weiden, P. J. (2000). Predicting medication noncompliance after hospital discharge among patients with schizophrenia. *Psychiatric Services, 51*(2), 216–222.

Palmer, B. A., Pankratz, V. S., & Bostwick, J. M. (2005). The lifetime risk of suicide in schizophrenia: A reexamination. *Archives of General Psychiatry, 62*(3), 247–253.

Perkins, D. O. (2002). Predictors of noncompliance in patients with schizophrenia. *Journal of Clinical Psychiatry, 63*(12), 1121–1128.

Perkins, D. O., Gu, H., Weiden, P. J., McEvoy, J. P., Hamer, R. M., & Lieberman, J. A. (2008). Comparison of atypicals in first episode study group. Predictors of treatment discontinuation and medication nonadherence in patients recovering from a first episode of schizophrenia, schizophreniform disorder, or schizoaffective disorder: A randomized, double-blind, flexible-dose, multicenter study. *Journal of Clinical Psychiatry, 65*(1), 77–83; 69(1), 106–113.

Pharoah, F., Mari, J., Rathbone, J., & Wong, W. (2010). Family intervention for schizophrenia. *Cochrane Database of Systematic Reviews, 8*(12): CD000088.

Pilling, S., Bebbington, P., Kuipers, E., Garety, P., Geddes, J., Orbach, G., & Morgan, C. (2002). Psychological treatments in schizophrenia: I. Meta-analysis of family intervention and cognitive behaviour therapy. *Psychological Medicine, 32,* 763–782.

Pinikahana, J., Happell, B., & Keks, N. A. (2003). Suicide and schizophrenia: A review of literature for the decade (1990–1999) and implications for mental health nursing. *Issues in Mental Health Nursing, 24*(1), 27–43.

Pitschel-Walz, G., Leucht, S., Baumi, J., Kissling, J., & Engel, R. R. (2001). The effect of family interventions on relapse and rehospitalization in schizophrenia: A meta-analysis. *Schizophrenia Bulletin, 27*(1), 73–92.

Pompili, M., Amador, X. F., Girardi, P., Harkavy-Friedman, J., Harrow, M., Kaplan, K., . . . Tatarelli, R. (2007). Suicide risk in schizophrenia: learning from the past to change the future. *Annals of General Psychiatry, 6,* 10.

Popovic, D., Benabarre, A., Crespo, J. M., Goikolea, J. M., González-Pinto, A., Gutiérrez-Rojas, L., . . . Vieta, E. (2014). Risk factors for suicide in schizophrenia: Systematic review and clinical recommendations. *Acta Psychiatrica Scandinavica, 130*(6), 418–426.

Prentice-Dunn, S., Wilson, D. R., & Lyman, R. D. (1981). Client factors related to outcome in a residential and day treatment program for children. *Journal of Clinical Child Psychology, 10,* 188–191.

Qin, P., & Nordentoft, M. (2005). Suicide risk in relation to psychiatric hospitalization: Evidence based on longitudinal registers. *Archives of General Psychiatry, 62*(4), 427–432.

Radomsky, E. D., Haas, G. L., Mann, J. J., & Sweeney, J. A. (1999). Suicidal behavior in patients with schizophrenia and other psychotic disorders. *American Journal of Psychiatry, 156,* 1590–1595.

Ran, M. S., Leff, J., Hou, Z. J., Xiang, M. Z., & Chan, C. L. (2003). The characteristics of expressed emotion among relatives of patients with schizophrenia in Chengdu, China. *Culture, Medicine & Psychiatry, 27*(1), 95–106.

Rathod, S., Phiri, P., & Kingdon, D. (2010). Cognitive behavioral therapy for schizophrenia. *Psychiatric Clinics of North America, 33*(3), 527–536.

Regier, D. A., Narrow, W. E., Rae, D. S., Manderscheid, R. W., Locke, B. Z., & Goodwin, F. K. (1993). The de facto US mental and addictive disorders service system. Epidemiologic catchment area prospective 1-year prevalence rates of disorders and services. *Archives of General Psychiatry, 50*(2), 85–94.

Remschmidt, H. E., Schulz, E., Martin, M., Warnke, A., & Trott, G. E. (1994). Childhood-onset schizophrenia: History of the concept and recent studies. *Schizophrenia Bulletin, 20*(4), 727–745.

Reutfors, J., Bahmanyar, S., Jönsson, E. G., Brandt, L., Bodén, R., Ekbom, A., & Ösby, U. (2013). Medication and suicide risk in schizophrenia: A nested case–control study. *Schizophrenia Research, 150*(2–3), 416–420.

Robinson, D. G., Woerner, M. G., Alvir, J. M., Bilder, R., Goldman, R., Geisler, S., . . . Lieberman, J. A. (1999). Predictors of relapse following response from a first episode of schizophrenia or schizoaffective disorder. *Archives of General Psychiatry, 56*(3), 241–247.

Robinson, D. G., Woerner, M. G., Alvir, J. M., Geisler, S., Koreen, A., Sheitman, B., . . . Lieberman, J. A. (1999). Predictors of treatment response from a first episode of schizophrenia or schizoaffective disorder. *American Journal of Psychiatry, 156*(4), 544–549.

Robinson, D. G., Woerner, M. G., Delman, H. M., & Kane, J. M. (2005). Pharmacological treatments for first-episode schizophrenia. *Schizophrenia Bulletin, 31*(3), 705–722.

Ropcke, B., & Eggers, C. (2005). Early-onset schizophrenia: A 15-year follow-up. *European Child & Adolescent Psychiatry, 14*(6), 341–350.

Rosenfarb, I. S., Miklowitz, D. J., Goldstein, M. J., Harmon, L., Nuechterlein, K. H., & Rea, M. M. (2001). Family transactions and relapse in bipolar disorder. *Family Process, 40*(1), 5–14.

Rosmarin, D. H., Bigda-Peyton, J. S., Öngur, D., Pargament, K. I., & Björgvinsson, T. (2013). Religious coping among psychotic patients: Relevance to suicidality and treatment outcomes. *Psychiatry Research, 210*(1), 182–187.

Saha, S., Chant, D., & McGrath, J. (2007). A systematic review of mortality in schizophrenia: Is the differential mortality gap worsening over time? *Archives of General Psychiatry, 64,* 1123–1131.

Sanchez-Gistau, V., Baeza, I., Arango, C., González-Pinto, A., de la Serna, E., Parellada, M., . . . Castro-Fornieles, J. (2013). Predictors of suicide attempt in early-onset, first episode psychoses: A longitudinal 24-month follow-up study. *The Journal of Clinical Psychiatry, 74*(1), 59–66.

Schmidt, M., Blanz, B., Dippe, A., Koppe, T., & Lay, B. (1995). Course of patients diagnosed as having schizophrenia during first episode occurring under age 18 years. *European Archives of Psychiatry & Clinical Neuroscience, 245*(2), 93–100.

Sinclair, J. M., Mullee, M. A., King, E. A., & Baldwin, D. S. (2004). Suicide in schizophrenia: A retrospective case-control study of 51 suicides. *Schizophrenia Bulletin, 30*(4), 803–811.

Sinyor, M., & Remington, G. (2012). Is psychiatry ignoring suicide? The case for clozapine. *Journal of Clinical Psychopharmacology, 32*(3), 307–308.

Siris, S. G. (2001). Suicide and schizophrenia. *Journal of Psychopharmacology, 15*(2), 127–135.

Siris, S. G., Addington, D., Azorin, J.- M., Falloon, I. R. H., Gerlach, J., & Hirsch, S. R. (2001). Depression in schizophrenia: Recognition and management in the USA. *Schizophrenia Research, 47,* 185–197.

Sullivan, G., Wells, K. B., Morgenstern, H., & Leake, B. (1995). Identifying modifiable risk factors for rehospitalization: A case-control study of seriously mentally ill persons in Mississippi. *American Journal of Psychiatry, 152*(12), 1749–1756.

Suokas, J. T., Perälä, J., Suominen, K., Saarni, S., Lönnqvist, J., & Suvisaari, J. M. (2010). Epidemiology of suicide attempts among persons with psychotic disorder in the general population. *Schizophrenia Research, 124*(1–3), 22–28.

Svedberg, B., Mesterton, A., & Cullberg, J. (2001). First-episode non-affective psychosis in a total urban population: A 5-year follow-up. *Social Psychiatry & Psychiatric Epidemiology, 36*(7), 332–337.

Tai, S., & Turkington, D. (2009). The evolution of cognitive behavior therapy for schizophrenia: Current practice and recent developments. *Schizophrenia Bulletin, 35*(5), 865–873.

Thomas, K. L., Jiang, Y., & McCombs, J. S. (2015). Clozapine revisited: Impact of clozapine vs. olanzapine on health care use by schizophrenia patients on Medicaid. *Annals of Clinical Psychiatry, 27*(2), 90–99.

Tiihonen, J., Wahlbeck, K., Lonnqvist, J., Klaukka, T., Ioannidis, J. P., Volavka, J., & Haukka, J. (2006). Effectiveness of antipsychotic treatments in a nationwide cohort of 2,230 patients in community care after first hospitalization due to schizophrenia and schizoaffective disorder: Observational follow up study. *British Medical Journal, 333,* 224.

Togay, B., Noyan, H., Tasdelen, R., & Ucok, A. (2015). Clinical variables associated with suicide attempts in schizophrenia before and after the first episode. *Psychiatry Research, 229*(1–2), 252–256.

Vasconcelos e Sa, D., Wearden, A., Hartley, S., Emsley, R., & Barrowclough, C. (2016). Expressed emotion and behaviourally controlling interactions in the daily life of dyads experiencing psychosis. *Psychiatry Research, 245*(30), 406–413.

Verdoux, H., Lengronne, J., Liraud, F., Gonzales, B., Assens, F., Abalan, F., & van Os, J. (2000). Medication adherence in psychosis: Predictors and impact on outcome: A 2-year follow-up of first-admitted subjects. *Acta Psychiatrica Scandinavica, 102*(3), 203–210.

Verdoux, H., Liraud, F., Assens, F., Abalan, F., & van Os, J. (2002). Social and clinical consequences of cognitive deficits in early psychosis: A two-year follow-up study of first-admitted patients. *Schizophrenia Research, 56*(1–2), 149–159.

Vyas, N. S., Kumra, S., & Puri, B. K. (2010). What insights can we gain from studying early-onset schizophrenia? The neurodevelopmental pathway and beyond. *Expert Review of Neurotherapeutics, 10,* 1243–1247.

Wade, M., Tai, S., Awenat, Y., & Haddock, G. (2017). A systematic review of service-user reasons for adherence and nonadherence to neuroleptic medication in psychosis. *Clinical Psychology Review, 51,* 75–95.

Walsh, E., Buchanan, A., & Fahy, T. (2002). Violence and schizophrenia: Examining the evidence. *The British Journal of Psychiatry, 180*(6), 490–495.

Wasserman, D., Rihmer, Z., Rujescu, D., Sarchiapone, M., Sokolowski, M., Titelman, D., . . . Carli, V. (2012). The European Psychiatric Association guidance on suicide treatment and prevention. *European Psychiatry*, 27(2), 129–141.

Webb, R. T., Långström, N., Runeson, B., Lichtenstein, P., & Fazel, S. (2011). Violent offending and IQ level as predictors of suicide in schizophrenia: National cohort study. *Schizophrenia Research*, 130(1–3), 143–147.

Welham, J. L., Thomis, R. J., & McGrath, J. J. (2004). Age-at-first-registration for affective psychosis and schizophrenia. *Schizophrenia Bulletin*, 30, 849–853.

Werry, J. S., McClellan, J. M., & Chard, L. (1991). Childhood and adolescent schizophrenic, bipolar, and schizoaffective disorders: A clinical and outcome study. *Journal of the American Academy of Child & Adolescent Psychiatry*, 30(3), 457–465.

Wu, E. Q., Birnbaum, H. G., Shi, L., Ball, D. E., Kessler, R. C., Moulis, M., & Aggarwal, J. (2005). The economic burden of schizophrenia in the United States in 2002. *Journal of Clinical Psychiatry*, 66(9), 1122–1129.

Wyatt, R. J., Damiani, L. M., & Henter, I. D. (1998). First-episode schizophrenia: Early intervention and medication discontinuation in the context of course and treatment. *British Journal of Psychiatry— Supplementum*, 172(33), 77–83.

Yildiz, M., Yazici, A., & Böke, O. (2010). Demographic and clinical characteristics in schizophrenia: A multicenter cross-sectional case record study. *Turkish Journal of Psychiatry*, 21(3), 213–224.

Zipurskya, R. B., Menezesa, N. M., & Streinera, D. L. (2013). Risk of symptom recurrence with medication discontinuation in first-episode psychosis: A systematic review. *Schizophrenia Research*, 152(2–3), 408–414.

CHAPTER NINE

SUBSTANCE-RELATED DISORDERS AND SUICIDE

This chapter examines the relationship between substance-related disorders and risk of suicidality. Substance use and abuse has been associated with increased risk of suicide attempt and completion (Abroms & Sher, 2016; Dhossche, Meloukheia, & Chakravorty, 2000; Lamis & Malone, 2012; Maris, Berman, & Silverman, 2000; Masferrer, Garre-Olmo, & Caparros, 2016; Sher et al., 2005, 2006b). Diagnosed and undiagnosed substance-related disorders are very prevalent in society. Research recommends that every individual using or abusing substances, not merely those with depression, should be assessed for the presence of suicide ideation and risk (Lamis & Malone, 2012; Mino, Bousquet, & Broers, 1999; Sher, 2006a). Similarly, it has been recommended that all suicide attempters be assessed for substance abuse (Dhossche et al., 2000; Lamis & Malone, 2012; Sher, 2006a, 2006b).

GOALS AND OBJECTIVES

An understanding of:

- *Diagnostic and Statistical Manual of Mental Disorders (DSM)* criteria for alcohol and substance use disorders
- Course of illness of alcohol and substance use disorders
- Etiology and epidemiology of alcohol and substance use disorders
- Relationship between alcohol and substance use disorders and suicide
- Risk factors for suicide unique to individuals with alcohol and substance use disorders
- Protective factors for suicide unique to individuals with alcohol and substance use disorders
- Evidence-based practices for alcohol and substance use disorders

---

Substance abuse is a significant concern across cultures and societies. Research has identified that individuals with alcohol use disorders are nearly 10 times more likely to die by suicide, and individuals who inject drugs are approximately 14 times more likely to commit suicide (Wilcox, Conner, & Caine, 2004; Yuodelis-Flores & Ries, 2015). In the United States, the total economic burden associated with drug dependence is $67 billion annually (which includes the costs of crime, lost work productivity, foster care, and other social problems related to substance use and abuse; McLellan, Lewis, O'Brien, & Kleber, 2000), and excessive drinking is estimated to cost over \$249 billion annually (Quinn, Brolin, Stewart, Evans, & Horgan, 2016; Sacks, Gonzales, Bouchery, Tomedi, & Brewer, 2015).

The mental health impacts of substance abuse are significant. Alcohol and drug use and abuse have a strong association with major depression and suicidality (Agosti & Levin, 2006; Britton & Conner, 2010; Capron et al., 2016; Goldstein & Levitt, 2006; Hung et al., 2015; Pompili et al., 2010; Smith, 2016). Recent or acute alcohol ingestion is also associated with an elevated risk of impulsive suicide completion (Binelli et al., 2015; Borges & Rosovsky, 1996; Fudalej et al., 2015; Lejoyeux, Huet, Claudon, Fichelle, Casalino, & Lequen, 2008; Modesto-Lowe, Brooks, & Ghani, 2006; Preuss et al., 2002; Sher et al., 2007). Binge drinking in adults was associated with suicidal thoughts, plans, and attempts in females, and suicidal thoughts in males (Glasheen et al., 2015).

Research using psychological autopsies has found that individuals abusing alcohol also seem prone to suicide completions, specifically among adolescents (Giner et al., 2007). In addition, research has found that a significant percentage (40%–62%) of suicide attempts presenting in emergency departments have recently consumed alcohol, whereas prevalence of alcohol intake among all emergency patients is 2% (Lejoyeux et al., 2008; Saliou, Fichelle, McLoughlin, Thauvin, & Lejoyeux, 2005; Suokas & Lonnqvist, 1995). Further, research indicates that adolescent males may be at more risk of suicidality due to alcohol use, while suicidality may lead to increased alcohol use or abuse among females (Lee, Wu, Chen, & Wang, 2014; Light, Grube, Madden, & Gover, 2003; Rajapakse, Griffiths, Christensen, & Cotton, 2014).

Drug use has been associated with an elevated risk in suicide attempts and completions. However, the risk varies across the type of drug and nature of use/abuse. There is little published research on marijuana use and suicide risk. The minimal exploratory research that exists suggests that adolescents with a cannabis abuse or dependence may be at a higher risk of suicide attempts (Beautrais, Joyce, & Mulder, 1999; Kelly, Cornelius, & Lynch, 2002). especially those from disadvantaged sociodemographic backgrounds (Wilcox, 2004). A recent meta-analysis on cannabis use and suicidality found that currently there is a lack of evidence indicating that acute cannabis use increases imminent risk for suicidality; however, evidence does indicate that chronic cannabis use can predict suicidality (Borges, Bagge, & Orozco, 2016). The authors caution interpretation of these findings due to the limitations and methodological issues of the studies evaluated. Research findings on opioid use and suicide are also mixed (Ilgen et al., 2016).

Stereotypes regarding individuals with substance-related disorders pervade our society. There are a number of competing and contrasting values, judgments, and beliefs associated with this issue. Consequently, individuals who abuse substances are often unfortunately characterized as weak, corrupt, amoral, unpredictable, unproductive, and dangerous. These assumptions and stereotypes can stigmatize and negatively impact the quality of clinical engagement and treatment with individuals with reorganized mental health disorders. It is essential for clinicians to recognize their personal and professional values regarding substance abusers.

Individual Exercise 9.1

1. When you hear the term "substance abuser," what are the first words or thoughts that come to your mind?
2. When you hear the word "alcoholic," what are the first words or thoughts that come to your mind?
3. Are your listed words or thoughts generally positive or negative? Did they surprise you in any way? If so, how?

4. What personal *and* professional considerations and assumptions may make it hard for you to work with this population?
5. What personal *and* professional considerations may make it easy for you to work with this population?

SUBSTANCE DISORDERS AND *DSM-5* DIAGNOSIS

Substance-related disorders refer to the taking of a number of legal and illegal substances, such as alcohol, drugs, medications, or toxins. There are a number of classes of substance-related and addictive disorders categorized in the *DSM-5* (5th ed.; American Psychiatric Association [APA], 2013). These substance-related diagnostic areas focus on alcohol, caffeine, cannabis, hallucinogens, inhalants, nicotine, opioids, sedatives, hypnotics, anxiolytics, tobacco, and stimulants (APA, 2013). All substance-related disorders are categorized into two main groups: substance use disorders and substance-induced disorders. The essential features of substance use disorder revolve around a core cluster of cognitive, behavioral, and physiological symptoms resulting from the substance use despite significant substance-related problems (APA, 2013). Substance-induced disorders are subdivided into substance-induced intoxication disorders, substance-induced withdrawal disorders, and other substance/medication-induced mental disorders (APA, 2013).

Substance use disorders are usually characterized by a pathological pattern of behavior composed of impaired control, social impairment, risky use, and pharmacological criteria. Impaired control over the substance use often involves the individual (a) taking larger amounts or over a longer period of time than intended; (b) expressing persistent desire to reduce the amount used and may report multiple episodes of trying unsuccessfully to decrease or discontinue use; (c) spending more time obtaining or using the substance, or recovering from the effects; and (d) increasing urge or more intense desire to use the substance (APA, 2013). Social impairment as a result of substance use includes three criteria: impairing the individual's ability to fulfill major role obligations (e.g., at work, school, or home), having persistent or recurrent social or interpersonal problems, and/or giving up on or withdrawing from family activities and hobbies (APA, 2013). Risky use centers on two criteria: the individual using substances in situations that are physically hazardous, or continuing use despite an awareness of the physical or psychological problems that result from such use (APA, 2013). Pharmacological criteria include two components: increased tolerance for the substance that requires large amounts to achieve the desired effect and withdrawal symptoms.

Substance-induced intoxication and withdrawal disorders revolve around the development of a reversible substance specific syndrome. Criteria include behavioral or psychological changes associated with intoxication, such as changes in perception, wakefulness, attention, thinking, judgment, psychomotor behavior, and interpersonal behavior (APA, 2013).

EPIDEMIOLOGY AND PROGNOSIS

According to the National Survey on Drug Use and Health (Substance Abuse and Mental Health Services Administration [SAMHSA], 2016), 21.5 million American adults (aged 12 years and older) battled a substance use disorder in 2014 (Center for Behavioral Health Statistics and Quality [CBHSQ], 2015). Of those, approximately 80% struggled with an alcohol use disorder and one out of every eight individuals struggled with polysubstance use (SAMHSA, 2015). Further, approximately 8 million adults in the United States struggled with a comorbid mental health disorder and a substance use disorder (CBHSQ, 2015). Among young adults aged 18 and 25 years, approximately one out of every six struggled with a substance use disorder representing the highest percentage of any age group at 16.3% (CBHSQ, 2015). Among adolescents, approximately 5% suffered from a substance use disorder representing 1.3 million teens, or 1 in every 12 adolescents (CBHSQ, 2015).

Alcohol dependence is one of the most common psychiatric disorders, with an estimated 16.6 million American adults (18 years and older) struggling with an alcohol use disorder (SAMHSA, 2014). In Western developed countries, an estimated 90% of individuals have used alcohol, with approximately one-third developing alcohol-related difficulties (Erinoff et al., 2004). It is further estimated that approximately 10% of men and 3% to 5% of women will develop severe alcohol-related life impairments or alcohol dependence during their lives (Sher, Sperling, Zalsman, Vardi, & Merrick, 2006). According to the Centers for Disease Control and Prevention (CDC, 2009), during the period of 2001 to 2005, an estimated annual 79,646 alcohol-attributable deaths (AAD) and 2.3 million years of potential life lost (YPLL) were attributed to the harmful effects of excessive alcohol use.

The National Comorbidity Survey conducted in the United States found that the 12-month prevalence of alcohol dependence was 10.7% for males and 3.7% for females, while the lifetime prevalence was 20.1% for males and 8.2% for females (Kessler et al., 1994). Other research has found that adult men in the United States struggle with an alcohol use disorder at double the rate of women, 10.8 million as compared to 5.8 million (CBHSQ, 2016). In a replication of the National Comorbidity Survey, males continued to have greater rates of substance disorders in comparison to females (Kessler et al., 2005). Between 2005 and 2006, the CDC (2009) found that the overall prevalence of alcohol intoxication was nearly 24% among suicide decedents tested for alcohol, with the highest rates occurring among American Indian/Alaska Natives (AI/ANs; 37%), followed by Hispanics (29%) and persons aged 20 to 49 years (28%). Excessive alcohol use is one of the top causes of death in the United States with over 240 alcohol-related deaths occurring daily (Mokdad , Marks, Stroup, & Gerberding, 2004; Quinn et al., 2016; Stahre, Roeber, Kanny, Brewer, & Zhang, 2014). Additionally, 78 people die from an opioid overdose each day (CDC, 2016).

Relapse is a common and prevalent issue among individuals with substance-related disorders. Only approximately 10.9% of the individuals who require treatment in a specialized facility for substance use or dependency actually received it (CBHSQ, 2015). However, more than 95% of those who required specialty substance abuse treatment and did not receive it reported that they did not think that they needed it (CBHSQ, 2015). It is estimated that between 40% and 60% of individuals treated for alcohol or other drug dependence will relapse within a year following treatment discharge (Adler et al., 2012; McLellan et al., 2000). Research indicates that patterns of relapse following alcohol treatment are similar for women and men (Walitzer & Dearing, 2006). However, several studies have found that women are disadvantaged prognostically at pretreatment (Foster, Peters, & Marshall, 2000; Glenn & Parsons, 1991) and that alcohol has a more deleterious effect on women (Walitzer & Dearing, 2006). In regards to drug abuse, research findings indicate that women are less likely to relapse post substance use treatment (Walitzer & Dearing, 2006). Among adolescents recently completing an outpatient drug treatment program, two-thirds (66%) relapsed to drug use within 6 months with the median time to drug relapse being slightly less than 2 months or 54 days. The three most commonly given reasons for relapse were social pressure, withdrawal, and negative affect (Cornelius et al., 2003).

In a review of responses to addiction treatments, most demonstrated significant reductions in drug use, improved personal health, and reduced social pathology; however, they did not attain long-term cure (McLellan et al., 2000). Factors associated with relapse include problems of poverty, lack of family support, and psychiatric comorbidity (McLellan et al., 2000).

In comparison to alcohol use disorders, illicit drug use is a major contributor to the global burden of disease. Illicit drug dependence directly accounted for 8% of global all-cause disability-adjusted life years (DALYs; 20 million DALYs; Degenhardt et al., 2013). The proportion of all-cause DALYs attributed to drug dependence is 20 times higher in some countries than others, with an increased proportion of burden in countries with the highest incomes. Countries with the highest rate of burden (>650 DALYs per 100,000 population) include the United States, United Kingdom, Russia, and Australia (Degenhardt et al., 2013).

Approximately 4.2 million American adults struggle with a marijuana use disorder (CBHSQ, 2015). Prescription drugs are also abused at high rates, with the most common types of psychotherapeutic drugs abused reported as pain relievers, tranquilizers, stimulants, and sedatives, respectively. Pain relievers are the most common cause of a substance use disorder among prescription drug users, with over 2 million adults in the United States struggling with an opioid pain reliever abuse disorder (CBHSQ, 2016). In 2015, research found that approximately 590,000 adults in the United States struggle with a substance use disorder involving heroin (CBHSQ, 2016). According to the CDC, the rate of heroin abuse and addiction has increased across all population and demographic groups in the United States over the past few years. Heroin use, for example, more than doubled among young adults aged 18 to 25 years in the past decade (CDC, 2009). Finally, research also indicates that over 900,000 American adults struggle with a cocaine use disorder (CBHSQ, 2016).

SUBSTANCE-RELATED DISORDERS AND SUICIDE

Suicide among individuals with alcohol use disorders remains underinvestigated. Nevertheless, it is clear that alcoholism poses a major risk factor for suicidal behavior. It has been estimated that the lifetime mortality due to suicide in alcohol dependence is between 2.2% and 18% (Roy & Linnoila, 1986; Sher et al., 2006). Psychological autopsy studies demonstrate that between 19% and 63% of all suicides suffered from substance use disorders, mainly alcohol use disorders (Caces & Harford, 1998; Pirkola, Isometsa, Heikkinen, & Lönnqvist, 2000; Schneider, 2009).

The rate of suicide attempt among individuals with alcohol use disorders is also alarming with rates of completed suicide found to be as high as 69% (Cherpitel, Borges, & Wilcox, 2004; Pirkola et al., 2000) and attempted suicide as high as 73% (Kolves, Varnik, Tooding, & Wasserman, 2006). Among individuals with comorbid depression and alcoholism, 40% of inpatients had attempted suicide in the prior week to admission and 70% had attempted suicide at some point in their lives (Cornelius, Salloum, Day, Thase, & Mann, 1996; Ries, Yuodelis-Flores, Roy-Byrne, Nilssen, & Russo, 2009; Roy, 2003; Zahl & Hawton, 2004).

Research into opioid use and suicide is mixed. Suicide as a risk of amphetamine dependence accounted for 854,000 DALYs, as a risk of opioid dependence for 671,000 DALYs, and as a risk of cocaine dependence for 324,000 DALYs (Degenhardt et al., 2013). Individuals dependent on heroin are more likely to die of suicide compared to the general population (Pan et al., 2014). However, among heroin users, research suggests that lifetime prevalence for suicide ideation is between 50% and 60% (Rossow, Groholt, & Wichstrom, 2005; Vingoe, Welch, Farrell, & Strang, 1999) with approximately one-third attempting suicide (Rossow et al., 2005). Although some investigations have found that opioid dependence was related to suicidal behavior, other studies found that opioid dependence did not make a unique contribution to the risk of suicide attempts (Maloney, Degenhardt, Darke, Mattick, & Nelson, 2007).

One study, which investigated cocaine and alcohol use preceding suicide, found that over 40% of White adolescents had used one or both substances within 48 hours prior to suicide, compared with less than 20% of Black youth (Garlow, Purselle, & Heninger, 2007).

However, the pattern of cocaine use or abuse before suicide is different in adults, where research has found that over 15% of Black adults had used cocaine before death compared with less than 10% in White adults (Garlow, 2002).

Among adolescents, one study compared 10 different types of drugs for their effect on suicidal ideation, suicide plan, suicide attempt, and severe suicide attempt requiring medical attention within the past year (Wong, Zhou, Goebert, & Hishinuma, 2013). Results indicate that adolescents reporting a history of heroin use have the strongest association with suicidal ideation, suicide plans, suicide attempts, and severe suicide attempts in the past year, followed by users of methamphetamines, closely followed by users of steroids, and then users of cocaine, ecstasy, hallucinogens, and inhalants. Users of marijuana, alcohol, and tobacco also had an increased odds ratio of suicidality; however, this was a more moderate effect than the preceding substances (Wong, 2013). Increases in risk of suicidality were also found as the number of substances used increased (Wong, 2013).

Substance and alcohol use disorders have unique relationships with depressive disorders, bipolar disorders, and schizophrenia. While this section has focused on the overall relationship between substance and alcohol use disorders and suicide, the specific relationship between individual psychiatric diagnoses and substance and alcohol use disorders is more directly examined in Chapters 7 through 9.

Risk Factors

There are a number of established risk factors for suicidal acts among individuals with alcohol and substance use disorders. These include:

- Aggression and impulsivity (Greenwald, Reznikoff, & Plutchik, 1994; Horesh, Gothelf, & Ofek, 1999; Ilgen et al., 2009; Koller, Preuss, Bottlender, Wenzel, & Soyka, 2002; Lipsey, Wilson, Cohen, & Derzon, 1997; Maloney, Degenhardt, Darke, & Nelson, 2009; Mann, Waternaux, Haas, & Malone, 1999; Plutchik & Van Praag, 1989; Sher et al., 2005; Wojnar et al., 2009)
- Life stressors (Conner, Conwell, Duberstein, & Eberly, 2004; Duberstein, Conwell, & Caine, 1993; Henriksson et al., 1993; Lester, 1992)
- Hopelessness (Hewitt, Norton, Flett, Callander, & Cowan, 1998; Kingree, Thompson, & Kaslow, 1999; Wright & Obitz, 1984)
- Living alone (Henriksson et al., 1993; Masferrer et al., 2016; Sher et al., 2006)
- Unemployment (Henriksson et al., 1993; Masferrer et al., 2016)
- Financial difficulties (Henriksson et al., 1993; Preuss et al., 2002; Sher et al., 2006; Yuodelis-Flores & Ries, 2015)
- Lack of school connectedness (Govender et al., 2013)
- Interpersonal losses, particularly the end of a romantic relationship (Conner, Beautrais, & Conwell, 2003; Conner et al., 2001; Dubersteinet al., 1993; Pirkola et al., 2000; Preuss, 2002; Yuodelis-Flores & Ries, 2015)
- Younger age at onset of alcohol use (Cheng, 1995; Conner et al., 2004; Sher et al., 2005)
- Longer duration of alcohol use (Cheng, 1995; Conner et al., 2004; Sher et al., 2005)
- Family history of alcoholism (Yaldizli, Kuhl, Graf, Wiesbeck, & Wurst, 2010)
- History of substance abuse, especially cocaine abuse (Britton & Conner, 2010; Sher et al., 2006; Vijayakumar, Kumar, & Vijayakumar, 2011) and sedative abuse (Olsson, Bradvik, Öjehagen, & Hakansson, 2016)
- Comorbidity, especially with major depressive episode (Christiansen & Jensen, 2009; Fudalej et al., 2009; Ganz & Sher, 2009; Preuss et al., 2002; Riihimäki, Vuorilehto, Melartin, Haukka, & Isometsä, 2014; Schneider, 2009; Sher et al., 2006)

- History of suicidal behavior (Britton & Conner, 2010; Monnin et al., 2012; Preuss, et al., 2002; Rojas, Bujarski, Babson, Dutton, & Feldner, 2014; Yuodelis-Flores & Ries, 2015)
- Family history of suicide (Masferrer et al., 2016; Olsson et al., 2016; Preuss, et al., 2002; Roy, 2010)
- Consumption of a greater amount of alcohol (Borges & Rosovsky, 1996; Brent, Perper, & Allman, 1987; Cornelius et al., 1996; Hufford, 2001; Mattisson, Bogren, Öjehagen, Nordström, & Horstmann, 2011; Welte, Abel, & Wieczorek, 1988)
- Greater level of nicotine use (Hawton & van Heeringen, 2009; Keizer, Gex-Fabry, Eytan, & Bertschy, 2009; Riala, Hakko, & Räsänen, 2009; Yaworski, Robinson, Sareen, & Bolton, 2011)
- Recent use and/or intoxication (Fudalej et al., 2009; Vijayakumar et al., 2011; Wang & Stórá, 2009; Yuodelis-Flores & Ries, 2015). For example, in comparison to abstinence, alcohol intoxication increases suicide risk as much as 90 times (Borges & Rosovsky, 1996)
- History of sexual abuse (Cutajar et al., 2010; Vaszari, Bradford, Callahan O'Leary, Ben Abdallah, & Cottler, 2011; Yuodelis-Flores & Ries, 2015)
- Childhood physical abuse (Vaszari et al., 2011)
- Risky sexual behaviors (Vijayakumar et al., 2011)

Protective Factors

Conversely, a more limited number of protective factors against suicidal behavior have been identified among individuals with alcohol and substance use disorders. These include:

- Social support (Galanter, 1988; Hung et al., 2015; Sher, 2006c), which is recognized as the strongest protective factor
- Effective clinical care for psychiatric and physical illness (Sher, 2006c)
- Access to clinical interventions (Sher, 2006c)
- Financial independence (Hung et al., 2015)
- Support for seeking help (Sher, 2006c)
- Restricted access to lethal means of suicide (Sher, 2006c)
- Strong problem-solving skills (Sher, 2006c)
- Strong conflict resolution skills (Sher, 2006c)
- Cultural and religious beliefs that discourage suicide (Sher, 2006c)

Case Vignette 9.1

Adam is a 19-year-old single White, Jewish male. He is a high school graduate and completed 1 year of college. He was raised in an upper-middle-class family where academic and career success was extremely important, as was their Orthodox faith. Adam was the last of five children. Seven years apart from the next youngest of his siblings, Adam was an unplanned child. He was a good student but had to work hard to earn his grades. He had several friends and dated occasionally throughout high school, but never had a serious girlfriend or a best friend.

After graduation from high school, Adam went away to college. He did well in his first semester and passed all of his classes with above-average grades, but the adjustment to living away from home and college life was not easy. He found it hard to make friends and could not relax in social situations. During the spring semester, Adam began to socialize more, which negatively impacted his studying and class attendance. He began to rely on the use of alcohol to cope with academic stress, and to feel comfortable in social situations. When he came home for the summer after his first year, his parents noted that his sleep pattern was disrupted. He was often irritable during the day, and would seem to relax only after he had a drink. After some time they asked him about it, and he indicated that he was drinking more than he had in the past but did not think it was a problem. While they were concerned, his parents agreed they would "wait and see if he got any worse" before they "jumped to any conclusions that Adam was in need of help." Adam returned to school that fall, but due to his continued alcohol consumption, he was unable to attend most of his classes and failed the semester, at which point he dropped out of school. Over the next year, Adam became more isolated as friends increasingly commented on his drinking and noted their concerns. His parents finally insisted that he see a mental health professional after an episode during which he disappeared for 2 days due to a drinking spree.

On mental status examination, Adam is alert and oriented x3. His clothes are disheveled and his grooming is poor. He has constricted range of affect and acknowledges feeling depressed, and at times acting impulsively. He denies that his drinking is a problem and reports feeling attacked and criticized by others. According to Adam, it is the unreasonable expectations of others that led him to drop out of school. As for the recent episode, he reports being unable to remember what happened during those 2 days. He said "this is no big deal. It has happened to me before at school."

ROLE-PLAY 9.1

Using Case Vignette 9.1, in groups of three (clinician, client, and observer), engage the client and conduct an assessment for substance-related disorders and suicide risk. What specific risk and protective factors should you consider? Be aware of your personal and professional attitudes in working with this client. What other information would you need to know?

Case Vignette 9.2

Using the same case vignette and role-play exercise (9.1), change the following:

Gender: From Adam (male) to Anne (female)

Environment: Note that Anne was physically abused by her boyfriend while at college

Case Vignette 9.3

Using the same case vignette and role-play exercise (9.1), change the following:

Sexual orientation: From heterosexual to homosexual

Religion: From Judaism to Catholicism

CURRENT PRACTICE GUIDELINES AND EVIDENCE-BASED PRACTICE

A number of treatments are available for individuals with a substance use disorder; however, treatment access can be limited by recent client suicidality. Research has found that often addiction treatment programs will not accept clients with recent suicidal behavior;

up to 40% of clients who are seeking treatment for substance dependence have reported a history of suicide attempts (CDC, 2016; Roy, 2009, 2010; Roy & Janal, 2007; Yuodelis-Flores et al., 2015).

The main treatment modalities used to address suicidality among alcohol and substance abusers are Alcoholics Anonymous (AA), Narcotics Anonymous (NA), cognitive behavioral therapy (CBT), motivational enhancement therapy (MET), and psychopharmacological treatment (Sher et al., 2006). Across modalities, treatment is aimed at achieving abstinence from use, stabilizing acute medical and psychiatric problems, increasing motivation for recovery, assisting the patient in getting social support for recovery, enhancing coping and relapse prevention skills, and promoting maintenance of recovery (Babor, Kranzler, Hernandez-Avila, & Ungemack, 2003; Oyserman, Bybee, Mowbray, & Hart-Johnson, 2005; Schuckit, 2005; Sher et al., 2006).

AA and NA are well-known established psychosocial treatments for alcohol and substance abusers. The foundation of AA and NA is a 12-step program through which a person with alcohol or substance abuse needs to progress to maintain recovery. Members of AA and NA are able to access help 24 hours a day and are paired with a senior sober member of the group who serves as a sponsor (Sher et al., 2006).

CBT has been found to be an effective treatment for persons with alcoholism (Feeney, Connor, Young, Tucker, & McPherson, 2004; Sher, 2002). The focus of CBT is on the process of relapse and recovery. Treatment focuses on changing (a) cognitions regarding expectancy of substance effects, self-efficacy for coping, attributions for success or setbacks; (b) behavior such as coping with high-risk situations and developing functional alternatives such as relaxation and exercise; and (c) lifestyle via balancing social relationships and support, and spiritual life (Sher et al., 2006).

MET uses a patient's intrinsic motivation for change as the focus of treatment (Sellman, Sullivan, Dore, Adamson, & MacEwan, 2001). The therapist seeks to develop a discrepancy in the patient's current behavior and his or her future goals. Emphasis is placed on commitment to change and on recognizing change talk (Sher et al., 2006).

Notwithstanding the growing treatments targeting individuals with a substance use disorder and their positive impacts, a recent study of 2,966 clients who received treatment found that 12 months following treatment, 2.6% of clients had attempted suicide (Britton, Wines, & Conner, 2010). This study highlights not only the importance of treatment but also follow-up care related to monitoring ongoing suicidality.

There has been a growing use of medications for the treatment of alcoholism. Disulfiram, an alcohol-sensitizing agent, is being widely used (Babor et al., 2003; Oyserman et al. 2005; Schuckit, 2005; Swift, 1999). Drinking alcohol precipitates an uncomfortable physical reaction, including nausea, vomiting, and changes in blood pressure in individuals taking disulfiram. Disulfiram is effective in individuals with a high level of motivation (Sher et al., 2006).

Naltrexone helps to reduce drinking and maintain abstinence by reducing the pleasurable effects of alcohol and the craving for alcohol (Babor et al. 2003; Oyserman et al., 2005; Schuckit, 2005; Swift, 1999). Individuals who drink during treatment with naltrexone report experiencing less alcohol high and are less likely to progress to heavy drinking. Naltrexone reduces craving for alcohol in both patients with alcoholism and social drinkers (Sher et al., 2006).

Acamprosate reduces craving and distress during early abstinence and thus decreases the need to consume alcohol (Anton, 2001; Babor et al., 2003; Mason, 2001; Oyserman et al.; Schuckit, 2005). Acamprosate is safe for use in conjunction with disulfiram and naltrexone (Sher et al., 2006).

Research demonstrates that selective serotonin reuptake inhibitors (SSRIs) lead to decreases in alcohol consumptions (Anton, 2001; Babor et al., 2003; Cornelius et al., 1997; Oyserman et al., 2005; Schuckit, 2005). Finally, anticonvulsants such as topiramate also have been shown to be an effective treatment for alcoholism (Johnson et al., 2003).

Practice guidelines for suicidal patients with alcoholism or substance abuse recommend the following:

1. Patients with alcoholism who report a suicide plan or intent should be hospitalized and observed closely until the suicidal ideation dissipates even if it is the result of a temporary alcohol-induced depression. Hospitalization should also be considered if an individual with alcoholism exhibits severe agitation, psychotic symptoms, thought disorder, increased impulsivity, hopelessness, and/or has a history of suicide attempt (Cornelius, Clark, Salloum, Bukstein, & Kelly, 2004).
2. When the suicidality has decreased, discharge from inpatient care may be considered. Before discharge, the family of the patient should be advised to remove all items of danger from the home, such as guns and poisons, and to closely observe the patient after discharge. Referral to an alcohol abuse treatment program should be made (Cornelius et al., 2004).

SUMMARY

The vast majority of individuals diagnosed with a substance-related disorder do not complete suicide. It is important to recognize that individuals with a substance problem are at an elevated risk for both suicide attempts and completions. Clinicians need to be aware of the unique risk and protective factors associated with suicide in this population. For engagement, treatment, and long-term management of individuals with substance-related disorders, it is necessary to consider the impact of personal stereotypes, assumptions, and bias in working with this population.

KEY POINTS

1. Substance-related disorders are often characterized by periods of remission and relapse.
2. Relapse following treatment for substance use has similar patterns for both males and females.
3. Prevalence of substance-related disorders is higher for males than for females.
4. Prognosis is complicated by problems of poverty, lack of family support, and psychiatric comorbidity.
5. Individuals with alcoholism have a 60 to 120 times greater suicide risk than the general population.
6. Among heroin users, research suggests that the lifetime prevalence for suicide ideation is between 50% and 60%.
7. The main treatment modalities used for substance-related disorders are AA/NA, CBT, MET, and psychopharmacological treatment.

ELECTRONIC RESOURCES

HOTLINES AND SUPPORT ORGANIZATIONS

Alcoholics Anonymous

www.aa.org/?Media=PlayFlash

Narcotics Anonymous

www.na.org

Alcohol Treatment Hotline
www.NationalHotline.org
Adult Children of Alcoholics Worldwide Service Organization
www.adultchildren.org
Al-anon/Alateen
www.al-anon.org
Alcohol and Drug Problems Association of North America
www.adpana.com

INFORMATION AND RESOURCES

www.learn-about-alcoholism.com
American Foundation for Addiction Research
www.addictionresearch.com
Drug Abuse Resistance Education (DARE)
www.dare.com
National Association of Addiction Treatment Providers (NAATP)
www.naatp.org
National Council on Alcoholism and Drug Dependence (NCADD)
www.ncadd.org
National Institute on Alcohol Abuse and Alcoholism, National Institutes of Health
www.niaaa.nih.gov

KNOWLEDGE ACQUISITION TEST (KAT)

True or False

1. More adults in the United States abuse heroin than marijuana.
2. The relapse rate of substance use is higher for males than for females.
3. Prevalence of alcohol use disorders is higher in males than in females.
4. The rate of completed suicide among individuals with substance-related disorders is over 75%.
5. Impulsivity is not a risk factor for suicide among individuals with substance-related disorder.
6. Alcohol dependence is one of the most common psychiatric disorders.
7. Binge drinking is a similar risk factor for suicidal behavior for males and females.
8. Alcohol intoxication increases suicide risk.

Short Answer

9. Substance use disorders are usually characterized by pathological pattern of behavior in what four areas?
10. List the key risk factors for suicide among individuals with substance disorders.
11. List the key protective factors for suicide among individuals with substance disorders.
12. List the recommended evidence-based treatments of individuals with substance-related disorders.

Multiple Choice

13. Which is not a category in substance-induced disorders?
    A. Intoxification
    B. Withdrawal
    C. Other substance/medication-induced disorders
    D. Tolerance
    E. All of the above
    F. None of the above
14. Which of the following is not a criteria group for substance use disorders?
    A. Impaired control
    B. Social impairment
    C. Restriction and isolation
    D. Risky use
    E. Pharmacological criteria
    F. None of the above
15. Which of the following items is a risk factor for suicidality among individuals with substance-related disorders?
    A. Impulsivity
    B. Comorbid depression
    C. Hallucinations
    D. Interpersonal losses
    E. All of the above
    F. None of the above

REFERENCES

Abroms, M., & Sher, L. (2016). Dual disorders and suicide. *Journal of Dual Diagnosis, 12*(2), 148–149.

Adler, M. W., Brady, K., Brigham, G., Carroll, K. M., Clayton, R. R., Cottier, L. B., . . . Woody, G. (2012). *Principles of drug addiction treatment: A research-based guide* (3rd ed.). Bethesda, MD: National Institute on Drug Abuse. Retrieved from https://www.drugabuse.gov/publications/principles-drug -addiction-treatment-research-based-guide-third-edition

Agosti, V., & Levin, F. R. (2006). One-year follow-up study of suicide attempters treated for drug dependence. *The American Journal on Addictions, 15*(4), 293–296.

American Psychiatric Association. (2013). *Diagnostic and statistical manual of mental disorders, text revision* (5th ed.). Arlington, VA: American Psychiatric Publishing.

Anton, R. F. (2001). Pharmacologic approaches to the management of alcoholism. *Journal of Clinical Psychiatry, 62*(Suppl. 20), 11–17.

Babor, T. F., Kranzler, H. R., Hernandez-Avila, C. A., & Ungemack, J. A. (2003). *Substance abuse: Alcohol use disorders.* Chichester, UK: John Wiley.

Beautrais, A. L., Joyce, P. R., & Mulder, R. T. (1999). Cannabis abuse and serious suicide attempts. *Addiction, 94*, 1155–1164.

Binelli, C., Muñiz, A., Sanches, S., Ortiz, A., Navines, R., Egmond, E., . . . Martín-Santos, R. (2015). New evidence of heterogeneity in social anxiety disorder: Defining two qualitatively different personality profiles taking into account clinical, environmental and genetic factors. *European Psychiatry, 30*(1), 160–165.

Borges, G., Bagge, C. L., & Orozco, R. (2016). A literature review and meta-analyses of cannabis use and suicidality. *Journal of Affective Disorders, 195*, 63–74.

Borges, G., & Rosovsky, H. (1996). Suicide attempts and alcohol consumption in an emergency room sample. *Journal of Studies on Alcohol, 57*, 543–548.

Brent, D. A., Perper, J. A., & Allman, C. J. (1987). Alcohol, firearms, and suicide among youth: Temporal trends in Allegheny County, Pennsylvania, 1960 to 1983. *Journal of the American Medical Academy, 257*, 3369–3372.

Britton, P. C., & Conner, K. R. (2010). Suicide attempts within 12 months of treatment for substance use disorders. *Suicide and Life-Threatening Behavior, 40*(1), 14–21.

Britton, P. C., Wines, J. D., & Conner, K. R. (2010). Non-fatal overdose in the 12 months following treatment for substance use disorders. *Drug and Alcohol Dependence, 107*(1), 51–55.

Caces, F. E., & Harford, T. (1998). Time series analysis of alcohol consumption and suicide mortality in the United States, 1934–1987. *Journal of Studies on Alcohol and Drugs, 59*, 455–461.

Capron, D. W., Bujarski, S. J., Gratz, K. L., Anestis, M. D., Fairholme, C. P., & Tull, M. T. (2016). Suicide risk along male substance users in residential treatment: Evaluation of the depression-distress amplification model. *Psychiatry Research, 237*, 22–26.

Center for Behavioral Health Statistics and Quality. (2015). *Behavioral health trends in the United States: Results from the 2014 National Survey on Drug Use and Health* (HHS Publication No. SMA 15-4927, NSDUH Series H-50). Retrieved from https://www.samhsa.gov/data/sites/default/files/NSDUH -FRR1-2014/NSDUH-FRR1-2014.htm

Center for Behavioral Health Statistics and Quality. (2016). Key substance use and mental health indicators in the United States: Results from the 2015 National Survey on Drug Use and Health (HHS Publication No. SMA 16-4984, NSDUH Series H-51). Retrieved from http://www.samhsa.gov/data

Centers for Disease Control and Prevention. (2009). Alcohol and suicide among racial/ethnic populations–17 states, 2005–2006. *Morbidity and Mortality Weekly Report, 58*(23), 637–641.

Centers for Disease Control and Prevention. (2016). Opioid overdose: Understanding the epidemic. Retrieved from https://www.cdc.gov/drugoverdose/epidemic/index.html

Cheng, A. T. (1995). Mental illness and suicide: A case-control study in east Taiwan. *Archives of General Psychiatry, 52*, 594–603.

Cherpitel, C. J., Borges, G. L., & Wilcox, H. C. (2004). Acute alcohol use and suicidal behavior: A review of the literature. *Alcoholism: Clinical and Experimental Research, 28*, 18S–28S.

Christiansen, E., & Jensen, B. F. (2009). A nested case-control study of the risk of suicide attempts after discharge from psychiatric care: The role of comorbid substance use disorder. *Nordic Journal of Psychiatry, 63*(2), 132–139.

Conner, K. R., Beautrais, A. L., & Conwell, Y. (2003). Risk factors for suicide and medically serious suicide attempts among alcoholics: Analyses of Canterbury Suicide Project Data. *Journal of Alcohol Studies, 64*, 551–554.

Conner, K. R., Conwell, Y., Duberstein, P. R., & Eberly, S. (2004). Aggression in suicide among adults age 50 and over. *American Journal of Geriatric Psychiatry, 12*, 37–42.

Conner, K. R., Cox, C., Duberstein, P. R., Tian, L., Nisbet, P. A., & Conwell, Y. (2001). Violence, alcohol, and completed suicide: A case-control study. *American Journal of Psychiatry, 158*, 1701–1705.

Cornelius, J. R., Clark, D. B., Salloum, I. M., Bukstein, O. G., & Kelly, T. M. (2004). Interventions in suicidal alcoholics. *Alcoholism: Clinical and Experimental Research, 28*(5 Suppl), 89S–96S.

Cornelius, J. R., Maisto, S. A., Pollock, N. K., Martin, C. S., Salloum, I. M., Lynch, K. G., & Clark, D. B. (2003). Rapid relapse generally follows treatment for substance use disorders among adolescents. *Addictive Behaviors, 28*(2), 381–386.

Cornelius, J. R., Salloum, I. M., Day, N. L., Thase, M. E., & Mann, J. J. (1996). Patterns of suicidality and alcohol use in alcoholics with major depression. *Alcoholism: Clinical and Experimental Research, 20*, 1451–1455.

Cornelius, J. R., Salloum, I. M., Ehler, J. G., Jarrett, P. J., Cornelius, M. D., Perel, J. M., . . . Black, A. (1997). Fluoxetine in depressed alcoholics: A double-blind, placebo-controlled trial. *Archives of General Psychiatry, 54*, 700–705.

Cutajar, M. C., Mullen, P. E., Ogloff, J. R., Thomas, S. D., Wells, D. L., & Spataro, J. (2010). Suicide and fatal drug overdose in child sexual abuse victims: A historical cohort study. *Medical Journal of Australia, 192*(4), 184–187.

Degenhardt, L., Whiteford, H. A., Ferrari, A. J., Baxter, A. J., Charlson, F. J., Hall, W. D., . . . Vos, T. (2013). Global burden of disease attributable to illicit drug use and dependence: Findings from the Global Burden of Disease Study 2010. *Lancet, 382*(9904), 1564–1574.

Dhossche, D. M., Meloukheia, A. M., & Chakravorty, S. (2000). The association of suicide attempts and comorbid depression and substance abuse in psychiatric consultation patients. *General Hospital Psychiatry, 22*(4), 281–288.

Duberstein, P. R., Conwell, Y., & Caine, E. D. (1993). Interpersonal stressors, substance abuse, and suicide. *Journal of Nervous and Mental Disease, 181*, 80–85.

Erinoff, L., Anthony, J. C., Brown, G. K., Caine, E. D., Conner, K. R., Dougherty, D. M., . . . Yen, S. (2004). Overview of workshop on drug abuse and suicidal behavior. *Drug and Alcohol Dependence, 76*(Suppl. 7), S3–S9.

Feeney, G. F., Connor, J. P., Young, R. M., Tucker, J., & McPherson, A. (2004). Alcohol dependence: The impact of cognitive behaviour therapy with or without naltrexone on subjective health status. *Australian and New Zealand Journal of Psychiatry, 38*, 842–848.

Foster, J. H., Peters, T. J., & Marshall, E. J. (2000). Quality of life measures and outcome in alcohol-dependent men and women. *Alcohol, 22*, 45–52.

Fudalej, S., Ilgen, M., Fudalej, M., Wojnar, M., Matsumoto, H., Barry, K. L., . . . Blow, F. C. (2009). Clinical and genetic risk factors for suicide under the influence of alcohol in a Polish sample. *Alcohol, 44*(5), 437–442.

Fudalej, S., Ilgen, M., Kołodziejczyk, I., Podgórska, A., Serafin, P., Barry, K., . . . Bohnert, A. (2015). Somatic comorbidity and other factors related to suicide attempt among Polish methadone maintenance patients. *Journal of Addiction Medicine, 9*(6), 433–439.

Galanter, M. (1988). Research on social supports and mental illness. *American Journal of Psychiatry, 145*, 1270–1227.

Ganz, D., & Sher, L. (2009). Suicidal behavior in adolescents with comorbid depression and alcohol abuse. *Minerva Pediatrica, 61*(3), 333–347.

Garlow, S. J. (2002). Age, gender, and ethnicity differences in patterns of cocaine and ethanol use preceding suicide. *American Journal of Psychiatry, 159*, 615–619.

Garlow, S. J., Purselle, D. C., & Heninger, M. (2007). Cocaine and alcohol use preceding suicide in African American and White adolescents. *Journal of Psychiatric Research, 41*(6), 530–536.

Giner, L., Carballo, J. J., Guija, J. A., Sperling, D., Oquendo, M. A., Garcia-Parajua, P., . . . Giner, L. (2007). Psychological autopsy studies: The role of alcohol use in adolescent and young adult suicides. *International Journal of Adolescent Medicine and Health, 19*(1), 99–113.

Glasheen, C., Pemberton, M. R., Lipari, R., Copello, E. A., & Mattson, M. E. (2015). Binge drinking and the risk of suicidal thoughts, plans, and attempts. *Addictive Behavior, 43*, 42–49.

Glenn, S. W., & Parsons, O. A. (1991). Prediction of resumption of drinking in posttreatment alcoholics. *International Journal of the Addictions, 26*, 237–254.

Goldstein, B. I., & Levitt, A. J. (2006). Is current alcohol consumption associated with increased lifetime prevalence of major depression and suicidality? Results from a pilot community survey. *Comprehensive Psychiatry, 47*(5), 330–333.

Govender, K., Naicker, S. N., Meyer-Weitz, A., Fanner, J., Naidoo, A., & Penfold, W. L. (2013). Associations between perceptions of school connectedness and adolescent health risk behaviors in South African high school learners. *Journal of School Health, 83*(9), 614–622.

Greenwald, D. J., Reznikoff, M., & Plutchik, R. (1994). Suicide risk and violence risk in alcoholics: Predictors of aggressive risk. *Journal of Nervous and Mental Disease, 182*, 3–8.

Hawton, K., & van Heeringen, K. (2009). Suicide. *Lancet, 373*(9672):1372–1381.

Henriksson, M. M., Aro, H. M., Marttunen, M. J., Heikkinen, M. E., Isometsä, E. T., Kuoppasalmi, K. I., & Lonnqvist, J. K. (1993). Mental disorders and comorbidity in suicide. *American Journal of Psychiatry, 150*, 935–940.

Hewitt, P. L., Norton, G. R., Flett, G. L., Callander, L., & Cowan, T. (1998). Dimensions of perfectionism, hopelessness, and attempted suicide in a sample of alcoholics. *Suicide and Life-Threatening Behavior, 28*, 395–406.

Horesh, N., Gothelf, D., & Ofek, H. (1999). Impulsivity as a correlate of suicidal behaviour in adolescent psychiatric inpatients. *Crisis, 20*, 8–14.

Hufford, M. R. (2001). Alcohol and suicidal behavior. *Clinical Psychology Review, 21*(5), 797–811.

Hung, G. C., Cheng, C. T., Jhong, J. R., Tsai, S. Y., Chen, C. C., & Kuo, C. J. (2015). Risk and protective factors for suicide mortality among patients with alcohol dependence. *Journal of Clinical Psychiatry, 76*(12), 1687–1693.

Ilgen, M. A., Bohnert, A. S., Ganoczy, D., Bair, M. J., McCarthy, J. F., & Blow, F. C. (2016). Opioid dose and risk of suicide. *Pain, 157*(5), 1079–1084. doi:10.1097/j.pain.0000000000000484

Ilgen, M. A., Chermack, S. T., Murray, R., Walton, M. A., Barry, K. L., Wojnar, M., & Blow, F. C. (2009). The association between partner and non-partner aggression and suicidal ideation in patients seeking substance use disorder treatment. *Addictive Behavior, 34*(2), 180–186.

Johnson, B. A., Ait-Daoud, N., Bowden, C. L., DiClemente, C. C., Roache, J. D., Lawson, K., . . . Ma, J. Z. (2003). Oral topiramate for treatment of alcohol dependence: A randomised controlled trial. *Lancet, 361*, 1677–1685.

Keizer, I., Gex-Fabry, M., Eytan, A., & Bertschy, G. (2009). Smoking in psychiatric inpatients: Association with working status, diagnosis, comorbid substance abuse and history of suicide attempts. *Addictive Behavior, 34*(10), 815–820.

Kelly, T. M., Cornelius, J. R., & Lynch, K. G. (2002). Psychiatric and substance use disorders as risk factors for attempted suicide among Aadolescents: A case control study. *Suicide and Life-Threatening Behavior, 32*, 301–312. doi:10.1521/suli.32.3.301.22168

Kessler, R. C., Berglund, P., Demler, O., Jin, R., Merikangas, K. R., & Walters, E. E. (2005). Lifetime prevalence and age-of-onset distributions of *DSM-IV* disorders in the national comorbidity. *Archives of General Psychiatry, 62*, 593–602.

Kessler, R. C., McGonagle, K. A., Zhao, S., Nelson, C. B., Hughes, M., Eshleman, S., . . . Kendler, K. S. (1994). Lifetime and 12-month prevalence of *DSM-III-R* psychiatric disorders in the United States. Results from the National Comorbidity Survey. *Archives of General Psychiatry, 5*, 8–19.

Kingree, J. B., Thompson, M. P., & Kaslow, N. J. (1999). Risk factors for suicide attempts among low-income women with a history of alcohol problems. *Addictive Behavior, 24*, 583–587.

Koller, G., Preuss, U. W., Bottlender, M., Wenzel, K., & Soyka, M. (2002). Impulsivity and aggression as predictors of suicide attempts in alcoholics. *European Archives of Psychiatry & Clinical Neuroscience, 252*(4), 155–160.

Kolves, K., Varnik, A., Tooding, L. M., & Wasserman, D. (2006). The role of alcohol in suicide: A case-control psychological autopsy study. *Psychological Medicine, 36*, 923–930.

Lamis, D. A., & Malone, P. S. (2011). Alcohol-related problems and risk of suicide among college students: The mediating roles of belongingness and burdensomeness. *Suicide and Life-Threatening Behavior, 41*(5), 543–553.

Lee, C. Y., Wu, Y. W., Chen, C. K., & Wang, L. J. (2014). The rate of fatality and demographic characteristics associated with various suicide methods: A community-based study in Northern Taiwan. *Crisis, 35*(4), 245–252.

Lejoyeux, M., Huet, F., Claudon, M., Fichelle, A., Casalino, E., & Lequen, V. (2008). Characteristics of suicide attempts preceded by alcohol consumption. *Archives of Suicide Research, 12*(1), 30–38.

Lester, D. (1992). *Why people kill themselves*. Springfield, IL: Charles Thomas.

Light, J. M., Grube, J. W., Madden, P. A., & Gover, J. (2003). Adolescent alcohol use and suicidal ideation: A non-recursive model. *Addictive Behaviors, 28*, 705–724.

Lipsey, M. W., Wilson, D. B., Cohen, M. A., & Derzon, J. H. (1997). Is there a causal relationship between alcohol use and violence? A synthesis of evidence. *Recent Developments in Alcoholism, 13*, 245–282.

Maloney, E., Degenhardt, L., Darke, S., Mattick, R. P., & Nelson, E. (2007). Suicidal behaviour and associated risk factors among opioid-dependent individuals: A case-control study. *Addiction, 102*(12), 1933–1941.

Maloney, E., Degenhardt, L., Darke, S., & Nelson, E. C. (2009). Impulsivity and borderline personality as risk factors for suicide attempts among opioid-dependent individuals. *Psychiatry Research, 169*(1), 16–21.

Mann, J. J., Waternaux, C., Haas, G. L., & Malone, K. M. (1999). Towards a clinical model of suicidal behavior in psychiatric patients. *American Journal of Psychiatry, 156*, 181–189.

Maris, R. W., Berman, A. L., & Silverman, M. M. (2000). *Comprehensive textbook of suicidology*. New York, NY: Guilford Press.

Masferrer, L., Garre-Olmo, J., & Caparros, B. (2016). Risk of suicide: Its occurrence and related variables among bereaved substance users. *Journal of Substance Use, 21*(2), 191–197.

Mason, B. J. (2001). Treatment of alcohol-dependent outpatients with acamprosate: A clinical review. *Journal of Clinical Psychiatry, 62*(Suppl. 20), 42–48.

Mattisson, C., Bogren, M., Öjehagen, A., Nordström, G., & Horstmann, V. (2011). Mortality in alcohol use disorder in the Lundby Community Cohort: A 50-year follow-up. *Drug and Alcohol Dependence, 118*(2–3), 141–147.

McLellan, A. T., Lewis, D. C., O'Brien, C. P., & Kleber, H. D. (2000). Drug dependence, a chronic medical illness: Implications for treatment, insurance, and outcomes evaluation. *Journal of American Medical Association, 284*(13), 1689–1695.

Mino, A., Bousquet, A., & Broers, B. (1999). Substance abuse and drug-related death, suicidal ideation, and suicide: A review. *Crisis: Journal of Crisis Intervention & Suicide, 20*(1), 28–35.

Modesto-Lowe, V., Brooks, D., & Ghani, M. (2006). Alcohol dependence and suicidal behavior: From research to clinical challenges. *Harvard Review of Psychiatry, 14*(5), 241–248.

Mokdad, A. H., Marks, J. S., Stroup, D. F., & Gerberding, J. L. (2004). Actual causes of death in the United States, 2000. *JAMA, 291*, 1238–1245. doi:10.1001/jama,291.10.1238

Monnin, J., Thiemard, E., Vandel, P., Nicolier, M., Tio, G., Courtet, P., . . . Haffen, E. (2012). Sociodemographic and psychopathological risk factors in repeated suicide attempts: Gender differences in a prospective study. *Journal of Affective Disorders, 136*(1–2), 35–43.

Olsson, M. O., Bradvik, L., Öjehagen, A., & Hakansson, A. (2016). Risk factors for unnatural death: Fatal accidental intoxication, undetermined intent and suicide: Register follow-up in a criminal justice population with substance use problems. *Drug and Alcohol Dependence, 162*, 176–181.

Oyserman, D., Bybee, D., Mowbray, C., & Hart-Johnson, T. (2005). When mothers have serious mental health problems: Parenting as a proximal mediator. *Journal of Adolescence, 28*, 443–463.

Pan, C. H., Jhong, J. R., Tsai, S. Y., Lin, S. K., Chen, C. C., & Kuo C. J. (2014). Excessive suicide mortality and risk factors for suicide among patients with heroin dependence. *Drug and Alcohol Dependence, 145*, 224–230.

Pirkola, S. P., Isometsä, E. T., Heikkinen, M. E., & Lönnqvist, J. K. (2000). Suicides of alcohol misusers and non-misusers in a nationwide population. *Alcohol and Alcoholism, 35*, 70–75.

Plutchik, R., & Van Praag, H. (1989). The measurement of suicidality, aggressivity and impulsivity. *Progress in Neuropsychopharmacology and Biological Psychiatry, 13*(Suppl.), 23–34.

Preuss, U. W., Schuckit, M. A., Smith, T. L., Buckman, K., Bierut, L., Bucholz, K. K., . . . Reich, T. (2002). Comparison of 3190 alcohol-dependent individuals with and without suicide attempts. *Alcoholism, Clinical and Experimental Research, 26*, 471–477.

Pompili, M., Serafini, G., Innamorati, M., Dominici, G., Ferracuti, S., Kotzalidis, G. D., . . . Lester, D. Suicidal Behavior and Alcohol Abuse. *International Journal of Environmental Research and Public Health, 7*, 1392–1431. doi:10.3390/ijerph7041392

Quinn, A. E., Brolin, M., Stewart, M. T., Evans, B., & Horgan, C. (2016). Reducing risky alcohol use: What health care systems can do (Issue Brief No.46). Waltham, MA: Massachusetts Health Policy Forum.

Rajapakse, T., Griffiths, K. M., Christensen, H., & Cotton, S. (2014). A comparison of non-fatal self-poisoning among males and females, in Sri Lanka. *BioMed Central Psychiatry, 14*, 221. doi:10.1186/s12888-014-0221-z

Riala, K., Hakko, H., & Räsänen, P.; Study-70 Workgroup. (2009). Nicotine dependence is associated with suicide attempts and self-mutilation among adolescent females. *Comprehensive Psychiatry, 50*(4), 293–298. doi:10.1016/j.comppsych.2008.08.012

Ries, R. K., Yuodelis-Flores, C., Roy-Byrne, P. P., Nilssen, O., & Russo, J. (2009). Addiction and suicidal behavior in acute psychiatric inpatients. *Comprehensive Psychiatry, 50*, 93–99.

Riihimäki, K., Vuorilehto, M., Melartin, T., Haukka, J., & Isometsä, E. (2014). Incidence and predictors of suicide attempts among primary-care patients with depressive disorders: A 5-year prospective study. *Psychological Medicine, 44*(2), 291–302.

Rojas, S. M., Bujarski, S., Babson, K. A., Dutton, C. E., & Feldner, M. T. (2014). Understanding PTSD comorbidity and suicidal behavior: Associations among histories of alcohol dependence, major depressive disorder, and suicidal ideation and attempts. *Journal of Anxiety Disorders, 28*(3), 318–325.

Rossow, I., Groholt, B., & Wichstrom, L. (2005). Intoxicants and suicidal behaviour among adolescents: Changes in levels and associations from 1992 to 2002. *Addiction, 100*(1), 79–88.

Roy, A. (2003). Distal risk factors for suicidal behavior in alcoholics: Replications and new findings. *Journal of Affective Disorders, 77,* 267–271.

Roy, A. (2009). Characteristics of cocaine dependent patients who attempt suicide. *Archives of Suicide Research, 13,* 46–51. doi:10.1080/13811110802572130

Roy, A. (2010). Risk factors for attempting suicide in heroin addicts. *Suicide and Life- Threatening Behavior, 40*(4), 416–420.

Roy, A., & Janal, M. N. (2007). Risk factors for suicide among alcohol-dependent patients. *Archives of Suicide Research, 11,* 211–217.

Roy, A., & Linnoila, M. (1986). Alcoholism and suicide. *Suicide and Life-Threatening Behavior, 16,* 244–273.

Sacks, J. J., Gonzales, K. R., Bouchery, E. E., Tomedi, L. E., & Brewer, R. D. (2015). 2010 national and state costs of excessive alcohol consumption. *American Journal of Preventive Medicine, 49*(5), e73–e79. Epub 2015 Oct 1. doi:10.1016/j.amepre.2015.05.031

Saliou, V., Fichelle, A., McLoughlin, M., Thauvin, I., & Lejoyeux, M. (2005). Psychiatric disorders among patients admitted to a French medical emergency service. *General Hospital Psychiatry, 27,* 263–268.

Schneider, B. (2009). Substance use disorders and risk for completed suicide. *Archives of Suicide Research, 13*(4), 303–316.

Schuckit, M. A. (2005). *Alcohol-related disorders.* Philadelphia, PA: Lippincott, Williams & Wilkins.

Sellman, J. D., Sullivan, P. F., Dore, G. M., Adamson, S. J., & MacEwan, I. (2001). A randomized controlled trial of motivational enhancement therapy (MET) for mild to moderate alcohol dependence. *Journal of Studies on Alcohol and Drugs, 62,* 389–396.

Sher, L. (2002). Behavioural therapy for the treatment of alcohol abuse and dependence. *Canadian Journal of Psychiatry, 47,* 586.

Sher, L. (2006a). Alcohol consumption and suicide. *Quarterly Journal of Medicine, 99*(1), 57–61.

Sher, L. (2006b). Alcohol and suicide: Neurobiological and clinical aspects. *Scientific World Journal, 6,* 700–706.

Sher, L. (2006c). Alcoholism and suicidal behavior: A clinical overview. *Acta Psychiatrica Scandinavica, 113,* 13–22.

Sher, L., Oquendo, M. A., Galfalvy, H. C., Grunebaum, M. F., Burke, A. K., Zalsman, G., & Mann, J. J. (2005). The relationship of aggression to suicidal behavior in depressed patients with a history of alcoholism. *Addictive Behavior, 30*(6), 1144–1153.

Sher, L., Sperling, D., Stanley, B. H., Carballo, J. J., Shoval, G., Zalsman, G., . . . Oquendo, M. A. (2007). Triggers for suicidal behavior in depressed older adolescents and young adults: Do alcohol use disorders make a difference? *International Journal of Adolescent Medicine & Health, 19*(1), 91–98.

Sher, L., Sperling, D., Zalsman, G., Vardi, G., & Merrick, J. (2006). Alcohol and suicidal behavior in adolescents. *Minerva Pediatrica, 58*(4), 333–339.

Stahre, M., Roeber, J., Kanny, D., Brewer, R. D., & Zhang, X. (2014). Contribution of excessive alcohol consumption to deaths and years of potential life lost in the United States. *Preventing Chronic Disease, 11,* E109. doi:10.5888/pcd11.130293

Substance Abuse and Mental Health Services Administration. (2015). *Behavioral health trends in the United States: Results from the 2014 National Survey on Drug Use and Health.* Retrieved from https://www.samhsa.gov/data/sites/default/files/NSDUH-FRR1-2014/NSDUH-FRR1-2014.pdf

Substance Abuse and Mental Health Services Administration. (2016). *Results from the 2015 National Survey on Drug Use and Health: Detailed tables.* Retrieved from https://www.samhsa.gov/data/sites/default/files/NSDUH-DetTabs-2015/NSDUH-DetTabs-2015/NSDUH-DetTabs-2015.pdf

Suokas, J., & Lonnqvist, J. (1995). Suicide attempts in which alcohol is involved: A special group in general hospital emergency rooms. *Acta Psychiatrica Scandinavica, 91,* 36–40.

Swift, R. M. (1999). Drug therapy for alcohol dependence. *New England Journal of Medicine, 340,* 1482–1490.

Vaszari, J. M., Bradford, S., Callahan O'Leary, C., Ben Abdallah, A., & Cottler, L. B. (2011). Risk factors for suicidal ideation in a population of community-recruited female cocaine users. *Comprehensive Psychiatry, 52*(3), 238–246.

Vijayakumar, L., Kumar, M. S., & Vijayakumar, V. (2011). Substance use and suicide. *Current Opinion in Psychiatry, 24*(3), 197–202.

Vingoe, L., Welch, S., Farrell, M., & Strang, J. (1999).Heroin overdose among a treatment sample of injecting drug misusers: Accident or suicidal behaviour? *Journal of Substance Use, 4*, 88–91.

Walitzer, K. S., & Dearing, R. L. (2006). Gender differences in alcohol and substance use relapse. *Clinical Psychology Review, 26*(2), 128–148.

Wang, A. G., & Stórá, T. (2009). Core features of suicide: Gender, age, alcohol and other putative risk factors in a low-incidence population. *Nordic Journal of Psychiatry, 63*(2), 154–159.

Welte, J. W., Abel, E. L., & Wieczorek, W. (1988). The role of alcohol in suicides in Erie County, NY, 1972–84. *Public Health Reports, 103*(66), 648–652.

Wilcox, H. C. (2004). Epidemiological evidence on the link between drug use and suicidal behaviors among adolescents. *Canadian Child and Adolescent Psychiatry Review, 13*(2), 27–30.

Wilcox, H. C., Conner, K. R., & Caine, E. D. (2004). Association of alcohol and drug use disorders and completed suicide: An empirical review of cohort studies. *Drug and Alcohol Dependence, 76*(Supp.), S11–S19.

Wojnar, M., Ilgen, M. A., Czyz, E., Strobbe, S., Klimkiewicz, A., Jakubczyk, A., . . . Brower, K. J. (2009). Impulsive and non-impulsive suicide attempts in patients treated for alcohol dependence. *Journal of Affective Disorders, 115*(1–2), 131–139.

Wong, S. S., Zhou, B., Goebert, D., & Hishinuma, E. S. (2013). The risk of adolescent suicide across patterns of drug use: A nationally representative study of high school students in the United States from 1999 to 2009. *Social Psychiatry & Psychiatric Epidemiology, 48*(10), 1611–1620.

Wright, M. H., & Obitz, F. W. (1984). Alcoholics and nonalcoholics' attributions of control of future life events. *Journal of Studies on Alcohol and Drug, 45*, 138–143.

Yaldizli, O., Kuhl, H. C., Graf, M., Wiesbeck, G. A., & Wurst, F. M. (2010). Risk factors for suicide attempts in patients with alcohol dependence or abuse and a history of depressive symptoms: A subgroup analysis from the WHO/ISBRA study. *Drug and Alcohol Review, 29*(1), 64–74.

Yaworski, D., Robinson, J., Sareen, J., & Bolton, J. M. (2011). The relation between nicotine dependence and suicide attempts in the general population. *Canadian Journal of Psychiatry, 56*(3):161–170.

Yuodelis-Flores, C., & Ries, R. K. (2015). Addiction and suicide: A review. *The American Journal on Addictions, 24*(2), 98–104.

Zahl, D. L., & Hawton, K. (2004). Repetition of deliberate self-harm and subsequent suicide risk: Long-term follow-up study of 11,583 patients. *British Journal of Psychiatry, 185*, 70–75.

CHAPTER 10

PERSONALITY DISORDERS AND SUICIDE

Personality disorders (PDs) are common psychiatric disorders strongly associated with suicide ideation, attempts, and completions. Overall, research indicates that the prevalence rate of suicide among individuals with PDs, with suicide among borderline personality disorder (BPD), approximates 10% (Schneider, Schnabel, & Wetterling, 2008). The rate of suicide attempt is estimated to be as high as 80% (Linehan et al., 2006; Soloff, Lynch, Kelly, Malone, & Mann, 2000). In this chapter, the relationship between PDs and risk of suicidality is explored. Special attention is given to the borderline PD as it is among the most common PDs and has a significant body of research regarding its epidemiology, course, and treatment.

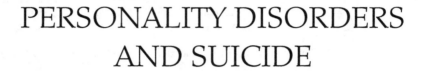

GOALS AND OBJECTIVES

An understanding of:

- *Diagnostic and Statistical Manual of Mental Disorders (DSM)* criteria for PDs
- Course of illness of borderline PD
- Etiology and epidemiology of borderline PDs
- Relationship between borderline PD and suicide
- Risk factors for suicide unique to individuals with borderline PD
- Protective factors for suicide unique to individuals with borderline PD
- Evidence-based practices for borderline PD

The prevalence of PDs generally ranges from 5% to 10% (Lenzenweger, 2008; Paris, 2013; Samuels, 2011; Trull, Jahng, Tomko, Wood, & Sher, 2010) and are associated with suicide attempts and completed suicide, specifically BPDs (Linehan et al., 2006; Soloff et al., 2000). PDs are characterized by a persistent and enduring pattern of inner experiences and behaviors that are pervasive, inflexible, and stable over time (American Psychiatric Association [APA], 2013). PDs manifest across a broad range of social and personal situations that result in distress or impairment in areas of social, occupational, and other areas of functioning (APA, 2013).

PDs generally become recognizable in adolescence and early adulthood (APA, 2013). Among mental disorders, PDs, specifically BPD, have one of the highest suicide risks (Chesney, Goodwin, & Fazel, 2014; Li et al., 2011; Pompili et al., 2005). Research has suggested that the lifetime rate of mortality for PDs is notably elevated (Biskin, 2015). A recent systematic review found that the reduction in life expectancy associated with PDs was between 13 and 22 years (Chesney et al., 2014).

PDs are associated with a high level of stigma, especially a diagnosis of BPD. Individuals with BPD are commonly labeled as manipulative and exploitative (Aviram, Brodsky, & Stanley, 2006; Bodner et al., 2015; Sansone & Sansone, 2013). This stigma is not relegated to the general public. Research demonstrates that the stigma associated with BPD may also affect how clinicians tolerate the actions, thoughts, and emotional reactions of individuals with BPD and may also lead to minimizing symptoms and overlooking client strengths (Aviram et al., 2006; Bodner et al., 2015; Sansone & Sansone, 2013). As a result of the extreme emotional dysregulation and instability experienced by individuals with BPD, they are often hypersensitive to rejection and abandonment. Therefore, a clinician's reactions to a client diagnosed with BPD are especially critical, and efforts to distance oneself from a client with BPD may have a profound effect above and beyond what was intended. It is essential that clinicians consider their own reactions and beliefs regarding individuals with PDs in order to ensure that an effective, appropriate therapeutic alliance can be developed and maintained.

Individual Exercise 10.1

1. When you hear the words "PD" or "borderline," what are the first words or thoughts that come to your mind?
2. Are your listed words or thoughts generally positive or negative? Did they surprise you in any way? If so, how?
3. What personal *and* professional considerations and assumptions may make it hard for you to work with a client with a PD?
4. What personal *and* professional considerations may make it easy for you to work with a client with a PD?

DSM-5 DIAGNOSIS

The *DSM-5* (5th ed.; APA, 2013) brought many changes to a number of diagnostic categories, including the development of new stand-alone chapters (e.g., Trauma- and Stressor-Related Disorders, Obsessive-Compulsive and Related Disorders), new, but empirically supported diagnoses (e.g., disruptive mood dysregulation disorder, excoriation disorder), and the refining of several diagnostic criteria informed by research. However, the chapter, diagnoses, and criteria related to PDs remain unchanged from the *DSM-IV* (4th ed.; APA, 1994). Notwithstanding the efforts of the working group established to focus on updating PDs and incorporating decades on new research, differing perspectives, proposed changes, and lack of scientific support for the new directions resulted in their work being excluded from the diagnostic section of the *DSM*. In December 2012, these proposed changes were rejected on scientific grounds and with no time to revise, the *DSM-IV* PD section was reinstated for the *DSM-5* (Paris, 2013). Much of their work can be found in Section III of the *DSM-5*, Emergent Measures and Models; future research may incorporate and adapt aspects of its work into subsequent *DSM* editions or updates (APA, 2013).

Consequently, the only notable change, which is significant, is that PDs are no longer coded on Axis II in the *DSM-5*, because in *DSM-5* the duplicative and confusing multiaxial diagnostic coding was removed (APA, 2013). In prior *DSM* editions (*DSM-III* and *DSM-IV*), PDs were located in their own Axis II (along with intellectual ability) that oddly diminished and separated PDs from all other diagnoses situated in Axis I, resulting in the minimization or failure to recognize, diagnose, and treat these conditions (Paris, 2013). Separating PDs into their own axis was justified as these disorders were (incorrectly understood as) inflexible, durable, chronic, and incurable. However, research has demonstrated that PDs show remission and recovery with treatment over time (Gunderson et al., 2011; Paris, 2013). Thus, the *DSM-5's* removal of the past multiaxial system was a significant step for PDs.

According to the *DSM-5*, there are 10 PDs including paranoid, schizoid, schizotypal, antisocial, borderline, histrionic, narcissistic, avoidant, dependent, and obsessive-compulsive. A PD is an enduring pattern of inner experience and behavior (that deviates from one's culture) that is pervasive, inflexible, and stable over time, typically beginning in late adolescence or early adulthood and leading to distress or impairment (APA, 2013). This pattern typically emerges in two or more of the following areas: cognition, affectivity, interpersonal functioning, and impulse control; and is enduring across a range of social and personal situations that result in distress or impairment in areas of functioning (e.g., social, occupational; APA, 2013).

BPDs have received special attention in suicidology. According to the *DSM-5*, the general criteria for BPD includes enduring and persistent patterns of unstable interpersonal relationships, self-image, affect, with notable impulsivity, and five or more of the following criteria:

- Efforts to avoid real or imagined abandonment
- Unstable and intense interpersonal relationships
- Identity disturbance
- Impulsivity
- Recurrent suicidal behaviors, gestures, and threats
- Affective instability
- Feelings of emptiness
- Inappropriate and intense anger
- Stress-related paranoid ideation

EPIDEMIOLOGY AND PROGNOSIS

PDs are traditionally considered maladaptive patterns in interacting with oneself, others, and the world resulting from dysfunctional early childhood environments that limited that development of adaptive patterns of perceptions and responses (APA, 2013). In addition, research has highlighted the genetic contributions to PDs and their symptoms (Newlin & Weinstein, 2015; Reichborn-Kjennerud, 2010). Notwithstanding, continued research is required to further clarify the etiology and multiple influences on the development of a PD.

Research into PDs has found a wide range of prevalence rates in the general community from as high as nearly 15% of adults (Grant et al., 2004), to 10.6% (Lenzenweger, 2008), to estimated 6% to 10% of individuals (Samuels, 2011), to as low as just over 4% (Cold, Yang, Tyrer, Roberts, & Ullrich, 2006). While the higher rates have been questioned, researchers recognize that even rates around 5% would constitute a significant problem (Paris, 2013, 2010). PDs are frequently co-occurring with other mental disorders, including mood disorders, anxiety disorders, and alcohol and other substance use disorders (Samuels, 2011). In addition, PDs are associated with sleep disturbance, cardiovascular disease, arthritis, obesity, pain conditions, and other chronic health conditions (Dixon-Gordon, Whalen, Layden, & Chapman, 2015). Overall, PDs carry substantial societal costs (Frankenburg & Zanarini, 2004; van Asselt, Dirksen, Arntz, & Severens, 2007).

The following factors are associated with an increased risk of BPD:

- Comorbid anxiety (Riihimäki, Vuorilehto, & Isometsä, 2014)
- Comorbid substance use disorders (Riihimäki et al., 2014)
- Previous depressive episodes (Riihimäki et al., 2014)
- Suicidal ideation (Riihimäki et al., 2014)

- Previous suicide attempts (Riihimäki et al., 2014)
- Unemployment (Riihimäki et al., 2014)
- Severe economic difficulties (Riihimäki et al., 2014)
- Disorganized controlling childhood behavior (Lyons-Ruth, Bureau, Holmes, Easterbrooks, & Brooks, 2013)
- Negative parent–child interaction during infancy and/or childhood (Lyons-Ruth et al., 2013)

BPD AND SUICIDE

BPD is associated with an elevated risk of suicide ideation, suicide attempt, and completed suicide (Ansell et al., 2015; Linehan et al., 2006, 2015; Pompili et al., 2005; Sher et al., 2016; Tucker et al., 2016) and represents 9% to 33% of all suicides (Pompili et al., 2005). Approximately 15% to 50% of psychiatric inpatients and 11% of psychiatric outpatients meet current criteria for BPD and the rate of suicide among BPD patients is estimated to be 10% (Oumaya et al., 2008; Schneider, 2008), which is more than 50 times the rate of suicide in the general population (Zeng et al., 2015). The rate of suicide attempt, however, is much higher than completed suicides and is estimated to be between 69% and 80% (Linehan et al., 2006; Soloff et al., 2000). Annually, approximately 100,000 diagnosed with BPD complete suicide (Pompili et al., 2005).

Research from long-term follow-up studies of individuals with BPD has established that the age of suicide attempts and completions vary within the context of BPD. That is, most often attempts peak early in the course of BPD, when patients are in their 20s, and suicide completions occur much later in the life span (Paris & Zweig-Frank, 2001). Limited research has examined the relationship between suicidality and race/ethnicity within BPD. This research finds that African–American women with BPD present with more severe symptoms of lack of anger control and fewer suicidal behaviors than Caucasian women with BPD (De Genna & Feske, 2013).

Risk Factors

There are a number of established risk factors for suicidal acts among individuals with BPD. These include:

- Comorbid depression (Pompili et al., 2005)
- Comorbid anxiety (Ferrer et al., 2010; Maloney, Degenhardt, Darke, & Nelson, 2009; Mehlum, Friis, Vaglum, & Karterud, 1994; Pompili et al., 2005)
- Comorbid substance abuse (Links, Heslegrave, Mitton, van Reekum, & Patrick, 1995; Maloney et al., 2009; Pompili et al., 2005; Soloff et al., 2000)
- Previous suicide attempts (Pompili et al., 2005)
- Higher levels of aggressivity (Sher et al., 2016)
- Higher levels of affective dysregulation (Sher et al., 2016)
- Higher levels of impulsivity (May & Klonsky, 2016; Pompili et al., 2005; Soloff et al., 2000)
- Hopelessness (Pompili et al., 2005; Soloff et al., 2000)
- Despondency (Tucker et al., 2016)
- Fragility (Tucker et al., 2016)
- History of child abuse (Kaplan et al., 2016), especially co-occurring physical and sexual abuse (Kaplan, 2015)
- Female gender (Maloney et al., 2009)
- Adolescent onset of disorder (Lundin, Lundberg, Allebeck, & Hemmingsson, 2011)
- Maternal withdrawal during infancy (Lyons-Ruth et al., 2013)

Protective Factors

Although significantly fewer, a small number of protective factors have been identified among individuals with BPD that serve to reduce the risk of suicide. These include:

- Lower levels of impulsivity (Lin, Zhang, Zhou, & Jiang, 2016)
- Greater emotional stability (Ferrer, 2015)
- Reward-dependent attachment style (Chapman, Derbidge, Cooney, Hong, & Linehan, 2009)

Case Vignette 10.1

Anne is a 19-year-old single White, Jewish female. She is a high school graduate and completed 1 year of college. She was raised in an upper-middle-class family where academic and career success was extremely important, as was their Orthodox faith. Anne was the last of five children. Seven years apart from the next youngest of her siblings, Anne was an unplanned child. She was a good student throughout middle school and high school, but had to work hard to earn her grades. She had few close friends, and although she dated occasionally throughout high school, she never had a serious boyfriend or a best friend. In fact, she seemed to frequently shift her focus of attention from one individual to another before ever establishing a meaningful connection.

After graduation from high school, Anne went away to college. She did well in her first semester and passed all of her classes with above-average grades, but the adjustment to living away from home and college life was not easy. By the spring semester, Anne began to have increasing trouble keeping up her grades and often reported to her mother that she felt as if the professors were treating her unfairly and picking on her. She also started having trouble with the new friendships she had started forming in the fall semester. She felt that some of the other girls were jealous of her, and therefore, trying to exclude her from their group. She accused the girls of going out together behind her back. She would become full of rage and lash out at them and then feel guilty and lonely and reach out to them only to be turned away, making her angry once again. As a result, she would often go out on her own, get drunk, and sleep through her early morning classes the next day. Her behavior was impulsive, cutting classes, going out with strangers she met at the bar the night before, dying her hair, and stealing money from her roommate.

When Anne came home for the summer after her first year, her parents noted that she did not engage with her old friends from high school and that she seemed "angry and emotional." She was frequently out very late at night and then slept during the day. They did not know where she was or who she was with or where she got the money to pay for her nights out, and Anne would become very angry when they questioned her about it. Her appetite dropped off and she seemed to be dressing very provocatively, which was a dramatic shift from her conservative upbringing and style during high school.

Anne returned to school that fall but was unable to concentrate in class and was placed on academic probation for missing so many classes. During the winter break, she returned home and told her family that she did not plan on returning to school for the spring semester. She no longer wanted to be a pediatrician, veterinarian, lawyer, or teacher (her major had changed several times in the last year and a half), but rather an artist or actor. She said that school just was not for her; it was too restrictive and the people there did not understand her. She needed a place where she could be creative and thrive, and not have to conform to everyone else's rules. Anne exploded with rage when her parents confronted her about the dramatic shifts in her appearance, friend groups, goals, and behavior. She threw a vase and smashed a painting against a chair. She then curled up like a baby, sobbing on the floor asking for forgiveness saying she was a failure and didn't deserve to be alive.

Her parents were worried about her temper tantrums and rage and were increasingly concerned about her impulsive behavior and her late nights out doing who knows what. They finally insisted that she see a psychiatrist.

On mental status examination, Anne is alert and oriented x3, although she kept her head down and rarely made eye contact. Her clothes are unclean and mismatched. She had noticeable body odor. She displays limited range of affect and frequently answers in monosyllabic monotones. Anne denies that she hears voices. In the past few months, Anne had lost 23 pounds and described a very minimal appetite. She cannot recall the last time she laughed, and is not concerned by her inability to smile. She sees life as a never-ending burden. She admits long-standing suicide ideation. Although she denies any prior suicide attempts, she noted collecting pills.

Case Vignette 10.2

Using the same Case Vignette (10.1), change the following:

Gender: From Anne (female) to Adam (male)
Religion: From Judaism to Christianity

Case Vignette 10.3

Using the same Case Vignette (10.1), change the following:

Sexual orientation: From heterosexual to homosexual
Religion: From Judaism to Muslim

Case Vignette 10.4

Using the same Case Vignette (10.1), change the following:

Immigration status: From born in the United States to immigrated from Algeria
Family history: Mother has a history of self-harm behaviors

ROLE-PLAY 10.1

Using Case Vignettes 10.1 and 10.2, in groups of three (clinician, client, and observer), engage the client and conduct an assessment for BPD and suicide risk. What specific risk and protective factors should you consider? Be aware of your personal and professional attitudes in working with this client. What other information would you need to know? How do the changes in the vignette impact your answers to these questions?

CURRENT PRACTICE GUIDELINES AND EVIDENCE-BASED PRACTICE

Psychotherapy has been found to be effective for addressing the elevated risk of suicide within the context of BPD (Calati, 2016). Dialectical behavioral therapy (DBT) is one of the main empirically supported treatments for reducing suicide attempts and nonsuicidal self-injury among individuals with BPD (Linehan et al., 2015). This approach to treatment is discussed in detail in Chapter 18. DBT consists of multiple components, including (a) individual therapy, (b) skills training, (c) telephone coaching, and (d) a therapist consultation team. Research has examined which of these components are required to achieve the best possible outcome (Linehan et al., 2015). This research has compared skills training plus case management (DBT-S), DBT individual therapy plus activities group (DBT-I), and standard DBT including skills training and individual therapy. Findings suggest that all three treatment conditions result in similar improvements in the frequency and severity of suicide attempts, suicide ideation, use of crisis services due to suicidality, and reasons for living (Linehan et al., 2015). Compared with the DBT-I group, the standard DBT group had lower dropout rates from treatment, were less likely to use crisis services during the follow-up period, and had fewer psychiatric hospitalizations (Linehan et al., 2015).

Mentalization-based therapy (MBT) has also been shown to be effective at reducing self-harm behaviors within the context of BPD (Bateman & Fonagy, 1999, 2001, 2010). It has also been found to be effective when delivered by mental health professionals with only limited additional training and with moderate levels of supervision (Bateman & Fonagy, 2010). MBT is a psychodynamically oriented treatment. Although mentalization is a component in most traditional models of psychotherapy, in MBT it is the primary focus rather than just an additional component of treatment.

MBT has as its central focus the goal of helping people to differentiate and separate out their own thoughts and feelings from those around them (Bateman & Fonagy, 2010). Mentalization is the capacity to understand both behavior and feelings and how they are associated with specific mental states in ourselves and in others. MBT proposes that individuals with BPD have a decreased capacity for mentalization. More specifically, individuals with BPD have unstable and intense relationships and often find it difficult or impossible to recognize the effects that their behavior has on other individuals or to put themselves in other people's shoes and to empathize with others (Bateman & Fonagy, 2010). MBT suggests that individuals with BPD have a history of disorganized attachment leading to problems in affect regulation, attention, and self-control and that these problems are mediated through a failure to develop a healthy, strong mentalizing capacity (Bateman & Fonagy, 2010).

The first task in MBT is to help the individual learn to stabilize his or her emotional expression as uncontrolled affect leads to impulsivity and only when affect is regulated can the individual begin to improve his or her sense of self (Bateman & Fonagy, 2010). The therapist is expected to (a) refrain from acting as an expert, (b) have patience in taking time to identify differences in perspectives, (c) validate and accept divergent perspectives, (d) actively question the patient about his or her experiences (asking for detailed descriptions of experience rather than explanations), and (e) seek clarification to ensure accurate understanding of the individual's experience (i.e., saying explicitly that something is unclear; Bateman & Fonagy, 2010).

The primary mechanism of change by which mentalization is enhanced is via the attachment between the therapist and the client. Therefore, exploration and interpretation of transference is a major component of MBT (Bateman & Fonagy, 2010). The technique of mentalizing the transference refers to the therapist's goal of encouraging clients to consider in detail the relationship they are currently in (i.e., with the therapist) and to focus their attention on the other (i.e., therapist), and then to assist them in contrasting their own perceptions of themselves with how they are perceived by others (e.g., the therapist). This intense examination is used to achieve the ultimate goal of MBT, to reinstate mentalizing when it is lost, or to help to maintain it in circumstances when it might be lost or is being lost (Bateman & Fonagy, 2010).

Research has found that MBT is more effective than treatment as usual at treating individuals with BPD (Bateman & Fonagy 1999, 2001; Linehan et al. 2006). Research has also found that individuals who received 18 months of MBT were at lower risk of suicidality and reported greater clinical improvements and greater global levels of functioning at 5 years posttreatment termination than those who received treatment as usual (Bateman & Fonagy, 2008).

SUMMARY

PDs are associated with an increased risk of suicidality. In particular, individuals diagnosed with BPD struggle with impulsivity and emotional dysregulation leading to increased risk of completed suicide and high rates of suicide attempts and ideation. To engage, develop a therapeutic alliance, and effectively treat individuals with BPD at risk of suicide, it is essential for clinicians to become informed of not only the risk and protective factors but also their own personal and professional beliefs regarding the disorder. A lack

KEY POINTS

1. PDs are characterized by an enduring pattern of inner experiences and behaviors (that deviates from one's culture) that is pervasive and inflexible, typically beginning in late adolescence or early adulthood and leading to distress and/or impairment.
2. BPD is among the most commonly studied PD related to suicidal behavior.
3. Approximately 9% to 33% of all suicides occur in persons with a BPD.
4. Lifetime prevalence of PDs range from 5% to 10%, but has been estimated to be as high as 15%.
5. PDs are frequently comorbid with mood and anxiety disorders.
6. Lifetime rate of mortality secondary to suicide has been estimated to be 10% for individuals with BPD.
7. Key predictors of suicide for individuals diagnosed with BPD include comorbid depression, anxiety, and substance use; previous suicide attempts; higher levels of aggressivity; higher levels of affective dysregulation; higher levels of impulsivity; hopelessness; despondency; fragility; history of child abuse; female gender; adolescent onset of disorder; and maternal withdrawal during infancy.

of awareness may hinder the ability to effectively build an alliance with such clients and prevent effective treatment delivery.

ELECTRONIC RESOURCES

NATIONAL INSTITUTE OF MENTAL HEALTH

www.nimh.nih.gov/health/topics/borderline-personality-disorder/index.shtml

NATIONAL ALLIANCE ON MENTAL ILLNESS

www.nami.org/Learn-More/Mental-Health-Conditions/Borderline-Personality-Disorder

EDUCATIONAL AND INFORMATIVE SITES

www.borderlinepersonalitydisorder.com/what-is-bpd/bpd-overview
www.behavioraltech.org
www.narsad.org
www.bpddemystified.com
www.bpdworld.org
www.cartercenter.org/health/mental_health/index.html
www.borderlinepersonalitydisorder.com
www.nmha.org
http://thefightwithinus.com
www.psych.org

KNOWLEDGE ACQUISITION TEST (KAT)

True or False

1. Males with borderline personality disorder (BPD) are more likely to attempt suicide than females with BPD.
2. Individuals with BPD endorsing higher levels of impulsivity are less likely to complete suicide.
3. Up to 80% of individuals with BPD are likely to attempt suicide.
4. Aggression is a risk factor for suicide among individuals with BPD.
5. Dialectical behavioral therapy is the only empirically supported treatment for BPD.
6. Improving affect regulation is a main goal of any treatment for BPD.
7. More individuals with personality disorders (PDs) complete suicide than those with depression.
8. There are no differences in the rate of suicide attempt among individuals with BPD based on ethnicity.

Short Answer

9. List the key risk factors for suicide among individuals with BPD.
10. List the key protective factors against suicide among individuals with BPD.
11. Describe the theory upon which mentalization-based therapy is based.
12. Describe how the *DSM-5* defines a PD.

Multiple Choice

13. Which item in the following list is not a *DSM-5* criteria for BPD?
    A. Impulsivity
    B. Feelings of emptiness
    C. Intense inappropriate anger
    D. Loss of interest
    E. All of the above
    F. None of the above
14. Which of the following is not a PD?
    A. Narcissistic
    B. Obsessive-compulsive
    C. Borderline
    D. Paranoid
    E. All of the above
    F. None of the above
15. PDs are often associated with which of the following?
    A. Arthritis
    B. Diabetes
    C. Depression
    D. Sleep disturbance
    E. All of the above
    F. None of the above

REFERENCES

American Psychiatric Association. (1994). *Diagnostic and statistical manual of mental disorders* (4th ed.). Washington, DC: Author.

American Psychiatric Association. (2013). *Diagnostic and statistical manual of mental disorders* (5th ed., text rev.). Arlington, VA: American Psychiatric Publishing.

Ansell, E. B., Wright, A. G. C., Markowitz, J. C., Sanislow, C. A., Hopwood, C. J., Zanarini, M. C., . . . Grilo, C. M. (2015). Personality disorder risk factors for suicide attempts over 10 years of follow-up. *Personality Disorders: Theory, Research and Treatment, 6*(2), 161–167.

Aviram, R. B., Brodsky, B. S., & Stanley, B. (2006). Borderline personality disorder, stigma and treatment implications. *Harvard Review of Psychiatry, 14*(5), 249–256.

Bateman, A., & Fonagy, P. (1999). The effectiveness of partial hospitalization in the treatment of borderline personality disorder: A randomised controlled trial. *American Journal of Psychiatry, 156,* 1563–1569.

Bateman, A., & Fonagy, P. (2001). Treatment of borderline personality disorder with psychoanalytically oriented partial hospitalisation: An 18-month follow-up. *American Journal of Psychiatry, 158,* 36–42.

Bateman, A., & Fonagy, P. (2008). 8-year follow-up of patients treated for borderline personality disorder: Mentalization-based treatment versus treatment as usual. *American Journal of Psychiatry, 165*(5), 631–638.

Bateman, A., & Fonagy, P. (2010). Mentalization-based treatment for borderline personality disorder. *World Psychiatry, 9*(1), 11–15.

Biskin, R. S. (2015). The lifetime course of borderline personality disorder. *Canadian Journal of Psychiatry, 60*(7), 303–308.

Bodner, E., Cohen-Fridel, S., Mashiah, M., Segal, M., Grinshpoon, A., Fischel, T., & Iancu, I. (2015). The attitudes of psychiatric hospital staff toward hospitalization and treatment of patients with borderline personality disorder. *BioMed Central Psychiatry, 15*(1), 2-14.

Chapman, A. L., Derbidge, C. M., Cooney, E., Hong, P. Y., & Linehan, M. M. (2009). Temperament as a prospective predictor of self-injury among patients with borderline personality disorder. *Journal of Personality Disorders, 23*(2), 122–140.

Chesney, E., Goodwin, G. M., & Fazel, S. (2014). Risks of all-cause and suicide mortality in mental disorders: A meta-review. *World Psychiatry, 13*(2), 153–160.

Cold, J., Yang, M., Tyrer, P., Roberts, A., & Ullrich, S. (2006). Prevalence and correlates of personality disorder in Great Britain. *The British Journal of Psychiatry, 188*(5), 423–431.

De Genna, N. M., & Feske, U. (2013). Phenomenology of borderline personality disorder: the role of race and socioeconomic status. *Journal of Nervous and Mental Diseases, 201*(12), 1027–1034.

Dixon-Gordon, K. L., Whalen, D. J., Layden, B. K., & Chapman, A. L. (2015). A systematic review of personality disorders and health outcomes. *Canadian Psychology, 56*(2), 168–190.

Ferrer, M., Andión, Ó, Matali, J., Valero, S., Navarro, J. A., Ramos-Quiroga, J. A., . . . Casas, M. (2010). Comorbid attention-deficit/hyperactivity disorder in borderline patients defines an impulsive subtype of borderline personality disorder. *Journal of Personality Disorders, 24,* 812–822.

Frankenburg, F. R., & Zanarini, M. C. (2004). The association between borderline personality disorder and chronic medical illnesses, poor health-related lifestyle choices, and costly forms of health care utilization. *Journal of Clinical Psychiatry, 65,* 1660–1665.

Grant, B. F., Hasin, D. S., Stinson, F. S., Dawson, D. A., Chou, S. P., Ruan, W. J., & Pickering, R. P. (2004). Prevalence, correlates, and disability of personality disorders in the United States: Results from the national epidemiologic survey on alcohol and related conditions. *Journal of Clinical Psychiatry, 65*(7), 948–958.

Gunderson, J. G., Stout, R. L., McGlashan, T. H., Shea, M. T., Morey, L. C., Grilo, C., . . . Skodol, A. E. (2011). Ten-year course of borderline personality disorder: psychopathology and function from the Collaborative Longitudinal Personality Disorders study. *Archives of General Psychiatry, 68*(8), 827–837.

Kaplan, C., Tarlow, N., Stewart, J. G., Aguirre, B., Galen, G., & Auerbach, R. P. (2016). Borderline personality disorder in youth: The prospective impact of child abuse on non-suicidal self-injury and suicidality. *Comprehensive Psychiatry, 71,* 86–94. doi:10.1016/j.comppsych.2016.08.016

Lenzenweger, M. F. (2008). Epidemiology of personality disorders. *Psychiatric Clinics of North America, 31*(3), 395–403.

Lin, L., Zhang, J., Zhou, L., & Jiang, C. (2016). The relationship between impulsivity and suicide among rural youths aged 15–35 years: A case-control psychological autopsy study. *Psychological Health Medicine, 21*(3), 330–337.

Linehan, M. M., Comtois, K. A., Murray, A. M., Brown, M. Z., Gallop, R. J., Heard, H. L., . . . Lindenboim, N. (2006). Two-year randomized controlled trial and follow-up of dialectical behavior therapy vs. therapy by experts for suicidal behaviors and borderline personality disorder. *Archives of General Psychiatry, 63*(7), 757–766.

Linehan, M. M., Korslund, K. E., Harned, M. S., Gallop, R. J., Lungu, A., Neacsiu, A. D., . . . Murray-Gregory, A. M. (2015). Dialectical behavior therapy for high suicide risk in individuals with borderline personality disorder: A randomized clinical trial and component analysis. *Journal of the American Medical Association Psychiatry, 72*(5), 475–482.

Links, P. S., Heslegrave, R. J., Mitton, J. E., van Reekum, R., & Patrick, J. (1995). Borderline personality disorder and substance abuse: Consequences of comorbidity. *Canadian Journal of Psychiatry, 40*(9), 9–14.

Lundin, A., Lundberg, I., Allebeck, P., & Hemmingsson, T. (2011). Psychiatric diagnosis in late adolescence and long-term risk of suicide and suicide attempt. *Acta Psychiatrica Scandinavica, 124*(6), 454–461.

Lyons-Ruth, K., Bureau, J. F., Holmes, B., Easterbrooks, A., & Brooks, N. H. (2013). Borderline symptoms and suicidality/self-injury in late adolescence: Prospectively observed relationship correlates in infancy and childhood. *Psychiatry Research, 206*(2–3), 273–281.

Maloney, E., Degenhardt, L., Darke, S., & Nelson, E. C. (2009). Impulsivity and borderline personality as risk factors for suicide attempts among opioid-dependent individuals. *Psychiatry Research, 169*(1), 16–21.

May, A. M., & Klonsky, E. D. (2016). 'Impulsive' suicide attempts: What do we really mean? *Personality Disorders: Theory, Research and Treatment, 7*(3), 293–302.

Mehlum, L., Friis, S., Vaglum, P., & Karterud, S. (1994). The longitudinal pattern of suicidal behaviour in borderline personality disorder: A prospective follow-up study. *Acta Psychiatrica Scandinavica, 90*(124), 30.

Newlin, E., & Weinstein, B. (2015, June). Personality disorders. *Continuum: Lifelong learning in neurology, 21*(3, Behavioral Neurology and Neuropsychiatry), 806–817.

Oumaya, M., Friedman, S., Pham, A., Abou, A. T., Guelfi, J. D., & Rouillon, F. (2008). Borderline personality disorder, self-mutilation and suicide: Literature review. *Encephale, 34*(5), 452–458.

Paris, J. (2010). Estimating the prevalence of personality disorders in the community. *Journal of Personality Disorders, 24*(4), 405–411.

Paris, J. (2013). *The intelligent clinician's guide to the DSM-5.* Oxford, UK: Oxford Press.

Paris, J., & Zweig-Frank, H. A. (2001). A 27-year follow-up of patients with borderline personality disorder. *Comprehensive Psychiatry, 42,* 482–487.

Pompili, M. I., Girardi, P., Ruberto, A., & Tatarelli, R. (2005). Suicide in borderline personality disorder: A meta-analysis. *Nordic Journal of Psychiatry, 59*(5), 319–324.

Reichborn-Kjennerud, T. (2010). The genetic epidemiology of personality disorders. *Dialogues in Clinical Neuroscience, 12*(1), 103–114.

Riihimäki, K., Vuorilehto, M., & Isometsä, E. (2014). Borderline personality disorder among primary care depressive patients: A five-year study. *Journal of Affective Disorders, 155,* 303–306.

Samuels, J. (2011). Personality disorders: Epidemiology and public health issues. *International Review of Psychiatry, 23*(3), 223–233.

Sansone, R. A., & Sansone, L. A. (2013). Responses of mental health clinicians to patients with borderline personality disorder. *Innovations in Clinical Neuroscience, 10*(5–6), 39–43.

Schneider, B., Schnabel, A., & Wetterling, T. (2008). How do personality disorders modify suicide risk? *Journal of Personality Disorders, 22,* 233–245.

Sher, L., Fisher, A. M., Kelliher, C. H., Penner, J. D., Goodman, M., Koenigsberg, H. W., . . . Hazlett, E. A. (2016). Clinical features and psychiatric comorbidities of borderline personality disorder patients with versus without a history of suicide attempt. *Psychiatry Research, 246,* 261–266.

Soloff, P. H., Lynch, K. G., Kelly, T. M., Malone, K. M., & Mann, J. J. (2000). Characteristics of suicide attempts of patients with major depressive episode and borderline personality disorder: A comparative study. *American Journal of Psychiatry, 157*(4), 601–608.

Trull, T. J., Jahng, S., Tomko, R. L., Wood, P. K., & Sher, K. J. (2010). Revised NESARC Personality disorder diagnoses: Gender, prevalence, and comorbidity with substance dependence disorders. *Journal of Personality Disorders, 24*(4), 412–426.

Tucker, R. P., Lengel, G. J., Smith, C. E., Capron, D. W., Mullin-Sweatt, S. N., & Wingate, L. R. (2016). Maladaptive Five Factor Model personality traits associated with borderline personality disorder indirectly affect susceptibility to suicide ideation through increased anxiety sensitivity cognitive concerns. *Psychiatry Research, 246,* 432–437.

van Asselt, A. D. I., Dirksen, C. D., Arntz, A., & Severens, J. L. (2007). The cost of borderline personality disorder: Societal cost of illness in BPD-patients. *European Psychiatry, 22,* 354–361.

Zeng, R., Cohen, L. J., Tanis, T, Qizilbash, A., Lopatyuk, Y., Yaseen, Z. S., & Galynker, I. (2015). Assessing the contribution of borderline personality disorder and features to suicide risk in psychiatric inpatients with bipolar disorder, major depression and schizoaffective disorder. *Psychiatry Research, 226*(1), 361–367.

PART IV

At-Risk Populations

CHAPTER ELEVEN

ACTIVE MILITARY PERSONNEL AND VETERANS

Serving in the military presents many challenges, opportunities, and risks. Recently, the suicide rates among military service members and veterans have trended upward and reached unprecedented levels (Kuehn, 2009; Nock et al., 2013). Individuals who are currently serving or have served in the military are specific populations that are highlighted in this chapter due to their importance and distinct vulnerability. This chapter explores the statistics, epidemiology, and trends in active military personnel and veteran suicide. In addition, the specific risk factors (psychiatric, sociodemographic, interpersonal, and other associated factors) for military personnel and veterans are drawn from evidence-based research. Also, protective factors identified in the literature for military service members and veterans are presented. Finally, treatment considerations and interventions for active military personnel and veterans are explored.

GOALS AND OBJECTIVES

An understanding of:

- Influence of being an active military personnel or veteran on suicidality
- Prevalence of suicide among military personnel or veterans
- Influence of gender on active military personnel or veteran suicidality
- Risk factors for active military personnel or veteran suicidality
- Protective factors against active military personnel or veteran suicidality
- Key considerations in mental health treatment of suicidal active military personnel or veterans
- Some gaps and limitations in the mental health treatment of suicidal active military personnel or veterans

Suicidality is widely recognized as a serious problem facing military personnel and veterans. Historically, the rates of suicide among military personnel were lower than that of the civilian population (Kemp & Bossarte, 2012; Nock et al., 2014). In fact, the term "healthy soldier effect" was coined to describe the decrease in all-cause mortality traditionally found in military members, especially in the period immediately after they leave the service (Lineberry & O'Connor, 2012). However, beginning in 2008, the rate of suicide among U.S. soldiers exceeded that of the civilian population for the first time in decades (Kuehn,

2009). Further, while suicide rates once varied greatly among the different branches of the military (Helmkamp, 1995), at present, rates across sectors of the military are now rather similar (Eaton, Messer, Garvey Wilson, & Hoge, 2006). Veterans also present as at significant risk for suicide (U.S. Department of Veterans Affairs, 2016). Although veterans represent 8.5% of the U.S. adult population, they account for 18% of all adult suicides (U.S. Department of Veterans Affairs, 2016).

Despite the fact that preenlistment screening interviews inquire about suicide and mental health history and that applicants who report such a history are excluded from service, suicide is the second leading cause of death among active-duty military personnel (Centers for Disease Control and Prevention [CDC], 2007). Nearly half of the soldiers who report lifetime suicide attempts also report that their first attempt occurred prior to the age at enlistment (Nock et al., 2014). Further, preenlistment mental disorders are associated with more than one-third of postenlistment first suicide attempts (Nock et al., 2014). This suggests that relying on self-report of these issues during initial screening is not a sufficient way to identify potentially at-risk individuals. It also highlights the need for strong outreach and treatment programs for new soldiers given the significant number of recruits who enter service with a history of suicidal behavior and mental disorders.

The military evokes strong reactions in many individuals. Many struggle with reconciling a recognition of the necessity of war while upholding the value of all life. As mental health professionals, active-duty soldiers and veteran clients alike may trigger a number of positive and/or negative ideas, preconceptions, assumptions, or biases. Professional awareness of the epidemiology, unique risk and protective factors, and special treatment considerations relevant for military personnel and veterans should serve to inform effective practice. Additionally, awareness of one's personal reactions, thoughts, and beliefs connected to military personnel and veterans is critical to ensure such reactions do not infringe upon accurate assessment of risk and effective clinical treatment of this client population.

Individual Exercise 11.1

1. Write down your initial reaction upon hearing the following words. Be honest and unfiltered in your response. Remember, answers are personal and there are no correct or incorrect answers: military, veteran, war, soldier, and combat.
2. Examine your responses. Are you surprised by anything you wrote down? In what way?

Small Group Exercise 11.1

In groups of two to three,

1. Share, as you feel comfortable, your responses to question 1 in Individual Exercise 11.1.
2. Were there similarities in your responses? What accounts for these similarities?
3. Were there differences in your responses? What accounts for these differences?
4. How might these perceptions influence positively or negatively clinical practice with active military personnel and veterans?

Reflect on your responses to question 1 in Small Group Exercise 11.1:

1. Which responses were you comfortable sharing? What made those responses easier to share?
2. Which were you not comfortable sharing? What made those responses difficult for you to share?
3. How might this awareness impact your work with military personnel and veterans?

STATISTICS, EPIDEMIOLOGY, AND TRENDS IN ACTIVE MILITARY PERSONNEL AND VETERAN SUICIDE

Suicide is the second leading cause of death among active-duty military personnel (CDC, 2007). The overall suicide rate among military personnel is as much as 20% higher than the suicide rate among civilians (Eaton et al., 2006; Scoville, Gubata, Potter, White, & Pearse, 2007; Sentell, Lacroix, Sentell, & Finstuen, 1997). Suicide attempts have been on the rise since the Army began tracking. Overall, among active military personnel, rates of suicide have doubled since 2005 (Miller, 2012). Approximately 17.3 per 100,000 troops or 2,100 military personnel completed suicide in 2006 (Lorge, 2008), the highest in 26 years (Hefling, 2008), up from 350 military personnel in 2002. It is hypothesized that due to the deployments in Iraq and Afghanistan, suicide rates in the military are higher than ever (Rutherford, 2008). Before the wars in Iraq and Afghanistan, for example, the incidence of suicide in active-duty U.S. service members was consistently 25% lower than that of civilians (Hoge & Castro, 2012).

Veterans in the United States are at an increased risk of suicide, and veterans associated with the conflicts in Afghanistan and Iraq have higher levels of functional impairment and psychiatric morbidity (Kaplan, Huguet, McFarland, & Newsom, 2007). The rate of suicide among veterans reached an average of 20 deaths each day in 2014 (U.S. Department of Veterans Affairs, 2016).

A comprehensive study by Ursano et al. (2015) examining the rate of suicide attempts in the U.S. Army during the wars in Afghanistan and Iraq found a sharp increase in attempts (Ursano et al., 2015). Study findings across the period between 2004 and 2009 identified that enlisted soldiers, which represent nearly 83.5% of active-duty Army soldiers, constitute 98.6% of all suicide attempts (overall prevalence rate of 377.0 per 100,000 individuals), whereas officers that represent 16.5% of active-duty regular Army soldiers accounted for only 1.4% of all suicide attempts (overall prevalence rate of 27.9 per 100,000 individuals; Ursano et al., 2015). Another study found that the suicide rate among U.S. Army soldiers increased by 80% from 2004 to 2008 (Archuleta et al., 2014). One study of 119 active-duty U.S. Army soldiers found that they made a total of 175 suicide attempts during military service, 121 of which occurred during the preceding year (C. J. Bryan, Garland, & Rudd, 2016).

One important study used the 2005 to 2012 National Violent Death Reporting System data from 16 states to examine the county-level distribution of suicides among current military and veteran decedents aged 18 to 35 years (Logan, Fowler, Patel, & Holland, 2016). Approximately 262 (33%) current military suicides occurred in just 10 (1.0%) counties, and 391 (33%) veteran suicides occurred in 33 (3.4%) counties. Suicides among regular-duty military personnel occur at a higher rate than among recruits (Scoville, Gardner, & Potter, 2004). It is suggested that the lower rate of suicide among recruits is due to the close supervision and limited access to alcohol and motor vehicles during the training period (Scoville et al., 2004). Suicide rates among male recruits outweigh the rate among female recruits by 3.5 times (Scoville et al., 2007). Regular-duty military males also have a higher rate of suicide than regular-duty military females (Sentell et al., 1997).

Findings regarding rates of suicide among military personnel by ethnicity vary. Some have found a higher rate of suicide among minority males and females as compared to nonminority males and females (Hourani, Warrack, & Coben, 1999), while others have found a higher rate of suicide among Caucasian military personnel (Helmkamp, 1995; Maguen, Skopp, Zhang, & Smolenski, 2015; Ursano et al., 2015). Scoville et al. (2007) found that the most common method of suicide among U.S. Air Force, Army, Marine Corps, and Navy military recruits was firearms (Scoville et al., 2007). Others have found firearms to be the leading method of suicide among regular-duty military personnel as well (Helmkamp, 1995; Mahon, Tobin, Cusack, Kelleher, & Malone, 2005).

In a 2-year prospective cohort study investigating suicide ideation among military veterans identified that a significant minority (13.7%) of U.S. veterans has chronic, onset, or remitted suicide ideation (Smith et al., 2016). In general, research has found the prevalence of suicidality among veterans is similar to previous estimates of ideation and attempts among adults in the U.S. general population (Bossarte et al., 2012). However, others report that suicides among veterans climbed to 22 per day in 2010 with male veterans having twice the risk of dying from suicide as their civilian counterparts (Lazar, 2014).

Individual Exercise 11.3

1. Among active military personnel and veterans, what would be the hardest military subpopulation (veterans from World War II, Korea, Vietnam, Gulf War, Iraq, or Afghanistan; dishonorably discharged personnel; individuals with psychiatric illness, trauma, or physical disabilities; homeless veterans; active-duty personnel) for you to professionally work with? Why?
2. What personal and/or professional considerations may make it harder for you to work with this population?
3. What would be the easiest military subpopulation group (veterans from World War II, Korea, Vietnam, Gulf War, Iraq, or Afghanistan; dishonorably discharged personnel; individuals with psychiatric illness, trauma, or physical disabilities; homeless veterans; active-duty personnel) for you to professionally work with? Why?
4. What personal and/or professional considerations may make it easier for you to work with this population?

Small Group Exercise 11.2

In small groups of two to three, please discuss, as you are comfortable, your responses to Individual Exercise 11.3. Remember, answers are personal and there are no correct or incorrect answers.

1. What were the response similarities in your group?
2. What were the response differences in your group?
3. Did you find any surprises in the group discussion? If so, what were they and how were you surprised?

RISK FACTORS FOR SUICIDE

Psychiatric Risk Factors

A history of suicide attempt prior to enlistment is a significant risk factor for later attempts both during and after service (Mahon et al., 2005; Ritchie, Keppler, & Rothberg, 2003; Yacobi, Fruchter, Mann, & Shelef, 2013). Among military personnel who made a suicide attempt during or after military service, approximately 50% experienced suicidal ideation and up to 25% made a suicide attempt prior to joining the military. Military personnel and veterans who made suicide attempts prior to joining the military were more than six times more likely to make a later suicide attempt after joining the military (C. J. Bryan, Ray-Sannerud, Morrow, & Etienne, 2013).

Research has also found that the primary motive for suicide attempts among military personnel is a desire to reduce or alleviate emotional distress, similar to motives reported by those in nonmilitary samples (C. J. Bryan, Rudd, & Wertenberger, 2016). However, few studies have examined factors that motivate military personnel to make a repeat suicide attempt. One study of 134 active-duty soldiers found that they were more likely to have made multiple suicide attempts if they were younger at the time of their first attempt, were not admitted to a hospital or treatment program after their first attempt, or experienced emotional and psychological relief immediately following their initial attempt (C. J. Bryan, Rudd, & Wertenberger, 2016).

Nonsuicidal self-injury (NSSI) is also a significant risk factor for suicidality in this population (C. J. Bryan, Rudd, Wertenberger, Young-McCaughon, & Peterson, 2015; Ganz & Sher, 2013). As one study of 422 military personnel and veterans reported, of those with a history of suicide attempt, NSSI emerged prior to the first attempt (91%) more often than the reverse (9%; C. J. Bryan, Rudd, et al., 2015). Conversely, suicide ideation emerged before NSSI in the majority of cases rather than the reverse (67% vs. 17%, respectively; C.J. Bryan, Rudd, et al., 2015). Therefore, NSSI may be a risk factor for attempts but not for ideation.

Psychiatric illness prior to enlistment, during active duty, and postenlistment is a significant risk factor for suicidality among military personnel and veterans. Among U.S. Army personnel, the estimated lifetime prevalence of any *Diagnostic and Statistical Manual of Mental Disorders* (4th ed.; *DSM-IV*; American Psychiatric Association [APA], 1994) anxiety, mood, behavior, or substance disorder has been found to be as high as 53% (Gadermann et al., 2012). When examining specific disorder, lifetime prevalence rates of approximately 18% for mood disorders, 27% for anxiety disorders, 23% for behavior disorders, and 14% for substance use disorders have been found (Gadermann et al., 2012). Findings also demonstrated that of the 53% of soldiers with psychiatric disorders, approximately 92% had onsets prior to enlistment (Gadermann et al., 2012). Findings further revealed that 82% had onset of suicidal ideation and 68% had suicide plans prior to enlistment (Gadermann et al., 2012). Another study found that approximately 85% of military personnel who self-identified as having had a mental health disorder reported that the problem began prior to joining the Army (Kessler, 2014).

Nock et al. (2013) highlight that many soldiers enlist while in the age range in which the risk for first onset of mental disorders is highest and may become ill only after joining the Army, especially after experiencing war-related stressors (i.e., the stress of basic training, the loss of family support). In a study of over 5,000 nondeployed soldiers, recruitment interviews showed that approximately 14% of soldiers considered suicide at some point in their lifetime, 5% made a suicide plan, and 3% attempted suicide, with between 47% and 60% of these outcomes first occurring prior to enlisting in the armed services (Nock et al., 2014). Results further showed that preenlistment mental disorders, particularly panic disorder and posttraumatic stress disorder (PTSD), were associated with increased rates of suicide attempts postenlistment. Further, almost one-third of postenlistment suicide attempts tied back to preenlistment mental disorders and pre- and postenlistment mental disorders accounted for 60% of first suicide attempts in the Army (Nock et al., 2014).

Among military personnel and veterans, depression (Britton et al., 2015; Conner et al., 2014; Corson et al., 2013; Cox et al., 2016; Ganz & Sher, 2013; LeardMann et al. 2013; Logan et al., 2016; Logan, Skopp, Karch, Reger, & Gahm, 2012; Mahon et al., 2005; Ritchie et al., 2003) and PTSD (Haller, Angkaw, Hendricks, & Norman, 2016; Ganz & Sher, 2013; Fanning & Pietrzak, 2013; Pompili et al., 2013; Wisco et al., 2014) are the most highly associated psychiatric disorders with suicidal ideation, attempts, and completions. For example, one systematic review identified 80 articles focusing on the relationship between PTSD and veterans and confirmed the relationship between PTSD in veterans and increased risk of suicide attempts (Pompili et al., 2013). One study of active-duty soldiers in the U.S. Army who attempted suicide found that while only 25% of attempters received mental health treatment prior to their attempt, 77% were diagnosed with moderate-to-severe mental disorders after their attempt (Yacobi, 2013). Results also identified personality disorders as a primary risk factor for suicide attempt (Yacobi, 2013).

Alcohol and substance use are significant risk factors for active military personnel (Arias et al., 2016; Britton et al., 2015; Fuehrlein et al., 2016; Ganz & Sher, 2013; Kim et al., 2012; Maguen 2015). A study of active-duty U.S. Army soldiers found that alcohol use during the 24 hours preceding a suicide attempt was associated with a significantly faster transition from suicidal impulse to action (C. J. Bryan, Garland, & Rudd, 2016). Drug use during the 24 hours leading up to an attempt, on the other hand, was unrelated to speed of transition or attempt lethality. Further, among suicide attempts in the past year, lethality significantly increased as the length of time since the last alcoholic drink increased. This suggests that the rapid transition may contribute to the use of less lethal attempt methods during periods of active drinking (C. J. Bryan, Garland, & Rudd 2016), or perhaps, that being under the influence of alcohol-skewed judgment or led to misestimation of risk, less lethal methods were unintentionally chosen.

A study of active-duty U.S. Army soldiers examining external life events and internal experiences (i.e., emotional distress and trauma-related thoughts) occurring within the 24 hours preceding suicide attempts not surprisingly found that soldiers experienced multiple external stressors and internal states in the 24 hours preceding their suicide attempts. Interestingly, however, emotional distress was found to be the most common risk factor while trauma-related thoughts were much less frequently reported in the 24 hours preceding suicide attempts. Emotional experiences were found to be directly related with suicidal intent, and to explain the relationship between external events and suicidal intent. Lethality was not found to be associated with any external events, emotional experiences, or trauma-related thoughts. Greater emotional distress and trauma-related thoughts were found to be associated with shorter deliberation about whether or not to attempt suicide (Bryan, Morrow, Etienne, & Ray-Sannerud, 2012; Bryan & Rudd, 2012). Other studies have also demonstrated the relationship between emotional distress and increased suicide attempt risk in this population (Bryan, Hernandez, Allison, & Clemans, 2013).

Other psychiatric risk factors for suicide among military personnel include history of inpatient hospitalization (Luxton, Trofimovich, & Clark, 2013) and suicidal ideation (May, Overholser, Ridley, & Raymond, 2015).

Sociodemographic Risk Factors

Traditionally, male gender has been identified as an elevated risk factor for suicidal attempts and completions within the military and for veterans (Mahon et al., 2005; Sentell et al., 1997). However, findings regarding the risk of suicidality among military personnel associated with gender have become rather inconsistent with several studies noting greater risk among female soldiers (Street et al., 2015; Ursano et al., 2015; Wise, 2015). This may result from the fact that over the past two decades there has been an increase in the number of women entering all branches of the U.S. Armed Forces, including holding direct combat positions (Ganzer, 2016). Now that women in the military are no longer prohibited from holding direct combat positions, like males, they are often exposed to traumatic events that place them at higher risk for psychiatric illness and suicide (Conard, Armstrong, Young, & Hogan, 2015; Ganzer, 2016). For example, a recent study identified that suicide attempts were more likely among soldiers who were women with deployment status (Ursano et al., 2016). Another study found that the suicide rate of currently deployed women was 3.1 to 3.5 times the rates of never-deployed or previously deployed women (Street et al., 2015). In contrast, research studies also identify male gender as a risk factor for suicide among current and former U.S. military personnel between 2001 and 2008 (LeardMann et al., 2013).

When examining the relevance of other risk factors noted in this chapter across genders, research has demonstrated that female and male soldiers have more similarities than differences when in terms of the risk factors associated with suicide (Maguen, 2015). In one retrospective study of 1,857 U.S. Army soldiers who died by suicide or attempted suicide between 2008 and 2010, the only gender difference approaching significance was workplace difficulties, which was more strongly associated with suicide among female as compared to male soldiers (Maguen, 2015). Across genders, the most common risk factor was having a failed intimate relationship in the 90 days prior to suicide. Among those who attempted suicide, across genders, the most common risk factor was a major psychiatric diagnosis (Maguen, 2015). There have been gender differences found, however, in respect to risk factors for repeat suicide attempts among military personnel, particularly among military inpatients with single versus multiple suicide attempts. Males with multiple suicide attempts were more likely to have a substance use problem and a mood disorder diagnosis, while females with a multiple-attempt history were more likely to have a history of childhood sexual abuse (Kochanski-Ruscio, Carreno-Ponce, DeYoung, Grammer, & Ghahramanlou-Holloway, 2014).

Sexual minority status has also been established as a risk factor for suicidality among military personnel. Research has found that military personnel with a history of same-sex partners or LGBT status report significantly increased rates of suicide ideation, NSSI, and suicide attempts (Blosnich, Bossarte, & Silenzio, 2012; Ray-Sannerud, Bryan, Perry, & A. O. Bryan, 2015).

Relationship status has also been examined as a risk factor for suicide in military personnel (Armed Forces Health Surveillance Center [AFHSC], 2012; Hyman, Ireland, Frost, & Cottrell, 2012; Martin et al., 2013; Ursano et al., 2015). One study by the Armed Forces Health Surveillance Center (AFHSC) of 2,990 service members who died by suicide while on active duty during 1998 to 2001 found that suicide death rates were 24% higher among divorced/separated service members than those who were single, never married (AFHSC, 2012). Others have identified that married veterans are at lower risk of suicide than those who are unmarried (Jakupcak et al., 2010).

Age has been examined as a risk factor for suicide among military personnel and veterans. Among active-duty military personnel, younger age has been found to be a significant risk factor for suicidality (Mahon et al., 2005). Further, among active-duty personnel, being 25 years or older at enlistment is associated with increased risk (Ursano et al., 2016). Among veterans, those in the young and middle-age groups have higher suicide rates than nonveterans; however, older age is associated with a lower risk of suicidality compared to civilians (Kaplan, McFarland, Huguet, & Valenstein, 2012). Among veterans who die by suicide, mental health, substance abuse, and financial and relationship problems have been found to be more common in younger than older veterans, whereas health problems are more prevalent in the older veterans who die by suicide. More older veterans use firearms as their means of suicide than do younger veterans (Kaplan et al., 2012).

Other sociodemographic risk factors for suicide include educational level of less than high school (Ursano et al., 2015), history of legal problems (Holmes, Mateczun, Lall, & Wilcove, 1998), disrupted or disturbed sleep, which may be a risk factor or warning sign (Pigeon, Bishop, & Titus, 2016), homelessness (Bossarte, Blosnich, Piegari, Hill, & Kane, 2013; Lee, Iglewicz, Golshan, & Zisook, 2013; Schinka, Bossarte, Curtiss, Lapcevic, & Casey, 2016), veteran's spiritual struggle (Kopacz & Pollitt, 2015), guilt and shame (C. J. Bryan, Ray-Sannerud, et al., 2013), particularly combat-related guilt (Ganz & Sher, 2013), history of physical injury and/or traumatic brain injury (Ganz & Sher, 2013; Gradus et al., 2015; Wisco et al., 2014), severe pain (Ilgen et al., 2010; Magruder, Yeager, & Brawman-Mintzer, 2012), and access to firearms (Anestis & Capron, 2016; Ganz & Sher, 2013; Smith, Currier, & Drescher, 2015).

Interpersonal Risk Factors

The relationship between child abuse exposure and suicidality in military personnel relative to civilians has also received attention. One study found that the prevalence of childhood trauma among active-duty Army soldiers was 43.3% among the suicide cases and 64.7% among the attempt cases (Perales, Gallaway, Forys-Donahue, Spiess, & Millikan, 2012). All types of child abuse exposures and childhood trauma exposures have been shown to be associated with increased odds of suicidal ideation, suicide plans, and suicide attempts among military personnel (Afifi et al., 2016; McGuinness & Waldrop, 2015; Perales, et al., 2012).

Adult exposure to sexual trauma has also received attention as a risk factor for suicidality among military personnel and veterans. A study by Kimerling, Makin-Byrd, Louzon, Ignacio, and McCarthy (2016) evaluated associations between military sexual trauma and suicide risk within the Veterans Health Administration services in fiscal years 2007 to 2011 that included records for 5,991,080 men and 360,774 women (Kimerling et al., 2016). Results demonstrated that sexual trauma was reported by 1.1% of men and 21.2% of women, and military sexual trauma for men and women was significantly associated with elevated suicide risk (Kimerling et al., 2016). Similar results have been identified in other research (C. J. Bryan, Bryan, & Clemens, 2015; Klingensmith, Tsai, Mota, Southwick, & Pietrzak, 2014; Monteith et al., 2016; Monteith, Menefee, Forster, Wanner, & Bahraini, 2015; Schry et al., 2015). One study, in particular, investigating the association of military sexual trauma with suicide risk examined 464 U.S. military personnel and veterans enrolled in college classes. Results of the study indicate that premilitary sexual assault was significantly associated with increased risk for suicide ideation, plans, and attempts during military service. Unwanted sexual experiences occurring during military service were significantly associated with increased risk for suicide ideation and suicide plans; however, only among male participants. Premilitary sexual trauma showed relatively stronger associations with suicide risk among women whereas military sexual trauma showed relatively stronger associations with suicide risk among men (C. J. Bryan, Bryan, & Clemens, 2015).

Other interpersonal risk factors for suicide among military personnel include intimate partner violence (C. J. Bryan & Hernandez, Allison, & Clemans, 2013; Logan et al., 2016), loneliness (Cacioppo et al., 2016), lack of social support (Ganz & Sher, 2013), and lower level of unit cohesion (Griffith, 2015).

Other Associated Risk Factors

Ursano et al. (2015) examined suicide attempts in the U.S. Army during the wars in Afghanistan and Iraq (between 2004 and 2009) and identified the following significant risk factors associated with suicide attempts: (a) enlisted women having nearly 13 times the risk of female officers, (b) being early on in years of service with enlisted soldiers during their first year in Army service at high risk and with the risk peaking in the second month of service, (c) deployment status with never-deployed enlisted soldiers having higher risk as compared to those who have been deployed, and (d) history of mental illness with enlisted soldiers with a recent mental health diagnosis, specifically in the previous month at highest risk (Ursano et al., 2015). A follow-up study on the timing of suicide attempts found that soldiers who were never deployed had the highest risk in the second month of service, whereas for soldiers on their first deployment, the highest risk period was in the sixth month of deployment, and for soldiers returning from deployment, the risk was highest at 5 months after their return (Ursano et al., 2016).

Suicides among military personnel most often occur in the morning shortly after duty commencement, most probably because this is the time when personnel gain access to firearms (Mahon et al., 2005). Thus, being on morning duty is an independent risk factor for suicide among military personnel. Receiving a recent medical downgrade is another service-related risk factor for suicide (Mahon et al., 2005), as are receiving a low performance evaluation and having a history of military problems (Holmes et al., 1998).

Some have studied occupational cohorts within the military for corresponding suicide risk. For example, one study using data from the Department of Defense (DoD) active component population between 2001 and 2010 examined rates of suicide based on military occupational categories. Results demonstrated that the combined infantry, gun crews, and seamanship specialist group were at increased risk of suicide compared to the overall military population even when adjusted for gender, age, and deployment history (Trofimovich, Reger, Luxton, & Oetjen-Gerdes, 2013). Another study compared reservists to active-duty personnel and found that reservists who had been deployed reported higher rates of suicidal ideation and attempts than did active-duty personnel who had been deployed (Lane, Hourani, Bray, & Williams, 2012).

A unique and potential risk factor for military veterans that has begun to receive scientific scrutiny is the transition period of separation from the military back to civilian life (Kline, Ciccone, Falca-Dodson, Black, & Losonczy, 2011; Pease, Billera, & Gerard, 2016; Reger, Skopp, & Smolenski, 2015). Research has identified that the transition and adjustment to civilian life for combat veterans can be problematic and difficult (Reger, Skopp, & Smolenski, 2015). Veterans typically are managing a number of stressors transitioning to civilian life including relationship difficulties with their partners and other family members, feelings of disconnection from their families, employment or financial concerns, or educational challenges (Pease et al., 2016). This initial period of reintegration into civilian life and the resulting stressors may increase the risk of suicide thoughts of behaviors for military veterans (Pease et al., 2016). More specifically, research has found an increased rate of suicide associated with separation from military service, regardless of whether service members were deployed or not (Reger, Smolenski, et al., 2015). This research also shows that rates of suicide were also elevated for service members who separated with less than 4 years of military service or who did not separate with an honorable discharge (Reger, Smolenski, et al., 2015). Others have found that readjustment troubles are widespread, with 45% of veterans endorsing one or more financial or family problems with the first 3 months postdeployment (Kline, 2011). Even after adjusting for mental health issues and combat exposure, veterans who reported the highest number of readjustment stressors were at a five-and-a-half times greater risk of suicidal ideation than those who reported no stressors (Kline, 2011).

Given the increase in suicidal behaviors among military personnel and veterans since the beginning of combat operations in Afghanistan and Iraq, many have questioned the potential causal role of combat on suicide risk. It is important to note that, to date, research is inconsistent in this area. One study examined both direct and indirect effects of combat exposure on suicide risk and found that greater combat exposure was directly associated with fearlessness about death and PTSD severity, but did not show either a direct or indirect effect on suicide risk (C. J. Bryan, Hernandez, Allison, & Clemans, 2013). Other studies have found that deployment, independent of exposure to combat, is also not associated with increased risk of suicide (Reger, Smolenski, et al., 2015). However, in a narrative review and meta-analysis of 22 studies examining the relationship of deployment-related predictors (i.e., deployment, deployment to a combat zone, combat experience, and exposure to specific combat events) with suicide-related outcomes (i.e., suicide ideation, attempt, and death), a 25% increased risk for suicide-related outcomes among those who have been deployed was found. Further, among those studies examining the relationship between exposure to killing and atrocities, a 43% increased risk for suicide-related outcomes was found for those who were exposed to killing or atrocity (C. J. Bryan, Hernandez, et al., 2013). Others have found that while combat veterans are not only more likely to have suicidal ideation, they are more likely to act on a suicidal plan (Sher, Braquehais, & Casas, 2012).

PROTECTIVE FACTORS AGAINST SUICIDE

Most protective factors tested to date have involved facets of social or familial support. In a recent review, the most frequently identified protective factors were social and family support, resiliency, emotional intelligence, coping skills, and access and utilization of mental health services (Nock et al., 2013). Other protective factors against suicide attempt include positive attitude toward help-seeking and mental health treatment and increased awareness regarding mental illness (Knox, Litts, Talcott, Feig, & Caine, 2003). Also, protective factors include female gender, military duties with limited access to firearms, and older age (Knox et al., 2003). Regarding age, research has identified that being 40 years of age or older was found to be a protective factor for enlisted soldiers and officers (Ursano et al., 2015).

It is important to recognize the influence of the larger social environment to fully understand the risk of suicidality within military populations. In the case of military personnel, the context of the military community is crucial to consider. Although the membership in the military would appear to bring along several protective factors including common values, customs, and traditions; a strong support network; and a sense of common purpose, involvement in the military also requires being separated from family, social isolation, restricting independence, promoting aggression, and easy access to firearms (Rosanov, Mokhovikov, & Stiliha, 2002). These factors may promote suicidal behavior in vulnerable military personnel.

Research has also examined the role of self-forgiveness as a protective factor among military personnel and veterans against suicide attempt and ideation (C. J. Bryan, Bryan, & Clemens, 2015). Self-forgiveness is considered the act of generosity and kindness shown toward oneself following self-perceived inappropriate action (C. J. Bryan, Bryan, & Clemens, 2015). Research has found that self-forgiveness is the lowest among military personnel and veterans who had made a suicide attempt and that self-forgiveness significantly differentiates participants who have attempted suicide from those who had only thought about it (C. J. Bryan, Bryan, & Clemens, 2015).

Research has indicated the protective effect of optimism against suicidality among military personnel. According to Bryan and colleagues (2013), optimism is associated with less severe suicidal ideation and can buffer the effects of hopelessness (C. J. Bryan, Graham, & Roberge, 2015).

Others have examined the role of spirituality as a protective factor against suicide for military personnel and have looked at self-forgiveness as a component of spirituality (A. O. Bryan, Theriault, & Bryan, 2015; Currier, 2015a, 2015b). Research posits that the existential components of spirituality (i.e., meaning in life and the capacity to forgive oneself for perceived transgressions) may potentially reduce risk even more so than the explicit religious aspects of spirituality (i.e., the belief in a higher power). Findings suggest that interventions and treatments that foster personal meaning and self-compassion in addition to decreasing feelings of guilt, shame, and self-deprecation can reduce suicidal behavior among military personnel and veterans (A. O. Bryan et al., 2015).

As veterans leave the military and transition into civilian life, successful reintegration that includes a sense of belonging has been identified as a protective factor against depression (A. O. Bryan, et al., 2015) and suicide risk (Joiner, 2005; Pease et al., 2016).

TREATMENT CONSIDERATIONS FOR ACTIVE MILITARY PERSONNEL AND VETERANS

A study examining primary health care utilization prior to the suicide of active-duty military personnel found that 38% of suicide cases had contact with a primary care physician (PCP) within the past month before death (Hochman et al., 2014). Findings further revealed that only 28% of active military personnel who completed suicide had contact with a mental health specialist during their entire service time (Hochman et al., 2014). A study of active-duty military personnel found that only 23% to 40% of returning military who met strict criteria for any mental health problem had received professional help in the past year (Lazar, 2014). Another study examined the outpatient experiences of active-duty service members prior to completed suicide during 2001 to 2010. Results found that 45% of service members who completed suicide had outpatient encounters within 30 days prior to suicide. Primary care was the most frequently visited clinical service prior to suicide. Service members with suicidal behavior had especially high rates of outpatient visit within, but not prior to, 60 days of their death (Trofimovich, Skopp, Luxton, & Reger, 2012).

Research has examined the likelihood of active-duty soldiers disclosing suicidal thoughts and/or behaviors during mandated screenings. One such study examined soldiers' willingness to report and seek treatment for behavioral health problems during DoD-mandated screenings (Whalen, 2015). After controlling for stigma and other barriers to care, results of the study demonstrated that soldiers with high combat exposure and high levels of PTSD symptoms were significantly more willing to report these symptoms during the DoD-mandated screening. Additionally, those soldiers who perceived their unit leader as willing to take action on findings from the anonymous Unit Behavioral Health Needs Assessment Survey were significantly more likely to report a willingness to disclose symptoms and seek treatment (Whalen, 2105).

In terms of veterans and mental health service utilization, one study that surveyed veterans between 2011 and 2013 found that approximately 90,000 veterans had mental health needs and 200,000 reported serious thoughts of suicide during the preceding 12 months; however, three of four veterans with mental health needs received either inadequate or no mental health care (Tran, Grant, & Aydin, 2016). Another study examined 300 veterans who died by suicide in 1 year across 11 states and who had received Veterans Affairs (VA) health care services in the 6 months prior to their death. Just under half of the veterans studied were seen in primary care ($n = 136$; 46%). Over half of these visits were for routine follow-up ($n = 168$; 57%). Less than 20% were assessed for suicidal ideation, and of these, 38% endorsed having such thoughts (Denneson et al., 2016).

As some have noted, veterans in need of social services may access many different community-based organizations within the public and private sector. These organizations have the potential to serve as a pipeline for helping veterans obtain needed health, mental health, and benefits services. However, many service providers lack information on how to determine where veterans should go to access services within their local community (Matthieu, Gardiner, Ziegemeier, & Buxton, 2014). This may partially explain the high rates of underutilization of services among veterans, and the inability to receive effective support in locating relevant services.

The Army Study to Assess Risk and Resilience in Service (Army STARRS) members is a very large, multicomponent epidemiological and neurobiological study that was designed to generate actionable evidence-based recommendations to both reduce U.S.

Army suicides and increase basic knowledge about determinants of suicidality among military personnel (Heeringa et al., 2013). Results of this study inform much of what has been identified regarding risk and protective factors for suicidality among military personnel. At the same time, several structural changes concerning the management of mental health issues within the armed services were identified. Specifically, the U.S. Army Medical Command has implemented significant programmatic changes to facilitate the delivery of high-quality standardized mental health services for military personnel. These changes include centralized workload management; consolidation of psychiatry, psychology, psychiatric nursing, and social work services under integrated behavioral health departments; creation of satellite mental health clinics embedded within brigade work areas; incorporation of mental health providers into primary care; routine mental health screening throughout soldiers' careers; standardization of clinical outcome measures; and improved services for family members (Hoge, 2016). These changes have resulted in a reduction in psychiatric hospitalization and improved continuity of care.

However, significant gaps remain. For example, at present, Veterans Administration/ DoD treatment guidelines do not recognize the need for intensive and extended psychotherapies for the chronic and complex psychiatric conditions suffered by active-duty personnel and veterans including personality disorders and chronic anxiety and depressive disorders (Lazar, 2014). However, studies demonstrate that the prevalence of 30-day *DSM-IV* psychiatric disorders in active-duty military service members, including PTSDs and major depressive disorder, is greater than among their civilian counterparts with 25% of regular Army soldiers meeting criteria for a 30-day *DSM-IV* mental disorder (Lazar, 2014). Those military personnel diagnosed with PTSD and major depressive disorder frequently have comorbid psychiatric illnesses and an increased death rate from homicide, injury, cardiovascular disease, and suicide (Lazar, 2014). They also have been found to be at increased risk of medical illness, smoking and substance abuse, decreased employment and work productivity, marital and family dysfunction, and homelessness (Lazar, 2014).

Research suggests that PCP education is an important consideration and approach to suicide prevention in a military setting (Hochman et al., 2014). One study found that, whereas 38% of active-duty military personnel suicide cases contacted a PCP within the past month before death, only 28% contacted a mental health specialist during their entire service time (Hochman et al., 2014).

Research also indicates that some mental health service providers within the military and VA feel underprepared to work with at-risk clients. One study noted that chaplains, in particular, play an important role in supporting the mental health of both active-duty personnel and veterans and surveyed 440 VA and 1,723 DoD chaplains for their self-perceived preparedness for dealing with suicidality. Compared to DoD chaplains, VA chaplains encountered at-risk service users more frequently and reported feeling less prepared for dealing with suicidality (Kopacz et al., 2016). Another study found that training on interventions to address suicidality among soldiers was associated with increased efficacy and lower levels of stigma among chaplains (Ramchand, Ayer, Geyer, & Kofner, 2016).

A systematic review was performed to identify active, externally funded randomized controlled trials (RCTs) that target suicidal ideation or behavior as a primary or secondary outcome among U.S. military service members, guard–reservists, and veterans. Only 23 studies were identified. These were largely funded by the U.S. DoD or U.S. Department of Veterans Affairs. Several innovations in intervention modality were identified targeting suicide deaths or attempts as primary outcome, including the delivery of interventions through technology (i.e., telehealth and ehealth programs; Bossarte et al., 2014; Conner & Simons, 2015; Gallegos, Streltzov, & Stecker, 2016; Kasckow et al., 2016) and/or outside clinical settings, and examinations of rarely studied treatments for use with this population (Conner & Simons, 2015).

Cognitive behavioral therapy (CBT) has also been examined as a potential treatment approach for reducing suicide attempt risk among military personnel. Rudd et al. (2015) conducted a small randomized control trial of a brief CBT intervention for the prevention of suicide attempts among active-duty Army soldiers who either attempted suicide or experienced suicidal ideation with intent. Results indicate that from baseline to the 24-month follow-up assessment period, significantly fewer soldiers in the brief CBT group attempted suicide at least one time than those in the treatment as usual group (14% vs. 40%, respectively), suggesting that soldiers who received brief CBT were approximately 60% less likely to make a suicide attempt (Rudd et al., 2015). Similarly, another study examining CBT-based treatment with veterans revealed that CBT for depression (CBT-D) was associated with significant decreases in suicide ideation and depression (Brown et al., 2016). These promising results point to CBT as a potentially effective treatment for addressing suicide risk in military personnel, which warrants further investigation (for more information about CBT, see Chapter 16).

However, it is important to note that another systematic review was able to identify only five published studies on military suicide prevention programs and their outcomes. Not only did results find substantial research design and methodological issues across these five studies, but also one study identified reported statistically significant results; thus, indicating a significant lack of empirical evidence demonstrating effective suicide prevention programs within the U.S. Armed Forces (Harmon, Cooper, Nugent, & Butcher, 2016).

Among veterans, more recent research on interventions to reduce risk of suicidality has focused on mindfulness-based stress reduction (MBSR; Bergen-Cico, Possemato, & Pigeon, 2014; Gallegos, Cross, & Pigeon, 2015; Serpa, Taylor, & Tillisch, 2104). Preliminary research indicated that MBSR is effective at reducing anxiety, depression, and suicidal ideation in veterans (Serpa, 2104). Other research has examined the effectiveness of Veterans Crisis Line calls as a means of reducing suicide risk and connecting veterans to needed mental health services. One study demonstrated that approximately 84% of calls to the Veterans Crisis Line ended with a favorable outcome, 25% ended with resolution, and 59% with a referral to a local service provider. Calls from high-risk callers were more likely to end with a referral than without a resolution or referral. Responders most frequently used caller intent to die, known risk and protective factors, and the absence of future plans to determine caller risk (Britton, Bossarte, Thompson, Kemp, & Conner, 2013).

ROLE-PLAY 11.1

A veteran of the war in Afghanistan recently discharged enters outpatient treatment for the first time upon the recommendation of his partner. He clearly indicates having little faith or expectations that you will be able to assist him with his sleeping and other undescribed difficulties. He refuses to talk about his ongoing suicide ideation, which is in the phone intake form. In fact, he refers to the so-called mental health field with disgust and amusement. How you would start the first clinical interview?

Break into groups of three and assume the role of the mental health clinician and the new patient in the outpatient agency. The third member will act as a recorder and can be called upon to consult and assist the mental health clinician.

Part B: Vary the client, by changing gender, mandated or voluntary nature of referral, an active-duty military personnel or a veteran, presenting in a wheelchair or with PTSD, and so forth.

An innovative study that explored veterans with past suicide attempts found that the most common recommendation for the improvement of care was to increase clinicians' empathy, compassion, and listening skills (Montross et al., 2014). Other findings recommended efforts to strengthen social supports as a means to diminish suicide events (Montross et al., 2014).

SUMMARY

Membership in at-risk groups, such as the active military personnel and veterans, poses additional issues and complications for individuals experiencing suicidality. In addition, mental health professionals working with active military personnel and veterans need to become aware of the unique risk and protective factors that may exert further influence on these groups. Professional and personal awareness is essential for mental health clinicians engaging, assessing, and treating members of active military personnel and veterans.

KEY POINTS

1. Rates of suicide among active military personnel sharply increased since 2008.
2. Suicide is the second leading cause of death among the military.
3. Veterans account for less than 9% of the population but over 18% of all suicides.
4. Many unique risk factors related to deployment, exposure to combat, timing of service, and rank exist for military personnel.
5. Established protective factors against suicide for military personnel and veterans are very limited; however, social support has been identified as especially important in reducing suicide risk in this population.
6. Guidelines have recently been developed to improve services to soldiers in need of mental health treatment.
7. Evidence-based practices to address/prevent suicide in this population are sorely lacking.

ELECTRONIC RESOURCES

MILITARY PERSONNEL

www.WoundedWarriorProject.org

www.SCUV.org

www.vetfriends.com

www.troopsupports.com

www.theVeteransvoice.com

www.hireahero.com

www.anysoldier.com

http://troopssupport.com

www.Road2Healing.com

KNOWLEDGE ACQUISITION TEST (KAT)

True or False

1. Suicide rates among the active military personnel and veterans are comparable to suicide rates in the general population.
2. Military personnel suicide rates have remained consistent over the past two decades.
3. Suicide is among the leading causes of death among the military.
4. Sexual minority status is not a risk factor for suicidality among military personnel.
5. More than 4 in 10 active-duty Army soldiers who completed suicide had experienced childhood trauma, whereas more than 6 in 10 active-duty Army soldiers who attempted suicide had experienced childhood trauma.
6. Lower level of unit cohesion has been associated with increased risk of suicide among active military personnel.
7. Optimism has a protective effect against suicidality among military personnel.
8. Veterans Crisis Lines are not effective interventions for veterans.

Short Answer

9. Discuss how the U.S. Army has attempted to address the unmet mental health challenges of active-duty military personnel.
10. Discuss a major gap in mental health care that exists in regard to active-duty soldiers and veterans' mental health needs.
11. Discuss the role of spirituality as a protective factor for suicide among active-duty military personnel and veterans.
12. Discuss the willingness of soldiers to disclose their suicidality.

Multiple Choice

13. Suicide is the _____ leading cause of death among military personnel.
    A. Second
    B. Fourth
    C. Sixth
    D. Eighth
    E. Tenth
14. Risk factors among active members of the U.S. Army include which of the following?
    A. Enlisted rank (compared to officers)
    B. Being in the first year of service
    C. History of mental illness
    D. Educational level of less than high school
    E. B and C only
    F. All of the above
15. Protective factors against suicide among active military personnel and veterans include which of the following?
    A. Emotionally detached
    B. Sense of belonging
    C. Self-compassion
    D. Avoidance
    E. B and C only
    F. All of the above

REFERENCES

Afifi, T. O., Taillieu, T., Zamorski, M. A., Turner, S., Cheung, K., & Sareen, J. (2016). Association of child abuse exposure with suicidal ideation, suicide plans, and suicide attempts in military personnel and the general population in Canada. *Journal of the American Medical Association Psychiatry*, 73(3), 229–238.

Anestis, M., & Capron, D. W. (2016). The associations between state veteran population rates, handgun legislation, and statewide suicide rates. *Journal of Psychiatric Research*, 74, 30–34.

Archuleta, D., Jobes, D. A., Pujol, L., Jennings, K., Crumlish, J., Lento, R. M., . . . Crow, B. (2014, October–December). Raising the clinical standard of care for suicidal soldiers: An army process improvement initiative. *U.S. Army Medical Department Journal*, 55–66.

Arias, S. A., Dumas, O., Sullivan, A. F., Boudreaux, E. D., Miller, I., & Camargo, C. A., (2016). Substance use as a mediator of the association between demographics, suicide attempt history, and future suicide attempts in emergency department patients. *Crisis: The Journal of Crisis Intervention and Suicide Prevention*, 37(5), 385–391.

Armed Forces Health Surveillance Center. (2012). Deaths by suicide while on active duty, active and reserve components, U.S. Armed Forces, 1998–2011. *Medical Surveillance Monthly Report*, 19(6), 7–10.

Bergen-Cico, D., Possemato, K., & Pigeon, W. (2014). Reductions in cortisol associated with primary care brief mindfulness program for veterans with PTSD. *Medical Care*, 12(Suppl. 5), S25–S31. doi:10.1097/MLR.0000000000000224

Blosnich, J. R., Bossarte, R. M., & Silenzio, V. M. (2012). Suicidal ideation among sexual minority veterans: Results from the 2005–2010 Massachusetts behavioral risk factor surveillance survey. *American Journal of Public Health*, 102(Suppl. 1), S44–S47. doi:10.2105/AJPH.2011.300565

Bossarte, R. M., Blosnich, J. R., Piegari, R. I., Hill, L. L., & Kane, V. (2013). Housing instability and mental distress among US veterans. *American Journal of Public Health*, 103(Suppl. 2), S213–S216. doi:10.2105/AJPH.2013.301277

Bossarte, R. M., Karras, E., Lu, N., Tu, X., Stephens, B., Draper, J., & Kemp, J. E. (2014). Associations between the Department of Veterans Affairs' suicide prevention campaign and calls to related crisis lines. *Public Health Reports*, 129(6), 516–525.

Bossarte, R. M., Knox, K. L., Piegari, R., Altieri, J., Kemp, J., & Katz, I. R. (2012). Prevalence and characteristics of suicide ideation and attempts among active military and veteran participants in a national health survey. *American Journal of Public Health*, 102(Suppl. 1), S38–S40.

Britton, P. C, Bossarte, R. M., Thompson, C., Kemp, J., & Conner, K. R. (2013). Influences on call outcomes among veteran callers to the National Veterans Crisis Line. *Suicide and Life-Threatening Behavior*, 43(5), 494–502.

Britton, P. C., Stephens, B., Wu, J., Kane, C., Gallegos, A., Ashrafioun, L., . . . Conner, K. R. (2015). Comorbid depression and alcohol use disorders and prospective risk for suicide attempt in the year following inpatient hospitalization. *Journal of Affective Disorders*, 187, 151–155.

Brown, G. K., Karlin, B. E., Trockel, M., Gordienko, M., Yesavage, J., & Taylor, C. B. (2016). Effectiveness of cognitive behavioral therapy for veterans with depression and suicidal ideation. *Archives of Suicide Research*, 20(4), 677–682.

Bryan, A. O., Theriault, J. L., & Bryan, C. J. (2015). Self-forgiveness, posttraumatic stress, and suicide attempts among military personnel and veterans. *Traumatology*, 21(1), 40–46.

Bryan, C. J., Bryan, A. O., & Clemans, T. A. (2015). The association of military and premilitary sexual trauma with risk for suicide ideation, plans, and attempts. *Psychiatry Research*, 227(2–3), 246–252.

Bryan, C. J., Garland, E. L., & Rudd, M. D. (2016). From impulse to action among military personnel hospitalized for suicide risk: Alcohol consumption and the reported transition from suicidal thought to behavior. *General Hospital Psychiatry*, 41, 13–19.

Bryan, C. J., Graham, E., & Roberge, E. (2015). Living a life worth living: Spirituality and suicide risk in military personnel. *Spirituality in Clinical Practice*, 2(1), 74–78.

Bryan, C. J., Hernandez, A. M., Allison, S., & Clemans, T. (2013). Combat exposure and suicide risk in two samples of military personnel. *Journal of Clinical Psychology*, 69(1), 64–77.

Bryan, C. J., Morrow, C. E., Etienne, N., & Ray-Sannerud, B. (2012). Guilt, shame, and suicidal ideation in a military outpatient clinical sample. *Depression and Anxiety*, 30(1), 55–60. doi:10.1002/da.22002

Bryan, C. J., Ray-Sannerud, B. N., Morrow, C. E., & Etienne, N. (2013). Optimism reduces suicidal ideation and weakens the effect of hopelessness among military personnel. *Cognitive Therapy and Research*, 37(5), 996–1003.

Bryan, C. J., & Rudd, M. D. (2012). Life stressors, emotional distress, and trauma-related thoughts occurring in the 24 h preceding active duty U.S. soldiers' suicide attempts. *Journal of Psychiatric Research, 46*(7), 843–848.

Bryan, C. J., Rudd, M. D., & Wertenberger, E. (2016). Individual and environmental contingencies associated with multiple suicide attempts among U.S. Military personnel. *Psychiatry Research, 242,* 88–93.

Bryan, C. J., Rudd, M. D., Wertenberger, E., Young-McCaughton, S., & Peterson, A. (2015). Nonsuicidal self-injury as a prospective predictor of suicide attempts in a clinical sample of military personnel. *Comprehensive Psychiatry, 59,* 1–7. doi: 10.1016/j.comppsych.2014.07.009. Epub 2014 Jul 11

Cacioppo, J. T., Cacioppo, S., Adler, A. B., Lester, P. B., McGurk, D., Thomas, J. L., & Chen, H. J. (2016). The cultural context of loneliness: Risk factors in active duty soldiers. *Journal of Social and Clinical Psychology, 35*(10), 865–882.

Centers for Disease Control and Prevention. (2007). Web-based Injury Statistics Query and Reporting System (WISQARS). Retrieved from https://www.cdc.gov/injury/wisqars/index.html

Conard, P. L., Armstrong, M. L., Young, C., & Hogan, L. M. (2015). Suicide assessment and action for women veterans. *Journal of Psychosocial Nursing and Mental Health Services, 53*(4), 33–42.

Conner, K. R., Bossarte, R. M., He, H., Arora, J., Lu, N., Tu, X. M., & Katz, I. R. (2014). Posttraumatic stress disorder and suicide in 5.9 million individuals receiving care in the Veterans Health Administration health system. *Journal of Affective Disorders, 166,* 1–5.

Conner, K. R., & Simons, K. (2015). State of innovation in suicide intervention research with military populations. *Suicide and Life-Threatening Behavior, 3,* 281–292.

Corson, K., Denneson, L. M., Bair, M. J., Helmer, D. A., Goulet, J. L., & Dobscha, S. K. (2013). Prevalence and correlates of suicidal ideation among operation enduring freedom and operation Iraqi freedom veterans. *Journal of Affective Disorder, 149*(1–3), 291–298. doi:10.1016/j.jad.2013.01.043

Cox, K. S., Mouilso, E. R., Venners, M. R., Defever, M. E., Duvivier, L., Rauch, S. A. M., . . . Tuerk, P. W. (2016). Reducing suicidal ideation through evidence-based treatment for posttraumatic stress disorder. *Journal of Psychiatric Research, 80,* 59–63.

Currier, J. M., Kuhlman, S., & Smith, P. N. (2015a). Empirical and ethical considerations for addressing spirituality among veterans and other military populations at risk for suicide. *Spirituality in Clinical Practice, 2*(1), 68–73.

Currier, J. M., Kuhlman, S., & Smith, P. N. (2015b). Spirituality, meaning, and suicide. *Spirituality in Clinical Practice, 2*(1), 82–83.

Denneson, L. M., Kovas, A. E., Britton, P. C., Kaplan, M. S., McFarland, B. H., & Dobscha, S. K. (2016). Suicide risk documented during veterans' last Veterans Affairs health care contacts prior to suicide. *Suicide and Life-Threatening Behavior, 46*(3), 363–374.

Eaton, K. M., Messer, S. C., Garvey Wilson, A. L., & Hoge, C. W. (2006). Strengthening the validity of population-based suicide rate comparisons: An illustration using U.S. military and civilian data. *Suicide and Life-Threatening Behavior, 36*(2), 182–191.

Fanning, J. R., & Pietrzak, R. H. (2013). Suicidality among older male veterans in the United States: Results from the National Health and Resilience in Veterans Study. *Journal of Psychiatric Research, 47*(11), 1766–1775. doi:10.1016/j.jpsychires.2013.07.015

Fuehrlein, B. S., Mota, N., Arias, A. A., Trevisan, L. A., Kachadourian, L. K., Krystal, J. H., . . . Pietrzak, R. H. (2016). The burden of alcohol use disorders in US military veterans: Results from the National Health and Resilience in Veterans Study. *Addiction, 111*(10), 1786–1794.

Gadermann, A. M., Gilman, S. E., McLaughlin, K. A., Nock, M. K., Petukhova, M., Sampson, N. A., & Kessler, R. C. (2012). Projected rates of psychological disorders and suicidality among soldiers based on simulations of matched general population data. *Military Medicine, 177*(9), 1002–1010.

Gallegos, A. M., Cross, W., & Pigeon, W. R. (2015). Mindfulness-based stress reduction for veterans exposed to military sexual trauma: Rationale and implementation considerations. *Military Medicine, 180*(6):684–689. doi:10.7205/MILMED-D-14-00448

Gallegos, A. M., Streltzov, N. A., & Stecker, T. (2016). Improving treatment engagement for returning operation enduring freedom and operation Iraqi freedom veterans with posttraumatic stress disorder, depression, and suicidal ideation. *Journal of Nervous and Mental Disease, 204*(5), 339–343.

Ganz, D., & Sher, L. (2013). Educating medical professionals about suicide prevention among military veterans. *International Journal of Adolescent Medicine and Health, 25*(3), Special Issue: Education of health professionals about adolescent psychiatry, 187–191.

Ganzer, C. A. (2016). CE: Veteran women: Mental health-related consequences of military service. *American Journal of Nursing, 116*(11), 32–39.

Gradus, J. L., Wisco, B. E., Luciano, M. T., Iverson, K. M., Marx, B. P., & Street, A. E. (2015). Traumatic brain injury and suicidal ideation among U.S. operation enduring freedom and operation Iraqi freedom veterans. *Journal of Traumatic Stress, 28*(4), 361–365. doi:10.1002/jts.22021

Griffith, J. (2015). Cross (Unit)-level effects of cohesion on relationships of suicide thoughts to combat exposure, post deployment stressors, and post deployment social support. *Behavioral Medicine, 41*(3), 98–106. doi:10.1080/08964289.2014.987719

Haller, M., Angkaw, A. C., Hendricks, B. A., & Norman, S. B. (2016). Does reintegration stress contribute to suicidal ideation among returning veterans seeking PTSD treatment? *Suicide and Life-Threatening Behavior, 46*(2):160–171.

Harmon, L. M., Cooper, R. L., Nugent, W. R., & Butcher, J. J. (2016). A review of the effectiveness of military suicide prevention programs in reducing rates of military suicides. *Journal of Human Behavior in the Social Environment, 26*(1), 15–24.

Heeringa, S. G., Gebler, N., Colpe, L. J., Fullerton, C. S., Hwang, I., Kessler, R. C., . . . Ursano, R. J. (2013). Field procedures in the army study to assess risk and resilience in service members (Army STARRS). *International Journal of Methods in Psychiatric Research, 22*(4), 276–287. doi:10.1002/mpr.1400

Hefling, K. (2008). Iraq war vets' suicide rates analyzed high numbers found among members of guard, reserves [Electronic Version]. Retrieved from http://www.sfgate.com/cgi-bin/article.cgi?f=/c/a/2008/02/13/MNPSV110J.DTL

Helmkamp, J. C. (1995). Suicides in the military: 1980–1992. *Military Medicine, 160*(2), 45–50.

Hochman, E., Shelef, L., Mann, J. J., Portugese, S., Krivoy, A., Shoval, G., . . . Fruchter, E. (2014). Primary health care utilization prior to suicide: A retrospective case-control study among active-duty military personnel. *Journal of Clinical Psychiatry, 75*(8), e817–e823. doi:10.4088/JCP.13m08823

Hoge, C. W., & Castro, C. A. (2012). Preventing suicides in US service members and veterans: Concerns after a decade of war. *JAMA, 308*(7), 671–672.

Holmes, E. K., Mateczun, J. M., Lall, R., & Wilcove, G. L. (1998). Pilot study of suicide risk factors among personnel in the United States Marine Corps (Pacific Forces). *Psychological Reports, 83*(1), 3–11.

Hourani, L. L., Warrack, A. G., & Coben, P. A. (1999). Suicide in the U.S. Marine Corps, 1990 to 1996. *Military Medicine, 164*(8), 551–555.

Hyman, J., Ireland, R., Frost, L., & Cottrell, L. (2012). Suicide incidence and risk factors in an active duty US military population. *American Journal of Public Health, 102*(Suppl. 1), S138–S146. doi:10.2105/AJPH.2011.300484

Ilgen, M. A., Zivin, K., Austin, K. L., Bohnert, A. S. B., Czyz, E. K., Valenstein, M., & Kilbourne, A. M. (2010). Severe pain predicts greater likelihood of subsequent suicide. *Suicide and Life-Threatening Behavior, 40*(6), 597–608.

Jakupcak, M., Vannoy, S., Imel, Z., Cook, J. W., Fontana, A., Rosenheck, R., & McFall, M. (2010). Does PTSD moderate the relationship between social support and suicide risk in Iraq and Afghanistan war veterans seeking mental health treatment? *Depression and Anxiety, 27*(11), 1001–1005.

Joiner, T. E. (2005). Why people die by suicide. Cambridge, MA: Harvard University Press.

Kaplan, M. S., Huguet, N., McFarland, B. H., & Newsom, J. T. (2007). Suicide among male veterans: A prospective population-based study. *Journal of Epidemiological and Community Health, 61*, 619–624.

Kaplan, M. S., McFarland, B. H., Huguet, N., & Valenstein, M. (2012). Suicide risk and precipitating circumstances among young, middle-aged, and older male veterans. *American Journal of Public Health, 102*(Suppl. 1), S131–S137. doi:10.2105/AJPH.2011.300445

Kasckow, J., Zickmund, S., Gurklis, J., Luther, J., Fox, L., Taylor, M., . . . Haas, G. L. (2016). Using telehealth to augment an intensive case monitoring program in veterans with schizophrenia and suicidal ideation: A pilot trial. *Psychiatry Research, 239*, 111–116. doi:10.1016/j.psychres.2016.02.049

Kemp, J. E., & Bossarte, R. (2012). *Suicide data report.* Washington, DC: Department of Veterans Affairs; 2013. Retrieved from http://ajph.aphapublications.org/doi/ref/10.2105/AJPH.2013.301507

Kessler, R. C., Heeringa, S. G., Stein, M. B., Colpe, L. J., Fullerton, C. S., Hwang, I., . . . Ursano, R. J. (2014).Thirty-day prevalence of DSM-IV mental disorders among non-deployed soldiers in the U.S. Army: Results from the Army Study to Assess Risk and Resilience in Service members (Army STARRS). *Journal of the American Medical Association Psychiatry, 71*(5), 504–513.

Kim, H. M., Smith, E. G., Ganoczy, D., Walters, H., Stano, C. M., Ilgen, M. A., . . . Valenstein, M. (2012). Predictors of suicide in patient charts among patients with depression in the Veterans Health Administration health system: Importance of prescription drug and alcohol abuse. *Journal of Clinical Psychiatry, 73*(10). 1269–1275. doi:10.4088/JCP.12m07658

Kimerling, R., Makin-Byrd, K., Louzon, S., Ignacio, R. V., & McCarthy, J. F. (2016). Military sexual trauma and suicide mortality. *American Journal of Preventive Medicine, 50*(6), 684–691.

Kline, A., Ciccone, D. S., Falca-Dodson, M., Black, C. M., & Losonczy, M. (2011). Suicidal ideation among National Guard troops deployed to Iraq: the association with post deployment readjustment problems. *Journal of Nervous and Mental Disease, 199*(12), 914–920.

Klingensmith, K., Tsai, J., Mota, N., Southwick, S. M., & Pietrzak, R. H. (2014). Military sexual trauma in US veterans: Results from the National Health and Resilience in Veterans Study. *The Journal of Clinical Psychiatry, 75*(10), e1133–e1139.

Knox, K. L., Litts, D. A., Talcott, G. W., Feig, J. C., & Caine, E. D. (2003). Risk of suicide and related adverse outcomes after exposure to a suicide prevention programme in the US Air Force: Cohort study. *British Medical Journal, 327*(7428), 1376–1381.

Kochanski-Ruscio, K. M., Carreno-Ponce, J. T., DeYoung, K., Grammer, G., & Ghahramanlou-Holloway, M. (2014). Diagnostic and psychosocial differences in psychiatrically hospitalized military service members with single versus multiple suicide attempts. *Comprehensive Psychiatry, 55*(3), 450–456.

Kopacz, M. S., & Pollitt, M. J. (2015). Delivering chaplaincy services to veterans at increased risk of suicide. *Journal of Health Care Chaplaincy, 21*(1), 1–13.

Kopacz, M. S., Nieuwsma, J. A., Jackson, G. L., Rhodes, J. E., Cantrell, W. C., Bates, M. J., & Meador, K. G. (2016). Chaplains' engagement with suicidality among their service users: Findings from the VA/DoD Integrated Mental Health Strategy. *Suicide and Life-Threatening Behavior, 46*(2), 206–212.

Kuehn, B. M. (2009). Soldier suicide rates continue to rise: Military, scientists work to stem the tide. *Journal of the American Medical Association, 301*(11), 1111–1113.

Lane, M. E., Hourani, L. L., Bray, R. M., & Williams, J. (2012). Prevalence of perceived stress and mental health indicators among reserve-component and active-duty military personnel. *American Journal of Public Health, 102*(6), 1213–1220. doi:10.2105/AJPH.2011.300280

Lazar, S. G. (2014). The mental health needs of military service members and veterans. *Psychodynamic Psychiatry, 42*(3), 459–478.

LeardMann, C. A., Powell, T. M., Smith, T. C., Bell, M. R., Smith, B., Boyko, E. J., . . . Hoge, C. W. (2013). Risk factors associated with suicide in current and former US military personnel. *Journal of the American Medical Association, 310*(5), 496–506. doi:10.1001/jama.2013.65164

Lee, H., Iglewicz A, Golshan S, & Zisook, S. (2013). A tale of two veterans: Homeless vs domiciled veterans presenting to a psychiatric urgent care clinic. *Annals of Clinical Psychiatry, 25*(4), 275–282.

Lineberry, T. W., & O'Connor, S. S. (2012). Suicide in the US Army. *Mayo Clinic Proceedings, 87*(9), 871–878.

Logan, J., Skopp, N. A., Karch, D., Reger, M. A., & Gahm, G. A. (2012). Characteristics of suicides among US army active duty personnel in 17 US states from 2005 to 2007. *American Journal of Public Health, 102*(Suppl. 1), S40–S44. doi:10.2105/AJPH.2011.300481

Logan, J. E., Fowler, K. A., Patel, N. P., & Holland, K. M. (2016). Suicide among military personnel and veterans aged 18–35 years by county—16 states. *American Journal of Preventive Medicine, 51*(5 Suppl. 3), S197–S208.

Lorge, E. M. (2008). Army responds to rising suicide rates. Retrieved from http://www.army.mil/-news/2008/01/31/7222-army-responds-to-rising-suicide-rates

Luxton, D. D., Trofimovich, L., & Clark, L. L. (2013). Suicide risk among US Service members after psychiatric hospitalization, 2001–2011. *Psychiatric Services, 64*(7), 626–629. doi:10.1176/appi.ps.201200413

Magruder, K. M., Yeager, D., & Brawman-Mintzer, O. (2012). The role of pain, functioning, and mental health in suicidality among Veterans Affairs primary care patients. *American Journal of Public Health, 102*(Suppl. 1), S118–S124. doi:10.2105/AJPH.2011.300451

Maguen, S., Skopp, N. A., Zhang, Y., & Smolenski, D. J. (2015). Gender differences in suicide and suicide attempts among US Army soldiers. *Psychiatry Research, 225*(3), 545–549.

Mahon, M. J., Tobin, J. P., Cusack, D. A., Kelleher, C., & Malone, K. M. (2005). Suicide among regular-duty military personnel: A retrospective case-control study of occupation-specific risk factors for workplace suicide. *American Journal of Psychiatry, 162*(9), 1688–1696.

Martin, J. S., Ghahramanlou-Holloway, M., Englert, D. R., Bakalar, J. L., Olsen, C., Nademin, E. M., . . . Branlund, S. (2013). Marital status, life stressor precipitants, and communications of distress and suicide intent in a sample of United States Air Force suicide decedents. *Archives of Suicide Research, 17*(2), 148–160.

Matthieu, M. M., Gardiner, G., Ziegemeier, E., & Buxton, M. (2014). Using a service sector segmented approach to identify community stakeholders who can improve access to suicide prevention services for veterans. *Military Medicine, 179*(4), 388–395.

May, C. N., Overholser, J. C., Ridley, J., & Raymond, D. (2015). Passive suicidal ideation: A clinically relevant risk factor for suicide in treatment-seeking veterans. *Illness, Crisis, & Loss, 23*(3), 261–277.

McGuinness, T. M., & Waldrop, J. R. (2015). Adverse childhood experiences and the mental health of veterans. *Journal of Psychosocial Nursing Mental Health Services, 53*(6), 23–26.

Miller, M. (2012). Preventing suicide by preventing lethal injury: The need to act on what we already know. *American Journal of Public Health, 102*(Suppl. 1), e1–e3. doi:10.2105/AJPH.2012.300662

Monteith, L. L., Bahraini, N. H., Matarazzo, B. B., Gerber, H. R., Soberay, K. A., & Forster, J. E. (2016). The influence of gender on suicidal ideation following military sexual trauma among veterans in the Veterans Health Administration. *Psychiatry Research, 244*, 257–265.

Monteith, L. L., Menefee, D. S., Forster, J. E., Wanner, J. L., & Bahraini, N. H. (2015). Sexual trauma and combat during deployment: Associations with suicidal ideation among OEF/OIF/OND veterans. *Journal of Traumatic Stress, 28*(4), 283–288. doi:10.1002/jts.22018

Montross, T. L. P., Palinkas., L. A., Meier, E. A., Iglewicz, A., Kirkland, T., & Zisook, S. (2014). Yearning to be heard: What veterans teach us about suicide risk and effective interventions. *Crisis: The Journal of Crisis Intervention and Suicide Prevention, 35*(3), 161–167.

Nock, M. K., Deming, C. A., Fullerton, C. S., Gilman, S. E., Goldenberg, M., Kessler, R. C., . . . Ursano, R. J. (2013). Suicide among soldiers: A review of psychosocial risk and protective factors. *Psychiatry, 76*, 97–125.

Nock, M. K., Stein, M. B., Heeringa, S. G., Ursano, R. J., Colpe, L. J., Fullerton, C. S., . . . Kessler, R. C. (2014). Prevalence and correlates of suicidal behavior among soldiers: Results from the Army Study to Assess Risk and Resilience in Service members (Army STARRS). *Journal of the American Medical Association Psychiatry, 71*(5), 514–522.

Pease, J. L., Billera, M., & Gerard, G. (2016). Military culture and the transition to civilian life: Suicide risk and other considerations. *Social Work, 61*(1), 83–86.

Perales, R., Gallaway, M. S., Forys-Donahue, K. L., Spiess, A., & Millikan, A. M. (2012). Prevalence of childhood trauma among U.S. Army soldiers with suicidal behavior. *Military Medicine, 177*(9), 1034–1040.

Pigeon, W. R., Bishop, T. M., & Titus, C. E. (2016). The relationship between sleep disturbance, suicidal ideation, suicide attempts, and suicide among adults: A systematic review. *Psychiatric Annals, 46*(3), 177–186.

Pompili, M., Sher, L., Serafini, G., Forte, A., Innamorati, M., Dominici, G., . . . Girardi, P. (2013). Posttraumatic stress disorder and suicide risk among veterans: A literature review. *Journal of Nervous and Mental Disease, 201*(9), 802–812.

Ramchand, R., Ayer, L., Geyer, L., & Kofner, A. (2016). Factors that influence chaplains' suicide intervention behavior in the army. *Suicide and Life-Threatening Behavior, 46*(1), 35–45. doi:10.1111/sltb.12170

Ray-Sannerud, B. N., Bryan, C. J., Perry, N. S., & Bryan, A. O. (2015). High levels of emotional distress, trauma exposure, and self-injurious thoughts and behaviors among military personnel and veterans with a history of same sex behavior. *Psychology of Sexual Orientation and Gender Diversity, 2*(2), 130–137.

Reger, M. A., Skopp, N. A., & Smolenski, D. J. (2015). On deployment and military suicide risk: Reply. *Journal of the American Medical Association Psychiatry, 72*(9), 950–951.

Reger, M. A., Smolenski, D. J., Skopp, N. A., Metzger, A., Bamukang, M. J., Kang, H. K., . . . Gahm, G. A. (2015). Risk of suicide among US military service members following operation enduring freedom or operation Iraqi freedom deployment and separation from the US military. *Journal of the American Medical Association Psychiatry, 72*, 561–569.

Ritchie, E. C., Keppler, W. C., & Rothberg, J. M. (2003). Suicidal admissions in the United States military. *Military Medicine, 186*(3), 177–181.

Rosanov, V. A., Mokhovikov, A. N., & Stiliha, R. (2002). Successful model of suicide prevention in the Ukraine military environment. *Crisis: The Journal of Crisis Intervention and Suicide Prevention, 23*(4), 171–177.

Rudd, M. D., Bryan, C. J., Wertenberger, E. G., Peterson, A. L., Young-McCaughan, S., Mintz, J., . . . Bruce, T. O. (2015). Brief cognitive-behavioral therapy effects on post-treatment suicide attempts in a military sample: Results of a randomized clinical trial with 2-year follow-up. *The American Journal of Psychiatry, 172*(5), 441–449.

Schinka, J. A., Bossarte, R. M., Curtiss, G., Lapcevic, W. A., & Casey, R. J. (2016). Increased mortality among older veterans admitted to VA homelessness programs. *Psychiatric Services, 67*(4), 465–468.

Schry, A. R., Hibberd, R., Wagner, H. R., Turchik, J. A., Kimbrel, N. A., Wong, M., . . . Strauss, J. L. (2015). Veterans Affairs Mid-Atlantic Mental Illness Research, Education and Clinical Center Workgroup:

Functional correlates of military sexual assault in male veterans. *Psychological Services,12*(4), 384–393. doi:10.1037/ser0000053

Scoville, S. L., Gardner, J. W., & Potter, R. N. (2004). Traumatic deaths during U.S. Armed Forces basic training, 1977–2001. *American Journal of Preventive Medicine, 26*(3), 194–204.

Scoville, S. L., Gubata, M. E., Potter, R. N., White, M. J., & Pearse, L. A. (2007). Deaths attributed to suicide among enlisted U.S. Armed Forces recruits, 1980–2004. *Military Medicine, 172*(10), 1024–1031.

Sentell, J. W., Lacroix, M., Sentell, J. V., & Finstuen, K. (1997). Predictive patterns of suicidal behavior: The United States armed services versus the civilian population. *Military Medicine, 162*(3), 168–171.

Serpa, J. G., Taylor, S. L., & Tillisch, K. (2014). Mindfulness-based stress reduction (MBSR) reduces anxiety, depression, and suicidal ideation in veterans. *Medical Care, 52*(12 Suppl. 5), S19–S24. doi:10.1097/MLR.0000000000000202

Sher, L., Braquehais, M. D., & Casas, M. (2012). Posttraumatic stress disorder, depression, and suicide in veterans. *Cleveland Clinic Journal of Medicine, 79*(2), 92–97. doi:10.3949/ccjm.79a.11069

Smith, N. B., Mota, N., Tsai, J., Monteith, L., Harpaz-Rotem, I., Southwick, S. M., & Pietrzak, R. H. (2016). Nature and determinants of suicidal ideation among U.S. veterans: Results from the National Health and Resilience in Veterans study. *Journal of Affective Disorders, 197*, 66–73.

Smith, P. N., Currier, J., & Drescher, K. (2015). Firearm ownership in veterans entering residential PTSD treatment: Associations with suicide ideation, attempts, and combat exposure. *Psychiatry Research, 229*(1–2), 220–224.

Street, A. E., Gilman, S. E., Rosellini, A. J., Stein, M. B., Bromet, E. J., Cox, K. L., . . . Army STARRS. (2015). Understanding the elevated suicide risk of female soldiers during deployments. *Psychological Medicine, 45*(4), 717–726.

Tran, L. D., Grant, D., & Aydin, M. (2016). The mental health status of California veterans. *Policy Brief UCLA Center of Health Policy Research PB2016-3*, 1–10.

Trofimovich, L., Reger, M. A., Luxton, D. D, & Oetjen-Gerdes, L. A. (2013). Suicide risk by military occupation in the DoD active component population. *Suicide and Life-Threatening Behavior, 43*(3), 274–278.

Trofimovich, L., Skopp, N. A., Luxton, D. D., & Reger, M. A. (2012). Health care experiences prior to suicide and self-inflicted injury, active component, U.S. Armed Forces, 2001–2010. *Medical Surveillance Monthly Report, 19*(2), 2-6.

Ursano, R. J., Kessler, R. C., Stein, M. B., Naifeh, J. A., Aliaga, P. A., Fullerton, C. S., . . . Heeringa, S. G. (2015). Suicide attempts in the US Army during the wars in Afghanistan and Iraq, 2004 to 2009. *JAMA Psychiatry, 72*(9), 917–926.

Ursano, R. J., Kessler, R. C., Stein, M. B., Naifeh, J. A., Aliaga, P. A., Fullerton, C. S., . . . Heeringa, S.G. (2016). Risk factors, methods, and timing of suicide attempts among US Army soldiers. *JAMA Psychiatry, 73*(7), 741–749.

U.S. Department of Health and Human Services. (2001). *Summary of national strategy for suicide prevention: Goals and objectives for action [National Strategy for Suicide Prevention Website]*. Retrieved from https://www.surgeongeneral.gov/library/reports/national-strategy-suicide-prevention/index.html

U.S. Department of Veterans Affairs. (2016). Suicide among veterans and other Americans 2001–2014. Retrieved from https://www.mentalhealth.va.gov/docs/2016suicidedatareport.pdf

Whalen, R. J. (2015, January–March). Predicting willingness to report behavioral health problems and seek treatment among US male soldiers deployed to Afghanistan: A retrospective evaluation. *US Army Medical Department Journal*, 88–92.

Wisco, B. E., Marx, B. P., Wolf, E. J., Miller, M. W., Southwick, S. M., & Pietrzak, R. H. (2014). Posttraumatic stress disorder in the US veteran population: Results from the National Health and Resilience in Veterans Study. *Journal of Clinical Psychiatry, 75*(12), 1338–1346. doi:10.4088/JCP.14m09328

Wise, J. (2015). Army suicide attempts are most likely among enlisted soldiers on first tour of duty and female soldiers, US study finds. *British Medical Journal, 351*, h3702. doi:10.1136/bmj.h3702

Yacobi, A., Fruchter, E., Mann, J. J., & Shelef, L. (2013). Differentiating Army suicide attempters from psychologically treated and untreated soldiers: A demographic, psychological and stress-reaction characterization. *Journal of Affective Disorders, 150*(2), 300–305. doi:10.1016/j.jad.2013.04.009

CHAPTER TWELVE

LESBIAN, GAY, BISEXUAL, TRANSGENDER, AND QUEER/QUESTIONING

In considering sexual orientation, it is important to acknowledge that orientation is a broader construct than simply same-sex activity (Cochran, Mays, & Sullivan, 2003; Sell, 1997). The term "LGBTQ" incorporates a number of constructs including lesbian, gay, bisexual, transgendered/transsexual, and queer/questioning. LGBTQ will be used to more inclusively and accurately represent the diversity of individuals who identify as such or with nonheterosexual orientations. "Sexual minority status" has more recently become a common term to represent these sexual identity groups. Research demonstrates an increased prevalence of suicidal ideation, attempts, and completions among sexual minority groups across age groups, gender, race, and ethnicity. This chapter examines the prevalence of suicide risk for within and across sexual minority groups and presents relevant specific risk for and protective factors against suicidal thoughts and behaviors. In addition, this chapter explores the influence of the larger social environment on LGBTQ suicide risk. Lastly, this chapter discusses key factors to consider in the treatment of suicidal LGBTQ individuals.

GOALS AND OBJECTIVES

An understanding of:

- Influence of sexual orientation on suicidality
- Impact of the general public's attitudes, views, and opinions on the suicide risk of sexual minority groups
- Influence of mental health professional's attitudes, views, and opinions on the suicide risk of sexual minority groups
- Prevalence of suicide among sexual minority groups
- Risk factors for LGBTQ suicidality
- Protective factors against LGBTQ suicidality
- Key considerations in mental health treatment of suicidal LGBTQ individuals

---

Research has demonstrated that LGBTQ individuals experience an elevated rate of suicidal thoughts, attempts, and completions. Despite consistent reports of this elevated risk for over four decades, minimal attention has been given to the problem of suicidal behavior in this population (Haas et al., 2011). Sexual minorities are defined in respect to two main characteristics, namely, sexual orientation and gender identity. Sexual orientation is defined as having three main domains including sexual self-identification, sexual behavior, and sexual attraction or fantasy (Saewyc et al., 2004; Sell, 1997). Of these, the most commonly used criteria is self-identification as either gay/lesbian, bisexual or heterosexual, or the gender of one's sexual partners (same sex, both same and opposite sex, or opposite sex; Haas et al., 2011). In juxtaposition to sexual orientation, gender identity refers to a person's internal sense of being masculine, feminine, or androgynous and includes degrees of masculinity to femininity and maleness to femaleness, as well as identification as primarily neither male or female (Haas et al., 2011).

Sexual minority clients, like other vulnerable populations, may evoke a number of positive and/or negative ideas, conceptualizations, and biases or stigmas in individuals, including mental health professionals. It is essential for mental health professionals to understand suicidality across sexual minority groups for several fundamental reasons. One, professional awareness of the epidemiology, risk and protective factors, misconceptions, societal issues, and treatment considerations that are unique to LGBTQ individuals can help guide clinicians in their practice. Two, personal awareness of your response, thoughts, and beliefs connected to suicidality and sexual minority groups impacts your clinical assessment, interaction, and treatment of LGBTQ clients. Without such awareness, effective clinical treatment is not possible.

Individual Exercise 12.1

1. Write down your initial reaction upon hearing the following words. Be honest and unfiltered in your response. Remember, answers are personal and there are no correct or incorrect answers: lesbian, gay, bisexual, transgender, queer.
2. Examine your responses. Are you surprised by anything you wrote down? In what way?

Small Group Exercise 12.1

In groups of two to three,

1. Share, as you feel comfortable, your responses to question 1 in Individual Exercise 12.1.
2. Were there similarities in your responses? What accounts for these similarities?
3. Were there differences in your responses? What accounts for these differences?
4. How might these perceptions influence positively or negatively clinical practice with LGBTQ clients?

Individual Exercise 12.2

Reflect on your responses to question 1 in Small Group Exercise 12.1:

1. Which responses were you comfortable sharing? What made those responses easier to share?
2. Which were you not comfortable sharing? What made those responses difficult for you to share?
3. How might this awareness impact your work with LGBTQ clients?

STATISTICS, EPIDEMIOLOGY, AND TRENDS IN LGBTQ SUICIDE

Approximately, 2.8% of men and 1.4% of women in the United States identify themselves as homosexual (Haas et al., 2011). However, more individuals report same-sex sexual behavior (3% of men and 1.6% of women), and even more report same-sex attraction (7.7% of men and 7.5% of women), than identify themselves as gay or lesbian (Black, Gates, Sanders, & Taylor, 2000; Pedersen & Kristiansen, 2008; Wells, McGee, & Beautrais, 2010).

Same-sex orientation has been associated with an elevated risk for suicide ideation, suicide attempt, and completed suicide across age groups and racial and ethnic groups (Bostwick et al., 2014; Bouris et al., 2016; Hottes, Bogaert, Rhodes, Brennan, & Gesink, 2016; Lea, de Wit, & Reynolds, 2014; Levy, Russon, & Diamond, 2016; Remafedi, 1999a, 1999b; Remafedi, French, Story, Resnick, & Blum, 1998; Semlyen, King, Varney, & Hagger-Johnson, 2016; Shadick, Backus Dagirmanjian, & Barbot, 2015; Smith, Armelie, Boarts, Brazil, & Delahanty, 2016; Tsypes, Lane, Paul, & Whitlock, 2016). A systematic review of 199 studies examining sexual minorities reported an elevated risk of depression, anxiety, suicide attempts or suicides, and substance-related problems for both sexual minority men and women, across adolescents and adults from many geographic regions, and across sexual orientation dimensions (behavior, attraction, and identity; Ploderl & Tremblay, 2015; Mustanski & Liu, 2013). Among community-based samples, research demonstrates that 20% of sexual minority adults have attempted suicide (Hottes et al., 2016). Research also shows that LGB adults have a higher prevalence of poor mental health and low well-being when compared to heterosexuals, particularly younger and older LGB adults (Semlyen et al., 2016).

Research has examined the trajectory of suicide risk across the life span among five sexual identity groups including, heterosexual, mostly heterosexual, bisexual, mostly gay, and gay. Results of this research found that the percentage of participants reporting suicidal ideation decreased significantly in all groups except for the mostly gay group (Cardom, Rostosky, & Danner, 2013). The percentage of participants reporting suicide attempts declined in all groups except the bisexual group (Cardom et al., 2013). Further, depressive symptoms diminished in young adulthood in all groups (Cardom et al., 2013). Overall, results suggest that gay and bisexual young adults do not report the same significant declines in risk as their counterparts (Cardom et al., 2013).

A majority of studies have found an increased risk of suicidality among both LGBTQ males and females, but findings indicate that males have a higher risk for suicidality (Meyer, Dietrich, & Schwartz, 2008; Remafedi, 1999a; van Heeringen & Vincke, 2000; Wang, Plöderl, Häusermann, & Weiss, 2015). In regard to females, those who first wondered about their sexual identity in early, middle, or late adolescence had greater odds of lifetime suicidal ideation than those women who questioned their sexual identity in adulthood. Further, among women, parental support is independently associated with suicidal ideation (Dirkes, Hughes, Ramirez-Valles, Johnson, & Bostwick, 2016). Among adults who ever attempted suicide, homosexual men have been found to have almost seven times higher risk of lifetime suicide attempts than heterosexual men (Blosnich, Nausti, Mays, & Cochran, 2016). Further, sexual minority women had a younger age of index attempt than heterosexual women (Blosnich et al., 2016).

Among trans individuals, compared to individuals with no plans to transition, individuals with plans or who were living as their identified gender report greater odds of lifetime suicidal ideation (Rood, Puckett, Pantalone, & Bradford, 2015). In a systematic review of 31 studies exploring the rates of nonsuicidal self-injury (NSSI) and suicidality in trans individuals, results indicated that trans individuals have a higher prevalence of both NSSI and suicidality compared to cisgender (nontrans) individuals (Marshall, Claes, Bouman, Witcomb, & Arcelus, 2016). Compared with cisgender-matched controls, transgender youths have been found to have a twofold to threefold increased risk of suicidal ideation, suicide attempt, self-harm without lethal intent, depression, anxiety disorder, and both inpatient and outpatient mental health treatment (Reisner et al., 2015).

In regard to bisexual individuals, research indicated that while all sexual minority subgroups are at increased risk for suicidality, bisexual individuals are at the highest risk in the majority of studies (Ploderl & Tremblay, 2015). Another national study indicated that gay, but not bisexual, men were more likely to report suicide ideation and attempts than heterosexual men, whereas bisexual, not lesbian, women were more likely to report suicide ideation and attempts (Swannell, Martin, & Page, 2016). Other research comparing bisexuals, heterosexuals, and homosexual men and women found that bisexual women had a nearly sixfold increased risk of lifetime suicide attempts than heterosexual women (Blosnich et al., 2016), and again found increased risk among bisexual women compared to lesbians (Colledge, Hickson, Reid, & Weatherburn, 2015).

Among LGBTQ ethnically diverse adults, research has found an increased risk of suicide attempts among racial–ethnic minority LGB individuals compared to White individuals (O'Donnell, Meyer, & Schwartz, 2011). Similar findings of increased risk have been found among LGB college students of color and indicate that they have elevated suicide risk relative to heterosexual peers (Lytle, De Luca, & Blosnich, 2014; Shadick et al., 2015). Other research examining risk of suicide among LGBQ college students across ethnicities and religious affiliations found that among LGBQ students, Latino college students had lower odds of reporting both past 12-month passive and active suicidal ideation than their non-Hispanic White LGBQ counterparts. This study also found that compared to Christian LGBQ students, agnostic/atheist LGBQ college students had greater odds of reporting past 12-month passive suicidal ideation, and Jewish LGBQ students were less likely to endorse past 12-month passive and/or active suicidal ideation (Lytle, De Luca, Blosnich, & Brownson, 2015).

Research indicates that LGB adolescents are three times more likely than their heterosexual peers to consider suicide (Whitaker, Shapiro, & Shields, 2016). Elevated suicide risk in LGBTQ youths has also been found across ethnicity and race, including White, African American, and Hispanic/Latino (Consolacion, Russell, & Sue, 2004). In a national longitudinal study, 17% of adolescents identifying as lesbian, gay, or bisexual reported suicide ideation in comparison to 6% of heterosexual-identified adolescents (Silenzio, Pena, Duberstein, & Knox, 2007). Others have reported that 28% of sexual minority youths report suicidal ideation and between 15% and 40% make a suicide attempt each year (Levy et al., 2016). A study of 21,927 sexually active youths found that, among LGBTQ adolescents, over half reported suicidal thoughts with 37% attempting suicide (Eisenberg & Resnick, 2006). Among LGBTQ youths, research demonstrates that substance interacts with posttraumatic stress disorder (PTSD) symptoms and depression to increase the risk of suicide attempt (Smith et al., 2016; see Chapter 9 for further information on youth suicide). Other research finds that LGBTQ-identified students are 3.3 times as likely to think about suicide, 3.0 times as likely to attempt suicide, and 1.4 times as likely to skip school as heterosexual-identified students within the same school who reported equivalent levels of peer victimization (Robinson & Espelage, 2012). Research on adolescence has found that between 9% and 14% of male high school students reported being bullied because of perceived sexual orientation (PSO), whereas 6% to 11% of female students endorsed being bullied for PSO (Patrick, Bell, Huang, Lazarakis, & Edwards, 2013). Described further in the Risk Factors for Suicide and Protective Factors Against Suicide sections, bullying has been identified as a frequently identified risk factor for the LGBTQ population.

1. What would be the hardest sexual minority group for you to professionally work with (lesbian, gay, bisexual, transgendered, queer/questioning)? Why?
2. What personal and/or professional considerations may make it harder for you to work with this population?
3. What would be the easiest at-risk group for you to professionally work with (lesbian, gay, bisexual, transgendered, queer/questioning)? Why?
4. What personal and/or professional considerations may make it easier for you to work with this population?

In small groups of two to three, please discuss, as you are comfortable, your responses to Individual Exercise 12.3. Remember, answers are personal and there are no correct or incorrect answers.

1. What were the response similarities in your group?
2. What were the response differences in your group?
3. Did you find any surprises in the group discussion? If so, what were they and how were you surprised?

RISK FACTORS FOR SUICIDE

Psychiatric Risk Factors

Suicide attempt history has been frequently identified as a risk factor among LGBTQ youths, including a number of psychiatric-related factors. Research has demonstrated that prior attempted suicide is associated with a 10 times greater odds of making another attempt in the following year than youths with no previous attempt (Mustanski & Lui, 2013).

Among gay males, specifically, one study found that the most frequently reported reason for attempting suicide was social/interpersonal problems (Wang et al., 2015). Problems with love, relationship, and accepting one's homosexuality were consistently among the top three reasons for attempting as reported by gay men and were associated with the strongest intent to die and also were reported as reasons for making multiple attempts. Problems with family are among the most common perceived causes for a first attempt and are associated with the greatest medical severity of all the perceived causes (Wang et al., 2015). Only 10% of the gay men participating in the study cited depression as a cause for their attempt, and when it was reported it was associated with a weaker intent to die (Wang et al., 2015).

Sociodemographic Risk Factors

A number of individual and sociodemographic factors have been found to be associated with an increased risk for suicide among LGBTQ individuals. For example, coping style has been found to be a significant risk factor for suicidality among LGBTQ. Research has also found that among ethnically diverse lesbian, bisexual, queer, or "other" non-heterosexual-identified cisgender women coping styles significantly explain 20.3% of the variance in past suicidal ideation and 30.4% of the variance in lifetime history of suicide attempts (Rabinovitch, Perrin, Tabaac, & Brewster, 2015). Specifically, a self-blaming coping style positively predicted past suicidal ideation, while religious coping and venting coping styles were associated with a higher lifetime history of suicide attempts (Rabinovitch et al., 2015).

Religiosity has also been examined as a risk factor for suicide among LGBTQ individuals, although to a significantly lesser extent than among heterosexual individuals. Findings suggest that LGBT young adults who are raised in religious contexts have higher odds of suicidal thoughts, and more chronic suicidal thoughts, as well as suicide attempts compared to other LGBT young adults (Gibbs & Goldbach, 2015).

The two negative interpersonal cognitions of thwarted belongingness and perceived burdensomeness have been increasingly investigated as risk factors within the LGBTQ community. According to researchers, Joiner et al. (2009) and Van Orden and colleagues (2010) perceived burdensomeness reflects self-beliefs that the self is so flawed as to be a liability on others and reflects affectively laden cognitions of self-hatred (Joiner et al., 2009; Van Orden et al., 2010). Thwarted belongingness encompasses a feeling of social isolation coupled with a real need to belong (Baams, Grossman, & Russell, 2015; Cramer, Burks et al., 2015; Joiner et al., 2009; Van Orden et al., 2010). In research that has examined the coming-out process and factors that may mediate the experience of suicidal thoughts and behaviors during this process has found that for all gender and sexual identity groups, the association of sexual orientation victimization with depression and suicidal ideation was mediated by perceived burdensomeness (Baams et al., 2015). For gay, lesbian, and bisexual girls, in particular, coming-out stress was also found to be related to depression and suicidal ideation, mediated by perceived burdensomeness. These results suggest that feeling like a burden to important individuals in their lives is a critical factor explaining higher levels of depression and suicidal ideation among LGB youths (Baams et al., 2015).

Other sociodemographic risk factors for LGBTQ suicide identified in research include psychological stress, low self-esteem, and increased levels of hopelessness (van Heeringen & Vincke, 2000).

Interpersonal Risk Factors

Interpersonal risk factors for suicide are highly associated with an increased suicide risk among LGBTQ individuals. One such risk factor is the coming-out process, where individuals disclose their nonexclusive heterosexuality to self and others (Bagley & Ramsay, 1997; Fenaughty & Harre, 2003; Michaels, Parent, & Torrey, 2016).

Among bisexual youths, interpersonal risk factors for suicide established in research include related victimization, peer judgments, and family rejection (Pompili et al., 2014). Bisexual individuals also report higher rates of mental illness and substance abuse (Pompili et al., 2014).

History of being bullied in person or cyberbullying has been repeatedly identified as a risk factor for LGBTQ individuals (DeCamp & Bakken, 2016; McIntosh & Bialer, 2015; Peter & Taylor, 2014; Wiederhold, 2014). Studies of sexual minority youths indicate that in addition to bullying victimization (DeCamp & Bakken, 2016; McIntosh & Bialer, 2015), fighting, substance use, sexual behavior, depression, and unhealthy dieting behaviors are associated with increased risk of both NSSI and suicidal ideation (DeCamp & Bakken, 2016). Others have further examined the role of victimization in relation to increased risk for suicidality in sexual minority youths. This research found that although victimization explains part of the LGBTQ–heterosexual risk disparities, substantial differences persist even when the differences in victimization are taken into account (Robinson & Espelage, 2012). Also, significant differences were found in suicidal ideation and suicide attempts at both higher and lower levels of victimization (Robinson & Espelage, 2012). These findings have important implications and suggest that policies aimed solely at reducing bullying may not be sufficient to address the differential psychological and educational outcomes between LGBTQ youths and their heterosexual peers.

Among transgendered adults, specifically, violence, discrimination, and transition status significantly predict suicidal ideation (Rood et al., 2015). Other research also suggests that internalized transphobia may account in part for the increased risk in lifetime suicide attempts experienced by trans individuals (Perez-Brumer, Hatzenbuehler, Oldenburg, & Bockting, 2015).

Some research has examined the role of discrimination based on sexual orientation as compared to racism. Some research indicates that discrimination based on sexual identity and not racism is associated with an increased risk of suicidal ideation in LGBTQ ethnically diverse individuals (Sutter & Perrin, 2016). Other research, however, has found that both forms of mistreatment are associated with depressive symptoms and suicidal ideation among African American LGB adolescents, but, racism is more strongly associated with substance use than the risk of suicidality (Thoma & Huebner, 2013).

It is important to recognize the influence of the larger social environment on the risk of suicidality within the LGBTQ population. In population studies, research has consistently demonstrated that sexual orientation is associated with elevated risk for mental health disorders, such as depression, anxiety, and substance use (Cochran & Mays, 2000; Gilman et al., 2001; Sandfort, de Graaf, Bijl, & Schnabel, 2001). Research has also indicated that increased risk is not associated with an illness model of homosexuality (Gonsiorek, 1996), rather an elevated risk is likely associated with the theory of social stress (Cochran et al., 2003; Meyer, 2003; Meyer et al., 2008). According to social stress theories, stigma and experiences of prejudice, rejection, and concealing, as well as internalized homophobia and decreased coping skills, contribute to higher rates in certain mental disorders, such as depression, anxiety, and substance use (Cochran et al., 2003; Dohrenwend, 2000). Consequently, an increased risk of suicide may be associated with the LGBTQ population in comparison to heterosexuals.

Stigma remains a prevalent issue for LGBTQ. An early public opinion poll on attitudes, a Harris poll in 1965, found that 70% of Americans had a negative attitude toward gays and lesbians, and it was not until 1999 that public support for legalizing homosexual relations between consenting adults reached 50% (Herek, 2002; Hicks & Lee, 2006). Although polls have increasingly found public opinion to be more tolerant, a significant percentage of the population continues to hold negative attitudes toward the LGBTQ population (Hicks & Lee, 2006).

The negativity of public opinion and related stigma exert a number of direct and indirect influences on the LGBTQ population, specifically in the form of mental health treatment. Mental health clinicians who assess and treat individuals at risk of suicidality may also have personal values, attitudes, and opinions toward LGBTQ clients. Although most mental health professionals recognize the importance of providing treatment for all clients who need it, an individual clinician's opinion can affect his or her work.

Institutional discrimination is yet another societal level factor that creates risk for LGBTQ individuals. Institutional discrimination results from laws and public policies that create inequities or fail to protect against sexual orientation–based discrimination (i.e., insurance coverage, business and employment laws, same sex marriage laws; Haas et al., 2011; Hatzenbuehler, 2009). Research demonstrates that LGBTQ individuals who reside in states that lack specific protections against sexual orientation–based hate crimes or employment discrimination report a significantly higher prevalence of mood, anxiety, and substance use disorders than heterosexual adults living in those states as well as LGBTQ individuals living in states that have laws that provide protection in at least one of these areas (Hatzenbuehler, 2009). Additionally, research demonstrates that sexual minority individuals residing in states without protective policies are approximately five times more likely to experience more mental disorders and symptoms than those in other states (Hatzenbuehler, 2009).

Other interpersonal risk factors for suicide include childhood trauma (Peter & Taylor, 2014), lack of family support (Ploderl & Fartacek, 2005), negative family reaction (D'Augelli et al., 2005), family rejection (Klein & Golub, 2016; Ryan, Huebner, Diaz, & Sanchez, 2009), social isolation (Fenaughty & Harre, 2003; Johnson & Amella, 2014), being in a hostile environment (Paul et al., 2002) or a less supportive environment (Hatzenbuehler, 2011), particularly at school (Seil, Desai, & Smith, 2014), low socioeconomic status (Peter & Taylor, 2014), and a history of forced sex, discrimination, and victimization (Clements-Nolle, Marx, & Katz, 2006).

PROTECTIVE FACTORS AGAINST SUICIDE

Protective factors against suicide among LGBTQ include the implementation of inclusive policies attempting to improve school climates and reduce the effects of homophobia and transphobia in schools on suicide risk (Hatzenbuehler & Keyes, 2013; Peter, Taylor, & Campbell, 2016). Identified protective factors in schools and educational environments include more supportive school environments (Denny et al., 2016), greater school acceptance (Ploderl, Faistauer, & Fartacek, 2010), more positive and protective school climates (Birkett, Espelage, & Koenig, 2009; Hatzenbuehler, Birkett, Van Wagenen, & Meyer, 2014; Sivashanker, 2013), and inclusive anti-bullying policies (Hatzenbuehler & Keyes, 2013). Other protective factors identified in schools include educational institutions that promote school safety (Eisenberg & Resnick, 2006) and increased sense of school connectedness (Whitaker et al., 2016). These findings demonstrate that efforts to shift the balance of heteronormative discourse on the part of LGBTQ students can have profound effects on the experiences and perceptions of sexual and gender minority youths, which may reduce incidents of suicidality among LGBTQ youths (Peter et al., 2016).

Research has also identified other protective factors, including family connectedness (Eisenberg & Resnick, 2006; Reisner, Biello, Perry, Gamarel, & Mimiaga, 2014), adult caring (Eisenberg & Resnick, 2006), family acceptance, school and peer support, social support, positive support networks, and more developed coping mechanisms (Fenaughty & Harre, 2003; Moody, Fuks, Peláez, & Smith, 2015). Research has found that social support from family and significant others is a protective factor against suicidal ideation and lifetime attempts (Moody & Smith, 2013; Tabaac, Perrin, & Rabinovitch, 2016). For adolescents, parental support has been identified as a specific protective factor (Bouris et al., 2010; Needham & Austin, 2010). Self-esteem and a general optimism have also been identified as protective factors against suicide among LGBTQ (Fenaughty & Harre, 2003; Moody & Smith, 2013; Peter & Taylor, 2014).

Individual Exercise 12.4

1. Consider your own values, attitudes, biases, and thoughts toward individuals with a different sexual orientation than yours. What is your orientation? Are you more comfortable interacting professionally and/or personally with those of a similar orientation? Why or why not?
2. Consider some of the following questions in relation to your views, morality, values, or attitudes toward individuals who self-identify as LGBTQ. Do you believe that individuals who self-identify as LGBTQ are able to be effective parents? Should they be able to adopt? Babysit your children? Become teachers? Get married? Join the military? Live in your community? Be entitled to health benefits from their partner's employer? Hold political office? Be treated the same as a heterosexual client? If you are religious, do you believe that your God is accepting of LGBTQ individuals?
3. How did you develop these ideas, attitudes, and perspectives?

4. Have they changed over time? If so, what has changed and how?
5. How have they or may they potentially impact your clinical practice?
6. Would further training, education, exposure, and/or supervision in this area improve your ability to work with individuals who self-identify as LGBTQ? Why or why not?

TREATMENT CONSIDERATIONS FOR LGBTQ INDIVIDUALS

For decades, being homosexual was considered a mental disorder in the American Psychiatric Association's *Diagnostic and Statistical Manual of Mental Disorders (DSM)*. After considerable controversy and challenges to this unsupported diagnosis, psychiatrists and other mental health professionals were able to remove homosexuality as a psychiatric diagnosis in 1973. In mental health practice, any sexual orientation beyond heterosexuality was considered to be sexually deviant, a mental disorder, and frequently morally wrong. Consequently, the acceptance or inculcation of this perception resulted in mental health professionals' treatment to center on repairing or curing individuals of any same-sex sexual attraction and/or behavior. The direct and indirect problems generated from these historical realities, unsubstantiated views, and resulting treatment practices are extensive and remain a source of stigma and detriment not only to the LGBTQ community but all mental health professionals and the larger society. Although it has been decades since homosexuality was removed from the DSM, there continues to exist some mental health professionals who without scientific support and despite evidence that these approaches are ineffective and harmful, persist in practicing curative, reparative, or conversion therapies for LGBTQ individuals (American Psychiatric Association, 2000; Haas et al., 2011; Panozzo, 2013).

Each mental health profession, including psychology, psychiatry, social work, counseling, and nursing, has studied the influence and attitudes of its members toward individuals within the LGBTQ community (Bhugra, 1990; Blackwell, 2006; Crawford, McLeod, Zamboni, & Jordan, 1999; Crisp, 2006; Crisp & McCave, 2007; Liddle, 1999; Liszcz & Yarhouse, 2005; Newman, 2002; Savage, Prout, & Chard, 2004; Smith, 1993). Although mental health professionals tend to hold less negative attitudes than the general public, each profession has found to some degree negative or homophobic attitudes (Blackwell, Dziegielewski, & Jacinto, 2007; Crisp, 2006; DeCrescenzo, 1984).

A study examining barriers to optimal care between physicians and LGBTQ youths found that the majority of physicians would not regularly discuss sexual orientation, sexual attraction, or gender identity while taking a sexual history from a sexually active adolescent even when an adolescent presented with depression, suicidal thoughts, or had attempted suicide (Kitts, 2010). Most physicians reported not having the needed skills to address issues of sexual orientation, but noted that sexual orientation should be addressed more often and included in their training (Kitts, 2010). Research has also found that education, exposure, and training in LGBTQ issues have been demonstrated to reduce negative opinion and increase tolerance in mental health clinicians. Furthermore, research has indicated that members of the LGBTQ population feel that they have different therapeutic needs (Bieschke, McClanahan, Tozer, Grzegorek, & Park, 2000; Silenzio et al., 2007), but some service providers may not consider any differences (Gambrill, Stein, & Brown, 1984). For example, one study that investigated LGB adults who attempted suicide found that 23% of individuals sought mental health or medical treatment and 14% sought religious or spiritual treatment prior to the suicide attempt (Meyer, Schwartz, & Teylan, 2015). Further, Black and Latino LGBs were underrepresented in mental health or medical treatment and Black LGBs were overrepresented in religious or spiritual treatment (Meyer et al., 2015). It is important for mental health professionals to consider not only the unique needs of sexual minority clients but also the larger professional bias and their personal perceptions.

Existing suicide prevention and intervention efforts often fail to address suicidal behavior or suicide risk within LGBT groups. Consequently, unless LGBT people are the specific focus of an intervention, they are generally overlooked. Although some guidelines have been established for increasing LGBT competency among human services organizations (Haas et al., 2011), there is little evidence that suicide prevention interventions are becoming more LGBT inclusive (Haas et al., 2011). In 2007, the American Foundation for Suicide Prevention partnered with the Suicide Prevention Resource Center and the Gay and Lesbian Medical Association to convene a conference designed to address the need for better understanding of suicidal behavior and suicide risk in LGBT populations (Haas et al., 2011). The following recommendations related to suicide prevention interventions specifically for LGBT individuals are the result of this collaboration:

To improve LGBT suicide prevention efforts:

- Address LGBT suicide risk and possible interventions for reducing risk in national and state suicide prevention strategies and plans.
- Provide educational and resource materials on LGBT suicide and suicide risk to LGBT organizations, and encourage consideration of how suicide prevention can be advanced within the context of each organization's mission and activities.
- Incorporate well-designed outcome evaluations into all interventions aimed at reducing suicidal behavior and suicide risk among LGBT people.
- Develop a wider range of interventions for reducing suicidal behavior and suicide risk in specific LGBT groups.
- Encourage a focus on LGBT groups within suicide prevention interventions and programs designed for the general population.
- Develop and implement educational programs for increasing competency in LGBT suicide risk within:

  - organizations and groups providing suicide prevention interventions for the general population; and
  - community gatekeepers including teachers and staff in youth programs, senior centers, aging services agencies, and others who come in contact with at-risk individuals.

- Encourage training in LGBT suicide risk for staff and volunteers of suicide crisis lines, law enforcement, emergency care professionals, and others who work with suicidal individuals.

SUMMARY

Individuals within the LGBTQ community are at increased risk of suicidality and may experience additional issues and complications when managing their suicide risk. Understanding the specific influence of the risk factors and protective factors for sexual minority status individuals may assist clinicians' approach, assessment, and treatment. In addition, professional and personal awareness is essential for mental health clinicians engaging, assessing, and treating members of these and other at-risk populations.

ELECTRONIC RESOURCES

LGBTQ POPULATION

http://thetrevorproject.org/helpline.aspx
www.glma.org
www.glaad.org
www.hrc.org

KNOWLEDGE ACQUISITION TEST (KAT)

True or False

1. Sexual minority status has been associated with an elevated risk for suicide ideation and suicide attempt.
2. LGBTQ females have a higher suicide risk than LGBTQ males.
3. Bullying does not increase the suicide risk for sexual minority status individuals.
4. Surprisingly, history of previous suicide attempts is not a risk factor for LGBTQ individuals.
5. Like other populations, religiosity is a protective factor.
6. Perceived burdensomeness, the feeling of being a burden to important individuals in their lives, is a critical factor explaining higher levels of depression and suicidal ideation among LGB youths.
7. School policies have yielded no real effect in reducing the suicide attempts and completions within the LGBTQ youth populations.
8. Research has found that homosexual men have almost three times higher risk of lifetime suicide attempts than heterosexual men.

Short Answer

9. Discuss how the larger social environment may influence the suicide risk within the LGBTQ population.
10. How can mental health professionals improve their ability to work within the LGBTQ population?
11. Describe how the two negative interpersonal cognitions of thwarted belongingness and perceived burdensomeness may be risk factors within the LGBTQ community.
12. In what ways can parents and families serve as a protective factor for sexual minority status individuals?

Multiple Choice

13. Which item may improve the effectiveness of mental health professionals working within the LGBTQ community?
    A. Education
    B. Exposure
    C. Training
    D. All of the above
    E. None of the above
14. Protective factors for LGBTQ youths in schools and educational environments include which of the following?
    A. Supportive school environments
    B. Greater school acceptance
    C. More positive and protective school climates
    D. Inclusive anti-bullying policies
    E. A and D only
    F. All of the above
15. Protective factors against suicide among LGBTQ include which of the following?
    A. Family connectedness/acceptance
    B. Engagement in hobbies

C. Higher levels of attention
D. Good grades
E. All of the above
F. None of the above

REFERENCES

American Psychiatric Association. (2013). *Diagnostic and statistical manual of mental disorders*, text revision (5 th ed.). Arlington, VA: American Psychiatric Publishing.

Baams, L., Grossman, A. H., & Russell, S. T. (2015). Minority stress and mechanisms of risk for depression and suicidal ideation among lesbian, gay, and bisexual youth. *Developmental Psychology, 51*(5), 688–696.

Bagley, C., & Ramsay, R. (1997). *Suicidal Behaviour in Adolescents and Adults: Research*, Taxonomy, and Prevention. Aldershot, UK: Ashgate Publishing.

Bhugra, D. (1990). Doctors' attitudes to male homosexuality: A survey. *Sexual & Marital Therapy, 5*(2), 167–174.

Bieschke, K. J., McClanahan, M., Tozer, E., Grzegorek, J. L., & Park, J. (2000). Programmatic research on the treatment of lesbian, gay, and bisexual clients: The past, the present, and the course for the future. In R. M. Perez, K. A. DeBord, & K. J. Bieschke (Eds.), *Handbook of counseling and psychotherapy with lesbian, gay, and bisexual clients* (pp. 309–335). Washington, DC: American Psychological Association.

Birkett, M., Espelage, D. L., & Koenig, B. (2009). LGB and questioning students in schools: The moderating effects of homophobic bullying and school climate on negative outcomes. *Journal of Youth and Adolescence, 38*(7), 989–1000.

Black, D., Gates, G., Sanders, S., & Taylor, L. (2000). Demographics of the gay and lesbian population in the United States: Evidence from available systematic data sources. *Demography, 37*(2), 139–154.

Blackwell, C. W. (2006). *Registered nurses' attitudes toward the protection of gays and lesbians in the workplace: An examination of homophobia and discriminatory beliefs.* Orlando: University of Central Florida.

Blackwell, C. W., Dziegielewski, S. F., & Jacinto, G. A. (2007). The use of a strength-based approach in addressing discrimination against gays and lesbians. *Journal of Human Behavior in the Social Environment, 14*(3), 1–17.

Blosnich, J. R., Nausti, L. I., Mays, V. M., & Cochran, S. D. (2016). Suicidality and sexual orientation: Characteristics of symptom severity, disclosure, and timing across the life course. *American Journal of Orthopsychiatry, 86*(1), 69–78.

Bostwick, W. B., Meyer, I., Aranda, F., Russell, S., Hughes, T., Birkett, M., & Mustanski, B. (2014). Mental health and suicidality among racially/ethnically diverse sexual minority youths. *American Journal of Public Health, 104*(6), 1129–1136.

Bouris, A., Everett, B. G., Heath, R. D., Elsaesser, C. E., & Neilands, T. B. (2016). Effects of victimization and violence on suicidal ideation and behaviors among sexual minority and heterosexual adolescents. *LGBT Health, 3*(2), 153–161.

Bouris, A., Guilamo-Ramos, V., Pickard, A., Shiu, C., Loosier, P. S., Dittus, P., Gloppen, K., & Waldmiller, J. M. (2010). A systematic review of parental influences on the health and well-being of lesbian, gay, and bisexual youth: Time for a new public health research and practice agenda. *The Journal of Primary Prevention, 31*(5–6), 273–309.

Cardom, R., Rostosky, S., & Danner, F. (2013). Does "it get better" for depressed sexual minority youth in young adulthood? *Journal of Adolescent Health, 53*(5), 671–673.

Clements-Nolle, K., Marx, R., & Katz, M. (2006). Attempted suicide among transgender persons: The influence of gender-based discrimination and victimization. *Journal of Homosexuality, 51*(3), 53–69.

Cochran, S. D., & Mays, V. M. (2000). Relation between psychiatric syndromes and behaviorally defined sexual orientation in a sample of the US population. *American Journal of Epidemiology, 151*(5), 516–523.

Cochran, S. D., Mays, V. M., & Sullivan, J. G. (2003). Prevalence of mental disorders, psychological distress, and mental health services use among lesbian, gay, and bisexual adults in the United States. *Journal of Consulting and Clinical Psychology, 71*(1), 53–61.

Colledge, L., Hickson, F., Reid, D., & Weatherburn, P. (2015). Poorer mental health in UK bisexual women than lesbians: Evidence from the UK 2007 Stonewall Women's Health Survey. *Journal of Public Health, 37*(3), 427–437.

Consolacion, T. B., Russell, S. T., & Sue, S. (2004). Sex, race/ethnicity, and romantic attractions: Multiple minority status adolescents and mental health. *Cultural Diversity & Ethnic Minority Psychology, 10*(3), 200–214.

Cramer, R. J., Burks, A. C., Stroud, C. H., Bryson, C. N., & Graham, J. (2015). A moderated mediation analysis of suicide proneness among lesbian, gay, and bisexual community members. *Journal of Social and Clinical Psychology, 34*(7), 622–641.

Crawford, I., McLeod, A., Zamboni, B. D., & Jordan, M. B. (1999). Psychologists' attitudes toward gay and lesbian parenting. *Professional Psychology: Research and Practice, 30*(4), 394–401.

Crisp, C. (2006). Correlates of homophobia and use of gay affirmative practice among social workers. *Journal of Human Behavior in the Social Environment, 14*(4), 119–143.

Crisp, C., & McCave, E. L. (2007). Gay affirmative practice: A model for social work practice with gay, lesbian, and bisexual youth. *Child & Adolescent Social Work Journal, 24*(4), 403–421.

D'Augelli, A. R., Grossman, A. H., Salter, N. P., Vassey, J. J., Starks, M. T., & Sinclair, K. O. (2005). Predicting the suicide attempts of lesbian, gay, and bisexual youth. *Suicide and Life-Threatening Behavior, 35*(6), 646–660.

DeCamp, W., & Bakken, N. W. (2016). Self-injury, suicide ideation, and sexual orientation: Differences in causes and correlates among high school students. *Journal of Injury and Violence Research, 8*(1), 15–24.

DeCrescenzo, T. (1984). *Homophobia: A study of the attitudes of mental health professionals toward homosexuality.* New York, NY: Harrington Park.

Denny, S., Lucassen, M. F., Stuart, J., Fleming, T., Bullen, P., Peiris-John, R., . . . Utter, J. (2016). The association between supportive high school environments and depressive symptoms and suicidality among sexual minority students. *Journal of Clinical Child & Adolescent Psychology, 45*(3), 248–261.

Dirkes, J., Hughes, T., Ramirez-Valles, J., Johnson, T., & Bostwick, W. (2016). Sexual identity development: Relationship with lifetime suicidal ideation in sexual minority women. *Journal of Clinical Nursing, 25*(23–24), 3545–3556.

Dohrenwend, B. P. (2000). The role of adversity and stress in psychopathology: Some evidence and its implications for theory and research. *Journal of Health & Social Behavior, 41*(1), 1–19.

Eisenberg, M. E., & Resnick, M. D. (2006). Suicidality among gay, lesbian and bisexual youth: The role of protective factors. *Journal of Adolescent Health, 39*(5), 662–668.

Fenaughty, J., & Harre, N. (2003). Life on the seesaw: A qualitative study of suicide resiliency factors for young gay men. *Journal of Homosexuality, 45*(1), 1–22.

Gambrill, E. D., Stein, T. J., & Brown, C. E. (1984). Social services use and need among gay/lesbian residents of the San Francisco Bay Area. *Journal of Social Work & Human Sexuality, 3*(1), 51–69.

Gibbs, J. J., & Goldbach, J. (2015). Religious conflict, sexual identity, and suicidal behaviors among LGBT young adults. *Archive Suicide Research, 19*(4), 472–488.

Gilman, S. E., Cochran, S. D., Mays, V. M., Hughes, M., Ostrow, D., & Kessler, R. C. (2001). Risk of psychiatric disorders among individuals reporting same-sex sexual partners in the National Comorbidity Survey. *American Journal of Public Health, 91*(6), 933–939.

Gonsiorek, J. C. (1996). *Mental health and sexual orientation.* Orlando, FL: Harcourt Brace College Publishers.

Haas, A. P., Eliason, M., Mays, V. M., Mathy, R. M., Cochran, S. D., D'Augelli, A. R., . . . Clayton, P. J. (2014). Suicide and suicide risk in lesbian, gay, bisexual, and transgender populations: Review and recommendations. *American Journal of Public Health, 104*(2), 279–286.

Hatzenbuehler, M. L. (2009). How does sexual minority stigma *"get under the skin"? A psychological mediation framework. Psychological Bulletin, 135*(5), 707.

Hatzenbuehler, M. L. (2011). The social environment and suicide attempts in lesbian, gay, and bisexual youth. *Pediatrics, 127*(5), 896–903.

Hatzenbuehler, M. L., Birkett, M., Van Wagenen, A., & Meyer, I. H. (2014). Protective school climates and reduced risk for suicide ideation in sexual minority youths. *American Journal of Public Health, 104*(2), 279–286.

Hatzenbuehler, M. L., & Keyes, K. M. (2013). Inclusive anti-bullying policies and reduced risk of suicide attempts in lesbian and gay youth. *The Journal of Adolescent Health : Official Publication of the Society for Adolescent Medicine, 53*(1 Suppl.), S21–S26.

Herek, G. M. (2002). Gender gaps in public opinion about lesbians and gay men. *Public Opinion Quarterly, 66*(1), 40–66.

Hicks, G. R., & Lee, T. (2006). Public attitudes toward gays and lesbians: Trends and predictors. *Journal of Homosexuality, 51*(2), 57–77.

Hottes, T. S., Bogaert, L., Rhodes, A. E., Brennan, D. J., & Gesink, D. (2016). Lifetime prevalence of suicide attempts among sexual minority adults by study sampling strategies: A systematic review and meta-analysis. *American Journal of Public Health, 106*(5), e1–e12.

Johnson, M. J., & Amella, E. J. (2014). Isolation of lesbian, gay, bisexual and transgender youth: A dimensional concept analysis. *Journal of Advanced Nursing, 70*(3), 523–532.

Joiner, T. E. Jr, Van Orden, K. A., Witte, T. K., Selby, E. A., Ribeiro, J. D., Lewis, R., & Rudd, M. D. (2009). Main predictions of the interpersonal–psychological theory of suicidal behavior: Empirical tests in two samples of young adults. *Journal of Abnormal Psychology, 118*(3), 634–646.

Kitts, R. L. (2010). Barriers to optimal care between physicians and lesbian, gay, bisexual, transgender, and questioning adolescent patients. *Journal of Homosexuality, 57*(6), 730–747.

Klein, A., & Golub, S. A. (2016). Family rejection as a predictor of suicide attempts and substance misuse among transgender and gender nonconforming adults. *LGBT Health, 3*(3), 193–199. doi:10.1089/lgbt.2015.0111

Lea, T., de Wit, J., & Reynolds, R. (2014). Minority stress in lesbian, gay, and bisexual young adults in Australia: Associations with psychological distress, suicidality, and substance use. *Archives of Sexual Behavior, 43*(8), 1571–1578.

Levy, S. A., Russon, J., & Diamond, G. M. (2016). Attachment-based family therapy for suicidal lesbian, gay, and bisexual adolescents: A case study. *Australian and New Zealand Journal of Family Therapy, 37*(2), 190–206.

Liddle, B. J. (1999). Gay and lesbian clients' ratings of psychiatrists, psychologists, social workers, and counsellors. *Journal of Gay & Lesbian Psychotherapy, 3*(1), 81–93.

Liszcz, A. M., & Yarhouse, M. A. (2005). A survey on views of how to assist with coming out as gay, changing same-sex behavior or orientation, and navigating sexual identity confusion. *Ethics & Behavior, 15*(2), 159–179.

Lytle, M. C., De Luca, S. M., & Blosnich, J. R. (2014). The influence of intersecting identities on self-harm, suicidal behaviors, and depression among lesbian, gay, and bisexual individuals. *Suicide and Life-Threatening Behavior, 44*(4), 384–391.

Lytle, M. C., De Luca, S. M., Blosnich, J. R., & Brownson, C. (2015). Associations of racial/ethnic identities and religious affiliation with suicidal ideation among lesbian, gay, bisexual, and questioning individuals. *Journal of Affective Disorder, 1*(178), 39–45.

Marshall, E., Claes, L., Bouman, W. P., Witcomb, G. L., & Arcelus, J. (2016). Non-suicidal self-injury and suicidality in trans people: A systematic review of the literature. *International Review of Psychiatry, 28*(1), 58–69.

McIntosh, C. A., & Bialer, P. A. (2015). Our youth at risk. *Journal of Gay & Lesbian Mental Health, 19*(2), 123–124.

Meyer, I. H. (2003). Prejudice, social stress, and mental health in lesbian, gay, and bisexual populations: Conceptual issues and research evidence. *Psychological Bulletin, 129*(5), 674–697.

Meyer, I. H., Dietrich, J., & Schwartz, S. (2008). Lifetime prevalence of mental disorders and suicide attempts in diverse lesbian, gay, and bisexual populations. *American Journal of Public Health, 98*(6), 1004–1006.

Meyer, I. H., Schwartz, S., & Teylan, M. (2015). The role of help-seeking in preventing suicide attempts among lesbians, gay men, and bisexuals. *Suicide and Life-Threatening Behavior, 45*(1), e25–e36.

Michaels, M. S., Parent, M. C., & Torrey, C. L. (2016). A minority stress model for suicidal ideation in gay men. *Suicide and Life-Threatening Behavior, 46*(1), 23–34.

Moody, C., & Smith, N. G. (2013). Suicide protective factors among trans adults. *Archives of Sex Behavior, 42*(5), 739–752.

Moody, C., Fuks, N., Peláez, S., & Smith, N. G. (2015). "Without this, I would for sure already be dead": A qualitative inquiry regarding suicide protective factors among trans adults. *Psychology of Sexual Orientation and Gender Diversity, 2*(3), 266–280. doi:10.1037/sgd0000130

Mustanski, B., & Liu, R. T. (2013). A longitudinal study of predictors of suicide attempts among lesbian, gay, bisexual, and transgender youth. *Archives of Sexual Behavior, 42*(3), 437–448.

Needham, B. L., & Austin, E. L. (2010). Sexual orientation, parental support, and health during the transition to young adulthood. *Journal of Youth Adolescence, 39*(10), 1189–1198.

Newman, B. S. (2002). Lesbians, gays, and religion: Strategies for challenging belief systems. *Journal of Lesbian Studies, 6*(3–4), 87–98.

O'Donnell, S., Meyer, I. H., & Schwartz, S. (2011). Increased risk of suicide attempts among Black and Latino lesbians, gay men, and bisexuals. *American Journal of Public Health, 101*(6), 1055–1059.

Panozzo, D. (2013). Advocating for an end to reparative therapy: Methodological grounding and blueprint for change. *Journal of Gay & Lesbian Social Services. 25*(3), 362–377.

Patrick, D. L., Bell, J. F., Huang, J. Y., Lazarakis, N. C., & Edwards, T. C. (2013). Bullying and quality of life in youths perceived as gay, lesbian, or bisexual in Washington state, 2010. *American Journal of Public Health, 103*(7), 1255–1261.

Paul, J. P., Catania, J., Pollack, L., Moskowitz, J., Canchola, J., & Mills, T. (2002). Suicide attempts among gay and bisexual men: Lifetime prevalence and antecedents. *American Journal of Public Health, 92*(8), 1338–1345.

Pedersen, W., & Kristiansen, H. W. (2008). Homosexual experience, desire, and identity among young adults. *Journal of Homosexuality, 54*(1–2), 68–101.

Perez-Brumer, A., Hatzenbuehler, M. L., Oldenburg, C. E., & Bockting, W. (2015). Individual- and structural-level risk factors for suicide attempts among transgender adults. *Behavioral Medicine, 41*(3), 164–171.

Peter, T., & Taylor, C. (2014). Buried above ground: A university-based study of risk/protective factors for suicidality among sexual minority youth in Canada. *Journal of LGBT Youth, 11*(2), 125–149.

Peter, T., Taylor, C., & Campbell, C. (2016). 'You can't break . . . When you're already broken': The importance of school climate to suicidality among LGBTQ youth. *Journal of Gay & Lesbian Mental Health, 20*(3), 195–213.

Plöderl, M., Faistauer, G., & Fartacek, R. (2010). The contribution of school to the feeling of acceptance and the risk of suicide attempts among Austrian gay and bisexual males. *Journal of Homosexuality, 57*(7), 819–841.

Plöderl, M., & Fartacek, R. (2005). Suicidality and associated risk factors among lesbian, gay, and bisexual compared to heterosexual Austrian adults. *Suicide and Life-Threatening Behavior, 35*(6), 661–670.

Plöderl, M., & Tremblay, P. (2015). Mental health of sexual minorities. A systematic review. *International Review of Psychiatry, 27*(5), 367–385.

Pompili, M., Lester, D., Forte, A., Seretti, M. E., Erbuto, D., Lamis, D. A., . . . Girardi, P. (2014). Bisexuality and suicide: A systematic review of the current literature. *The Journal of Sexual Medicine, 11*(8), 1903–1913.

Rabinovitch, A. E., Perrin, P. B., Tabaac, A. R., & Brewster, M. E. (2015). Coping styles and suicide in racially and ethnically diverse lesbian, bisexual, and queer women. *Psychology of Sexual Orientation and Gender Diversity, 2*(4), 497–504.

Reisner, S. L., Biello, K., Perry, N. S., Gamarel, K. E., & Mimiaga, M. J. (2014). A compensatory model of risk and resilience applied to adolescent sexual orientation disparities in nonsuicidal self-injury and suicide attempts. *American Journal of Orthopsychiatry, 84*(5), 545–556.

Reisner, S. L., Vetters, R., Leclerc, M., Zaslow, S., Wolfrum, S., Shumer, D., & Mimiaga, M. J. (2015). Mental health of transgender youth in care at an adolescent urban community health center: A matched retrospective cohort study. *Journal of Adolescent Health, 56*(3), 274–279.

Remafedi, G. (1999a). Sexual orientation and youth suicide. *Journal of the American Medical Association, 282*(13), 1291–1292.

Remafedi, G. (1999b). Suicide and sexual orientation: Nearing the end of controversy? *Archives of General Psychiatry, 56*(10), 885–886.

Remafedi, G., French, S., Story, M., Resnick, M. D., & Blum, R. (1998). The relationship between suicide risk and sexual orientation: Results of a population-based study. *American Journal of Public Health, 88*(1), 57–60.

Robinson, J. P., & Espelage, D. L. (2012). Bullying explains only part of LGBTQ–heterosexual risk disparities: Implications for policy and practice. *Educational Researcher, 41*(8), 309–319.

Rood, B. A., Puckett, J. A., Pantalone, D. W., & Bradford, J. B. (2015). Predictors of suicidal ideation in a statewide sample of transgender individuals. *LGBT Health, 2*(3), 270–275.

Ryan, C., Huebner, D., Diaz, R. M., & Sanchez, J. (2009). Family rejection as a predictor of negative health outcomes in White and Latino lesbian, gay, and bisexual young adults. *Pediatrics, 123*(1), 346–352.

Saewyc, E. M., Bauer, G., Skay, C., Bearinger, L., Resnick, M., & Reis, E. (2004). Measuring sexual orientation in adolescent health surveys: Evaluation of eight school-based surveys. *Journal of Adolescent Health, 35*(4), 345. e1–345.e15.

Sandfort, T. G., de Graaf, R., Bijl, R. V., & Schnabel, P. (2001). Same-sex sexual behavior and psychiatric disorders: Findings from the Netherlands Mental Health Survey and Incidence Study (NEMESIS). *Archives of General Psychiatry, 58*(1), 85–91.

Savage, T. A., Prout, H. T., & Chard, K. M. (2004). School psychology and issues of sexual orientation: Attitudes, beliefs, and knowledge. *Psychology in the Schools, 41*(2), 201–210.

Seil, K. S., Desai, M. M., & Smith, M. V. (2014). Sexual orientation, adult connectedness, substance use, and mental health outcomes among adolescents: Findings from the 2009 New York City Youth Risk Behavior Survey. *American Journal of Public Health, 104*(10), 1950–1956.

Sell, R. L. (1997). Defining and measuring sexual orientation: A review. *Archives of Sexual Behavior, 26*(6), 643–657.

Semlyen, J., King, M., Varney, J., & Hagger-Johnson, G. (2016). Sexual orientation and symptoms of common mental disorder or low well-being: Combined meta-analysis of 12 UK population health surveys. *BioMed Central Psychiatry, 16*, 67–76.

Shadick, R., Backus Dagirmanjian, F., & Barbot, B. (2015). Suicide risk among college students. The intersection of sexual orientation and race. *Crisis, 36*(6), 416–423.

Silenzio, V. M., Pena, J. B., Duberstein, P. R., & Knox, K. L. (2007). Sexual orientation and risk factors for suicidal ideation and suicide attempts among adolescents and young adults. *American Journal of Public Health, 97*(11), 2017–2019.

Sivashanker, K. (2013). Cyberbullying and the digital self. *Journal of the American Academy of Child & Adolescent Psychiatry, 52*(2), 113–115.

Smith, B. C., Armelie, A. P., Boarts, J. M., Brazil, M., & Delahanty, D. L. (2016). PTSD, depression, and substance use in relation to suicidality risk among traumatized minority lesbian, gay, and bisexual youth. *Archives of Suicide Research, 20*(1), 80–93.

Smith, G. B. (1993). Homophobia and attitudes toward gay men and lesbians by psychiatric nurses. *Archives of Psychiatric Nursing, 7*(6), 377–384.

Sutter, M., & Perrin, P. B. (2016). Discrimination, mental health, and suicidal ideation among LGBTQ people of color. *Journal of Counseling Psychology, 63*(1), 98–105.

Swannell, S., Martin, G., & Page, A. (2016). Suicidal ideation, suicide attempts and non-suicidal self-injury among lesbian, gay, bisexual and heterosexual adults: Findings from an Australian national study. *Australian and New Zealand Journal of Psychiatry, 50*(2), 145–153.

Tabaac, A. R., Perrin, P. B., & Rabinovitch, A. E. (2016). The relationship between social support and suicide risk in a national sample of ethnically diverse sexual minority women. *Journal of Gay and Lesbian Mental Health, 20*(2), 116–126.

Thoma, B. C., & Huebner, D. M. (2013). Health consequences of racist and antigay discrimination for multiple minority adolescents. *Cultural Diversity & Ethnic Minority Psychology, 19*(4), 404–413.

Tsypes, A., Lane, R., Paul, E., & Whitlock, J. (2016). Non-suicidal self-injury and suicidal thoughts and behaviors in heterosexual and sexual minority young adults. *Comprehensive Psychiatry, 65*, 32–43.

van Heeringen, C., & Vincke, J. (2000). Suicidal acts and ideation in homosexual and bisexual young people: A study of prevalence and risk factors. *Social Psychiatry & Psychiatric Epidemiology, 35*(11), 494–499.

Van Orden, K. A., Witte, T. K., Cukrowicz, K. C., Braithwaite, S. R., Selby, E. A., & Joiner, T. E., Jr. (2010). The interpersonal theory of suicide. *Psychological Review, 117*(2), 575–600.

Wang, J., Plöderl, M., Häusermann, M., & Weiss, M. G. (2015). Understanding suicide attempts among gay men from their self-perceived causes. *The Journal of Nervous and Mental Disease, 203*(7), 499–506.

Wells, J. E., McGee, M. A., & Beautrais, A. L. (2011). Multiple aspects of sexual orientation: Prevalence and sociodemographic correlates in a New Zealand national survey. *Archives of Sexual Behavior, 40*(1), 155–168.

Whitaker, K., Shapiro, V. B., & Shields, J. P. (2016). School-based protective factors related to suicide for lesbian, gay, and bisexual adolescents. *Journal of Adolescent Health, 58*(1), 63–68.

Wiederhold, B. K. (2014). Cyberbullying and LGBTQ youth: A deadly combination. *Cyberpsychology, Behavior, and Social Networking, 17*(9), 569–570.

CHAPTER THIRTEEN

AT-RISK GROUPS

Several diverse and unique groups within society are at an elevated risk for suicidality. These at-risk groups are frequently isolated from the larger society, either through stigma, being disenfranchised, separateness, exclusion, and/or sociodemographic characteristics. Although a number of at-risk populations exist, this chapter focuses on the following three groups: the homeless, Native Americans, and incarcerated individuals. Each of these populations is highlighted here due to its importance and distinct vulnerability. The prevalence of risk for each of these populations is highlighted as compared to the larger societal norms. In addition, the population-specific risk and protective factors are drawn from evidence-based research.

GOALS AND OBJECTIVES

An understanding of:

- Prevalence of suicide among the homeless
- Contextual factors related to suicidality among the homeless
- Risk and protective factors for suicide among the homeless
- Key considerations in mental health treatment of suicidal homeless individuals
- Prevalence of suicide among Native Americans
- Contextual factors related to suicidality among Native Americans
- Risk and protective factors for Native Americans
- Key considerations in mental health treatment of suicidal Native American individuals
- Prevalence of suicide among incarcerated individuals
- Contextual factors related to suicidality among incarcerated individuals
- Risk and protective factors for suicide among incarcerated individuals
- Key considerations in mental health treatment of suicidal incarcerated individuals

Suicide is a leading cause of death across countries, cultures, religions, gender, and the life span (Nock et al., 2008; U.S. Department of Health and Human Services, 2001). Although efforts continually need to be taken to address this phenomenon on a larger societal and global scale, there exist a number of specific groups and populations at increased risk for suicidality that require specific attention. It is essential for researchers and mental health professionals to understand and investigate these at-risk populations in order to more effectively identify their unique risk and protective factors, the specific societal and cultural contexts that influence suicide risk, and to effectively intervene to reduce their suicide risk. Effective clinical engagement, assessment, and treatment for these at-risk individuals require specific knowledge and understanding. The ability to effectively work with and treat one population does not necessarily translate into clinical success with another group.

A fundamentally important issue that arises for mental health professionals in working with at-risk populations is the influence and impact of their own personal attitudes, values, beliefs, views, and biases. Most, if not all, of these at-risk populations (homeless, Native Americans, and incarcerated individuals) are treated differently in society. These at-risk groups evoke a number of positive and/or negative ideas, preconceptions, stereotypes, and/or stigmas in individuals, including mental health professionals. Clinicians need to become aware of their own personal and professional perceptions related to members of these at-risk groups. Without such awareness, effective clinical treatment is not possible.

Individual Exercise 13.1

1. Write down your initial reaction upon hearing the following words. Be honest and unfiltered in your response. Remember, answers are personal and there are no correct or incorrect answers: homeless, Native American, American Indian, prisoner, convict, ex-convict, incarceration
2. Examine your responses. Are you surprised by anything you wrote down? In what way?

Small Group Exercise 13.1

In groups of two to three,

1. Share, as you feel comfortable, your responses to question 1 in Individual Exercise 13.1.
2. Were there similarities in your responses? What accounts for these similarities?
3. Were there differences in your responses? What accounts for these differences?
4. How might these perceptions influence positively or negatively clinical practice with these at-risk client groups?

Individual Exercise 13.2

Reflect on your responses to question 1 in Small Group Exercise 13.1:

1. Which responses were you comfortable sharing? What made those responses easier to share?
2. Which were you not comfortable sharing? What made those responses difficult for you to share?
3. How might this awareness impact your work with these at-risk client groups?

Individual Exercise 13.3

1. What would be the hardest at-risk group (homeless, Native Americans, and incarcerated individuals) for you to professionally work with? Why?
2. What personal and/or professional considerations may make it harder for you to work with this population?

3. What would be the easiest at-risk group (homeless, Native Americans, and incarcerated individuals) for you to professionally work with? Why?
4. What personal and/or professional considerations may make it easier for you to work with this population?

THE HOMELESS

On any given night, more than 600,000 individuals are homeless in the United States (Fazel, Geddes, & Kushel, 2014). Despite generalizations, stereotypes, and biases attributing homelessness to laziness or lack of intelligence, homelessness results from a complex combination of both individual and structural factors. Individual factors include such things as poverty, family problems, and mental health and substance use problems. Structural factors include the availability of low-cost housing, considered the most important structural determinant for homelessness (Fazel et al., 2014). Suicide among the homeless population has been recognized as a major public health problem. Suicide is among the leading causes of death among street youths (Hadland et al., 2015). It is important to understand the larger social context that may contribute to an elevated risk of suicidality among the homeless population.

Life on the streets is generally unsafe and is characterized by a lack of basic survival needs including food, water, shelter, and medical care (Rew & Horner, 2003). Attitudes of the nonhomeless population can help or hinder the homeless. In one qualitative study of homeless youths, for example, homeless adolescents reported that one resource for meeting basic survival needs was trusting strangers who were worried about homeless people finding food and items they needed to survive (Rew & Horner, 2003). However, homeless youths also reported the crucial skill of recognizing who can and cannot be trusted as many adults and nonhomeless youths alike often threaten, tease, and/or exploit them (Rew & Horner, 2003).

For homeless youths, it has been proposed that the effects of daily abuse and hardship of life on the streets lead to poor mental health functioning. This, in turn, results in their choosing ineffective and self-destructive coping strategies that negatively impact their overall physical health and general sense of well-being (Myburgh, Moolla, & Poggenpoel, 2015). A qualitative study of homeless youths presenting to a shelter found that children living on the streets report being threatened, exploited, and exposed to physical, sexual, and emotional abuse on a daily basis not only by the community and the authorities, but also by other street dwellers as well (Myburgh, Moolla, & Poggenpoel, 2015). Youths report that these experiences lead to feelings of sadness, fear, anxiety, misery, despair, hopelessness, helplessness, and suicide ideation (Myburgh, Moolla, & Poggenpoel, 2015). Despite this constant exposure to a range of negative experiences and associated negative emotions, these children also exhibited perseverance, resilience, a search for autonomy, and sympathy for other street children in their same position (Myburgh, Moolla, & Poggenpoel, 2015).

Statistics, Epidemiology, and Trends in Homeless Suicide

The lifetime prevalence of suicide attempt among homeless individuals has been found to be as high as 53% (Prigerson, Desai, Liu-Mares, & Rosenheck, 2003). Approximately 8% of homeless individuals report a history of repeat suicide attempts (Prigerson et al., 2003). Suicide ideation among the homeless is 10 times more common than in the general population (Patterson & Holden, 2012). The lifetime prevalence of suicidal ideation among the homeless has been estimated to be as high as 66% (Eynan et al., 2002; Prigerson et al., 2003).

Risk Factors for Suicide

Although some risk factors for suicide among the homeless population in the United States overlap with those associated with the general population, there are also several distinct risk factors for suicide in this population. Although most research examining risk factors among the homeless population focuses on adolescents, research indicates that middle-aged homeless individuals are actually at the highest risk for suicidality (Prigerson et al., 2003). Among homeless adults, alcohol and/or drug abuse (Pluck, Lee, & Parks, 2013; Prigerson et al., 2003; Torchalla et al., 2014; Torchalla, Strehlau, Li, & Krausz, 2011), younger age when first homeless (Pluck et al., 2013), psychiatric history, and inpatient hospitalizations (Prigerson et al., 2003) are main risk factors for suicide. Other research has found that a greater number of sources of psychological pain, past suicide attempts, and male gender predicted current suicidal thoughts among homeless adults (Coohey, Easton, Kong, & Bockenstedt, 2015). One longitudinal study following homeless individuals experiencing suicidal ideation over a 24-month period found that baseline diagnoses of mood and anxiety disorders, depressed mood, any type of substance abuse as well as polysubstance abuse were significantly associated with suicide ideation. Notably, a baseline of diagnosis of a psychotic disorder, daily substance use, intravenous drug use, recent arrest, multiple physical illnesses, and history of traumatic brain injury were not significantly associated with suicidal ideation (Noël et al., 2016).

Research has also examined the role of child maltreatment in homeless adults. Studies indicate that multiple types of maltreatment in childhood were associated with suicide risk (Torchalla, Strehlau, Li, Schuetz, & Krausz, 2012). Other research examining adverse life events among formerly homeless adults found that approximately 37% reported previous incarceration, 32% suicidality, 30% abandonment by one or both parents, and 34% the death of their mother (Padgett, Smith, Henwood, & Tiderington, 2012).

Among homeless women, survival sex has been examined as a risk factor for suicidal ideation and behaviors. Research has found that women engaging in survival sex are at an increased risk for suicide attempt (Warf et al., 2013). Further, women report engaging in survival sex largely out of either (a) desperation to meet basic needs, such as a place to stay, food, and/or money, (b) coercion, or (c) as a means to acquire drugs, and often experience regret and shame about their experience, potentially leading to their suicidality (Moskowitz, Stein, & Lightfoot, 2013; Warf et al., 2013).

Finally, a number of research studies have found that homeless veterans are at a higher risk of suicide (Bossarte, Piegari, Hill, & Kane, 2103; Goldstein, Luther, & Haas, 2012; Lee, Iglewicz, Golshan, & Zisook, 2013; Schinka, Bossarte, Curtiss, Lapcevic, & Casey, 2016; Schinka, Schinka, Casey, Kasprow, & Bossarte, 2012). In one study that examined homeless veterans versus domiciled veterans found that homeless veterans had significantly higher rates of past suicide attempts (47% vs. 27%; Lee et al., 2013). Suicide among active military personnel and military veterans is explored in more details in Chapter 11.

In terms of homeless youths, a recent study found that 88% of youths had a current mental health problem and 93% endorsed lifetime incidence of mental health problems (Hodgson, Shelton, & van den Bree, 2015; Oppong & Meyer-Weitz, 2015). Among homeless youths, alcohol and/or drug abuse (Rew, Taylor-Seehafer, & Fitzgerald, 2001; Votta & Manion, 2004), prescription drug use (Rhoades, Winetrobe, & Rice, 2014), low self-esteem (Yoder, 1999), mental health problems, especially depression (Votta & Manion, 2004; Yoder, 1999), legal and academic difficulties (Votta & Manion, 2004), prior suicide attempt (Votta & Manion, 2004), lesbian, gay, bisexual, transgender, and queer/questioning (LGBTQ) sexual orientation (Noël et al., 2001; Rohde, Noell, Ochs, & Seeley, 2001), and knowledge of peer suicide attempt (Yoder, 1999) are associated with increased risk of suicide. Gang involvement has also been noted as a risk factor for suicide attempt among homeless youths (Petering, 2016). Among runaway and homeless youths, female gender and LGBT youths were more likely to have attempted suicide; also recent stress was identified as a significant predictor of suicide attempts (Moskowitz, Stein, & Lightfoot, 2013; Walls, Potter, & Van Leeuwen, 2009).

Childhood maltreatment has received a lot of attention in the research examining homeless youths. Multiple types of childhood maltreatment, including sexual abuse (Hadland et al., 2015; Molnar, Shade, Kral, Booth, & Watters, 1998; Rew, Thomas, Horner, Resnick, & Beuhring, 2001; Yoder, 1999), physical abuse (Hadland et al., 2015; Molnar et al., 1998; Yoder, 1999), emotional abuse, and emotional neglect, have been found to be associated with subsequent risk of suicidal behavior among street youths (Hadland et al., 2015). For example, one study of young adults who had run away from home prior to the age of 16 found that 45.3% reported being bullied, 25.3% reported experiencing violence at home, and 8.8% reported experiencing unwanted sexual intercourse (Meltzer, Ford, Bebbington, & Vostanis, 2012).

Protective Factors Against Suicide

Homeless individuals who perceived themselves as resilient engage in fewer life-threatening behaviors (Oppong, 2015; Rew, Taylor-Seehafer, Thomas, & Yockey, 2004), and higher levels of self-reliance is a protective factor against suicide among homeless youths (Rew et al., 2004). Another study found youths with perceived resilience were associated with less suicidal ideation (Cleverley & Kidd, 2011). However, research also indicates that resilience may be protective only when levels of psychological distress are low and that it may not have any protective function in the face of high psychological distress (Cleverly & Kidd, 2011). Pride, moral principles, determination, commitment to personal relationships (Montgomery, 1994), self-confidence (McCormack & MacIntosh, 2001), and positive strategies for coping with loneliness (i.e., making friends, having a pet) have also been found to be protective against suicidality among homeless youths (Rew, 2000). Research has also found that homeless youths who report finding a family in their community of homeless peers that provides support and understanding often not found in their family of origin is a protective factor against suicidal behavior (Rew & Horner, 2003). Lastly, a trusting stranger who expresses concern for whether or not homeless individuals have access to food and other basic survival needs has been identified as a protective factor for homeless youths (Rew & Horner, 2003).

Treatment Considerations for Homeless Individuals

Common misperceptions of the homeless include that they are lazy, unwilling to work to better their situation, drug abusers, or mentally ill. These negative attitudes hinder outreach efforts designed to improve the life circumstances of the homeless. Intervention and prevention programs aimed at alleviating suicide and other mental health problems among the homeless would greatly benefit from incorporating campaigns designed to educate the public and improve public opinion of the homeless.

Research demonstrates that homeless individuals tend to underutilize medical and mental health services (Fazel et al., 2014; Hodgson, Shelton, & van den Bree, 2014). One study found that while the prevalence of psychiatric disorder among homeless young adults was startlingly high with 88% reporting current psychiatric illness and 93% reporting lifetime psychiatric illness, the rate of mental health service use was remarkably low at only 31% (Hodgson, 2014). However, other research does indicate that homeless adults do attend the emergency department more often than nonhomeless people (Fazel et al., 2014). This may be the result of limited access to private physicians and/or treatment centers but nevertheless suggests that the emergency department may serve as an important resource for outreach and intervention programs aimed at reducing suicide risk among the homeless.

Collins and colleagues (2012) investigated suicidality among chronically homeless individuals with alcohol problems and examined its trajectory following exposure to immediate, permanent, low-barrier housing, such as the Housing First program (i.e., Housing First). Longitudinal analyses found that severity of suicidal ideation decreased by 43% from baseline to follow-up and that no participants completed suicide during the 2-year follow-up (Collins et al., 2016).

However, it has also been suggested that housing programs aimed at reducing rates of homelessness also include access to mental health treatment to address the myriad mental health issues homeless individuals face (Strehlau, Torchalla, Kathy, Schuetz, & Krausz, 2012). Others suggest that given the experiences of trauma and loss across the life span of homeless adults and the cumulative effect these experiences have on suicidality and mental illness, prevention and intervention programs need to focus not simply on treating current mental illness but also on addressing previous adverse experiences (Padgett et al., 2012).

A recent study investigated the educational needs, experience, and exposure of clinical providers and paraprofessionals employed within homeless organizations regarding suicide (Hensley & Matthieu, 2011). Survey results found that 90% of homeless service providers had past contact with suicidal individuals, and 95% of the providers are willing to participate in continuing education on suicide prevention. Hensley and colleagues recommend that suicide prevention training could be essential and may serve as a preventative measure to address suicidal behaviors in the lives of their homeless clients (Hensley & Matthieu, 2011). Research finds that treatment and housing programs are recommended and need to be accompanied by multidisciplinary, specialized interventions that account for high rates of complex mental health conditions (Strehlau et al., 2012).

NATIVE AMERICANS

Suicide disproportionately affects Native Americans (Lizardi & Gearing, 2010; Wexler et al, 2015). It is important to recognize the larger social context that may contribute to an elevated risk of suicidality among Native Americans. In fact, research has highlighted that suicidal behaviors have been described by community members as an issue with very deep historical and contemporary structural roots that should not simply be understood as individualized pathology (Walls, Hautala, & Hurley, 2014). The legacy of colonization or historical trauma has been forwarded as a paradigm for understanding and explaining the heightened prevalence rates of mental disorders and social problems, including suicidality among American Indians (Alcantara & Gone, 2007; Duran, Duran, & Yellow Horse–Brave Heart, 1998; Yellow Horse–Brave Heart & DeBruyn, 1998). More specifically, it has been hypothesized that the high risk of suicide among Native American youths may be explained by a disconnect and a sense of loss of belonging to both their culture and community (Chandler, Lalonde, Sokol, Hallett, & Marcia, 2003). Although with mixed results, one study indicated that American Indians who more frequently engage in historical loss thinking may be susceptible to suicide ideation through more ruminative tendencies, including brooding (Tucker, Wingate, O'Keefe, Hollingsworth, & Cole, 2016). Others suggest that historical trauma plays a large role in the increased risk of suicide seen in this population (Gray & McCullagh, 2014; Taylor, Anderson, & Bruguier Zimmerman, 2014). More specifically, Native Americans were forcibly removed from their ancestral lands, experienced both famine and genocidal wars as a result of forced colonization, and were subject to forced acculturation through educational experiences (Gray & McCullagh, 2014). The effects of these historical traumas are still rampant throughout Native American reservations, which are largely characterized by extreme poverty, minimal access to mental health services and medical care, high rates of alcohol and drug use, substandard housing, limited educational and employment opportunities, and high rates of crime and violence (Gray & McCullagh, 2014). As a result, many Native Americans struggle with a lost sense of purpose, hopelessness, and disenfranchisement, all of which contribute to the increased risk of suicidality in this population (Wissow, 2000).

Statistics, Epidemiology, and Trends in Native American Suicide

There are 5.2 million American Indians and Alaska Natives in the United States, representing 1.7% of the total population (U.S. Census Bureau, 2010). Native Americans comprise 561 federally recognized tribes representing a diverse range of indigenous languages and cultural customs (U.S. Census Bureau, 2002). Suicide is the sixth leading cause of death among Native Americans (Andrew & Krouse, 1995) and is nearly double that of the overall U.S. rate (Indian Health Service [IHS], 2015). Suicide for Native Americans residing on reservations is even higher with rates 4 to 15 times the national averages (IHS, 2009; Mullany et al., 2009; Tingey et al., 2014). Research investigating American Indian youths have found that over 24% have attempted suicide one or more times in their lives (Chino & Fullerton-Gleason, 2006), with more than 16% attempting in the past year (Shaughnessy, Doshi, & Jones, 2004). Native American youths have the highest suicide rates in the United States (Bolton et al., 2014; Herne, Bartholomew, & Weahkee, 2014; Tingey et al., 2014). Specifically, adolescent males (15–24 years of age) are the highest risk group among Native Americans, with a suicide rate approximately 2.5 times higher than same-aged males in the general U.S. population (Wissow, 2000). Across genders, Native Americans aged 15 to 24 years complete suicide at a rate three times that of the national average for that age group (McLeigh, 2010). In addition, Native youths with a past attempt were more likely to engage in violence, sexual risk behavior, and use tobacco, drugs, and alcohol (Firestone et al., 2015; Shaughnessy et al., 2004). In one study, toxicology detected the presence of alcohol in 69% of all completed suicide by American Indians, with a higher prevalence in males over females (May et al., 2002).

Risk Factors for Suicide

Risk factors associated with suicidality among Native Americans include depression, drug and alcohol use, being a victim of violence (Alcantara & Gone, 2007; Andrew & Krouse, 1995; Chino & Fullerton-Gleason, 2006), previous suicide attempts (Borowsky, Resnick, Ireland, & Blum, 1999; Shaughnessy et al., 2004), friends or family members attempting or completing suicide, physical or sexual abuse, somatic symptoms, health concerns (Borowsky et al., 1999), family disruption, poor social support network, loss of ethnic/native identity, lack of religious or spiritual identification (Alcantara & Gone, 2007), and sadness/hopelessness (Manzo, Tiesman, Stewart, Hobbs, & Knox, 2015). For younger adult females, interpersonal conflict and partner violence are risk factors (Olson et al., 1999). Ballard and colleagues (2015) found that youths engaging in risky sexual behavior and with recent exposure to suicidal behavior were associated with higher risk for a suicide attempt (Ballard et al., 2015). Adverse childhood experiences (ACEs) are a significant risk factor for suicide attempt among Native American young adults (Brockie, Dana-Sacco, Wallen, Wilcox, & Campbell, 2015). One study found that ACEs are significantly associated with the risk of suicide attempt among young adults living on reservations, and for each additional ACE experienced, the odds of suicide attempt increase by 37% (Brockie et al., 2015).

Several studies have identified elevated suicide rates with acculturation stress (Lester, 1999). Also, Native Americans more often endorse alienation as a motivation for suicide than their White counterparts (Olson, Wahab, Thompson, & Durrant, 2011).

Protective Factors Against Suicide

Spirituality has been posited as an important buffer against suicidality for Native Americans (Alcantara & Gone, 2007; Garoutte et al., 2003). Research has also identified that connectedness and belonging serve as a culturally based protective factor against suicide among Native Americans (Hill, 2009; Mohatt, Fok, Burket, Henry, & Allen, 2011). Connectedness has been defined as the interrelated state of the individual, one's family, one's community, and the natural environment (Mohatt et al., 2011). Other research has similarly demonstrated that family connectedness, social support, emotional health, and affective relationships with tribal leaders have a protective effect against suicidality (Alcantara & Gone, 2007; Borowsky et al., 1999). One study investigating suicidality in sexually abused Native youths found that family attention; caring exhibited by family members, adults, or tribal leaders; parental expectations; and positive feelings toward school were protective factors for females (Pharris, Resnick, & Blum, 1997). Protective factors against suicidality for Native American males include school enjoyment; strong academic performance; and caring exhibited by family members, adults, or tribal leaders were protective factors against suicidality (Pharris et al., 1997). Individual psychological protective factors associated with lower levels of suicidal ideation that have been identified in the research include higher levels of hope and optimism (O'Keefe & Wingate, 2013).

Some research has also found engagement with cultural practices to be a protective factor against suicidality among Native Americans (Alcantara & Gone, 2007; Borowsky et al., 1999). For example, research has found a decreased risk of suicide to be associated with higher levels of traditional integration (Lester, 1999). Others have found that among Native American males, involvement in traditional activities was a protective factor (Pharris et al., 1997). However, it is important to note that studies examining the role of traditional engagement/integration have yielded mixed findings (Alcantara & Gone, 2007; Borowsky et al., 1999).

Treatment Considerations for Native Americans

Rates of mental health service utilization are rather low among Native Americans. One study found that Native American youths are less likely to receive outpatient mental health services than their White and non-Hispanic Black counterparts (Nestor, Cheek, & Liu, 2016). There are a multitude of reasons for why many Native Americans choose not to seek formal mental health treatment even when experiencing suicidal thoughts and/ or behaviors. Research has found that feelings of hopelessness, the desire to be self-reliant, the belief that they do not need help, and stigma associated with mental health care utilization are the strongest factors associated with a lack of help-seeking in this population. Others also note that the small, close-knit, rural nature of Native communities may influence a decision not to seek help as it would often be difficult if not impossible to do so confidentially. Further, some Native Americans may perceive mental health services as being an external agent to the tribal community and may be resistant to seeking care from an outside organization that they consider as a perpetrator of White norms and values (Grandbois, 2005; Gray & McCullagh, 2014). Given the social context of historical trauma and its impact on help-seeking, research suggests that suicide prevention and intervention efforts targeting Native Americans should occur across individual, community, and systemic levels (i.e., such as federal, state, local, and tribal health officials; Herne, Bartholemew, & Weahkee 2014; Taylor, Anderson, & Bruguier Zimmerman, 2014), and should also include integration of traditional healing methods (Taylor, Anderson, & Bruguier Zimmerman, 2014). Primary care, EDs, and schools can play an important role in the delivery of suicide prevention and intervention programs to this population (Taylor, Anderson, & Bruguier Zimmerman, 2014). Research examining service utilization data, for example, propose that EDs are critical locations for reservation-based suicide prevention, and that EDs should consider suicide screening for all at-risk patients (Ballard, Tingey, Lee, Suttle, Barlow, & Cwik, 2014).

A qualitative study by Isaak and colleagues further found that resilience was often presented as a journey of "survival" and "overcoming," and pathways to healing often incorporated traditional teachings (Isaak et al., 2015). The authors recommended that mental health clinicians strongly consider including, when appropriate, elements of traditional teachings into treatment to support recovery (DeCou, Skewes, & López, 2013; Isaak et al., 2015).

INCARCERATED INDIVIDUALS

One of every 100 American adults will serve time in prison (PEW Center on the States, 2008). Suicide rates in prisons are high. It is important to fully consider the contextual environment of incarcerated individuals including the unique aspects of prison life that contribute to suicide risk in this population. Prisons are characterized by social isolation and violence (Fruehwald et al., 2004). Incarcerated individuals most frequently have unaddressed mental health and substance abuse needs (Goss, Peterson, Smith, Kalb, & Brodey, 2002; Jenkins et al., 2005; Kariminia et al., 2007; Penn, Esposito, Schaeffer, Fritz, & Spirito, 2003; Skogstad, Deane, & Spicer, 2006). These factors combined with the negative attitude the public has toward prisons and incarcerated individuals greatly influence suicide risk.

Considering the larger social environment is particularly important in considering the rate of suicide among ex-convicts. The public at large has a negative attitude toward ex-convicts (Giguere & Dundes, 2002; Thacher, 2008). For individuals dealing with the stress of adjusting to life outside of prison where schedules are not regiments and imposed, the stress resulting from being stigmatized and marginalized can have serious negative consequences such as suicide.

One qualitative study of male prisoners examined motivation for nearly lethal suicide attempts (Rivlin, Ferris, Marzano, Fazel, & Hawton, 2013). Findings of the study point to five main domains of motivating factors for attempts among male prisoners including those that (1) were due to a prisoner being unable to cope in prison, (2) were motivated by psychotic symptoms, (3) had instrumental motives, (4) were unexpected, and (5) were associated with withdrawal from drugs (Rivlin et al., 2013).

Statistics, Epidemiology, and Trends in Incarcerated Individual Suicide

It is estimated that 30% to 50% of all deaths in custody are by suicide (Fazel & Benning, 2006; Mumola, 2005; Rivlin et al., 2013). Suicide among death row prisoners is five times higher than the suicide rate among the general population (Lester & Tartaro, 2002). Suicidal ideation and suicide attempts are more common among incarcerated adults than among the general population (Jenkins et al., 2005). Studies have reported that between 14% and 23% of male prisoners report a lifetime history of attempting suicide (Bland, Newman, Dyck, & Orn, 1990; Jenkins et al., 2005; Roy, Carli, Sarchiapone, & Branchey, 2014; Sarchiapone, Carli, Di Giannantonio, & Roy, 2009.

Suicide is the leading cause of death among juvenile detention centers (Casiano et al., 2016; Roberts & Bender, 2006). The suicide rate among adolescents in juvenile detention centers is four times higher than the rate of suicide among the general population (Gallagher & Dobrin, 2006; Hall & Gabor, 2004; Roberts & Bender, 2006). A study of adolescents in juvenile detention found that 21.5% of detained males reported past year suicidal ideation compared to 6.7% of males in the general population. This study further found that 58.1% of detained females reported past year suicidal ideation compared to 14.4% of females in the general population (Suk, 2009). In addition, incarcerated adolescents use more violent means of suicide than adolescents in the general population (Penn, Esposito, Schaeffer, Fritz, & Spirito, 2003).

Research shows that fewer than half of newly detained youths communicate their suicidal thoughts (Abram et al., 2008). Suicide risk among recently released ex-convicts is much greater than the suicide risk among the general population (Pratt, Piper, Appleby, Webb, & Shaw, 2006). This is particularly true among newly released ex-convicts among whom research has shown that during the first few weeks after release, male prisoners are 29 times more likely to die by suicide and female prisoners are 69 times more likely to die by suicide compared to the general population (Farrell & Marsden, 2008).

Risk Factors for Suicide

Risk factors for suicidality among incarcerated adults include psychosis, depression, personality disorder, younger age, not being married, Caucasian ethnicity, fewer years of education, and poor social support (Jenkins et al., 2005). Risk factors for youth detainee suicide include older age, female gender, living with only one parent, and being arrested for a felony or violent crime (Nolen et al., 2008).

Personality characteristics have also been examined as risk factors for suicide among prisoners. Research indicates that aggression, neuroticism, and introversion are all risk factors for suicide attempt among incarcerated adults (Sarchiapone, Carli, Di Giannantonio et al., 2009). Research has also indicated that high-impulsivity among incarcerated individuals was more prone to suicidal behavior (Carli et al., 2010). Research on offenders has identified that being single, unemployment, past abuse, physical disability, deliberate self-harm, family history of suicide, and mental health problems were associated with higher risk of suicidality (Byng, Howerton, Owens, and Campbell, 2015; Hawton, Zahl, & Weatherall, 2003, Qin, Agerbo, & Mortensen, 2003; Rivlin Hawton, Marzano, & Fazel, 2010).

Psychiatric illness, particularly mood disorder (Nolen et al., 2008; Penn et al., 2003), substance abuse (Nolen et al., 2008), and conduct disorders (Nolen et al., 2008) also increase suicide risk in this group. Among male incarcerated youths, anxiety disorders are also a risk factor for suicide (Nolen et al., 2008). Unlike the general population, there is no seasonal impact on the rate of suicide in custodial populations (Fruehwald et al., 2004).

Repeat attempts among prisoners are associated with greater endorsement of feeling that life was not worth living, more childhood trauma, and lower levels of resiliency as compared to those prisoners who report only one suicide attempt (Roy, 2014). Multiple attempters also reported a history of self-mutilation and greater severity of suicidal ideation (Roy, 2014).

Protective Factors Against Suicide

Few protective factors against suicide among incarcerated individuals have been identified. However, research indicates that programs designed to address the mental health needs and substance abuse treatment needs of prisoners, including specific screenings for suicidality, may reduce the rate of suicide in this group (Goss et al., 2002; Jenkins et al., 2005; Kariminia et al., 2007; Penn et al., 2003; Skogstad et al., 2006).

Treatment Considerations for Incarcerated Individuals

Very little research exists in terms of evidence-based practices to reduce suicide risk among incarcerated individuals. However, several guidelines and recommendations have been provided to address the distinct risk factors that incarcerated individuals face and the unique factors that influence suicidal behavior in this population. For example, Rivlin et al., 2013 suggest the following:

1. For prisoners struggling with being able to cope, focusing on finding a purpose in life and developing purposeful daily routines may help to mitigate some of the aspects of incarceration that these prisoners find particularly difficult. For instance, emphasizing constructive activities can help to reduce the degree of boredom that some prisoners note as contributory to their suicide attempts.
2. For prisoners experiencing psychotic symptoms, improving screening procedures upon arrival to prison and providing prompt access to mental health treatment when symptoms first appear are essential (Earthrowl, O'Grady, & Birmingham, 2003; Fazel & Baillargeon, 2011).
3. Prisoners who do not express an intent to die but seriously injure themselves nevertheless present a unique challenge. A case-by-case approach is suggested in order to determine the best management strategy as not responding to a prisoner's request can, in some instances, increase the likelihood that the severity of self-harm may escalate, whereas responding to every request may inadvertently encourage prisoners to engage in self-harm behaviors as a means to get their requests fulfilled.
4. Careful monitoring by prison staff of even those prisoners who do not present with histories of self-harm or other known risk factors is recommended as some suicide attempts are unexpected in that they appear to occur, even to the prisoners themselves, without warning. This suggests that staff have to be given the time to get to know prisoners well enough to be able to recognize when they may be in distress, which may be difficult in large, busy prisons with high turnover.
5. For prisoners who attempt suicide following or during drug withdrawal, an integrated approach that centers on providing prisoners with needed health care and appropriate psychopharmacological treatment is essential.

Case Study 13.1

You are a mental health professional working in a large community treatment agency. Recently, you were referred a new client. Before meeting him for the first time, you review the referral and intake forms, which contain the following information:

Your client is a 24-year-old male named Jon. His new medical doctor, following a general physical, referred him to you. According to his MD, Jon is mildly depressed, may be using substances to cope, and has reported some suicidal ideation.

Approximately 9 months earlier, he moved into the city for a new job. At first he liked his job, but less so recently. Jon has no family in the city and a limited support network. He describes meeting some people in the bar near his house some nights, but did not endorse having any close friends in the city. Increasingly, he reported thoughts of suicide, but feels that he would not attempt. He has no past history of suicide attempts, psychiatric diagnoses, or hospitalization. Jon indicated seeing a past therapist, but did not provide a description of the reason, services, or outcomes.

When Jon enters your office, he looks exceptionally despondent and depressed. He sits down and places his face in his hands. After a few moments, he lifts up his face and says "My name is Jon. I'm (an)_____. Although, I do not want to commit suicide, I'm not sure I want to live anymore."

Please fill in the blank with either:

1. *Homeless*
2. *Exconvict*
3. *Native American*

ROLE-PLAY 13.1

In groups of two or three (clinician, client, and observer), role-play the scenario described in Case Study 13.1. Engage the client and conduct an assessment. What specific risk and protective factors should you consider? Be aware of your personal and professional attitudes in working with this client.

SUMMARY

Membership in at-risk groups, such as the homeless, Native Americans, and incarcerated individuals, poses additional issues and complications for individuals experiencing suicidality. In addition, mental health professionals working with individuals need to become aware of the unique risk and protective factors that may exert further influence on these groups. Professional and personal awareness is essential for mental health clinicians engaging, assessing, and treating members of these and other at-risk populations.

KEY POINTS

1. There exist a number of specific groups or populations that are at an increased risk of suicide.
2. At-risk populations have unique and specific risk and protective factors.
3. The attitudes, biases, and opinions of mental health professionals may undermine their ability to effectively work with at-risk populations.
4. Suicidal ideation and attempts occur at an extremely high rate among the homeless.
5. The suicide rate among Native Americans in general is nearly double that of the overall U.S. rate, and for Native Americans residing on reservations, the rate is even higher at 4 to 15 times the national average.
6. Suicide is the leading cause of death of juvenile detainees.
7. The rate of suicide among incarcerated adults is elevated compared to that of the general population.
8. The first few weeks post release are an extremely high risk period for individuals who have been incarcerated.
9. The larger environmental context of each of these at-risk groups needs to be fully considered to understand the elevated rates of suicide in these groups.
10. Factors related to historical trauma greatly influence suicidality among Native Americans.
11. Stigma and bias associated with the homeless as lazy, unintelligent, dangerous, and/or violent greatly impact suicidality in this population.
12. Prison experiences characterized by social isolation, violence, and unaddressed mental health and substance abuse needs combined with negative public attitudes toward prisoners and ex-convicts greatly influence suicide risk in this population.

ELECTRONIC RESOURCES

NATIVE AMERICANS

www.sprc.org/grantees/pdf/nspl.pdf
www.cdc.gov/ncipc/factsheets/nativeamericans.htm
www.healthfinder.gov/Scripts/SearchContext.asp?topic=5101

HOMELESS INDIVIDUALS

www.alphaproject.org
www.careforthehomeless.org/services/susans_place.html
http://www.geocities.com/athens/agora/7076/hgroups.html

INCARCERATED INDIVIDUALS

http://www.who.int/mental_health/prevention/suicide/resource_jails_prisons.pdf
https://www.aclu.org/issues/prisoners-rights
www.newbridgefoundation.org.uk
www.stgilestrust.org.uk
www.nacro.org.uk
www.foundation-training.org
www.tomorrows-people.co.uk

KNOWLEDGE ACQUISITION TEST (KAT)

True or False

1. Older adult Native Americans have the highest risk of suicide among all other Native American age groups.
2. Newly released female ex-convicts have a higher rate of suicide than their male counterparts.
3. A greater connection with traditional identity and cultures is always associated with decreased suicide risk for Native Americans.
4. Previous attempts among Native American Indians are not a risk factor.
5. Incarcerated individuals have a higher rate of suicide than the general population.
6. Suicide is among the leading causes of death among homeless youths.
7. Homeless youths have the highest rate of suicide among all homeless age groups.
8. A major protective factor against suicide among the homeless is self-reliance.

Short Answer

9. Discuss how the larger social environment may influence the suicide risk within the homeless population.
10. How can mental health professionals improve their ability to work within the Native American populations?
11. Discuss how the larger cultural environment influences the suicide risk among the incarcerated population.
12. Describe the main risk factors for suicidality among the homeless.

Multiple Choice

13. Protective factors against suicide among Native Americans include which of the following?
    A. Spirituality
    B. Connectedness with parents and other caring family
    C. Connectedness with tribal leaders
    D. Connectedness with school
    E. All of the above
    F. None of the above
14. Protective factors against suicide among the homeless can include which of the following?
    A. Strategies for coping with loneliness
    B. Resiliency
    C. Having a pet
    D. All of the above
    E. None of the above
15. Risk factors for suicide among incarcerated adults include which of the following?
    A. Hispanic ethnicity
    B. Being married
    C. Younger age
    D. Greater level of education
    E. All of the above
    F. None of the above

REFERENCES

Abram, K. M., Choe, J. Y., Washburn, J. J., Teplin, L. A., King, D. C., & Dulcan, M. K. (2008). Suicidal ideation and behaviors among youths in juvenile detention. *Journal of the American Academy of Child & Adolescent Psychiatry, 47*(3), 291–300.

Alcantara, C., & Gone, J. P. (2007). Reviewing suicide in Native American communities: Situating risk and protective factors within a transactional-ecological framework. *Death Studies, 31*(5), 457–477.

Andrew, M. M., & Krouse, S. A. (1995). Research on excess deaths among American Indians and Alaska Natives: A critical review. *Journal of Cultural Diversity, 2*(1), 8–15.

Ballard, E. D., Musci, R. J., Tingey, L., Goklish, N., Larzelere-Hinton, F., Barlow, A., & Cwik, M. (2015). Latent class analysis of substance use and aggressive behavior in reservation-based American Indian youth who attempted suicide. *American Indian and Alaska Native Mental Health Research, 22*(1), 77–94.

Ballard, E. D., Tingey, L., Lee, A., Suttle, R., Barlow, A., & Cwik, M. (2014). Emergency department utilization among American Indian adolescents who made a suicide attempt: A screening opportunity. *Journal of Adolescent Health, 54*(3), 357–359.

Bland, R. C., Newman, S. C., Dyck, R. J., & Orn, H. (1990). Prevalence of psychiatric disorders and suicide attempts in a prison population. *Canadian Journal of Psychiatry, 35*(5), 407–413.

Bolton, S. L., Elias, B., Enns, M. W., Sareen, J., Beals, J., Novins, D. K., & Swampy Cree Suicide Prevention Team; & AI-SUPERPFP Team. (2014). A comparison of the prevalence and risk factors of suicidal ideation and suicide attempts in two American Indian population samples and in a general population sample. *Transcultural Psychiatry, 51*(1), 3–22.

Borowsky, I. W., Resnick, M. D., Ireland, M., & Blum, R. W. (1999). Suicide attempts among American Indian and Alaska Native youth: Risk and protective factors. *Archives of Pediatrics & Adolescent Medicine, 153*(6), 573–580.

Bossarte, R. M., Piegari, R., Hill, L., & Kane, V.. (2013). Age and suicide among veterans with a history of homelessness. *Psychiatric Services, 64*(7), 713–714.

Brockie, T. N., Dana-Sacco, G., Wallen, G. R., Wilcox, H. C., & Campbell, J. C. (2015). The relationship of adverse childhood experiences to PTSD, depression, poly-drug use and suicide attempt in reservation-based Native American adolescents and young adults. *American Journal of Community Psychology, 55*(3–4), 411–421.

Byng, R., Howerton, A., Owens, C. V., & Campbell, J. (2015). Pathways to suicide attempts among male offenders: The role of agency. *Sociology of Health and Illness, 37*, 936–951.

Carli, V., Roy, A., Bevilacqua, L., Maggi, S., Cesaro, C., & Sarchiapone, M. (2010). Insomnia and suicidal behavior in prisoners. *Psychiatry Research, 185*, 141–144.

Casiano, H., Bolton, S. L., Hildahl, K., Katz, L. Y., Bolton, J., & Sareen, J. (2016). A population-based study of the prevalence and correlates of self-harm in juvenile detention. *PLoS One, 11*(1), e0146918.

Centers for Disease Control and Prevention. (2007). Web-based Injury Statistics Query and Reporting System (WISQARS). Retrieved from https://www.cdc.gov/injury/wisqars/index.html

Chandler, M. J., Lalonde, C. E., Sokol, B. W., & Hallett, D. (2003). Personal persistence, identity, and suicide: A study of Native and non-Native North American adolescents. *Monographs for the Society for Research in Child Development, serial No. 273, 68*(2), vii–viii, 1–130.

Chino, M., & Fullerton-Gleason, L. (2006). Understanding suicide attempts among American Indian adolescents in New Mexico: Modifiable factors related to risk and resiliency. *Ethnicity & Disease, 16*(2), 435–442.

Cleverley, K., & Kidd, S. A. (2011). Resilience and suicidality among homeless youth. *Journal of Adolescence, 34*(5), 1049–1054.

Collins, S. E., Clifasefi, S. L., Dana, E. A., Andrasik, M. P., Stahl, N., Kirouac, M., . . . Malone, D. K. (2012). Where harm reduction meets housing first: Exploring alcohol's role in a project-based housing first setting. *International Journal of Drug Policy, 23*, 111–119.

Coohey, C., Easton, S. D., Kong, J., & Bockenstedt, J. K. W. (2015). *Suicide and Life-Threatening Behavior, 45*(3), 271–280.

DeCou, C. R., Skewes, M. C., & López, E. D. (2013). Traditional living and cultural ways as protective factors against suicide: Perceptions of Alaska Native university students. *International Journal of Circumpolar Health, 5*, 72–77.

Duran, B., Duran, E., & Yellow Horse–Brave Heart, M. (1998). Native Americans and the trauma of history. In R. Thorton (Ed.), *Studying native America: Problems and prospects* (pp. 60–76). Madison: University of Wisconsin.

Earthrowl, M., O'Grady, J., & Birmingham, L. (2003). Providing treatment to prisoners with mental disorders: development of a policy. Selective literature review and expert consultation exercise. *British Journal of Psychiatry, 182*, 299–302.

Eynan, R., Langley, J., Tolomiczenko, G., Rhodes, A. E., Links, P., Wasylenki, D., & Goering, P. (2002). The association between homelessness and suicidal ideation and behaviors: Results of a cross-sectional survey. *Suicide and Life-Threatening Behavior, 32*(4), 418–427.

Farrell, M., & Marsden, J. (2008). Acute risk of drug-related death among newly released prisoners in England and Wales. *Addiction, 103*(2), 251–155.

Fazel, S., & Baillargeon, J. (2011). The health of prisoners. *Lancet, 377*(9769), 956–965.

Fazel, S., & Benning, R. (2006). Natural deaths in male prisoners: A 20-year mortality study. *European Journal of Public Health, 16*(4), 441–444.

Fazel, S., Geddes, J. R., & Kushel, M. (2014). The health of homeless people in high-income countries: escriptive epidemiology, health consequences, and clinical and policy recommendations. *Lancet, 384*(9953), 1529–1540.

Firestone, M., Smylie, J., Maraclem, S., McKnight, C., Spiller, M., & O'Campo, P. (2015). Mental health and substance use in an urban First Nations population in Hamilton, Ontario. *Canadian Journal of Public Health, 106*(6), e375–e381.

Fruehwald, S., Frottier, P., Matschnig, T., Koenig, F., Lehr, S., & Eher, R. (2004). Do monthly or seasonal variations exist in suicides in a high-risk setting? *Psychiatry Research, 121*(3), 263–269.

Gallagher, C. A., & Dobrin, A. (2006). Deaths in juvenile justice residential facilities. [see comment]. *Journal of Adolescent Health, 38*(6), 662–668.

Garoutte, E. M., Goldberg, J., Beals, J., Herrell, R., Manson, S. M., & AI-SUPERPFP Team. (2003). Spirituality and attempted suicide among American Indians. *Social Science and Medicine, 56*, 1571–1579.

Giguere, R., & Dundes, L. (2002). Help wanted: A survey of employer concerns about hiring ex-convicts. *Criminal Justice Policy Review, 13*(4), 396–408.

Goldstein, G., Luther, J. F., & Haas, G. L. (2012). Medical, psychiatric and demographic factors associated with suicidal behavior in homeless veterans. *Psychiatry Research, 199*(1):37–43. doi:10.1016/j.psychres.2012.03.029

Goss, J. R., Peterson, K., Smith, L. W., Kalb, K., & Brodey, B. B. (2002). Characteristics of suicide attempts in a large urban jail system with an established suicide prevention program. *Psychiatric Services, 53*(5), 574–579.

Grandbois, D. (2005). Stigma of mental illness among American Indian and Alaska Native nations: Historical and contemporary perspectives. *Issues in Mental Health Nursing, 26*, 1001–1024.

Gray, J. S., & McCullagh, J. A. (2014). Suicide in Indian country: The continuing epidemic in rural Native American communities. *Journal of Rural Mental Health, Special Issue: Rural Suicide, 38*(2), 79–86.

Hadland, S. E., Wood, E., Dong, H., Marshall, B. D. L., Kerr, T., Montaner, J. S., & DeBeck, K. (2015). Suicide attempts and childhood maltreatment among street youth: A prospective cohort study. *Pediatrics, 136*(3), 440–449.

Hall, B., & Gabor, P. (2004). Peer suicide prevention in a prison. *Crisis: Journal of Crisis Intervention & Suicide, 25*(1), 19–26.

Hawton, K., Zahl, D., & Weatherall, R. (2003). Suicide following deliberate self-harm: Long-term follow-up of patients who presented to a general hospital. *The British Journal of Psychiatry, 182*(6), 537–542.

Hensley, M. A., & Matthieu, M. M. (2011). Educational needs assessment for homeless service providers on preventing suicide. *Social Work in Mental Health, 9*(2), 92–106.

Herne, M. A., Bartholomew, M. L., & Weahkee, R. L. (2014). Suicide mortality among American Indians and Alaska Natives, 1999–2009. *American Journal of Public Health, 104*(Suppl. 3), S336–S342. doi: 10.2105/AJPH.2014.301929

Hill, D. L. (2009). Relationship between sense of belonging as connectedness and suicide in American Indians. *Archives of Psychiatric Nursing, 23*(1), 65–74.

Hodgson, K. J., Shelton, K. J., & van den Bree, M. B. M. (2014). Mental health problems in young people with experiences of homelessness and the relationship with health service use: A follow-up study. *Evidence-Based Mental Health, 17*, 76–80.

Hodgson, K. J., Shelton, K. J., & van den Bree, M. B. M. (2015). Psychopathology among young homeless people: Longitudinal mental health outcomes for different subgroups. *British Journal of Clinical Psychology, 54*(3), 307–325.

Indian Health Service. (2015). *Trends in Indian health: 2014 edition*. Rockville, MD: Public Health Service, U.S. Department of Health and Human Services.

Isaak, C. A., Stewart, D. E., Mota, N. P., Munro, G., Katz, L. Y., & Sareen, J. (2015). Surviving, healing and moving forward: Journeys towards resilience among Canadian Cree adults. *International Journal of Social Psychiatry, 61*(8), 788–795.

Jenkins, R., Bhugra, D., Meltzer, H., Singleton, N., Bebbington, P., Brugha, T., . . . Paton, J. (2005). Psychiatric and social aspects of suicidal behaviour in prisons. *Psychological Medicine, 35*(2), 257–269.

Kariminia, A., Butler, T. G., Corben, S. P., Levy, M. H., Grant, L., Kaldor, J. M., . . . Law, M. (2007). Extreme cause-specific mortality in a cohort of adult prisoners—1988 to 2002: A data-linkage study. *International Journal of Epidemiology, 36*(2), 310–316.

Lee, H., Iglewicz, A., Golshan, S., & Zisook, S. (2013). A tale of two veterans: Homeless vs domiciled veterans presenting to a psychiatric urgent care clinic. *Annals of Clinical Psychiatry, 25*(4), 275–282.

Lester, D. (1999). Native American suicide rates, acculturation stress and traditional integration. *Psychological Reports, 84*(2), 398.

Lester, D., & Tartaro, C. (2002). Suicide on death row. *Journal of Forensic Sciences, 47*(5), 1108–1111.

Lizardi, D., & Gearing, R. E. (2010). Religion and suicide: Buddhism, Native American and African religions, atheism, and agnosticism. *Journal of Religion and Health, 49*(3), 377–384.

Manzo, K., Tiesman, H., Stewart, J., Hobbs, G. R., & Knox, S. S. (2015). A comparison of risk factors associated with suicide ideation/attempts in American Indian and White youth in Montana. *Archives of Suicide Research, 19*(1), 89–102.

May, P. A., Van Winkle, N. W., Williams, M. B., McFeeley, P. J., DeBruyn, L. M., & Serna, P. (2002). Alcohol and suicide death among American Indians of New Mexico: 1980–1998. *Suicide and Life-Threatening Behavior, 32*(3), 240–255.

McCormack, D., & MacIntosh, J. (2001). Research with homeless people uncovers a model of health. *Western Journal of Nursing Research, 23*, 679–697.

McLeigh, J. D. (2010). What are the policy issues related to the mental health of Native Americans? *American Journal of Orthopsychiatry, 80*(2), 177–182.

Meltzer, H., Ford, T., Bebbington, P., & Vostanis, P. (2012). Children who run away from home: Risks for suicidal behavior and substance misuse. *Journal of Adolescent Health, 51*(5), 415–421.

Mohatt, N. V., Fok, C. C. T., Burket, R., Henry, D., & Allen, J. (2011). Assessment of awareness of connectedness as a culturally-based protective factor for Alaska native youth. *Cultural Diversity and Ethnic Minority Psychology, 17*(4), 444–455.

Molnar, B. E., Shade, S. B., Kral, A. H., Booth, R. E., & Watters, J. K. (1998). Suicidal behavior and sexual/physical abuse among street youth. *Child Abuse & Neglect, 22*(3), 213–222.

Montgomery, C. (1994). Swimming upstream: The strengths of women who survive homelessness. *Advances in Nursing Science, 16*, 34–45.

Moskowitz, A., Stein, J. A., & Lightfoot, M. (2013). The mediating roles of stress and maladaptive behaviors on self-harm and suicide attempts among runaway and homeless youth. *Journal of Youth and Adolescence, 42*(7), 1015–1027.

Mullany, B., Barlow, A., Goklish, N., Larzelere-Hinton, F., Cwik, M., Craig, M., & Walkup, J. T. (2009). Toward understanding suicide among youths: Results from the White Mountain Apache tribally mandated suicide surveillance system, 2001–2006. *American Journal of Public Health, 99*(10), 1840–1848.

Mumola, C. J. (2015). *Suicide and Homicide in state prisons and local jails* (Special Report, NCJ 210036). Washington, DC: Bureau of Justice Statistics. Retrieved from https://www.prisonpolicy.org/scans/bjs/shsplj.pdf

Myburgh, C., Moolla, A., & Poggenpoel, M. (2015). The lived experiences of children living on the streets of Hillbrow. *Curationis, 38*(1), 1274–1281.

Nestor, B. A., Cheek, S. M., & Liu, R. T. (2016). Ethnic and racial differences in mental health service utilization for suicidal ideation and behavior in a nationally representative sample of adolescents. *Journal of Affective Disorders, 202*, 197–202.

Nock, M. K., Borges, G., Bromet, E. J., Alonso, J., Angermeyer, M., Beautrais, A., . . . William, D. (2008). Cross-national prevalence and risk factors for suicidal ideation, plans and attempts. *British Journal of Psychiatry, 192*(2), 98–105.

Noël, F., Moniruzzaman, A., Somers, J., Frankish, J., Strehlau, V., Schütz, C., & Krausz, M. (2016). A longitudinal study of suicidal ideation among homeless, mentally ill individuals. *Social Psychiatry & Psychiatric Epidemiology, 51*(1), 107–114.

Nolen, S., McReynolds, L. S., DeComo, R. E., John, R., Keating, J. M., & Wasserman, G. A. (2008). Lifetime suicide attempts in juvenile assessment center youth. *Archives of Suicide Research, 12*(2), 111–123.

O'Keefe, V. M., & Wingate, L. R. (2013). The role of hope and optimism in suicide risk for American Indians/Alaska Natives. *Suicide and Life-Threatening Behavior, 43*(6), 621–633.

Olson, L. M., Huyler, F., Lynch, A. W., Fullerton, L., Werenko, D., Sklar, D., & Zumwalt, R. (1999). Guns, alcohol, and intimate partner violence: The epidemiology of female suicide in New Mexico. *Crisis, 20*, 121–126.

Olson, L. M., Wahab, S., Thompson, C. W., & Durrant, L. (2011). Suicide notes among Native Americans, Hispanics, and Anglos. *Qualitative Health Research, 21*(11), 1484–1494.

Oppong, A. K. (2015). Exploring age and gender differences in health risk behaviours and psychological functioning among homeless children and adolescents. *International Journal of Mental Health Promotion, 17*(5), 278–292.

Oppong, A. K., & Meyer-Weitz, A. (2015). International note: Association between perceived resilience and health risk behaviours in homeless youth. *Journal of Adolescence, 39*, 36–39.

Padgett, D. K., Smith, B. T., Henwood, B. F., & Tiderington, E. (2012). Life course adversity in the lives of formerly homeless persons with serious mental illness: Context and meaning. *American Journal of Orthopsychiatry, 82*(3), 421–430.

Patterson, A. A., & Holden, R. R. (2012). Psychache and suicide ideation among men who are homeless: A test of Shneidman's model. *Suicide and Life-Threatening Behavior, 42*(2), 147–156.

Penn, J. V., Esposito, C. L., Schaeffer, L. E., Fritz, G. K., & Spirito, A. (2003). Suicide attempts and self-mutilative behavior in a juvenile correctional facility. *Journal of the American Academy of Child & Adolescent Psychiatry, 42*(7), 762–769.

Petering, R. (2016). Sexual risk, substance use, mental health, and trauma experiences of gang-involved homeless youth. *Journal of Adolescence, 48*, 73–81.

PEW Center on the States. (2008). *One in 100: Behind bars in America.* Public Safety Performance Project. Washington, DC: PEW Charitable Trusts.

Pharris, M. D., Resnick, M. D., & Blum, R. W. (1997). Protecting against hopelessness and suicidality in sexually abused American Indian adolescents. *Journal of Adolescent Health, 21*(6), 400–406.

Pluck, G., Lee, K. H., & Parks, R. W. (2013). Self-harm and homeless adults. *Crisis, 34*(5), 363–366.

Pratt, D., Piper, M., Appleby, L., Webb, R., & Shaw, J. (2006). Suicide in recently released prisoners: A population-based cohort study. *Lancet, 368*(9530), 119–123.

Prigerson, H. G., Desai, R. A., Liu-Mares, W., & Rosenheck, R. A. (2003). Suicidal ideation and suicide attempts in homeless mentally ill persons: Age-specific risks of substance abuse. *Social Psychiatry & Psychiatric Epidemiology, 38*(4), 213–219.

Qin, P., Agerbo, E., & Mortensen, P. B. (2003). Suicide risk in relation to socioeconomic, demographic, psychiatric, and familial factors: a national register-based study of all suicides in Denmark, 1981–1997. *American Journal of Psychiatry, 160*(4), 765–772.

Rew, L. (2000). Friends and pets as companions: Strategies for coping with loneliness among homeless youth. *Journal of Child and Adolescent Psychiatric Nursing, 13*, 125–140.

Rew, L., & Horner, S. D. (2003). Personal strengths of homeless adolescents living in a high-risk environment. *Advances in Nursing Science, 26*(2), 90–101.

Rew, L., Taylor-Seehafer, M., & Fitzgerald, M. L. (2001). Sexual abuse, alcohol and other drug use, and suicidal behaviors in homeless adolescents. *Issues in Comprehensive Pediatric Nursing, 24*(4), 225–240.

Rew, L., Taylor-Seehafer, M., Thomas, N. Y., & Yockey, R. D. (2004). Correlates of resilience in homeless adolescents. *Journal of Nursing Scholarship, 33*(1), 33–40.

Rew, L., Thomas, N., Horner, S. D., Resnick, M. D., & Beuhring, T. (2001). Correlates of recent suicide attempts in a triethnic group of adolescents. *Journal of Nursing Scholarship, 33*, 361–367.

Rhoades, H., Winetrobe, H., & Rice, E. (2014). Prescription drug misuse among homeless youth. *Drug Alcohol Dependence, 138*, 229–233.

Rivlin, A., Ferris, R., Marzano, L., Fazel, S., & Hawton, K. (2013). A typology of male prisoners making near-lethal suicide attempts. *Crisis, 34*(5), 335–347. doi: 10.1027/0227-5910/a000205

Rivlin, A., Hawton, K., Marzano, L., & Fazel, S. (2010). Psychiatric disorders in male prisoners who made near-lethal suicide attempts: case-control study. *British Journal of Psychiatry, 197*(4), 313–319.

Roberts, A. R., & Bender, K. (2006). Juvenile offender suicide: Prevalence, risk factors, assessment, and crisis intervention protocols. *International Journal of Emergency Mental Health, 8*(4), 255–265.

Rohde, P., Noell, J., Ochs, L., & Seeley, J. R. (2001). Depression, suicidal ideation, and STD-related risk in homeless older adolescents. *Journal of Adolescence, 24*(4), 447–460.

Roy, A., Carli, V., Sarchiapone, M., & Branchey, M. (2014). Comparisons of prisoners who make or do not make suicide attempts and further who make one or multiple attempts. *Archives of Suicide Research, 18*(1), 28–38.

Sarchiapone, M., Carli, V., Di Giannantonio, M., & Roy, A. (2009). Risk factors for attempting suicide in prisoners. *Suicide and Life-Threatening Behavior, 39*, 343–350.

Schinka, J. A., Bossarte, R. M., Curtiss, G., Lapcevic, W. A., & Casey, R. J. (2016). Increased mortality among older veterans admitted to VA homelessness programs. *Psychiatric Services, 67*(4), 465–468.

Schinka, J. A., Schinka, K. C., Casey, R. J., Kasprow, W., & Bossarte, R. M. (2012). Suicidal behavior in a national sample of older homeless veterans. *American Journal of Public Health, 102*(Suppl. 1), S147–S153.

Shaughnessy, L., Doshi, S. R., & Jones, S. E. (2004). Attempted suicide and associated health risk behaviors among Native American high school students. *Journal of School Health, 74*(5), 177–182.

Skogstad, P., Deane, F. P., & Spicer, J. (2006). Social-cognitive determinants of help-seeking for mental health problems among prison inmates. *Criminal Behaviour and Mental Health, 16*(1), 43–59.

Strehlau, V., Torchalla, I., Kathy, L., Schuetz, C., & Krausz, M. (2012). Mental health, concurrent disorders, and health care utilization in homeless women. *Journal of Psychiatric Practice, 18*(5), 349–360.

Suk, E., van Mill, J., Vermeiren, R., Ruchkin, V., Schwab-Stone, M., Doreleijers, T., & Deboutte, D. (2009). Adolescent suicidal ideation: A comparison of incarcerated and school-based samples. *European Child and Adolescent Psychiatry, 18*(6), 377–383.

Taylor, M. A., Anderson, E. M., & Bruguier Zimmerman, M. J. (2014). Suicide prevention in rural, tribal communities: The intersection of challenge and possibility. *Journal of Rural Mental Health, Special Issue: Rural Suicide, 38*(2), 87–97.

Thacher, D. (2008). *Prisoner re-entry and the professionalization of housing.* Paper presented at the Annual Meeting of the Law and Society, J.W. Marriott Resort, Las Vegas, NV.

Tingey, L., Cwik, M. F., Goklish, N., Larzelere-Hinton, F., Lee, A., Suttle, R., Walkup, J. T., & Barlow, A. (2014). Risk pathways for suicide among Native American adolescents. *Qualitative Health Research, 24*(11), 1518–1526.

Torchalla, I., Strehlau, V., Li, K., Aube Linden, I., Noel, F., & Krausz, M. (2014). Posttraumatic stress disorder and substance use disorder comorbidity in homeless adults: Prevalence, correlates, and sex differences. *Psychology of Addictive Behaviors, 28*(2), 443–452.

Torchalla, I., Strehlau, V., Li, K., & Krausz, M. (2011). Substance use and predictors of substance dependence in homeless women. *Drug and Alcohol Dependence, 118*(2–3), 173–179.

Torchalla, I., Strehlau, V., Li, K., Schuetz, C., & Krausz, M. (2012). The association between childhood maltreatment subtypes and current suicide risk among homeless men and women. *Child Maltreatment, 17*(2), 132–143.

Tucker, R. P., Wingate, L. R., O'Keefe, V. M., Hollingsworth, D. W., & Cole, A. B. (2016). An examination of historical loss thinking frequency and rumination on suicide ideation in American Indian young adults. *Suicide and Life-Threatening Behavior, 46*(2), 213–222.

U.S. Census Bureau. (2002). *The American Indian and Alaska Native population: 2000 (Census 2000 Brief).* Washington, DC: Author.

U.S. Census Bureau. (2010). Overview of race and Hispanic origin: 2010: 2010 Census briefs. Retrieved from https://www.census.gov/prod/cen2010/briefs/c2010br-02.pdf

U.S. Department of Health and Human Services. (2001). Summary of national strategy for suicide prevention: Goals and objectives for action [National Strategy for Suicide Prevention website]. Retrieved from https://www.surgeongeneral.gov/library/reports/national-strategy-suicide-prevention/full-report.pdf

Votta, E., & Manion, I. (2004). Suicide, high-risk behaviors, and coping style in homeless adolescent males' adjustment. *Journal of Adolescent Health, 34*(3), 237–243.

Walls, M. L., Hautala, D., & Hurley, J. (2014). "Rebuilding our community": *Hearing silenced voices on Aboriginal youth suicide. Transcultural Psychiatry, 51*(1), 47–72.

Walls, N. E., Potter, C., & Van Leeuwen, J. (2009). Where risks and protective factors operate differently: Homeless sexual minority youth and suicide attempts. *Child & Adolescent Social Work Journal, 26*(3), 235–257.

Warf, C. W., Clark, L. F., Desai, M., Rabinovitz, S. J., Agahi, G., Calvo, R., & Hoffmann, J. (2013). Coming of age on the streets: Survival sex among homeless young women in Hollywood. *Journal of Adolescence, 36*(6), 1205–1213.

Wexler, L., Chandler, M., Gone, J. P., Cwik, M., Kirmayer, L. J., LaFromboise, T., . . . Allen, J. (2015). Advancing suicide prevention research with rural American Indian and Alaska Native populations. *American Journal of Public Health, 105*(5), 891–899.

Wissow, L. S. (2000). *Suicide attempts among American Indian and Alaskan Natives.* Baltimore, MD: The Johns Hopkins University Press.

Yellow Horse-Brave Heart, M., & DeBruyn, L. M. (1998). The American Indian holocaust: Healing historical unresolved grief. *Journal of the National Center, 8*(2), 60–82.

Yoder, K., A. (1999). Comparing suicide attempters, suicide ideators, and non-suicidal homeless and runaway adolescents. *Suicide and Life-Threatening Behavior, 29*(1), 25–36.

PART V

Assessing Suicide

CHAPTER FOURTEEN

GUIDELINES FOR SUICIDE RISK ASSESSMENT

Assessment is the cornerstone of effective treatment for individuals with suicidality. Every individual presenting for clinical treatment should be assessed for risk of suicide at some level. Effective suicide risk assessment needs to be individualized based on the person, presenting issues, and personal and family history. Although there is no one universal assessment format, there are a number of key components essential to every suicide assessment. This chapter provides a comprehensive structure for assessing suicide risk including specific questions and recommendations for consideration.

GOALS AND OBJECTIVES

An understanding of:

- Role of sociodemographic data in relation to suicide assessment
- Importance of establishing identified problem/symptom history in relation to suicide assessment
- Influence of current suicidality in relation to suicide assessment
- Importance of determining suicide history in relation to suicide assessment
- How family/peer suicide history may impact suicide assessment
- Determining relevant risk factors in relation to suicide assessment
- Determining relevant protective factors in relation to suicide assessment
- Use of suicide rating scales
- Potential outcomes of assessment
- Core assessment recommendations

Suicide risk assessment should be seen as an individualized, ongoing process. Every individual presenting for treatment should be evaluated for past and current suicidality. Every contact with an individual deemed to be at some level of risk for suicide should incorporate monitoring for changes in risk status. Efficacious treatment begins with a thorough assessment. The more comprehensive and detailed the assessment, the more likely the prescribed treatment will be helpful.

Approximately 0.6% to 2.1% of individuals in the United States have attempted suicide, 1.1% to 3.1% have made suicide plans, and 3.9% to 9.2% of individuals have suicidal thoughts (Nock et al., 2008; SAMHSA, 2014). Given the prevalence of suicidality in the community, it is likely that you will encounter a suicidal individual in your practice.

Good clinical practice requires that all clinical evaluations include an assessment of suicidality.

Despite there being a number of well-researched screening and assessment tools available to clinicians, there remains a lack of consensus regarding a gold-standard suicide risk assessment measure (Bernett, 2014). Further, there exists a lack of universal terminology and definitions of suicidality that may further complicate the accurate detection of risk and hinder suicide prevention efforts (Bernett, 2014). For example, one major effort was undertaken by the Food and Drug Administration (FDA) to develop a standard international classification system, the prospective assessment and classification of suicidal ideation and behavior (FDA Draft Guidance 2012; Sheehan, Giddens, & Sheehan, 2014). The FDA began collecting suicide data as early as 2003, and first released its suicide classification system in 2010. This version of the guidelines was based on data collected by the FDA since 2003 during which suicide events were classified according to the nine-category classification system of the Columbia Classification Algorithm for Suicide Assessment (C-CASA; Posner, Oquendo, Gould, Stanley, & Davies, 2007), as well as data obtained from prospective trials that assessed suicidality according to the Columbia Suicide Severity Rating Scale (C–SSRS; Posner et al., 2011). This version was then revised and updated in 2012 when the FDA released its new draft guidance that recommends the prospective capture of suicide information using 11 categories that also appear to be based on the C–SSRS. Sheehan and colleagues (2014) conducted a critical review of the FDA's 2012 suicide classification system to determine its comprehensiveness and accuracy according to internally accepted standards of classification (i.e., categories are unambiguous, mutually exclusive, and robust; Sheehan et al., 2014). Results of the critical review indicate that the 2012 Draft Guidance does not capture the full range of suicidal ideation and behavior, making it susceptible to type II error. It further found that definitions used in the system are ambiguous (susceptible to multiple interpretations), and the potential for misclassification (type I and type II errors) is increased by frequent mismatches in category titles and definitions. The authors conclude that these issues have the potential to compromise data comparability not only within clinical trial sites but also across sites and over time, thereby significantly limiting the usefulness of the guidelines (Sheehan et al., 2014).

While there is no one "correct" approach to suicide assessment, all suicide assessments should incorporate both clinical judgment and comprehensive psychiatric evaluation (Jacobs & Brewer, 2004) and be applicable to client and any comorbid conditions. In addition, knowledge of the most recent evidence-based practice in your clinical area (e.g., youth with depression, adults with HIV, elderly with cancer) is also essential to supplement the general guidelines that follow (Roberts & Jennings, 2005; Simon, 2006).

CORE SUICIDE ASSESSMENT QUESTION

Suicide assessment should be clear, unambiguous, direct, and nonjudgmental. There is general agreement that the three fundamental components of suicide risk assessment include (a) specific inquiry regarding suicidal thoughts, (b) assessment of the risk factors for suicidal behavior present in the client's current circumstances, and (c) assessment of protective factors against suicidal behavior present in the client's current circumstances (Berman, 2006; Rudd, 2006; Rudd et al., 2006; Vikes, 2003; Shea, 2012). The assessment, therefore, should include initially asking the core suicide question "Are you suicidal?" or "Have you ever thought of killing yourself?" The manner in which this question is asked is fundamentally important. If asked with judgment, hesitation, anxiety, or accusation, the client will be less candid in his or her response. However, if the question is asked with genuine neutrality and openness, the client will be more likely to honestly respond. It is important to recognize that this core suicide assessment question is not a checklist question, but rather the beginning of a dialogue required for an effective clinical suicidal assessment.

There are three general categories of responses that often emerge from this question:

1. A clear denial of suicidal feelings, ideations, and/or plans
2. A clear endorsement of suicidal feelings, ideations, and/or plans
3. A vague, nebulous response that neither endorses nor denies suicidality

The categorical response will help determine the breadth and depth of the suicide assessment dialogue. Further, it is critical to note that even a clear denial requires follow-up assessment. It is recommended that every client regardless of his or her presentation or diagnosis be assessed with this core suicide assessment question. Not to do so is a clinical error.

ROLE-PLAY 14.1

Break into groups of three in which one person assumes the role of a mental health clinician, another the role of a new client in an emergency room, and the third an impartial observer. For this role-play, you can adopt the stance that the client is actively suicidal, passively suicidal (suicidal thoughts without intention to act), or not suicidal in the least. Engage in a role-play in which you ask the core suicide assessment question. Role-play this discussion for 2 to 4 minutes. The observer should record the verbal and nonverbal presentation of the question and the verbal and nonverbal response to the question and provide feedback to the group.

Small Group Exercise 14.1

Based on Role-Play 14.1, stay in your role-play groups and discuss the following questions. Remember, answers are personal and there are no correct or incorrect answers.

1. What were your thoughts and feelings as a mental health professional when you asked the core suicide assessment question?
2. What were your thoughts and feelings as a client when you were asked the core suicide assessment question?
3. Did you find any surprises in the responses to the first two questions? If so, what were they and how were you surprised?

FUNDAMENTAL SUICIDE ASSESSMENT COMPONENTS

The key components of the follow-up questions are to determine the presence, nature, and degree of the suicide risk. Beyond a traditional biopsychosocial assessment, when assessing suicide risk, a number of critical areas need to be considered and investigated.

Bernert, Hom, and Roberts (2014) conducted a systematic literature review to identify clinical practice guidelines for suicide risk assessment. Twenty-two studies were identified, of which 10 articles were formal clinical practice guidelines or practice parameters and 12 focused on additional resource documents such as nonformalized clinical guidelines, abbreviated recommendations, and tool kits. The authors also contacted 22 professional organizations (i.e., Association of Suicidology [AAS], American Foundation for Suicide Prevention [AFSP], American Medical Association [AMA], National Action Alliance for Suicide Prevention, National Association of Social Workers [NASW]) to provide further confirmation of identified guidelines. Overall, the study found that the majority of the identified guidelines consistently addressed five assessment categories and provided some degree of category-specific recommendations. The five categories included (a) assessment of evidence-based suicide risk factors (100%), (b) assessment of suicidal intent (80%), (c) recommended treatments (80%), (d) restricting access to means (80%), and (e) postvention practice recommendations (70%). The assessment of evidence-based risk factors for suicide was the only category that was included in all of the identified studies, which can be said to reflect a general consensus that a starting point for suicide risk assessment should be the identification of factors and warning signs known to be associated with risk (i.e., diagnostic, demographic, and psychosocial factors), as well as protective factors (Bernett, 2014).

This study also highlights some important existing gaps in clinical practice and management of suicidality. Although most guidelines recognized the need to assess risk level, relatively few actually offered recommendations regarding standardized risk level categorizations or decision-tree rules. This is important to note as such procedures may help in standardizing risk assessment, referral, and management procedures. Further problematic is that few of the guidelines actually recommended established screening measures and/or inventories to use. Of those that did, a possible 36 measures were mentioned. This wide range of tools makes it difficult to determine which to use and when, thereby limiting the ability to routinize assessment, clinical decision-making, and risk management procedures (Bernett, 2014).

Interestingly, a number of other important areas were less consistently addressed across the identified guidelines including suicide risk level categorizations, recommended risk assessment measures, tools for outpatient management, safety planning, confidentiality issues, training recommendations, ethical considerations, and legal issues. Several complex ethical issues exist in relation to suicide assessment and management including informed consent, confidentiality limits, legal issues, and safety concerns. Surprisingly, fewer than half of all guidelines included any consideration of these important ethical issues (Bernett, 2014).

Yet another systematic literature review aimed to identify existing literature focused on providing information, strategies, and guidelines to clinicians working with clients experiencing suicidal ideation who are not yet at imminent risk of suicidal behavior (Monaghan & Harris, 2015). Only 24 articles were identified in this review that were considered to have sufficient information to inform the practice of clinicians working with this client group. Overall, findings demonstrated that while the review articles provided some guidelines for working with clients with suicidal ideation, they often were wide-ranging principles that were general in nature and did not specifically address this client group. Further, none of the articles targeted early intervention; rather they provided a discussion of crisis management strategies following the onset of severe ideation or an attempt. Together, these studies highlight the need to establish consensus regarding gold-standard assessment techniques, across or within specific clinical populations (Bernett, 2014).

According to the established guidelines (Academy of Child & Adolescent Psychiatry, 2001; American Psychiatric Association (APA), 2003; Barber, Marzuk, Leon, & Portera, 2001; Jacobs, 1999; Posner, Oquendo, Gould, Stanley, & Davies, 2007; Rudd, 2006; Rudd, Cukrowicz, & Bryan, 2008; Shea, 2002; Wingate, Joiner, Walker, Rudd, & Jobes, 2004), it is important to recognize that it may not always be feasible to obtain all of the following recommended information. The APA (2003) Practice Guidelines for the Assessment and Treatment of Patients with Suicidal Behaviors provides an example of a comprehensive guideline for suicide assessment; however, it focuses on psychiatry. A clinician may have to begin with an assessment of the most pertinent categories and continue with a more in-depth evaluation during later sessions. A detailed assessment results in an effective treatment plan. The more detailed the assessment, the greater the clinician's ability to plan and implement an effective intervention. Therefore, the following seven areas require a detailed assessment:

1. Sociodemographic data
2. Identified problem/Symptom history
3. Current suicidality
4. Suicide history
5. Family/Peer suicide history
6. Risk factors
7. Protective factors

Sociodemographic Data

An assessment of demographic data is essential to any suicide assessment. Given that there is a different risk attributed to specific demographic characteristics (see Chapters 2 to 6), this assessment provides for the ability to determine the relevant risk and protective factors that may be present and subsequently incorporated into an individualized treatment plan. While not exhaustive, pertinent demographic information to assess includes the following:

- Age
- Gender
- Race
- Culture
- Ethnicity
- Immigration status/experience
- Acculturation
- Languages spoken
- Religion
- Marital status
- Domestic violence/Intimate partner violence
- Substance use and/or abuse
- Past or current abuse/neglect (e.g., physical, emotional, sexual, bullying)
- Sexual orientation (coming-out process)
- Socioeconomic status (SES)
- Education level
- Academic history (current and past academic status, changes in status, type of education)
- Occupation
- Employment history (current and past employment status, changes in status, type of work)
- Social support
- Where they live
- With whom they reside
- Recent changes, moves, births, deaths, separations, and so forth
- Overall health (including pregnancy, medications, smoking, any changes)
- Any sleep disturbances
- Current medical conditions (thyroid problems, AIDS, HIV status, and so forth)
- Past medical history (diagnoses, operations, time in hospital, and so forth)
- Developmental history (birth history, health problems as a child, developmental milestones, academic and cognitive functioning)
- Referral source and information

Identified Problem/Symptom History

In this section, the focus is on issues beyond current and past suicidality, which are assessed in detail in the following sections. A detailed history of the client's presenting problem, along with a detailed symptom history, allows a clinician to further assess suicide risk and to individualize a treatment plan targeting key issues and diagnostic features. Some key questions to assess in this area include the following:

- What is the client's main/chief concern/problem?
- Does the client have a *Diagnostic and Statistical Manual of Mental Disorders (DSM)* diagnosis (e.g., depressive disorder, anxiety disorder, substance abuse, schizophrenia)?
- When did the problem start, and how long has it been there?
- Is it constant, intermittent, episodic, and so forth?
- What makes it worse?
- What makes it better?
- How does it impact the client? Family/friends?
- How has the client managed/coped?
- Where in the client's life does it impact the most? Least?
- Why does the client think he or she has it?
- Who first identified/diagnosed the issue? When? Where? Why? How?
- What is the treatment/treatment history? What treatments (e.g., professional, personal, alternative) has the client sought out and/or received? Therapy, counseling, medication, other?
- If counseling/therapy, where? With whom? In what ways was it helpful and/or unhelpful?
- If medication, what name? Type? Dose? Treatment regimen? Did the medication work? Did/does the medication have side effects? Has the client changed the medication(s)? Was the client adherent? Why or why not?
- Has the client ever been hospitalized due to the problem (if so, provide details)?

Current Suicidality

There are several criteria that are essential to consider in assessing for current suicidality. These are ideation, intent, plan/planning, feasibility, lethality, timing, impulsivity/aggression, and hopelessness. In considering these factors, it is important to recognize that they are not a yes/no checklist, but rather, they frequently exist along a spectrum of severity. Assessment of current suicidality should specifically focus on the following:

- A. Ideation
  - a. Have they ever felt life is not worth living?
  - b. Are they tired of living?
  - c. What things in their life make them want to go on living?
  - d. Do they ever wish they were not born? Or would not wake up in the morning?
  - e. Have they ever felt trapped and that there is no way out?
  - f. Have they thought about death recently?
  - g. How comfortable are they with these thoughts?
  - h. When did they first have these thoughts?
  - i. What do they think led up to the thoughts?
  - j. Have they discussed these thoughts with anyone?
- B. Intent
  - a. How close have they come to acting on these thoughts?
  - b. On a scale of 1 to 10, 1 being not at all likely and 10 being extremely likely, how likely is it that they will act on these thoughts now?

    c. On a scale of 1 to 10, how likely do they think it is that they will act on them in the future?

    d. Do they want to die, no longer want to live, or can they just not think of any other solution to their problems?

    e. If there was another solution to their problem, would they take it?

C. Plan/planning (rehearsals)

    a. Have they made a specific plan to kill themselves? Is there more than one plan?

    b. If yes, what does the plan include? How detailed is it?

    c. Have they thought of a time when they will carry out the plan?

    d. Have they researched various means to kill themselves (e.g., Internet, books)?

    e. Have they ever started to act out a plan to hurt or kill themselves but then stopped (e.g., picked up a bottle of pills, picked up a knife, walked to a bridge)?

    f. Have they made any specific preparations?

        i. Purchased items to facilitate the plan?

        ii. Wrote a note?

        iii. Gave things away?

        iv. Stocked up on pills?

D. Feasibility

    a. Is the method readily available to them?

    b. Are they able to carry out the plan (e.g., cognitively and physically)?

    c. Do they have access to guns?

    d. Do they have access to weapons?

    e. Do they have access to pills or other drugs?

    f. Is there anything that prohibits them from carrying out the plan (e.g., supervision, environmental factors, and individual values/beliefs)?

    g. Did they invest sufficient planning so as not to be caught/interrupted?

E. Lethality

    a. What is the degree of lethality associated with the method?

    b. Is death likely?

    c. Have they researched whether the method is likely to end in death?

    d. Is it likely that they could be saved if medical intervention is sought?

F. Timing

    a. How often are the thoughts occurring?

    b. Do they occur more often when with certain individuals?

    c. Do they occur more often in certain places?

    d. Do they occur more often during certain times of the day or year?

    e. When do they not occur?

G. Impulsivity/aggression

    a. Do they have a history of acting impulsively? If yes, in what ways? Provide examples.

    b. Do they have a history of acting aggressively? If yes, in what ways? Provide examples.

    c. Do they feel they have control over their thoughts or behaviors?

    d. Have they ever acted impulsively while under the influence of a substance?

H. Hopelessness

    a. Do they feel hopeless?

    b. If yes, how long have they felt hopeless?

    c. What things in life have led them to feel more or less hopeless about the future?

Suicide History

An assessment of suicide history should begin by ascertaining whether or not the individual has a history of past suicide attempts. Whenever a history of suicidal behavior is present, a thorough assessment of current suicide risk requires an understanding of past attempts. It is important to consider the following areas in assessing for suicide history:

A. Number of attempts
   a. Total number of attempts they have made in their lifetime
   b. Breakdown of number of attempts in the last month, year, 5 years, total

For each attempt reported, assess the following areas, beginning with the most recent attempt:

B. Nature of attempt
   a. Describe the attempt
      i. Circumstances
         1. Who else was around, if anyone?
         2. Where did the attempt take place?
         3. When did the attempt take place?
      ii. Method
         1. What did the attempt consist of?
         2. Were alcohol and/or substances used?
         3. If yes, were they used to facilitate carrying out the method or as a means to increase lethality?
      iii. Purpose of the attempt
         1. Escaping their problems
         2. Reactions or manipulation of others
         3. Injury
         4. Death
         5. Unknown
      iv. Precipitants to the attempt
      v. Was the attempt completed, interrupted, or aborted?
      vi. Did they think they would be found?
C. Lethality/severity
   a. On a scale of 1 to 10, how lethal did they think their attempt would be?
   b. Did they research the lethality of their method?
   c. Did they think their life could be saved by medical intervention if they were found?
D. Postattempt factors
   a. Postvention
      i. Were they found by someone else? If yes, describe the circumstances.
      ii. Did they bring themselves in for help? Describe the circumstances.
      iii. Did they take no action yet the attempt resolved without causing injury?
   b. What were their thoughts and feelings after the attempt (e.g., relief, regret)?
   c. Did they tell someone they made an attempt?
   d. Reflecting on the attempt, what would they have done differently?
E. Consequences
   a. Medical attention
      i. Was there an emergency room visit/treatment? If yes, describe.
      ii. Were they hospitalized? If yes, describe.
   b. Outpatient referral
   c. Family support
   d. Nothing
F. Plan/planning (rehearsals)
   a. How long did they plan the attempt before acting on it?
   b. Was the attempt impulsive?
   c. What thoughts did they have prior to attempting?

    d. Did they leave a note?

    e. Did they tell others of their plans to attempt?

    f. Did they give personal items away?

    g. Did they create a will (e.g., on paper, electronically, or on the Internet)?

Family/Peer Suicide History

It is indicated that individuals who experience the suicide or attempted suicide of a relative or peer are at increased risk for attempting suicide themselves (Brent et al., 2002; Bridge, Goldstein, & Brent, 2006). Therefore, accurate assessment of suicide risk requires evaluation of the suicide history of an individual's support network. It is important to determine the nature of the relationship as the risk of suicide varies according to the degree of relation. This evaluation should begin with the question: Have any of your relatives and/or peers completed or attempted suicide? A more detailed history should then be gathered that assesses the following:

    A. If yes, what was your relationship to the individual?

    B. How closely did you identify with this individual?

    C. Number of attempts

      a. Total number of attempts made in the relative/peer's lifetime

      b. Recency of attempts

For each attempt reported, assess the following areas, beginning with the most recent attempt:

    D. Describe the attempt

      a. Circumstances

      b. Method

      c. Did the person tell you about the attempt or did you find him or her?

      d. Consequences

    E. Impact of attempt

      a. How did the attempt/completed suicide affect you?

      b. Did you feel responsible? If yes, in what ways?

Risk Factors

There are several established risk factors for suicidality. It is important to recognize that having one or more risk factor(s) does not make someone suicidal, nor does the absence of risk factors negate the risk. However, the number of risk factors present often correlates with the level of suicide risk. The following list of risk factors is not a checklist but should be the basis for a dialogue regarding the factors impacting an individual's risk. It is important to assess for whether these factors are acute or chronic. (Please refer to Chapters 4 to 6 for a comprehensive discussion of pertinent risk factors for suicide across the life span.)

    A. Social

      a. Who is in their family of origin?

      b. Who is in their current family? (Note any significant recent changes, e.g., divorce, separation, birth.)

      c. Is there a history of recent amorous crises?

      d. Is there a history of isolation/rejection?

      e. Is there a family history of psychiatric illness/mental health problems (including suicide/suicide attempts)?

      f. Is there a family medical history?

      g. Is there a family history of abuse, state involvement, children's services, and so forth?

    h. Is there a family economic status?

    i. Are there family ethnic/cultural customs or traditions (specifically those related to health and illness)?

    j. Are there family immigration history, issues, difficulties, current problems?

    k. Are there family religious/spiritual beliefs or customs?

    l. What does their family/partner/friends/social network think of the presenting problem? Do they exacerbate the issue? Do they support treatment?

B. Environmental

    a. Poverty

    b. Poor access to health and mental health care

    c. Safety (e.g., community, housing, family)

    d. Recent or pending changes in home, academic, and/or occupational status (e.g., moves, evictions, being fired)

    e. Involvement with the legal system

    f. Access to lethal means

C. Psychiatric

    a. Mental illness diagnosis

        i. Do they have a current *DSM* diagnosis (e.g., depressive disorder, substance abuse, schizophrenia)? If yes, how many?

        ii. Do they have a past *DSM* diagnosis? If yes, what were they?

    b. Current mental status

        i. Cognitive and emotional functioning

    c. Psychiatric treatment history

        i. Inpatient admissions

        ii. Outpatient treatment

        iii. Emergency room visits/treatment

        iv. Psychopharmacological treatments

        v. Adherence to treatment

D. Individual

    a. Poor coping skills

    b. Change in or loss of past coping strategies

    c. Limited problem-solving skills

    d. External loci of control

    e. Poor self-esteem

    f. Low self-efficacy

    g. Few reasons for living

    h. Shame

    i. Guilt

    j. Worthlessness

    k. Hopelessness

    l. Low frustration tolerance

    m. Perfectionism

    n. Increased impulsivity/aggression

    o. Nonsuicidal self-injury

    p. Impaired relatedness

    q. Burdensomeness

Protective Factors

Similar to risk factors, protective factors are highly individualized, yet there are several known factors that have been shown to be associated with decreased suicide risk. While risk factors are often explored, protective factors are often minimized. Therefore, it is essential to purposefully assess for these factors. It is important to note that while the opposite of a given risk factor is not necessarily a protective factor, often this is the case (e.g., having a positive support network vs. a negative support network).

The following list of protective factors should not be used as a checklist but should be the basis for a discussion regarding the factors impacting an individual's risk. Again, it is necessary to determine whether these factors are acute or chronic. Please refer to Chapters 4 to 6 for a comprehensive review of protective factors for suicide across the life span. The following four areas should be considered:

A. Social
   a. Their family of origin
   b. Quality/quantity of support network
   c. Their family/partner/friends/social network's opinion of the presenting problem. Are they supportive (i.e., interest/concern for the individual) or do they exacerbate the issue/treatment?
   d. Family strengths and resources
   e. Family religion/spiritual beliefs or customs
   f. Availability and willingness of family to be involved in treatment
   g. Family involvement in self-help groups (e.g., National Alliance for the Mentally Ill [NAMI])
   h. Ethnic/cultural health treatments (practices, folklore, remedies, alternative medication)
B. Environmental
   a. Stable SES
   b. Adequate access to health and mental health care
   c. Safety (e.g., community, housing, family)
   d. Restricted access to lethal means
C. Psychiatric
   a. Lack of a mental illness diagnosis
   b. Intact cognitive and emotional functioning
   c. Limited psychiatric history
   d. History of adherence to treatment recommendations
D. Individual
   a. Effective coping skills
   b. Comprehensive problem-solving skills
   c. Internal loci of control
   d. High self-esteem
   e. Self-efficacy
   f. Increased reasons for living
   g. Ability to relate to others
   h. Repulsion to death/attraction to life

SUICIDE RATING SCALES

There are a number of well-known psychiatric rating scales for assessing suicidality with established psychometric properties. While suicide rating scales can never replace a fundamental suicide assessment, they can enhance a clinician's determination of suicide risk. Suicide rating scales may evaluate the presence or absence of risk and protective factors, or they may focus more on specific aspects of suicidal thoughts and behaviors such as the degree of intent or lethality of plan. It is recommended that, when possible, suicide assessment be supplemented by the use of an established rating scale. Among the most well-known and widely used suicide rating scales worth considering are the following: (a) Scale for Suicidal Ideation (Beck, Kovacs, & Weissman, 1979), (b) Suicide Intent Scale (Beck, 1974), (c) Suicide Assessment Scale, (d) Columbia Suicide History Form (Oquendo, Halberstam, & Mann, 2003), and (e) Reasons for Living Inventory (Linehan, Goodstein, Nielsen, & Chiles, 1983). In addition, a number of scales have been designed, developed, and applied to specific presenting problems and populations. These scales may be important to consider as assessment tools based on the individual characteristics of the client presenting for treatment, such as assessments that focus on specific conditions (e.g., depression, bipolar disorder, substance use disorders), populations (e.g., military personnel), demographic groups (e.g., youth, older adults) across suicidality (e.g., intent, ideation, suicide history, suicidal behavior, suicide attempts), and other areas (e.g., suicide resilience, reasons for living, fearlessness about death).

Case Vignette 14.1

You are a mental health clinician in an outpatient psychiatric clinic. You are scheduled to do an intake with a new client who was self-referred for services.

Selena is a currently unemployed, 24-year-old female who recently graduated from college. She has been actively seeking employment for over 6 months to no avail and has been struggling with student loan payments and other expenses throughout this time. Usually a very independent person, Selena has become increasingly dependent on others for financial support. Two weeks ago, her boyfriend of 2.5 years who had moved away for graduate school, unexpectedly broke up with her via email. While she has suffered from bouts of depression in the past, Selena has no formal psychiatric history of major mental illness or suicidality.

ROLE-PLAY 14.1

Based on Case Vignette 14.1, engage in a role-play in which you conduct an assessment of suicide risk using the Fundamental Suicide Assessment Components described in the earlier section. One person takes on the role of the clinician, and one takes the role of the client, Selena. As the client, improvise the data regarding Selena's family history and risk/protective factors.

DETERMINING OUTCOMES BASED ON ASSESSMENT

The fundamental suicide assessment informs the level of suicide risk of the client. In essence, the level of risk will determine the disposition to follow. The level of risk can be seen as existing along a spectrum of risk ranging from an absence of suicide risk (where there is no suicide risk present) to acute, severe suicide risk (where the individual is actively suicidal and is unsafe to be left alone). The disposition ranges from no referral to outpatient referral with or without psychopharmacological intervention to immediate psychiatric hospitalization. Documentation of risk level and rationale for this determination is critical.

There are no absolute, scientific categories of suicide risk. However, treatment disposition can be seen across five general categories of suicide risk: (a) absence of risk, (b) low risk, (c) moderate risk, (d) high risk, and (e) severe risk. The following are broad possible dispositions based on the level of risk and are not to be considered disposition recommendations, which require full suicide assessment and cannot be determined without individual client contact.

- If the client presents with an absence of suicide risk, disposition should be based on the nature of the clinical presentation and other issues present (e.g., divorce, homelessness, depression).
- If the client presents with a low suicide risk, outpatient referral may be an acceptable disposition.
- If the client presents with a moderate suicide risk, an outpatient referral can be a reasonable disposition and psychopharmacological treatment may be considered to supplement outpatient psychotherapy.
- If the client presents with a high suicide risk, observation in the ER for up to 72 hours is often recommended.
- If the client presents with a severe suicide risk, admission to a psychiatric hospital is generally required.
- Clients who are not admitted to an ER or psychiatric hospital should be monitored at each contact for changes in their suicide risk level and may require safety planning and/or future crisis intervention.

Chu et al. (2015) propose several options for appropriately managing the various levels of risk, reinforcing and expanding on the aforementioned recommendations. On the low risk end of the spectrum, clinicians should encourage the individual to seek social support and provide them with emergency numbers. Individuals near the middle of the risk spectrum (i.e., low-to-moderate symptoms) should be provided with a safety plan organized in a hierarchy (i.e., first, engage in distracting activities; second, try repeating the list of activities more than once; and lastly, calling an emergency number and/or voluntarily go to the hospital). If an individual is above a moderate risk, all prior actions should be taken and frequent phone check-ins should be added. For individuals at the severe to extreme risk level, voluntary and involuntary hospitalization should be considered. Consultation with a trained and experienced colleague is always recommended. Lastly, in light of recent evidence for the efficacy of means safety, restricting access to means for suicide plans is strongly emphasized (Chu et al., 2015).

RECOMMENDATIONS FOR CONDUCTING A SUICIDE ASSESSMENT

It is critical to understand that the aforementioned guidelines provide comprehensive details on working with suicidality in general. It is necessary to individualize the assessment based on evidence-based knowledge regarding suicide within specific contexts. For example, assessing a 75-year-old with Stage IV prostate cancer, a 16-year old in the coming-out process with substance abuse, a 29-year old with anorexia nervosa, or a 35-year-old woman who recently lost her two children in a car accident requires unique and specific targeted assessment. The following recommendations are offered as a framework for conducting an effective suicide risk assessment. These recommendations are designed to support and facilitate the data-gathering dialogue described earlier.

1. A transparent, neutral, and nonjudgmental stance on the part of the clinician will improve engagement and facilitate more honest, open responses on the part of the client.
2. The development and maintenance of a therapeutic alliance enhances suicide risk assessment.
3. Being aware of the impact of culture and cultural customs on the client is important.

4. The patterning, flow, and sensitivity of questions are critical to the outcome of a suicide risk assessment. It is important to avoid an interrogational style. If the client is talking, he or she may answer many of your questions out of order or sequence, but this will encourage a more natural comfortable conversation.
5. The instillation of hope that alternative solutions to suicide exist is important.
6. Conveying to the client that effective assessment is only the first step in an ongoing process of intervention and is extremely important to engage and motivate his or her commitment to treatment.
7. A client's honest communication of his or her thoughts and feelings should be recognized and commended as a first step in the change process.
8. Knowledge of evidence-based practice in one's specific practice area, one's professional codes of ethics, and the laws regarding suicide within one's state of practice should be considered in and/or integrated into assessment as required.
9. Clinical supervision and guidance are vital in working with suicidal individuals. Professional supervision is particularly important when determining disposition based on the information gathered during the assessment.

SUMMARY

As clinicians it is imperative that we effectively assess every client for risk of suicide. Using the core suicide assessment question and the fundamental suicide assessment components can facilitate an informative, thorough assessment of suicide risk that aids clinicians in determining a client's level of suicide risk and developing an appropriate intervention and treatment plan. The level of suicide risk will vary over time. Although past suicide risk assessments may be helpful, they cannot serve as present indicators of suicide risk. The most comprehensive assessment is, at best, an assessment of risk at that moment. Therefore, clinicians should continually monitor clients for any changes in risk level.

KEY POINTS

1. Assessment is an ongoing process that should be revisited during every contact with clients at risk for suicide.
2. Every client is different; therefore suicide assessment must be individualized.
3. It is required to ask the core suicide assessment question of every client.
4. Every client with any level of suicide risk should participate in a fundamental suicide assessment.
5. The level of suicide risk exists along a continuum.
6. Suicide rating scales can enhance the evaluation of suicide risk.
7. Supervision is essential for effective suicide assessment and management.
8. Knowledge of evidence-based practice in the specific problem area of the client is essential.
9. Awareness of professional code of ethics and state laws regarding suicide is required.
10. An assessment should be followed by appropriate disposition.

ELECTRONIC RESOURCES

TRAINING INSTITUTE FOR SUICIDE ASSESSMENT

www.suicideassessment.com

SUICIDE INFORMATION & EDUCATION CENTRE

www.suicideinfo.ca

NATIONAL MENTAL ILLNESS SCREENING PROJECT

www.mentalhealthscreening.org

KNOWLEDGE ACQUISITION TEST (KAT)

True or False

1. There is one generally accepted standardized suicide risk assessment system.
2. Suicide risk assessment is a process.
3. The number of risk factors present often correlates with the level of suicide risk.
4. There are absolute, scientifically established categories of suicide risk.
5. The level of suicide risk can be said to exist along a spectrum.
6. Even a clear denial of a suicide intent requires further follow-up assessment.
7. An effective suicide assessment should take the form of a checklist rather than a dialogue.
8. Risk and protective factors are the key components of a thorough suicide risk assessment.

Short Answer

9. When asking the core suicide question "Are you suicidal?" or "Have you ever thought of killing yourself?" What are three general categories or responses?
10. List all seven components required in a detailed assessment.
11. Describe the rationale for including standard measures/scales in a suicide assessment and provide examples of some types of suicide scales.
12. Describe some of the key recommendations for conducting a suicide assessment.

Multiple Choice

13. Which of the following are key individual risk factors to include in an effective suicide risk assessment?
    A. Creativity
    B. Spirituality
    C. Change in coping skills
    D. Resilience
    E. All of the above
    F. None of the above
14. How should the core suicide risk assessment question be asked?
    A. Subtly so as to avoid assumption of the presence of suicidal thoughts/behaviors
    B. Directly without judgment
    C. Directly while indicating such thoughts/behaviors are inappropriate
    D. All of the above
    E. None of the above
15. Which of the following is a potential outcome based on assessment?
    A. Outpatient referral
    B. Psychiatric hospitalization
    C. Short-term observation in a psychiatric emergency room
    D. Initiation of psychiatric medication
    E. All of the above
    F. None of the above

REFERENCES

Academy of Child & Adolescent Psychiatry. (2001). Practice parameter for the assessment and treatment of children and adolescents with suicidal behavior. *Journal of the American Academy of Child & Adolescent Psychiatry, 40,* 24S–50S.

American Psychiatric Association. (2003). *Practice guideline for the assessment and treatment of patients with suicidal behaviors.* Washington, DC: American Psychiatric Association Press.

Barber, M. E., Marzuk, P. M., Leon, A. C., & Portera, L. (2001). Gate questions in psychiatric interviewing: The case of suicide assessment. *Journal of Psychiatric Research, 35*(1), 67–69.

Beck, A. T., Kovacs, M., & Weissman, A. (1979). Assessment of suicidal ideation: The scale for suicide ideation. *Journal of Consulting and Clinical Psychology, 47,* 343–352. Retrieved from https://pdfs .semanticscholar.org/c2de/a047d5d71cd6500d92d4cdf2c6e36129d8cf.pdf

Bernett, R. A. (2014). A review of multidisciplinary clinical practice guidelines in suicide prevention: Toward an emerging standard in suicide risk assessment and management, training and practice. *Academy of Psychiatry, 38*(5), 585–592. doi:10.1007/s40596-014-0180-1

Bernert, R. A., Hom, M. A., & Roberts, L. W. (2014). A review of multidisciplinary clinical practice guidelines in suicide prevention: Toward an emerging standard in suicide risk assessment and management, training and practice. *Academic Psychiatry, 38*(5), 585–592.

Brent, D. A., Oquendo, M., Birmaher, B., Greenhill, L., Kolko, D., Stanley, B., . . . Salazar, J. O. (2002). Familial pathways to early-onset suicide attempt: Risk for suicidal behavior in offspring of mood-disordered suicide attempters. *Archives of General Psychiatry, 59*(9), 801–807.

Bridge, J. A., Goldstein, T. R., & Brent, D. A. (2006). Adolescent suicide and suicidal behavior. *Journal of Child Psychology and Psychiatry, 47*(3–4), 372–394.

Chu, C., Klein, K. M., Buchman-Schmitt, J. M., Hom, M. A., Hagan, C. R., & Joiner, T. E. (2015). Routinized assessment of suicide risk in clinical practice: An empirically informed update. *Journal of Clinical Psychology, 71*(12), 1186–1200. doi: 10.1002/jclp.22210

Jacobs, D. (1999). *The Harvard guide to suicide assessment and intervention.* San Francisco, CA: Jossey-Bass.

Jacobs, D., & Brewer, M. (2004). APA Practice Guideline provides recommendations for assessing and treating patients with suicidal behaviors. *Psychiatric Annals, 34*(5), 373–380.

Linehan, M. M., Goodstein, J. L., Nielsen, S. L., & Chiles, J. A. (1983). Reasons for staying alive when you are thinking of killing yourself: the reasons for living inventory. *Journal of Consulting and Clinical Psychology, 51*(2), 276–286.

Monaghan, K., & Harris, M. (2015). Not at imminent risk: A systematic literature review. *Crisis, 36*(6), 459–463. doi:10.1027/0227-5910/a000337

Nock, M. K., Borges, G., Bromet, E. J., Alonso, J., Angermeyer, M., Beautrais, A., . . . Williams, D. (2008). Cross-national prevalence and risk factors for suicidal ideation, plans and attempts. *British Journal of Psychiatry, 192*(2), 98–105.

Oquendo, M.A., Halberstam, B., & Mann, J. J. (2003). Risk factors for suicidal behavior: The utility and limitations of research instruments. In M. B. First (Ed.), *Standardized Evaluation in Clinical Practice* (pp. 103–130). Washington, DC: American Psychiatric Publishing.

Posner, K., Brown, G. K., Stanley, B., Brent, D. A., Yershova, K. V., Oquendo, M. A., . . . Mann, J. J. (2011). The Columbia–Suicide Severity Rating Scale: Initial validity and internal consistency findings from three multisite studies with adolescents and adults. *American Journal of Psychiatry, 168,* 1266–1277.

Posner, K., Oquendo, M. A., Gould, M., Stanley, B., & Davies, M. (2007). Columbia Classification Algorithm of Suicide Assessment (C-CASA): Classification of suicidal events in the FDA's pediatric suicidal risk analysis of antidepressants. *American Journal of Psychiatry, 164*(7), 1035–1043.

Roberts, A. R., & Jennings, T. (2005). Hanging by a thread: How failure to conduct an adequate lethality assessment resulted in suicide. *Brief Treatment and Crisis Intervention, 5*(3), 251–260.

Rudd, M. D. (2006). *Assessment and management of suicidality.* Sarasota, FL: Professional Resource Press.

Rudd, M. D., Berman, A. L., Joiner, T. E., Jr., Nock, M. K., Silverman, M. M., Mandrusiak, M., . . . Witte, T. (2006). Warning signs for suicide: Theory, research, and clinical applications. *Suicide and Life-Threatening Behavior, 36*(3), 255–262.

Rudd, M. D., Cukrowicz, K. C., & Bryan, C. J. (2008). Core competencies in suicide risk assessment and management: Implications for supervision. *Training and Education in Professional Psychology, 2*(4), 219–228.

Shea, S. C. (2002). *The practical art of suicide assessment: A guide for mental health professionals and substance abuse counselors.* Hoboken, NJ: Wiley.

Shea, S. C. (2012). The interpersonal art of suicide assessment: Interviewing techniques for uncovering suicidal intent, ideation, and actions. In R. I. Simon & R. E. Hales (Eds.), *The American Psychiatric Publishing textbook of suicide assessment and management* (2nd ed., pp. 29–56). Washington, DC: American Psychiatric Publishing.

Sheehan, D. V., Giddens, J. M., & Sheehan, K. H. (2014). Current assessment and classification of suicidal phenomena using the FDA 2012 Draft Guidance document on suicide assessment: A critical review. *Innovations in Clinical Neuroscience, 11*(9–10), 54–65.

Simon, R. L. (2006). Suicide risk assessment: Is clinical experience enough? *Journal of the American Academy of Psychiatry and the Law, 34*(3), 276–278.

Substance Abuse and Mental Health Services Administration. (2014). Results from the 2013 National Survey on Drug Use and Health: Mental Health Findings, NSDUH Series H-49, HHS Publication No. (SMA) 14–4887. Rockville, MD: Author. Retrieved from https://www.samhsa.gov/data/sites/default/files/NSDUHmhfr2013/NSDUHmhfr2013.pdf

Vikes, M. (2013). Suicide risk assessment and formulation: An update. *Innovations in Clinical Neuroscience, 11*(9–10), 54–65.

Wingate, L., Joiner, T. E., Walker, R., Rudd, D. M., & Jobes, D. A. (2004). Empirically informed approaches to topics in suicide risk assessment. *Behavioral Sciences & the Law, 22*(5), 651–655.

PART VI

Evidence-Based Treatments

CHAPTER FIFTEEN

CRISIS INTERVENTION
AND SUICIDE

Although the vast majority of individuals will experience a crisis at some point or points in their lives, most of these experiences do not result in suicidality. However, when an individual is experiencing a suicidal crisis, crisis intervention may be an appropriate treatment modality. This chapter presents a model of crisis intervention for suicidal individuals, including traditional face-to-face approach, as well as hotline, online, and texting modalities of crisis intervention. Key stages and strategies are examined. Evidence regarding the application and effectiveness of crisis interventions is explored. Finally, recommendations for clinical practice when implementing crisis intervention are provided.

GOALS AND OBJECTIVES

An understanding of:

- Definition of crisis
- Key factors that constitute a crisis
- Crisis intervention models
- Robert's seven-stage crisis intervention model (RSSCIM)
- Core stages of crisis intervention
- Hotline, online, and texting crisis interventions
- Evidence to support the use of crisis interventions
- Populations for and settings in which crisis intervention is supported
- Clinical considerations when conducting crisis interventions
- Common errors or pitfalls when conducting crisis intervention
- Opportunity for positive change during a crisis period

A "crisis" can be defined as a time-limited response to an event or series of events that significantly burdens, disrupts, and distresses an individual and overwhelms his or her routine and established coping strategies. Literature further highlights that the crisis stimuli are typically unexpected (Westefeld & Heckman-Stone, 2003). The resultant disruption or distress has been described as a loss of psychological homeostasis (Roberts & Ottens, 2005) or a severe disequilibrium (Maris, Berman, & Silverman, 2000; Westefeld & Heckman-Stone, 2003), signifying a loss of stability and possible functional impairment due to a failure of existing coping mechanisms' ability to regulate one's response to the stimuli.

Interestingly, the Chinese symbol for crisis is composed of two separate symbols, those of "danger" and "opportunity" (Roberts & Dziegielewski, 1995). A moment of crisis often represents a threat to the individual, yet produces a time where positive change may occur. When an individual is in crisis and experiencing suicidality, effective crisis intervention is a treatment option that can ameliorate distress and provide motivation and mechanism for productive change.

Each crisis is different and individually defined, as what may qualify as a crisis for one individual may not produce a crisis for another individual or even for that same individual at a different time in his or her life. In order to effectively support and treat an individual experiencing a crisis, it is important to recognize your preconceived ideas regarding what constitutes a crisis and how a crisis can be managed.

Individual Exercise 15.1

Think of a past personal crisis. (This may evoke some distressing thoughts and feelings. If you prefer, you may consider skipping this exercise or reflecting on a historical experience in the distant rather than recent past or a less painful experience. The intention of this exercise is one of reflection and understanding related to crisis. It is not designed or intended for you to relive a traumatic event.)

1. How do you define a crisis? Be as specific as possible.
2. Are there events or situations that you feel would not produce a crisis for yourself or others? Be as specific as possible.
3. List events or situations that may result in a crisis and rank in order of severity. From your personal experience, reflect on a time when you have experienced a crisis.
4. What were the key elements of the experience that made it a crisis for you?
5. Which, if any, of the elements just described was the most critical for you during this experience?
6. During the time of the crisis, did it feel like it would never end?
7. In looking back at that prior experience, what was the first sign that the crisis was abating?
8. What helped you in resolving this crisis?
9. What, if anything, made the crisis more difficult to resolve? Or did any intended help have the opposite effect?

Small Group Exercise 15.1

In small groups of two to three, please discuss, as you are comfortable, your responses to questions 1 to 3 in Individual Exercise 15.1. Remember, answers are personal and there are no correct or incorrect answers.

1. What were the response similarities in your group?
2. What were the response differences in your group?
3. Did you find any surprises in the group discussion? If so, what were they and how were you surprised?
4. As every crisis is unique according to the individual, discuss how you think your ranking of crisis may impact the treatment you provide to a client in crisis, both positively and negatively?

███ Small Group Exercise 15.2 ███

In small groups of two to three, please discuss, as you are comfortable, your responses to questions 4 to 8 in Individual Exercise 15.1. Remember, answers are personal and there are no correct or incorrect answers.

1. What were the response similarities in your group?
2. What were the response differences in your group?
3. Did you find any surprises in the group discussion? If so, what were they and how were you surprised?
4. As a mental health clinician, how does hearing about others' experiences of crisis impact how you approach clients experiencing a crisis?

CRISIS INTERVENTION MODEL

There is no one universal crisis intervention model. Several models of crisis intervention exist in the literature. Despite differences, these models closely parallel each other in structure and composition. Some comprehensive crisis intervention models have been studied for effectiveness across populations and settings. An established recognized model in the literature is Roberts's RSSCIM; (Roberts, 1991; Roberts & Jennings, 2005; Roberts & Ottens, 2005).

The seven sequential stages of Robert's model include:

- plan and conduct a thorough biopsychosocial and assessment of lethality/imminent danger;
- rapidly establish a collaborative relationship;
- identify the major problems, including crisis precipitants;
- encourage an exploration of feelings and emotions;
- generate and explore alternatives and new coping strategies;
- restore functioning through implementation of an action plan;
- plan follow-up and booster sessions.

These stages of the RSSCIM model are intended to be completed sequentially with recognition that there may be overlap across some stages. All of the stages are considered necessary and include the following:

Stage I: Psychosocial and lethality assessment. Plan and conduct a thorough biopsychosocial assessment (see Chapter 17). This assessment may need to be conducted quickly and specifically target strengths, supports, stressors, coping strategies and resources, medications, medical needs, and substance use. This assessment should evaluate current lethality and intent of ideation or plan and should result in a determination of whether the client is in imminent danger (see Chapter 5).

Stage II: Rapidly establish rapport. Make psychological contact and rapidly establish the collaborative relationship. Empathy, reflective listening, reframing, reinforcing strengths, supporting existing coping strategies, and maintaining a nonjudgmental stance are essential skills during this stage to develop a positive working relationship with the client in a short period of time in order to address the crisis.

Stage III: Identify the major problems or crisis precipitants. Identify the major problems, including crisis precipitants. Elicit from the client what the current stimuli are that led to the crisis. Partializing problems is critical in order to determine which problem should be addressed first. Answering the questions "Why now?" and "Where to start?" are the two main components of this stage.

Stage IV: Deal with feelings and emotions. Encourage an exploration of feelings and emotions. The two main components of this stage include providing the opportunity for clients to express their feelings and to tell their story about the crisis. This stage involves employing active listening skills and supporting client statements and also requires gently challenging client maladaptive beliefs or negative cognitive schemas relating to their suicidal ideation, intent, or behavior to consider alternative viewpoints and coping mechanisms.

Stage V: Generate and explore alternatives. Generate and explore alternatives and new coping strategies. Often considered the most difficult stage of crisis intervention, this stage requires that clients acknowledge that suicide is not the only solution and consequently begin to identify more appropriate and effective means of coping. It is essential that Stage IV is sufficiently addressed in order for clients to let go of previous unhelpful and maladaptive coping mechanisms that may have resulted in suicidality. This solution-focused work is often more successful after some emotional stability has been achieved through Stage IV. Alternative coping mechanisms should be developed collaboratively between client and practitioner. These alternatives have a greater chance of success if they are owned by the client.

Stage VI: Implement an action plan. Restore functioning through implementation of an action plan. The strategies developed in the previous stage are transformed into an action plan in this stage. Critical components to consider include identifying and removing lethal means of suicide (e.g., pills, knives, guns); contracting for safety as a part of the overall plan; including family and friends in the plan to mobilize support, decrease isolation, and provide initial safety monitoring; address any outstanding mental or physical health issues (e.g., reducing anxiety or depression, improving sleep hygiene); identifying future action steps; and connecting the client to future treatment (e.g., outpatient treatment, hotlines, support groups).

Stage VII: Follow up. Plan follow-up and booster sessions. Following up on Stage VI, this stage involves determining a plan for follow-up contact with the client to evaluate postcrisis presentation. Areas to consider during postcrisis assessment include affect regulation, comfort and mastery with new coping skills, substance use, and ongoing support.

The RSSCIM is a model of intervention that can be effectively used across mental health professions. In addition to providing a framework for intervening, it is client-centered in that it incorporates client strengths and resiliency. The utility of RSSCIM model has been identified as a core source to provide mental health counselors an approach and strategies to work with suicidal clients in crisis (Granello, 2010).

A similar crisis intervention model, the ten-stage Integrated Problem-Solving Model (IPSM; Westefeld & Heckman-Stone, 2003) presents a parallel stage model but further subdivides and reorders RSSCIM and emphasizes different aspects of the crisis intervention process. Specifically, IPSM draws initial focus on establishing and maintaining rapport with the client as the first stage. In addition, the IPSM further delineates among the problem-solving model by dividing the tasks of setting goals, generating options, evaluating options, and selecting a plan of action as individual stages.

Frequently, the first professionals with whom an individual in suicidal crisis may interact are the police. As suicide crisis often involves both health/mental health providers and the police, the two fields of health care providers and law enforcement have partnered, often in mobile teams, to intervene with crisis in their communities. Research has begun to demonstrate the effectiveness of these joint police–mental health clinician units that can deliver a rapid multiskilled crisis response in the community (Lee, won Kim, & Enright, 2015; Ritter, Teller, Marcussen, Munetz, & Teasdale, 2011; Zealberg et al., 1992). These partnering units, police and clinicians, are able to respond quickly, deescalate, and provide resources to mitigate the immediate crisis. Also, the nature of the mobile interventions allows the individual in crisis to be immediately taken to the hospital emergency department for a fuller assessment and treatment or to be connected with appropriate community health and mental health services (Lee et al., 2015). However, research continues to investigate the effectiveness of mobile crisis teams in reducing suicide rate, managing crises, increasing training and skills of law enforcement, and reducing overutilization of emergency department visits (Lee et al., 2015; Zealberg et al., 1992).

HOTLINE, ONLINE, AND MOBILE METHODS OF CRISIS INTERVENTION

In addition to in-person psychotherapy approaches to crisis intervention, several other modalities have become more widespread in recent years, including crisis hotlines, online intervention programs, and mobile means of providing intervention, including text lines and phone applications. Call-in crisis hotlines have received the most attention in empirical studies. One such call-in program or hotline, The National Suicide Prevention Lifeline, represents a national network of over 160 community crisis centers in the United States that respond to approximately 1 million callers a year, about 25% of whom are suicidal (Gould et al., 2016).

As with most call-in programs, once Lifeline determines that a caller is at imminent risk, "Lifeline helpers" (those individuals who answer calls to the hotline) encourage callers to work toward securing their own safety (Draper, Murphy, Vega, Covington, & McKeon, 2015) using the least invasive interventions possible (e.g., voluntarily getting rid of means, agreeing to follow-up calls by the helper, agreeing to a consultation from a mobile crisis team, agreeing to take oneself to the nearest ER). In this respect, involuntary interventions (i.e., sending an ambulance or the police to the person's location without their request) are considered a last resort (Draper et al., 2015). When all other possible actions to prevent a caller from completing suicide have been exhausted, only then is "involuntary rescue" considered.

Studies have found great variation in response to calls across crisis centers. For example, Gould, Kalafat, Harrismunfakh, and Kleinman (2007) found that emergency rescue was initiated in approximately 38% of cases in which callers had engaged in some behavior to kill themselves immediately prior to calling the center. Another study examined calls that were made while a suicide attempt was in progress and found that emergency services were known to be dispatched in 18% of cases (Mishara et al., 2007). Another study found that callers actively engaged in collaborative interventions (e.g., creating a safety plan, caller agreeing to a follow-up call) on 76% of the calls (Gould et al., 2016; all other references in this paragraph are from that article). This study also found that emergency services were sent with the caller's collaboration on 19% of the calls while sending emergency services without the caller's request occurred on 25% of calls (Gould et al., 2016). Overall, research conducted a review of telephone crisis services over the past 45 years to provide a detailed overview of the evidence supporting the effectiveness of telephone crisis services on suicidal callers (Hvidt, Ploug, & Holm, 2016). Despite the wide time frame included in the review, only 18 studies were able to be identified that met the inclusion criteria of measuring either changes during calls, reutilization of service, compliance with advice, caller satisfaction, and/or counselor satisfaction, which indicates the need for more research on the effectiveness of this form of crisis intervention. Nevertheless, results demonstrate that the majority of studies included in the review showed evidence of a positive impact on both immediate and intermediate degrees of suicidal urgency, depressive mental states, and positive feedback from callers and counselors

(Hvidt et al., 2016). Importantly, this review suggests the lack of evidence regarding the long-term impact and randomized control trials, again highlighting the need for additional research in this area. One study did interview callers regarding their follow-up care after calling a crisis hotline and found that postcall utilization rates were only approximately 50% for suicidal crisis callers who received a mental health treatment referral (Gould, Munfakh, Kleinman, & Lake, 2012).

The national Veterans Crisis Hotline (VCL) has also received attention in the research. Studies have found that approximately 84% of calls to the VCL ended with a favorable outcome, specifically 25% ended with a resolution and 59% with a referral to the local health care provider. Reportedly, high-risk callers were more likely to receive a referral than to end the call without a resolution or referral (Britton, Bossarte, Thompson, Kemp, & Conner, 2013).

Training and effectiveness of helpline counselors have also been investigated. Research has found that helpline counselors are generally accurate in their judgments of risk for suicide-related behaviors (Karver, Tarquini, & Caporino, 2010). Recently, a method of training crisis hotline "helpers" has been the focus of study (Cross et al., 2014; Gould, Cross, Pisani, Munfakh, & Kleinman, 2013). Examinations of the Applied Suicide Intervention Skills Training (ASIST) program have demonstrated that improvements in caller outcomes were linked to ASIST-trained helpers, including the helpers' use of exploring reasons for living and informal support contacts. However, ASIST training was not found to yield more comprehensive suicide risk assessments (Gould et al., 2013). Another study found a wide variability in the fidelity of delivery of the ASIST program in trained helpers and also found that few had high levels of adherence and competence (Cross et al., 2014).

Further research is also needed to better understand who uses crisis hotlines. Research regarding utilization by youth, for example, remains inconsistent. One study surveying youths about their awareness, usage, and attitudes toward local and national crisis hotlines found that youths reported low rates of awareness and low rates of utilization, although they did express a strong interest in phone hotlines (41% vs. 59% for new media categories combined; Crosby & Sacks, 2002). A different study found that younger people are more likely to consider calling a hotline than going to an ER or calling 911 when faced with having to help a suicidal peer. They further found that young immigrants (in the United States <15 years) were more likely to call 911 and less likely to call a suicide hotline, while African Americans were more likely to go to the ER and call 911 than to call a hotline, and Hispanics were more likely to call 911 but less likely to call a suicide hotline (Larkin, Rivera, Xu, Rincon, & Beautrais, 2011). Spittal et al. (2015) found that being male or transgender, never having been married, and being older (until 55–64 years after which the rate decreases again) predict being a frequent hotline caller. Another study surveyed callers of a suicide crisis hotline to explore the self-reported characteristics of callers, their reasons for contacting the service, their evaluations of the services they received (Coveney, Pollock, Armstrong, & Moore, 2012). Results indicated that there were high incidences of expressed suicidality and mental health issues among callers and that regular and ongoing use of the service was rather common. Additionally, the callers surveyed indicated high satisfaction with and helpfulness of the services received and that they used the service for multiple, complex reasons and often as part of a larger network of support rather than in isolation or as a last resort. Still, other research has found that callers presenting as an imminent risk reported high levels of current suicidal desire including suicidal ideation, hopelessness, psychological pain, and high suicidal intent both in the form of a plan to kill themselves and expressed intent to die (Gould et al., 2016).

Online crisis intervention models have not been as widely studied but do have evidence of their effectiveness. One systematic review of research examining online-based crisis intervention identified 17 empirical studies comprising three crisis contexts:

(a) disasters, (b) risk/prevention of suicide, and (c) trauma. Of these, 11 distinct intervention programs were described and the predominant treatment approach was cognitive behavioral therapy. The study found that research examining online psychological crisis intervention models has been conducted in several different countries and that the users of these online programs report benefiting from them (De Silva et al., 2013).

Some have examined trained versus lay volunteers responding to distressed individuals who post on online support groups and have found that training leads to the implementation of a wider array of strategies and greater use of emotion-focused strategies and cognitive-focused strategies. The same study also found that self-disclosure was common among the responses of the lay individuals (Gilat, Tobin, & Shahar, 2012). Other studies have examined the use of online forums to serve in a gatekeeper role (Cross, Matthieu, Lezine, & Knox, 2010; Sueki & Ito, 2015). Specifically, placing advertisements on web search pages to promote mental health service use among Internet users with suicidal ideation is a form of online "gatekeeping" that preliminary research suggests may be feasible (Sueki & Ito, 2015). Others have found positive effects of online forums for support for suicidality that include help-seekers beginning to provide support for other help-seekers and developing an online community characterized by reciprocal help-seeking and help-providing (Greidanus & Everall, 2010). However, others have found that while many individuals turn to online forums for support out of fear of stigma from disclosing suicidal thoughts and/or behaviors in person to family members or professionals, many report high levels of stigma from online social networks and that stigma perceived from social network members was the best predictor of depression symptom severity (Frey, Hans, & Cerel, 2016).

One large review study examined current evidence regarding the operation and effectiveness of Internet programs for suicide and self-harm prevention that are run by professionals (Jacob, Scourfield, & Evans, 2014). Only 15 studies were identified targeting suicidal users. Studies either presented strategies that supported at-risk individuals ($n = 8$), supported professionals working with those at risk for suicide ($n = 6$), or attempted to improve website quality ($n = 1$). Results indicated that there is an overall lack of information regarding the evidence of the effectiveness of online prevention strategies (Jacob et al., 2014).

As with hotline and text lines, more research is needed to understand the users of online forums. One study found that suicide-related users reported significantly higher levels of social anxiety as well as lifetime and past year suicidal ideation than non-suicide-related users. They also reported a higher likelihood of future suicide and overall higher risk for suicide (Mok, Jorm, & Pirkis, 2016).

Crisis text lines and mobile applications (apps) have also been developed for individuals struggling with suicidal thoughts and behaviors. One app has been developed based on the concept of safety plan and proposition that the format of a mobile phone application would be more available and useful than traditional hard copy versions (Skovgaard, Frandsen, & Erlangsen, 2016). The MYPLAN app is designed to help at-risk individuals create a safety plan. The user creates an individualized safety plan by filling in templates with strategies, actions, and direct links to his or her identified contacts. The app has been downloaded approximately 8,000 times in 15 months since it has been made available, and developers of MYPLAN report that users and clinical staff have provided positive feedback on its effectiveness (Skovgaard et al., 2016).

Crisis Text Line, a texting version of the traditional call-in hotline, is aimed at young people who send text messages more frequently than they talk on their phones. Texting is attractive as an intervention modality as it is lower in cost, quick to provide, and easy to utilize. It offers responses by text message 24 hours per day, 7 days per week. A counselor answers within 5 minutes. Since its start in 2011, over 5 million texts have been received (Thomas, 2015).

Other research has found text messaging to be effective in preventing suicide repetition among suicide attempters (Berrouiguet et al., 2014). More specifically, text messages inquiring about the client's well-being and providing information regarding individual sources of help and evidence-based self-help strategies have been shown to reduce the risk of suicide attempt repetition among adults after self-harm (Berrouiguet et al., 2014). Overall, research suggests texting is an acceptable, feasible, and effective method of providing ongoing contact and support to suicide attempters experiencing crisis (Berrouiguet et al., 2014; Chen, Mishara, & Lui, 2010; Thomas, 2015).

EVIDENCE FOR CRISIS INTERVENTION

In general, there is a poverty of research examining the effectiveness of crisis intervention models. As far back as 1977, Auerbach and Kilmann conducted a review of outcome research regarding the effectiveness of crisis intervention and noted the dramatic lack of evidence in this area. Since that time, minimal work has been conducted. However, there is some evidence to support that RSSCIM is an effective mode of treatment for specific populations and in specific settings. Females ranging in age from 15 to 24 and 55 to 64 years have been found to benefit from suicide prevention and crisis intervention programs (Roberts, 2002). Individuals presenting with psychiatric crises also demonstrated positive outcomes from crisis intervention programs (Roberts, 2002; Roberts & Ottens, 2005). In-home intensive family-based crisis intervention has been shown to be highly effective at reducing child abuse and neglect in troubled families (Roberts & Everly, 2006). Studies indicate that Robert's model is effective for use with female domestic violence survivors and battered women (Burman, 2003; Lee, 2007). Adolescents experiencing problems with suicide, substance abuse, and loss also benefit from crisis intervention (Roberts, 2002). However, longitudinal and comparative studies are sorely needed (Roberts & Jennings, 2005) as are multicultural studies examining the impact of race, ethnicity, socioeconomic status, gender, and age in relation to the effectiveness of crisis intervention (Stone & Conley, 2004)

RECOMMENDED CLINICAL GUIDELINES FOR CRISIS INTERVENTION

Crisis intervention is a complex and delicate process. Above and beyond following a specific crisis intervention model, there are other practice considerations that require recognition. The following recommendations may aid clinicians in implementing and conducting crisis intervention with suicidal clients:

1. **Psychoeducation for support networks.** When possible, it is recommended that mental health practitioners educate family members and support networks regarding means of ensuring the safety of the individuals in suicidal crisis. According to McManus et al. (1997), 96% of suicide attempts occur at home and 94.4% of homes have at least one form of suicide available at the time an individual makes a suicide attempt. Among families who received psychoeducation regarding restricting access to lethal means, 86% locked up or disposed of means compared to only 32% of families who did not receive such psychoeducation. Although it is important to keep this recommendation in mind with all clients, it is specifically important when working with adolescents.
2. **Encouraging treatment engagement.** Having plans for follow-up treatment is not sufficient. It is important to recognize that approximately 60% of individuals who

present for initial treatment of suicidality attend their first scheduled follow-up outpatient treatment appointment (O'Brien, Holton, Hurren, Wyatt, & Hassanyeh, 1987). This is particularly concerning given that the 3-month period following a suicide attempt is the highest risk period for repeat suicidality (Rudd, Joiner, Jobes, & King, 1996). Consequently, it is recommended that specific attention be paid to and strategies be developed for supporting the individual's engagement in follow-up treatment. Such strategies may include addressing barriers to psychosocial barriers to treatment; providing additional contact via telephone, writing, or in-person to support attendance at outpatient treatment; and assessing and promoting the individual's motivation for treatment.

3. **Building resources.** In addition to enlisting the support of immediate family and significant others, it is recommended that clinicians working with individuals in suicidal crisis help their clients to develop resources they can access and implement during times of stress. Two important examples of such resource development include (a) a list of coping strategies that the client has found to be effective in managing prior stressors and (b) a list of individuals across social settings and networks who can be contacted in times of stress, such as extended family, neighbors, occupational or academic peers, social organizations (e.g., religious organizations, sports clubs), hotline numbers, support group information, and ER numbers, to name a few.

4. **Supervision.** Using formal supervision or clinical consultation with colleagues is highly recommended as a means of managing one's anxieties, concerns, and stress related to working with individuals in crisis. In addition, consultation can provide feedback and input on how the crisis intervention process is being carried out.

Crisis intervention can result in clinicians intentionally or unintentionally committing a number of possible errors or mistakes. It is important for clinicians not only to be aware of positive and effective recommendations but to be mindful of potential errors or pitfalls of crisis intervention. Some situations that mental health clinicians should guard against during a crisis intervention are listed as follows:

1. **Marginalize or dehumanize the client.** Mental health clinicians possess unequal power in their relationship with a client. During a crisis, clinicians can adopt an expert, directing, or evaluative position that increases this power imbalance or inequity. This may distance or marginalize the client (Shenassa, Rogers, Spalding, & Roberts, 2004).

2. **Contribute to the stigma of suicide.** Clinicians can directly add to a client's stigma or shame through their interactions or responses (e.g., self-reproach, judgment). More insidiously, clinicians can increase stigma by indirectly centering on the facts of the suicide and minimizing the process. The overwhelming focus on collecting data relating to the risk and lethality (i.e., the facts) with less attention on the narrative story, including the client's context and meaning (i.e., the process), can significantly contribute to a client's sense of being stigmatized (Shenassa et al., 2004).

3. **Superficial reassurance and/or minimization of intense affect.a** Clinicians may alienate their client by overly focusing on the positives, strengths, or optimistic aspects of the client's situation. This alienation can be further exacerbated by clinicians' avoidance or minimization of difficult, strong, and intense emotions (Neimeyer & Pfeiffer, 1994).

4. **Passivity and insufficient directiveness.** Overreliance on empathic responses during the crisis intervention process can have a negative impact on forming a collaborative relationship with the client. The crisis intervention process requires active, direct, and structured interventions (Neimeyer & Pfeiffer, 1994).

ROLE-PLAY 15.1

You are a mental health clinician in an outpatient mental health center. A client you treated briefly 2 years prior for depression unexpectedly presents to your office expressing suicidal ideation with intent.

Using this scenario, break into groups of three and assume the roles of the mental health clinician and the client. The third member will act as a recorder and can be called upon to consult and assist the mental health clinician. Engage in a role-play in which you would conduct a crisis intervention with this client.

ROLE-PLAY 15.2

You are a mental health clinician in an outpatient mental health center. A client you treated briefly 2 years prior for depression unexpectedly presents to your office expressing suicidal ideation with intent.

Using this scenario, break into groups of three and assume the roles of the mental health clinician and the supervisor. The third member will act as a recorder and can be called upon to consult and assist the mental health clinician. Engage in a role-play in which you would discuss this client with your supervisor. What questions might you ask? What kind of support might you try to elicit? Is the supervision for you? The client? Both?

SUMMARY

Treating individuals presenting in crisis, particularly a crisis involving suicide, can be an anxiety-provoking experience. As clinicians, our role often includes implementing a rational and empirically supported approach, as well as modeling a tone and pace in the intervention process that supports and facilitates management and resolution. It is essential to respond and interact according to the client's needs and situational context, while not overreacting to our own potential anxiety or concerns. Supervision and peer support from colleagues are important for any clinician conducting crisis intervention. There are several models of crisis intervention that can inform effective practice, yet it is essential to involve the client in every stage of the process.

1. Crisis is time limited.
2. Crisis stimuli are typically unexpected.
3. A crisis significantly disrupts and distresses an individual and overwhelms his or her coping strategies.
4. Crisis results in psychological disequilibrium.
5. Crisis intervention models are structured and sequential and, at times, the stages may overlap.
6. RSSCIM has been found to be an effective model of crisis intervention.
7. Mental health practitioners should provide psychoeducation to family members and support networks regarding means of ensuring the safety of the individual in suicidal crisis.
8. Collaborative work with clients throughout the crisis intervention process is essential to a successful outcome.
9. Crisis intervention is not a one-session process. It requires follow-up treatment with an emphasis on treatment engagement.
10. Accessing clients' strengths is important for crisis intervention, such as identifying coping strategies and building support networks.

ELECTRONIC RESOURCES

www.save.org
www.allaboutcounseling.com/crisis_hotlines.htm
www.suicidepreventionlifeline.org

KNOWLEDGE ACQUISITION TEST (KAT)

True or False

1. Nothing good can come from a crisis.
2. Crisis is a long-term, chronic process.
3. Individuals experiencing a crisis are unable to integrate new ideas or change.
4. The stages of crisis intervention are intended to be used sequentially.
5. There is limited research support for the use of crisis intervention models.
6. Reassurance is a key stage of Robert's seven-stage crisis intervention model (RSSCIM).
7. Assessment is not a requirement of crisis intervention models.
8. Good crisis intervention practice should incorporate supervision or consultation.
9. Families and extended support networks should not be included in crisis intervention.

Short Answer

10. Describe the key components of a crisis.
11. What are the seven stages of RSSCIM?
12. How may a clinician contribute to a client's feeling stigmatized through the process of crisis interventions?
13. Describe how technology is being used as a vehicle for crisis intervention.
14. What behaviors and actions should a clinician avoid when conducting crisis intervention?
15. Why would a mental health clinician avoid strong emotions expressed by a client during crisis intervention and what are the potential implications of this action?

Multiple Choice

16. Which is not a component of Stage V: Generate and explore alternatives in the RSSCIM?
    A. Clients acknowledge other solutions than suicide to their problems
    B. Brainstorming alternative solutions
    C. Can be completed before Stage IV
    D. Develop coping strategies
    E. All of the above
    F. None of the above
17. How can supervision assist mental health clinicians conducting crisis intervention with a client experiencing suicidality?
    A. Removes liability
    B. Can diffuse authority of the clinician
    C. Agency requirement
    D. Assists management of clinician's anxieties or stress
    E. All of the above
    F. None of the above
18. According to RSSCIM, which does not belong to Stage VI: Implement an action plan?
    A. Goal is to assist in improving the client's functioning
    B. Removal of lethal means of suicide

C. Plan should try to increase client support
D. Establish rapport
E. Identify future action steps

19. When considering ongoing treatment engagement to the plan following the initial treatment of suicidality, it is important for clinicians to remember that:
    A. Encouraging treatment engagement is not recommended as 95% of clients attend all recommended follow-up appointments.
    B. Treatment engagement to follow-up plans should be left to the client and not unduly influenced by the clinician.
    C. Encouraging treatment when the client is not ready to address his or her barriers to treatment is unethical.
    D. Client motivation develops over time and can be negatively impacted by an overly involved clinician.
    E. All of the above.
    F. None of the above.

20. Clinicians may contribute to a client's stigma or shame by:
    A. Centering on the facts of the suicide
    B. Minimizing the process of the crisis intervention
    C. Giving less attention to the client's narrative story
    D. Rushing over the client's meaning of events
    E. All of the above
    F. None of the above

REFERENCES

Berrouiguet, S., Alavi, Z., Vaiva, G., Courtet, P., Baca-García, E., Vidailhet, P., . . . Walter, M. (2014). SIAM (suicide intervention assisted by messages): The development of a post-acute crisis text messaging outreach for suicide prevention. *BioMed Central Psychiatry, 18,* 14–294.

Britton, P. C., Bossarte, R. M., Thompson, C., Kemp, J., & Conner, K. R. (2013). Influences on call outcomes among veteran callers to the national Veterans Crisis Line. *Suicide and Life-Threatening Behavior, 43*(5), 494–502.

Burman, S. (2003). Battered women: Stages of change and other treatment models that instigate and sustain leaving. *Brief Treatment and Crisis Intervention, 3*(1), 83–98.

Chen, H., Mishara, B. L., & Lui, X. X. (2010). A pilot study of mobile telephone message interventions with suicide attempters in China. *Crisis, 31*(2), 109–112.

Coveney, C. M., Pollock, K., Armstrong, S., & Moore, J. (2012). Callers' experiences of contacting a national suicide prevention helpline: Report of an online survey. *The Journal of Crisis Intervention and Suicide Prevention, 33*(6), 313–324.

Crosby, A. E., & Sacks, J. J. (2002). Exposure to suicide: Incidence and association with suicidal ideation and behavior: United States, 1994. *Suicide and Life-Threatening Behavior, 32*(3), 321–328.

Cross, W. F., Matthieu, M. M., Lezine, D., & Knox, K. L. (2010). Does a brief suicide prevention gatekeeper training program enhance observed skills? *Crisis, 31*(3), 149–159. http://doi.org/10.1027/0227-5910/a000014

Cross, W. F., Pisani, A. R., Schmeelk-Cone, K., Xia, Y., Tu, X., McMahon, M., . . . Gould, M. S. (2014). Measuring trainer fidelity in the transfer of suicide prevention training. *The Journal of Crisis Intervention and Suicide Prevention, 35*(3), 202–212.

De Silva, S., Parker, A., Purcell, R., Callahan, P., Liu, P., & Hetrick, S. (2013). Mapping the evidence of prevention and intervention studies for suicidal and self-harming behaviors in young people. *Crisis, 34,* 223–232.

Draper, J., Murphy, G., Vega, E., Covington, D. W., & McKeon, R. (2015). Helping callers to the National Suicide Prevention Lifeline who are imminent risk of suicide: The importance of active engagement, active rescue, and collaboration between crisis and emergency services. *Suicide and Life-Threatening Behavior, 45*(3), 261–270.

Frey, L. M., Hans, J. D., & Cerel, J. (2016). Perceptions of suicide stigma: How do social networks and treatment providers compare? *The Journal of Crisis Intervention and Suicide Prevention, 37*(2), 95–103.

Gilat, I., Tobin, Y., & Shahar, G. (2012). Responses to suicidal messages in an online support group: Comparison between trained volunteers and lay individuals. *Social Psychiatry and Psychiatric Epidemiology, 47*(12), 1929–1935.

Gould, M. S., Cross, W., Pisani, A. R., Munfakh, J. L., & Kleinman, M. (2013). Impact of applied suicide intervention skills training on the National Suicide Prevention Lifeline. *Suicide and Life-Threatening Behavior, 43*(6), 676–691.

Gould, M. S., Kalafat, J., Harrismunfakh, J. L., & Kleinman, M. (2007). An evaluation of crisis hotline outcomes. Part 2: Suicidal callers. *Suicide and Life-Threatening Behavior, 37,* 338–352. doi:10.1521/suli.2007.37.3.338

Gould, M. S., Lake, A. M., Munfakh, J. L., Galfavy, H., Kleinman, M., Williams, C., . . . McKeon, R. (2016). Helping callers to the National Suicide Prevention Lifeline who are at imminent risk of suicide: Evaluation of caller risk profiles and interventions implemented. *Suicide and Life-Threatening Behavior, 46*(2), 172–190.

Gould, M. S., Munfakh, J. L. Kleinman, M., & Lake, A. M. (2012). National Suicide Prevention Lifeline: Enhancing mental health care for suicidal individuals and other people in crisis. *Suicide and Life-Threatening Behavior, 42*(1), 22–35.

Granello, D. H. (2010). A suicide crisis intervention model with 25 practical strategies for implementation. *Journal of Mental Health Counseling, 32*(3), 218–235.

Greidanus, E., & Everall, R. D. (2010). Helper therapy in an online suicide prevention community. *British Journal of Guidance & Counseling, 38*(2), 191–204.

Hvidt, E. A., Ploug, T., & Holm, S. (2016). The impact of telephone crisis services on suicidal users: A systematic review of the past 45 years. *Mental Health Review Journal, 21*(2), 141–160.

Jacob, N., Scourfield, J., & Evans, R. (2014). Suicide prevention via the Internet: A descriptive review. *The Journal of Crisis Intervention and Suicide Prevention, 35*(4), 261–267.

Karver, M. S., Tarquini, S. J., & Caporino, N. E. (2010). The judgement of future suicide-related behavior: Helpline counselor's accuracy and agreement. *Crisis, 31*(5), 272–280.

Larkin, G. L., Rivera, H., Xu, H., Rincon, E., & Beautrais, A. L. (2011). Community responses to a suicidal crisis: Implications for suicide prevention. *Suicide and Life-Threatening Behavior, 41*(1), 79–86.

Lee, E., won Kim, S., & Enright, R. D. (2015). Case study of a survivor of suicide who lost all family members through parent-child collective suicide. *The Journal of Crisis Intervention and Suicide Prevention, 36*(1), 71–75.

Lee, M. (2007). Discovering strengths and competencies in female domestic violence survivors: An application of Roberts' continuum of the duration and severity of woman battering. *Brief Treatment and Crisis Intervention, 7*(2), 102–114.

Maris, R., Berman, A., & Silverman, M. (2000). *Comprehensive textbook of suicidology.* New York, NY: Guilford Press.

McManus, B. L., Kruesi, M. J., Dontes, A. E., Defazio, C. R., Piotrowski, J. T., & Woodward, P. J. (1997). Child and adolescent suicide attempts: An opportunity for emergency departments to provide injury prevention education. *The American Journal of Emergency Medicine, 15*(4), 357–360.

Mishara, B. L., Chagnon, F., Daigle, M., Balan, B., Raymond, S., Marcoux, I., . . . Berman, A. (2007). Which helper behaviors and intervention styles are related to better short-term outcomes in telephone crisis intervention? Results from a silent monitoring study of calls to the US 1–800-SUICIDE network. *Suicide and Life-Threatening Behavior, 37*(3), 308–321.

Mok, K., Jorm, A. F., & Pirkis, J. (2016). Who goes online for suicide-related reasons? A comparison of suicidal people who use the Internet for suicide-related reasons and those who do not. *Crisis: The Journal of Crisis Intervention and Suicide Prevention, 37*(2), 112–120.

Neimeyer, R. A., & Pfeiffer, A. M. (1994). Evaluation of suicide intervention effectiveness. *Death Studies, 18*(2), 131–166.

O'Brien, G., Holton, A., Hurren, K., Wyatt, L., & Hassanyeh, F. (1987). Deliberate self-harm and predictors of outpatient attendance. *British Journal of Psychiatry, 150*, 246–247.

Ritter, C., Teller, J. L. S., Marcussen, K., Munetz, M. R., & Teasdale, B. (2011). Crisis intervention team officer dispatch, assessment, and disposition: Interactions with individuals with severe mental illness. *International Journal of Law and Psychiatry, 34*(1), 30–38.

Roberts, A. R. (Ed.). (1991). *Conceptualizing crisis theory and the crisis intervention model.* Englewood Cliffs, NJ: Prentice-Hall.

Roberts, A. R. (2002). Assessment, crisis intervention, and trauma treatment: The integrative ACT intervention model. *Brief Treatment and Crisis Intervention, 2*(1), 17–18.

Roberts, A. R., & Dziegielewski, S. F. (Eds.). (1995). *Foundation skills and applications of crisis intervention and cognitive therapy.* Thousand Oaks, CA: Sage.

Roberts, A. R., & Everly, G. S. (2006). A meta-analysis of 36 crisis intervention studies. *Brief Treatment and Crisis Intervention, 6*(1), 10–21.

Roberts, A. R., & Jennings, T. (2005). Hanging by a thread: How failure to conduct an adequate lethality assessment resulted in suicide. *Brief Treatment and Crisis Intervention, 5*(3), 251–260.

Roberts, A. R., & Ottens, A. J. (2005). The seven-stage crisis intervention model: A road map to goal attainment, problem solving, and crisis resolution. *Brief Treatment and Crisis Intervention, 5*(4), 329–339.

Rudd, D., Joiner, T., Jobes, D., & King, C. (1996). The outpatient treatment of suicidality: An integration of science and recognition of its limitations. *Professional Psychology: Research and Practice, 30*(5), 437–446.

Shenassa, E. D., Rogers, M. L., Spalding, K. L., & Roberts, M. B. (2004). Safer storage of firearms at home and risk of suicide: A study of protective factors in a nationally representative sample. *Journal of Epidemiology and Community Health, 58*(10), 841–848.

Skovgaard Larsen, J. L., Frandsen, H., & Erlangsen, A. (2016). MYPLAN—A mobile phone application for supporting people at risk of suicide. *Crisis: The Journal of Crisis Intervention and Suicide Prevention, 37*(3), 236–240.

Spittal, M. J., Fedyszyn, I., Middleton, A., Bassilios, B., Gunn, J., Woodward, A., & Pirkis, J. (2015). Frequent callers to crisis helplines: Who are they and why do they call? *Australian and New Zealand Journal of Psychiatry, 49*(1), 54–64.

Stone, D. A., & Conley, J. A. (2004). A partnership between Roberts' crisis intervention model and the multicultural competencies. *Brief Treatment and Crisis Intervention, 4*(4), 367–375.

Sueki, H., & Ito, J. (2015). Suicide prevention through online gatekeeping using search advertising techniques: A feasibility study. *The Journal of Crisis Intervention and Suicide Prevention, 36*(4), 267–273.

Thomas, S. P. (2015). From the editor: A number to remember: 341741. *Issues in Mental Health Nursing, 36*(6), 395.

Westefeld, J. S., & Heckman-Stone, C. (2003). The integrated problem-solving model of crisis intervention: Overview and application. *Counseling Psychologist, 31*(2), 221–239.

CHAPTER SIXTEEN

COGNITIVE BEHAVIORAL THERAPY AND SUICIDE

Cognitive behavioral therapy (CBT) was originally conceived of as a treatment for depression (Beck, Rush, Shaw, & Emery, 1979). In the subsequent years since its development, a strong evidence base has been established for the use of CBT for individuals experiencing suicidality. This chapter presents CBT as a treatment model to address suicidal individuals. The theory behind CBT is outlined, and a thorough description of the key components and strategies of CBT is provided. Research examining the effectiveness of CBT across psychiatric disorders and settings is also explored. Recommendations for clinical practice when implementing CBT are also presented in this chapter.

GOALS AND OBJECTIVES

An understanding of:

- Theory behind CBT
- Major components of CBT
- Goals of CBT intervention
- Major tasks of CBT
- Treatment targets of CBT
- Core strategies used in CBT
- Evidence to support the use of CBT
- Populations for and settings in which CBT is supported
- Factors that impact the effectiveness of CBT
- Clinical considerations when conducting CBT

"CBT" is a term used to classify a type of psychotherapy that involves several approaches such as rational emotive behavioral therapy, cognitive therapy, rational behavioral therapy, and schema focused therapy, to name a few. Each approach has its own developmental history. This chapter focuses on cognitive therapy initially developed by Aaron Beck in the 1960s (Beck, 1964).

CBT grew out of cognitive theory and behavioral theory. *Cognitive theory* originated in the field of Psychology and the works of Alfred Adler (McMullin, 2000). Adler proposed that individuals are motivated by social drives and that behavior is shaped by beliefs regarding oneself, others, and the world (McMullin, 2000). This is known as the *cognitive triad* (Beck, 1976). Albert Ellis expanded Adler's theory by proposing that maladaptive emotions and behaviors were the result of irrational beliefs (Ellis, 1962). Ellis incorporated behavioral theory into CBT by adopting the stance that a person behaves in a certain way due to events that occur before and after the behavior is performed (antecedents, behaviors, and consequences). Aaron Beck refined Ellis's notion of the importance of irrational beliefs and devised a systematic treatment process known as *cognitive therapy* (Beck, 1976), commonly referred to under the umbrella term CBT.

Although initially developed to treat depression (Beck, 1976), CBT has subsequently become a time-limited effective approach for treating suicide (Beck, 2005; Brown et al., 2005; Weinberg, Gunderson, Hennen, & Cutter, 2006). CBT suggests that there is a connection between cognition, affect, and behavior. Feelings are based on ideas, and an individual can gain control over even the most overwhelming feelings by changing his or her thoughts. The goal is to determine the cognitions that are elicited by specific behaviors and to then modify those thoughts and behaviors (Beck, 1995; Beck et al., 1979). Also, individuals can develop coping and problem-solving strategies to better manage difficult thoughts and behaviors (Beck, 1995; Beck et al., 1979). In order to practice CBT effectively, a clinician needs to (a) be able to distinguish between thoughts and feelings, (b) recognize the connection between thoughts, feelings, and behaviors, and (c) understand that the way an individual interprets a given situation directly impacts his or her ensuing feelings and behaviors.

Individual Exercise 16.1

In this exercise, we are going to ask you to think of a past situation. This may evoke some distressing thoughts and feelings. You may consider skipping this exercise or reflecting on a historical experience in the distant rather than recent past, or a strong positive emotion rather than a negative one. The intention of this exercise is one of reflection and understanding related to CBT. It is not designed or intended for you to relive a traumatic event.

1. Think of a situation in which you experienced a strong emotion (frustration, anger, joy, etc.). Describe the situation with as much detail as possible.
2. Describe the various emotions that you felt with as much detail as possible.
3. What factors do you believe contributed to experiencing these emotions?
4. Prioritize these emotions in order of the most intense through least intense.
5. For questions 5 to 7, focus on your top two or three emotions. Is it possible you experienced these emotions for other reasons than the situation itself? Were there other factors that may have contributed to these emotions? Brainstorm and develop a list of other factors that may have accounted for the emotions you experienced.
6. On a scale of 1 to 10, 1 being "not strongly at all" and 10 being "very strongly," how strongly do you believe these other factors may have accounted for the emotions you felt?
7. What would it take to convince you that these other factors may have played a major role in the emotions you experienced?

Small Group Exercise 16.1

In small groups of two to three, please discuss, as you are comfortable, your responses to Individual Exercise 16.1. Remember, share only what you are comfortable to share. Answers are personal, and there are no correct or incorrect answers.

1. What were the response similarities in your group?
2. What were the response differences in your group?
3. Did you find any surprises in the group discussion? If so, what were they and how were you surprised?

COGNITIVE BEHAVIORAL THERAPY

CBT suggests that there is a connection between thoughts, emotions, and behavior. Intervention that targets or focuses on the thought processes can promote change in affect and behavior. CBT aims to identify and modify negative or maladaptive cognitions that contribute to problematic behaviors and emotions, which in turn further influence and maintain dysfunctional thought processes (Beck, 1995; Beck et al., 1979).

CBT posits that an individual's cognitions are based on attitudes or assumptions developed from earlier experiences (Beck, 1995; Beck et al., 1979). The manner in which an individual interprets and understands situations and information over time can lead to *maladaptive* or *dysfunctional* thought processes. Dysfunctional thoughts or beliefs can result in an individual distorting and misinterpreting experiences. Maladaptive thought processes include, but are not limited to, faulty *automatic thoughts* (thoughts that occur automatically without conscious effort or any attention). These thoughts can be true or untrue (Beck, 1967), overgeneralizations (using limited negative occurrences to make broad conclusions about a given issue), and *catastrophic thinking* (assuming or predicting the very worst possible outcome in all situations).

These cognitive deficits can impair an individual's capacity to regulate affect and manage interpersonal problems (Beck, 1995; Beck et al., 1979; Brent et al., 1997; Van der Sande, Buskens, Allart, van der Graaf, & van Engeland, 1997). For example, anxious individuals may have the maladaptive thought process of catastrophizing. This could negatively impact their ability to engage in effective, rewarding interpersonal relationships and may also negatively impact their academic and/or occupational performance.

CBT focuses on active identification and exploration of automatic thoughts, inferences, and assumptions (Beck, 1995; Beck et al., 1979). To understand the nature of an emotional episode or disturbance, it is essential to focus on the cognitive content of an individual's reaction to the upsetting event or stream of thoughts. The goal of CBT is to change the way clients think by using their automatic thoughts to identify core schema and to achieve cognitive restructuring. Interventions are then aimed at decreasing negative schemas (Beck, 1995; Beck et al., 1979; Rotherman-Borus, Piacentini, Miller, Graae, & Castro-Blanco, 1994). The literature also suggests that treatment should focus on decreasing cognitive distortions and rigidity to help clients develop more adaptive views of themselves, others, and the world, called the Cognitive Triad (Beck et al., 1979), to assist them in goal attainment (Emery, 1985).

Treatment also focuses on the client's behavior, specifically enhancing problem-solving skills as a coping mechanism. Individuals attempt to identify effective strategies (e.g., problem solving, relaxation, effective communication, social skills) for managing problems they encounter in everyday life (Beck, 1995; Pollock & Williams, 1998). Modifying and enhancing behavioral and coping skills influence one's thought processes and decisions (evaluating and adopting more adaptive beliefs) and the ability to tolerate difficult affect (e.g., anxiety, frustration, anger, low self-esteem).

Strategies are taught and assignments given aimed at the acquisition of behavioral and affect regulation (Beck, Rush, Shaw, & Emery, 1979; Blumenthal, 1990). Techniques include monitoring negative thoughts, countering catastrophic thinking, and identifying triggers to hopeless feelings and suicidal thoughts. Assignments include keeping a diary, completing automatic or dysfunctional thought records, setting up reinforcements for certain behaviors and activities, and physical exercise (Beck, 1995; Beck et al., 1979; Blumenthal, 1990). *Activity scheduling* is another major technique implemented in which the client schedules activities he or she enjoyed in the past in order to change emotions by changing behaviors. For example, a depressed client who has stopped meeting her friend for weekend lunches would be encouraged to plan this activity. Educating clients regarding the nature of the dysfunction and the treatment process, referred to as "psychoeducation," is also a major component of CBT (Beck, 1995; Beck et al., 1979; Brent et al., 1997).

There are several characteristics specific to CBT. Treatment is focused on the present, on the here and now, based on the idea that if one can correct current problematic or negative automatic thinking, then future emotional suffering will be reduced, if not eliminated. Treatment is goal oriented and problem focused (Beck, 1995).

CBT is considered a process of "guided discovery" (Beck, 1995), implying that the therapist acts as a catalyst and guide to help clients understand the connection between their thinking and the ways they feel and act. The major technique used to achieve this is Socratic questioning in which the therapist asks questions of the clients to help them discover for themselves the misconceptions under which they operate. When describing a situation that causes distress for a client, a clinician may ask a client the simple question, What would it mean to you if it were true? until the underlying belief is revealed.

CBT is also seen as a collaborative process that requires active engagement from both the mental health clinician and the client. Homework or between-session practice of skills developed in therapeutic sessions is important to the success of this approach. Mental health clinicians help frame client conclusions in the form of testable hypotheses. Clinicians are active, interactive, and engage the client through all phases of treatment (Beck, 1995).

The key strategy used in CBT is *cognitive restructuring* (Beck, 1995; Beck et al., 1979). Cognitive restructuring suggests that people can choose to think differently and this, ultimately, will lead to more constructive behavioral patterns. To change negative emotions and consequences, one must dispute and restructure negative, self-defeating thoughts. The goal is to replace one's negative irrational beliefs with more rational, constructive thoughts. Clients are taught to identify their "self-talk" (Beck, 1995; McMullin, 2000), the musts, shoulds, woulds, coulds, and oughts that they tell themselves about how they, others, and the world operate (McMullin, 2000).

CBT is a highly structured intervention. According to Beck (1995), a CBT mental health clinician's goals for an initial session include:

1. Establishing rapport and trust
2. Socializing the client into cognitive therapy
3. Educating the client about his or her disorder and the process of therapy for the disorder
4. Normalizing the client's difficulties and instilling hope
5. Eliciting (and correcting if necessary) the client's expectations for therapy
6. Gathering additional information about the client's difficulties
7. Using this information to develop a goal list

The recommended structure of this first session is to:

1. Set the agenda (providing a rationale for doing so)
2. Do a mood check
3. Briefly review the presenting problem and obtain an update
4. Identify problems and set goals
5. Educate the client about the cognitive model
6. Elicit the client's expectations for therapy
7. Educate the client about his or her disorder
8. Set homework
9. Provide a summary
10. Elicit feedback

The structure of subsequent sessions is recommended as follows (Beck, 1995):

1. Setting the agenda
2. Doing a mood check (including objective scores, such as standard measures)
3. Addressing agenda items including identifying automatic/intermediate/core thought, evaluating automatic/intermediate/core thoughts, modifying automatic/

intermediate/core thoughts, sharing cognitive conceptualization, and modifying goals as necessary

4. Setting homework
5. Providing a summary
6. Eliciting feedback

The tasks of CBT are hierarchical in nature. They are sequential and build upon one another. While the progress through which a client progresses through CBT is individualized, every client must pass through each task, in order. The first task of CBT is centered on teaching clients the theory behind CBT, often referred to as the *ABC model* (antecedents, events, and consequences; see Figure 16.1).

Clients are initially presented with the common misperception that their emotional or behavioral responses are caused by some triggering event or stimuli. This two-step model asserts that an experienced stimulus leads directly to a response. Clients are then presented with CBT's ABC model that posits that it is not the situation or event (event = A) that elicits a response (response = C), but rather thoughts about the situation or event that elicit the response (thoughts = B). The same situation can be interpreted in many different ways and that it is the thoughts or interpretation, the "B," rather than the situation, which is most important.

For example, a situation may occur in which a woman is sitting in a restaurant and noticing people staring at her and she begins to feel embarrassed. The two-step model would suggest that the staring led to her embarrassment. The ABC model, on the other hand, suggests that it is the way in which the staring was interpreted that led to her embarrassment. She could have had the thought "there must be food on my face," which led to her feeling embarrassed. Alternatively, if she had thought, "they are staring because I am beautiful" she may have felt happy or confident rather than embarrassed. If she had the thought "they are staring because I am ugly or I have been stood up" she may have felt depressed instead of embarrassed (Beck, 1995; McMullin, 2000). Consequently, CBT focuses on working with the client to understand his or her thoughts that are the "B" within the ABC model.

Once clients understand the ABC theory, they are taught to identify and modify their automatic thoughts. Automatic thoughts represent systematic negative bias in thought processes.

Clients are taught to identify actual words or images that go through their minds in stressful situations. The goal of this repeated review of distressing situations is the identification of themes and patterns of automatic thoughts (Beck, 1995; McMullin, 2000).

After clients have gained some mastery over identifying and modifying their automatic thoughts, the next task focuses on identifying and modifying intermediate thoughts. Intermediate beliefs represent rules, attitudes, and/or assumptions clients have about themselves, others, and the world, which give rise to specific automatic thoughts. The mental health practitioner stresses that there are a range of beliefs that the client could acquire and that they are learned, not innate, and therefore, can be revised. Mental health practitioners utilize behavioral experiments, rational–emotional role plays, and a cognitive continuum to modify intermediate beliefs (Beck, 1995; McMullin, 2000). Socratic questioning, also known as the "downward arrow" technique, is also a major tool utilized. In the downward arrow method, the clinician and client begin by discussing an upsetting event in which automatic thoughts occurred. The clinician then asks the client to

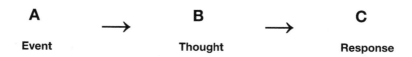

FIGURE 16.1 ABC model.

consider about each automatic thought: If this were true, what would it mean to you? This questioning continues until the underlying automatic thought is revealed (Burns, 1980; McMullin, 2000; Persons, 2008). For example, a client experienced an upsetting family reunion and after implementing the downward arrow technique, the client was able to recognize that he or she feels unlovable.

The task of identifying and modifying intermediate beliefs is followed by the task of identifying and modifying core beliefs. Core beliefs tend to be rigid, global ideas or generalizations clients hold about themselves and/or others. Core beliefs generally fall into two categories: helpless (e.g., I am needy, I am powerless) or unlovable (e.g., I am unwanted, I am bad). The groups or patterns of cognitions in which core beliefs occur are known as "schemas." Core beliefs represent the actual content of the schemas. Most individuals maintain positive core beliefs throughout their lives. It may be only in times of stress that negative core beliefs surface. For others, negative core beliefs may pervade their lives. While clients often identify traumatic events as the root of their core beliefs, often it is actually the smaller, less significant incidents that leave a standing impression. Core beliefs develop in childhood as a result of interactions with significant others. They serve as "life themes" that guide individuals throughout their lives. The fundamental goal of CBT is to uncover core beliefs. Several key strategies are used to identify and modify core beliefs, including Socratic questioning, creating a list of critical events, developing a master list of beliefs, and developing cognitive maps or cognitive conceptualization diagrams (Beck, 1995; McMullin, 2000).

EVIDENCE FOR CBT

CBT was initially developed for depression and has been found to be efficacious in its treatment (Beck et al., 1979). CBT's treatment of depression has been found to be effective across various age groups, including children, adolescents, and senior adults (Arnberg, 2014; Brent et al., 1998; Dubicka, 2010; March & Vitiello, 2009; Welch et al., 2010), concurrently with adolescents and parents (Spiriro et al., 2015) and older adults (Wilson, Mottram, & Vassilas, 2006). A recent literature review examining adolescent treatment of suicidality suggests that CBT interventions produce pre–post reductions in suicidality with moderate effect sizes and are at least as efficacious as pharmacotherapy in reducing suicidality (Devenish, Berk, & Lewis, 2016).

Similarly, CBT has demonstrated efficacy with the treatment of bipolar disorder (Scott et al., 2006; McMahon, Herr, Zerubavel, Hoertel, & Neacsiu, 2016), but research has not found it to be an effective treatment strategy for prevention of relapse in bipolar disorder (Lynch, Laws, & McKenna, 2010). Family-focused CBT (FF-CBT) was designed to treat youths with pediatric bipolar disorder and their family members and demonstrated efficacy in reducing youths' depressive symptoms (Weinstein, Henry, Katz, Peters, & West, 2015). Further research has found that FF-CBT may be efficacious in reducing acute mood symptoms and improving long-term psychosocial functioning among children with bipolar disorder (West et al., 2014). In regards to anxiety, CBT has been demonstrated effective in the treatment of phobias and generalized anxiety disorder in children (Walkup et al., 2008; Wolk, Kendal, & Beidas, 2015), adolescents (James, Soler, & Weatherall, 2005), and adults (Hunot, Churchill, Silva de Lima, & Teixeira, 2006). Similarly, CBT has been found to be effective in treating youths with obsessive-compulsive disorders (Turner, Heyman, Futh, & Lovell, 2009).

CBT has also shown some effectiveness in the treatment of feeding and eating disorders, including bulimia nervosa (Fairburn, Cooper, & Shafran, 2003; Fairburen et al., 1991; Wagner et al., 2016). A novel Internet-based cognitive behavioral treatment program has demonstrated a reduction of binge-eating episodes for individuals with binge-eating disorders (Wagner et al., 2016).

Trauma-related disorders, specifically posttraumatic stress disorder (PTSD), have increasingly applied CBT techniques and approaches (Bisson & Andrew, 2005; Cohen & Mannarino, 2008; Neely et al., 2013). Trauma-focused cognitive behavioral therapy (TF-CBT) is an evidence-based treatment for children with trauma symptoms including those with traumatic grief (Cohen et al., 2012; Cohen & Mannarino, 2011). Cognitive processing therapy (CPT) and prolonged exposure (PE) incorporated elements of CBT and have demonstrated positive outcomes in the treatment of individuals with PTSD, including decreased suicidal ideation and PTSD symptoms over the course of treatment (Gradus, Suvak, Wisco, Marx, & Resick, 2013).

Although CBT has not demonstrated efficacy in the treatment of schizophrenia (Lynch, et al., 2009), recent efforts are demonstrating some positive findings in CBT of specific components or symptoms related to psychosis (Freeman et al., 2015; Klingberg et al., 2012; Tarrier et al., 2014). For example, an adapted CBT approach, entitled Cognitive Behavioural Prevention of Suicide in psychosis protocol (CBSPp), has in a small clinical trial found the participants in the CBSPp group improved on primary outcome measures of suicidal ideation and suicide probability (Tarrier et al., 2014). Klingberg and colleagues (2012) investigated CBT and cognitive remediation in clients with schizophrenia; found no significant differences were identified (Klingberg et al., 2012). Another study investigating the effectiveness of CBT for obsessive-compulsive disorder co-occurring with psychosis found some evidence suggesting that CBT may be helpful treatment for obsessive-compulsive disorder (OCD)in these difficult-to-treat clients (Tundo et al., 2014). An investigation of CBT adapted for clients with persecutory delusions found the CBT intervention reduced worry and persecutory delusions in subjects (Freeman et al., 2015).

Increasingly, CBT is being adapted for other mental health conditions. While research is currently limited, investigations are applying CBT to personality disorders (Davidson & Tran, 2014; Davidson, Tyrer, Norrie, Palmer, & Tyrer, 2010; Norrie, Davidson, Tata, & Gumley, 2013) and body dysmorphic disorder (Enander et al., 2016).

CBT has not demonstrated efficacy in the treatment for bereaved individuals experiencing complicated grief (de Groot et al., 2007). While CBT treatment did not find a significant effect on complicated grief reactions, depression, and suicide risk factors among suicide survivors, it may serve as supportive counseling for suicide survivors (Wittouck, Van Autreve, Portzky, & van Heeringen, 2014). The versatility of CBT techniques has allowed for the model to be effectively adapted and applied to help individuals manage a number of health conditions including severe functional bowel disorders (Drossman et al., 2003), rheumatoid arthritis (Sharpe et al., 2001), breast cancer (Edelman, Bell, & Kidman, 1999), insomnia (Morgan, Dixon, Mathers, Thompson, & Tomeny, 2004), and multiple sclerosis (Fischer et al., 2015). In addition, CBT has demonstrated efficacy for treating depression in individuals following a stroke (Lincoln & Flannaghan, 2003) and after quitting smoking (Capron, Norr, Zvolensky, & Schmidt, 2014; Kahler et al., 2002; Kapson & Haaga, 2010).

CBT AND SUICIDE

CBT describes suicidal behavior as due to vulnerabilities that result from certain cognitive characteristics such as rigidity and poor problem solving and coping skills (Brown et al., 2005; Coleman & Casey, 2007; Freeman & Reinecke, 1994; Hetrick et al., 2014; Joiner, 2006; Pollock & Williams, 1998). Suicidal individuals, therefore, have difficulty generating solutions when faced with emotional problems (Brown et al., 2005; Freeman & Reinecke, 1994; Joiner, 2006; Pollock & Williams, 1998). They tend to have a negative attributional style, including negative views of themselves and of their future. Suicidal individuals will typically have experiences based on distortions, irrational beliefs, or pathological ways of viewing themselves and the world leading to hopelessness and a lack of positive expectations. Suicidal behavior is the result of erroneous or faulty logic (Beck et al., 1979). Such behavior is seen as an ineffective effort to resolve a problem (Rotherman-Borus, Piacentini, Miller, Graae, & Castro-Blanco, 1994).

A recent systematic review on the effectiveness of CBT in reducing suicidal cognitions and behavior in the adult population found that CBT treatments focusing on suicidal cognitions and behaviors were effective, but less evidence was found supporting that CBT, focusing on mental illness, reduces suicidal cognitions and behaviors (Mewton & Andrews, 2016). The authors recommend that clinicians should be trained in CBT techniques focusing specifically on suicidal cognitions and behaviors that are independent of the treatment of mental illness (Mewton & Andrews, 2016).

Another systematic review found that CBT-based psychotherapy, which combines cognitive behavioral and problem-solving therapies, was associated with fewer participants repeating self-harming behavior at 6- and 12-month follow-up, as well as significant improvements in the secondary outcomes of depression, hopelessness, suicidal ideation, and problem solving (Hawton et al., 2016).

Tarrier, Taylor, and Gooding (2008) conducted a meta-analysis that compared 28 studies treating suicidal behavior with CBT. Overall, findings indicated that CBT can reduce suicidal behavior in the immediate, short term and maintain significant, albeit less, reduction in suicidal behavior for the medium term. This review also found that CBT was significantly effective in the treatment of adults with suicidality but was not significant for adolescents (Tarrier, 2008). However, the authors recognize that there were limited studies focusing solely on adolescents, which may have contributed to this finding. In addition, CBT treatment is more effective when it directly focuses on some aspect or component of suicidal behavior, rather than when focused on other symptoms (e.g., depression) with a secondary focus on suicidality (Tarrier, 2008).

Two specific areas relating to the treatment of suicidality that CBT has demonstrated some promise in working with include changing negative schemas or automatic thoughts and improving problem-solving and coping skills. Adapting CBT to suicidality (ideation or behavior) has led to the specific tailoring of certain aspects of the approach, specifically the maladaptive thoughts or core schemas of hopelessness, worthlessness or self-criticism, and perfectionism (Coleman & Casey, 2007). Preliminary research has found that decreasing maladaptive automatic thoughts is associated with decreased suicidal ideation (Coleman & Casey, 2007).

Although CBT is typically delivered in a face-to-face approach, online applications of CBT have emerged, which tend to be more population focused (Guille, Zhao, Krystal, Nichols, Brady, & Sen, 2015; Lai, Maniam, Chan, & Ravindran, 2014; Mewton & Andrews, 2015; Millings & Carnelley, 2015; Robinson et al., 2014; Wagner et al., 2016; Wagner, Horn, & Maercker, 2014). For example, Guille and colleagues (2015) examined a brief web-based CBT treatment, called "wCBT program," which was developed as part of the training program for interning physicians (Guille et al., 2015). As a prevention program, wCBT was associated with reduced likelihood of suicidal ideation among medical interns (Guille et al., 2015). Another electronic adaptation of CBT, entitled Internet-delivered cognitive behavioral therapy (iCBT) for depression, was found to be a helpful method of reducing suicide ideation (Mewton & Andrews, 2015).

CBT, such as cognitive behavioral problem–solving therapy, which focuses on building and developing problem-solving skills, has also yielded some encouraging findings relating to reduced suicidality (Eskin, Ertekin, & Demir, 2008; Salkovskis, Atha, & Storer, 1990). Specifically, the targeting, development, and improvement of problem-solving skills may reduce levels of depression and suicide potential while increasing levels of protective factors, such as self-esteem and assertiveness (Eskin et al., 2008). CBT's focus on problem solving has also been adapted and applied to clients presenting with suicidal crises in psychiatric emergency services by helping clients and their families to develop problem-solving strategies and to enhance their ability to cope with immediate difficulties (Asarnow, Berk, & Baraff, 2009; Bilsker & Forster, 2003).

Emergent Models of CBT for Youths and Families

More recently, CBT has been adapted as a treatment for suicidality, specifically among adolescents. Research on these models to date has been limited and further research is needed to further demonstrate the populations for which these interventions can be effective at reducing suicide risk and the mechanisms of change in each model that result in their effectiveness. Nevertheless, these interventions are promising as the limited evidence that does exist suggests they are effective at reducing suicide risk.

The SAFETY Program (Asarnow, Berk, Hughes, & Anderson, 2015) is a model of cognitive behavioral family treatment for adolescent suicide attempters who utilize emergency services. The model is based on a social–ecological cognitive behavioral approach. The SAFETY Program proposes that in order to effectively address an adolescent's suicidality, treatment must emphasize enhancing protective supports within social systems (family, peers, and community) and includes one therapist for the youth and another focusing on the family and/or community.

The SAFETY Program addresses limitations of other approaches in several ways by looking at previously identified challenges in novel ways. The Program acknowledges that many youths receiving emergency-based services fail to attend or receive adequate follow-up mental health treatment. As such, in-home treatment is used for the first SAFETY session and then as needed. The family focus also aims to increase parental motivation and decrease family treatment barriers.

Additionally, the SAFETY Program recognizes that suicidal behavior can occur within multiple contexts and presentations. In order for any one approach to be effective, it needs to be broad enough to be relevant across diagnostic groups/presenting problems yet specific enough to address suicidal behavior. Therefore, the SAFETY Program uses core principles to guide treatment and targets treatment around a cognitive behavioral fit analysis (CBFA) conducted for each adolescent that specifies key risk and protective processes for each individual case that are likely to impact the risk of a repeat suicide attempt.

The SAFETY Program is a 12-week treatment designed to be integrated within emergency services. Sessions begin with an initial phase in which youths work with the youth therapist, while parents work with the parent therapist. This is followed by a second phase that is family focused where all come together to practice the skills identified as critical for preventing repeat suicide attempts.

Research has demonstrated that SAFETY Program results in improvements on measures of suicidal behavior, hopelessness, youth and parental depression, and youth social adjustment (Asarnow et al., 2015). However, other studies are needed to further provide support for the effectiveness of the model.

Cognitive behavioral therapy for suicide prevention (CBT-SP; Stanley et al., 2009) is a manualized treatment aimed specifically at reducing the risk for future suicidal behaviors in suicidal adolescents who attempted suicide within the past 3 months. CBT-SP focuses on developing the cognitive, behavioral, and interactional skills required to help the adolescent resist engaging in suicidal behavior. A main focus of CBT-SP is the identification of risk factors and stressors that are present immediately before and right after the adolescent's suicide attempt. This approach views these stressors as resulting from emotional, cognitive, behavioral, and/or family processes. Relevant risk factors are identified by conducting a detailed chain analysis of the events leading up to the suicidal crisis and the adolescent's reactions to these events.

CBT-SP assumes that adolescents experience deficits in their abilities or motivations to cope with suicidal crises. These deficits may include the difficulty in regulating emotions, resolving problems, tolerating distress, and managing negative thoughts or beliefs such as hopelessness or worthlessness. The main strategy of the treatment approach is to develop an individualized case conceptualization that identifies problem areas and details specific skills that can be implemented during periods of distress. These skills may include cognitive-restructuring skills (e.g., identifying and evaluating automatic thoughts), behavioral activation, problem-solving techniques, and emotion regulation techniques (e.g., mindfulness and distress tolerance skills).

As part of CBT-SP, parents also meet with their child's therapist for family sessions focused specifically on suicide risk reduction strategies. Family issues are addressed only to the extent that they are viewed by the patient, family, and clinician to be relevant to the prevention of future suicide attempts.

In addition to addressing relevant family issues, CBT-SP recognizes that suicidal crises occur within the context of the adolescents' environment and that environmental factors (including problematic peer or romantic relationships, the presence of abuse, poor school performance) often contribute to suicide risk. Therefore, these contextual factors are also the focus of treatment.

The CBT-SP model consists of an acute phase and a continuation phase, both of which are to be completed within 6 months. The acute phase comprises approximately 12 to 16 weekly sessions consisting mostly of individual sessions with up to six family sessions. The acute phase of treatment consists of three subphases of an initial, middle, and end-of-acute-treatment phase. This is followed by the continuation phase of treatment, which lasts an additional 12 weeks and consists of up to six sessions that are tapered in frequency and a maximum of up to three additional family sessions.

Research on the effectiveness of CBT-SP for adolescents indicates that it is a feasible intervention (Stanley et al., 2009); future research to determine its effectiveness is warranted. Integrated cognitive behavioral therapy (I-CBT; Esposito-Smythers, Spirito, Kahler, Hunt, & Monti, 2011) is another manualized treatment model of CBT adapted after several iterations (Donaldson, Spirito, & Esposito-Smythers, 2005; Esposito-Smythers, Spirito, Uth, & LaChance, 2006) for use specifically with adolescents with co-occurring substance abuse and suicidality. Based on a social-cognitive learning theory perspective, I-CBT proposes that mental health problems result, in part, from prior learning experiences, particularly the learning of social behaviors and core beliefs. Such learning experiences are based on operant and classical conditioning processes, social reinforcement, and observation and modeling of others (Bandura, 1986). In order to effect change in these areas, adolescents must relearn more adaptive ways of relating to self and others and be given the opportunity to develop self-efficacy in the use of these new skills. The relearning is achieved through the use of CBT, which focuses on both behavioral change as well as cognitive-restructuring techniques to facilitate new skill acquisition.

According to I-CBT, in order to effectively address the issues experienced by adolescents with comorbid substance use disorders and suicidality, treatment must target the common maladaptive behaviors and beliefs that underlie problems in these areas. These maladaptive behaviors tend to include cognitive distortions, poor coping, and poor communication skills. Therefore, I-CBT in individual sessions with the adolescents focuses largely on individual skill development (i.e., cognitive restructuring, problem solving, emotion regulation, communication).

I-CBT recognizes the role of parenting and suggests that ineffective parenting skills also contribute to the adolescent's problem behavior. Therefore, I-CBT includes family sessions and parenting skills training aimed at working with parents on developing appropriate modeling and parenting practices (e.g., affect management, monitoring, communication, contingency management). Consistent with social-cognitive learning theory, the I-CBT protocol integrated CBT techniques to remediate maladaptive cognitions and behaviors found to underlie both adolescent suicidality and alcohol and other drug (AOD) use disorders.

The model incorporates individual skills training along with family sessions across 12 months of treatment comprising a 6-month active phase, a 3-month continuation phase, and a 3-month maintenance treatment phase. In the acute treatment phase, adolescents attended weekly sessions while parents attended weekly to biweekly sessions. In the continuation treatment phase, adolescents attended biweekly sessions and parents biweekly to monthly sessions. In the maintenance treatment phase, adolescents attended monthly sessions and parents attended monthly sessions as needed. In addition to these sessions, I-CBT incorporates one motivational interviewing session for adolescents to improve readiness for treatment as well as one for parents aimed at facilitating treatment engagement.

Evidence from a preliminary randomized trial suggests that for adolescents with co-occurring alcohol or other drug-use disorders as well as suicidality, I-CBT is effective at reducing both substance use and suicidal behavior as well as significantly decreasing the use of additional health services, including inpatient psychiatric hospitalizations and emergency department visits (Esposito et al., 2011; Esposito-Smythers et al., 2006; Glenn et al., 2015). Specifically, as compared to treatment as usual, I-CBT has been found to result in greater reductions in heavy drinking days, days of marijuana use, and marijuana-related problems over the course of treatment (Esposito et al., 2011). Additionally, youths who received I-CBT reported fewer suicide attempts, psychiatric hospitalizations, and emergency room visits (Esposito et al., 2011).

RECOMMENDED CLINICAL GUIDELINES FOR CBT

CBT is an effective treatment approach for addressing suicidality. It is a structured approach that requires active participation of both the client and the therapist. As a mental health professional working with suicidal clients and practicing CBT, several recommended clinical guidelines to consider include the following:

1. *Automatic thoughts.* Just like clients, therapists too are subject to automatic thoughts that can interfere with the treatment process. Therapists may have automatic thoughts about their ability to manage a session, client, or issue, or they may have automatic thoughts about the responses their clients will have to an intervention they suggest or even to them as individuals. When working from a CBT approach, it is essential for therapists to monitor their own automatic thoughts and how they may be interfering with the treatment process (Beck, 1995).

2. *Summarize.* Providing a summary and seeking feedback throughout sessions and at the closing of sessions is critical. A clinician practicing CBT should never assume that a client understands what the therapist intends or that the therapist understands what the clients intends. It is important to clarify the understanding of both parties to ensure that the treatment process stays on track. Even if an issue seems very clear, it is recommended to always summarize the issue at hand for the client and seek the client's feedback regarding his or her understanding of the issue. As the client acclimates to the CBT process, he or she may take over the responsibility of making summarizations (Beck, 1995; Haarhoff, 2006).

3. *Homework.* For CBT to be effective, clients need to practice strategies and techniques outside of session. Homework plays a major role in this treatment approach. If homework is to be successful, it must be reinforced by the therapist. It is recommended that homework assignments always be reviewed. Even if there is a big issue that has arisen in between sessions or during a session that requires a change in the set agenda, it should never compromise the homework review. It may be that a client's distress necessitates the delay of the homework review until later in the session but it should not be forsaken altogether (Beck, 1995; Neimeyer & Feixas, 1990).

4. *CBT treatment for suicide needs to directly target suicidality.* If suicidality is the focus of treatment, CBT needs to target it directly and not indirectly or as a secondary symptom related to another presenting problem (e.g., depression). For treatment to be most effective, CBT suicide treatment needs to be designed, planned, tailored, and implemented around the client's suicidality (Tarrier, 2008). Areas of focus may include improving or changing maladaptive thoughts and enhancing client's coping and problem-solving abilities (Coleman & Casey, 2007; Eskin et al., 2008).

ROLE-PLAY 16.1

You are a mental health clinician in an outpatient mental health center. A client you treated briefly 2 years prior for depression unexpectedly presents to your office expressing suicidal ideation with intent.

Using this scenario, break into groups of three and assume the roles of the mental health clinician and the client. The third member will act as a recorder and can be called upon to consult and assist the mental health clinician. Engage in a role-play in which you would implement CBT with this client.

ROLE-PLAY 16.2

You are a mental health clinician in an outpatient mental health center. A client you treated briefly 2 years prior for depression unexpectedly presents to your office expressing suicidal ideation with intent.

Using this scenario, break into groups of three and assume the roles of the mental health clinician and the supervisor. The third member will act as a recorder and can be called upon to consult and assist the mental health clinician. Engage in a role-play in which you would discuss this client with your supervisor. What questions might you ask? What kind of support might you try to elicit? Is the supervision for you? The client? Both?

SUMMARY

CBT is a short-term, goal-oriented, evidence-based treatment approach for addressing suicidality. Initially developed for the treatment of depression, CBT has demonstrated wide applicability to a number of diagnoses and presenting problems, including suicidality. CBT focuses on the connection between thoughts, behaviors, and emotions. The goal of CBT is to identify and address maladaptive thought processes triggered by stressful events that result in clients experiencing difficult emotional and behavioral responses. CBT has demonstrated some promise in working with suicidal clients to change negative schemas or automatic thoughts as well as to improve problem-solving and coping skills.

KEY POINTS

1. CBT stresses the connection between cognition, affect, and behavior.
2. CBT focuses on active exploration of automatic thoughts, inferences, and assumptions.
3. Even the most overwhelming feelings can be modified by modifying one's thoughts.
4. The goal of CBT is to change the way clients think by using their automatic thoughts to identify core schema and to achieve cognitive restructuring.
5. Suicidality from a CBT perspective is the result of cognitive deficits such as rigidity, poor problem solving, and poor coping skills.
6. CBT follows the ABC model of understanding the connection between events, thoughts, and resulting responses (emotions and behaviors).
7. CBT has been found to be efficacious in the treatment of a number of mental disorders (e.g., depression, anxiety, and eating disorders) and other presenting problems (e.g., arthritis and insomnia).
8. CBT has been demonstrated to reduce suicidal behavior in the immediate, short term, and maintain reduction in suicidal behavior for the medium term.
9. CBT is significantly effective in the treatment of adults with suicidality but was not found to be significant for the treatment of adolescents with suicidality.
10. For the treatment of suicidality, CBT should focus directly on the client's suicidality.

ELECTRONIC RESOURCES

www.nacbt.org

www.the-iacp.com

www.cognitivetherapynyc.com

www.behavioralassociates.com/treatment_mot_cog.asp

www.med.upenn.edu/cct

www.cbtarena.com

KNOWLEDGE ACQUISITION TEST (KAT)

True or False

1. Cognitive behavioral therapy (CBT) is a long-term treatment approach.
2. CBT focuses on personality development.
3. The connection between cognitions, affect, and behavior is central to CBT.
4. CBT believes that specific situations lead directly to emotions.
5. Cognitive restructuring is a key strategy in CBT.
6. CBT has been found to effectively treat depression.
7. CBT has been found to effectively treat complicated grief.
8. CBT has been demonstrated to reduce suicidal behavior in the long term.
9. CBT has been shown to significantly treat adolescent suicide.
10. CBT can be used with suicidal clients in emergency departments.

Short Answer

11. Describe how CBT accounts for suicidality.
12. What are intermediate beliefs and what strategies are used to modify them?
13. What are core beliefs and what are the strategies used to modify them?
14. Describe the ABC model and provide an example.
15. For what conditions and diagnoses has CBT been demonstrated effective?
16. Under what conditions and diagnoses does CBT not have demonstrated efficacy?

Multiple Choice

17. Which of the following is a key characteristic of CBT?
    A. Is time limited
    B. Is highly structured
    C. Involves homework
    D. Monitors activities
    E. None of the above
    F. All of the above
18. Which of the following comes second in the ABC model?
    A. The event or situation
    B. The emotion experienced by the individual
    C. The thought the individual has about the event or situation
    D. None of the above
    E. All of the above
19. For which diagnoses has CBT not demonstrated treatment efficacy?
    A. Depression
    B. Schizophrenia
    C. Generalized anxiety disorder
    D. Posttraumatic stress disorder
    E. All of the above
20. CBT treatment for suicide is effective when it directly focuses on:
    A. Cognitive distortions
    B. Problem solving
    C. Coping strategies
    D. None of the above
    E. All of the above

REFERENCES

Arnberg, A. (2014). CBT for children with depressive symptoms: A meta-analysis. *Cognitive Behavioral Therapy, 43*(4), 275–288.

Asarnow, J. R., Berk, M. S., & Baraff, L. J. (2009). Family intervention for suicide prevention: A specialized emergency department intervention for suicidal youths. *Professional Psychology: Research and Practice, 40*(2, Special Section: Interventions for Suicidal Persons Across the Life Span), 118–125.

Asarnow, J. R., Berk, M., Hughes, J. L., & Anderson, N. L. (2015). The SAFETY Program: A treatment-development trial of a cognitive-behavioral family treatment for adolescent suicide attempters. *Journal of Clinical Child & Adolescent Psychology, 44*(1), 194–203.

Bandura, A. (1986). *Social foundations of thought and action: A social cognitive theory.* Englewood Cliffs, NJ: Prentice-Hall.

Beck, A. T. (1964). Thinking and depression II: Theory and therapy. *Archives of General Psychiatry, 10,* 561–571.

Beck, A. T. (1967). *Depression—Clinical experimental and theoretical aspects.* New York, NY: Harper & Row.

Beck, A. T. (Ed.). (1976). *Cognitive therapy and the emotional disorders.* New York, NY: International Universities Press.

Beck, A. T. (2005). The current state of cognitive therapy: A 40-year retrospective. *Archives of General Psychiatry, 62,* 953–959.

Beck, A. T., Rush, A. J., Shaw, B. F., & Emery, G. (Eds.). (1979). *Cognitive therapy of depression.* New York, NY: Guilford Press.

Beck, J. S. (Ed.). (1995). *Cognitive therapy: Basics and beyond.* New York, NY: Guilford Press.

Bilsker, D., & Forster, P. (2013). Problem-solving intervention for suicidal crises in the psychiatric emergency service. *Crisis, 24*(3), 134–136.

Blumenthal, S. J. (1990). Youth suicide: Risk factors, assessment, and treatment of adolescent and young adult suicidal patients. *Psychiatric Clinic of North America, 13*(3), 511–551.

Brent, D. A., Emslie, G. J., Clarke, G. N., Asarnow, J., Spirito, A., Ritz, L., . . . Keller, M. B. (2009). Predictors of spontaneous and systematically assessed suicidal adverse events in the treatment of SSRI-resistant depression in adolescents (TORDIA) study. *American Journal of Psychiatry, 166*(4), 418–426.

Brent, D. A., Greenhill, L. L., Compton, S., Emslie, G., Wells, K., Walkup, J. T., . . . Turner, J. B. (2009). The treatment of adolescent suicide attempters study (TASA): Predictors of suicidal events in an open treatment trial. *Journal of the American Academy of Child & Adolescent Psychiatry, 48*(10), 987–996.

Brent, D. A., Holder, D., Kolko, D., Birmaher, B., Baugher, M., & Roth, C., . . . Johnson, B. A. (1997). A clinical psychotherapy trial for adolescent depression comparing cognitive, family, and supportive therapy. *Archives of General Psychiatry, 54,* 877–885.

Brent, D. A., Kolko, D. J., Birmaher, B., Baugher, M., Bridge, J., Roth, C., & Holder, D. (1998). Predictors of treatment efficacy in a clinical trial of three psychosocial treatments for adolescent depression. *Journal of the American Academy of Child & Adolescent Psychiatry, 37*(9), 906–914.

Brown, G. K., Have, T. T., Henriques, G. R., Xie, S. X., Hollander, J. E., & Beck, A. T. (2005). Cognitive therapy for the prevention of suicide attempts: A randomized controlled trial. *Journal of the American Medical Association, 294,* 563–570.

Burns, D. D. (1980). Feeling good: The new mood therapy. New York, NY: Marrow.

Capron, D. W., Norr, A. M., Zvolensky, M. J., & Schmidt, N. B. (2014). Prospective evaluation of the effect of an anxiety sensitivity intervention on suicidality among smokers. *Cognitive Behavior Therapy, 43*(1), 72–82.

Cohen, J. A., & Mannarino, A. P. (2008). Trauma-focused cognitive behavioural therapy for children and parents. *Child and Adolescent Mental Health, 13*(4), 158–162.

Cohen, J. A., & Mannarino, A. P. (2011). Trauma-focused CBT for traumatic grief in military children. *Journal of Contemporary Psychotherapy, 41*(4), 219–227.

Coleman, D., & Casey, J. T. (2007). Therapeutic mechanisms of suicidal ideation: The influence of changes in automatic thoughts and immature defenses. *Crisis: Journal of Crisis Intervention & Suicide, 28*(4), 198–203.

Davidson, K. M., & Tran, C. F. (2014). Impact of treatment intensity on suicidal behavior and depression in borderline personality disorder: A critical review. *Journal of Personality Disorder, 28*(2), 181–197.

Davidson, K. M., Tyrer, P., Norrie, J., Palmer, S. J., & Tyrer, H. (2010). Cognitive therapy v. usual treatment for borderline personality disorder: Prospective 6-year follow-up. *British Journal of Psychiatry, 197*(6), 456–462.

de Groot, M., de Keijser, J., Neeleman, J., Kerkhof, A., Nolen, W., & Burger, H. (2007). Cognitive behaviour therapy to prevent complicated grief among relatives and spouses bereaved by suicide: Cluster randomised controlled trial. *British Medical Journalj, 334*(7601), 994.

Devenish, B., Berk, L., & Lewis, A. J. (2016). The treatment of suicidality in adolescents by psychosocial interventions for depression: A systematic literature review. *Australian and New Zealand Journal of Psychiatry, 50*(8), 726–740.

Donaldson, D., Spirito, A., & Esposito-Smythers, C. (2005). Treatment for adolescents following a suicide attempt: Results of a pilot trial. *Journal of the American Academy of Child and Adolescent Psychiatry, 44*, 113–120.

Drossman, D. A., Toner, B. B., Whitehead, W. E., Diamant, N. E., Dalton, C. B., Duncan, S.,.... Le, T. (2003). Cognitive-behavioral therapy versus education and desipramine versus placebo for moderate to severe functional bowel disorders. *Gastroenterology, 125*(1), 19–31.

Dubicka, B. (2010). Combined treatment with cognitive-behavioural therapy in adolescent depression: Meta-analysis. *British Journal of Psychiatry, 197*(6), 433–440.

Edelman, S., Bell, D. R., & Kidman, A. D. (1999). A group cognitive behaviour therapy programme with metastatic breast cancer patients. *Psycho-Oncology, 8*(4), 295–305.

Ellis, A. (Ed.). (1962). *Reason and emotion in psychotherapy.* New York, NY: Lyle Stuart.

Emery, G. (1985). Cognitive therapy: Techniques and applications. In A. T. Beck & G. Emery (Eds.), *Anxiety disorders and phobias: A cognitive perspective* (pp. 167–313). New York, NY: Basic Books.

Enander, J., Andersson, E., Mataix-Cols, D., Lichtenstein, L., Alström, K., Andersson, G., . . . Rück, C. (2016). Therapist guided internet based cognitive behavioural therapy for body dysmorphic disorder: Single blind randomised controlled trial. *British Medical Journal, 352*, i241.

Eskin, M., Ertekin, K., & Demir, H. (2008). Efficacy of a problem-solving therapy for depression and suicide potential in adolescents and young adults. *Cognitive Therapy and Research 32*, 227–245.

Esposito-Smythers, C., Spirito, A., Kahler, C. W., Hunt, J., & Monti, P. (2011). Treatment of co-occurring substance abuse and suicidality among adolescents: A randomized trial. *Journal of Consulting and Clinical Psychology, 79*(6), 728–739.

Esposito-Smythers, C., Spirito, A., Uth, R., & LaChance, H. (2006). Cognitive behavioral treatment for suicidal alcohol abusing adolescents: Development and pilot testing. *American Journal of Addiction, 15*, 126–130.

Fairburn, C. G., Cooper, Z., & Shafran, R. (2003). Cognitive behaviour therapy for eating disorders: A "transdiagnostic" theory and treatment. *Behaviour Research and Therapy, 41*(5), 509–528.

Fairburn, C. G., Jones, R., Peveler, R. C., Carr, S. J., Solomon, R. A., O'Connor, M. E., . . . Hope, R. A. (1991). Three psychological treatments for bulimia nervosa: A comparative trial. *Archives of General Psychiatry, 48*(5), 463–469.

Fischer, A., Schröder, J., Vettorazzi, E., Wolf, O. T., Pöttgen, J., Lau, S., . . . Gold, S. M. (2015). An online programme to reduce depression in patients with multiple sclerosis: A randomised controlled trial. *The Lancet Psychiatry, 2*(3), 217–223.

Freeman, A., & Reinecke, M. (Eds.). (1994). *Cognitive therapy of suicidal behavior.* New York, NY: Springer Publishing.

Freeman, D., Dunn, G., Startup, H., Pugh, K., Cordwell, J., Mander, H., . . . Kingdon, D. (2015). Effects of cognitive behaviour therapy for worry on persecutory delusions in patients with psychosis (WIT): A parallel, single-blind, randomised controlled trial with a mediation analysis. *The Lancet Psychiatry, 2*(4), 305–313.

Glenn, C. R., Franklin, J. C., & Nock, M. K. (2015). Evidence-based psychosocial treatments for self-injurious thoughts and behaviors in youth. *Journal of Clinical Child & Adolescent Psychology, 44*(1), 1–29.

Gradus, J. L., Suvak, M. K., Wisco, B. E., Marx, B. P., & Resick, P. A. (2013). Treatment of posttraumatic stress disorder reduces suicidal ideation. *Depression and Anxiety, 30*(10), 1046–1053.

Guille, C., Zhao, Z., Krystal, J., Nichols, B., Brady, K., & Sen, S. (2015). Web-based cognitive behavioral therapy intervention for the prevention of suicidal ideation in medical interns: A randomized clinical trial. *Journal of the American Medical Association Psychiatry, 72*(12), 1192–1198.

Haarhoff, B. A. (2006). The importance of identifying and understanding therapist schema in cognitive therapy training and supervision. *New Zealand Journal of Psychology, 35*(3), 126–131.

Hetrick, S., Yuen, H. P., Cox, G., Bendall, S., Yung, A., Pirkis, J., & Robinson, J. (2014). Does cognitive behavioural therapy have a role in improving problem solving and coping in adolescents with suicidal ideation? *The Cognitive Behaviour Therapist, 7*, e13.

Hawton, K., Witt, K. G., Taylor Salisbury, T. L., Arensman, E., Gunnell, D., Hazell, P., . . . van Heeringen, K. (2016, May). Psychosocial interventions for self-harm in adults. *Cochrane Database of Systematic Reviews*, (5), CD012189.

Hunot, V., Churchill, R., Teixeira, V., & de Lima, M. S. (2006). Psychological therapies for generalised anxiety disorder. *Cochrane Database of Systematic Reviews*. doi:10.1002/14651858.CDC1848.pub4

James, A. C. J., Soler, A., & Weatherall, R. (2005). Cognitive behavioural therapy for anxiety disorders in children and adolescents. *Cochrane Library*. doi:10.1002/14651858.CD004690.pub2

Joiner, T. (Ed.). (2006). *Why people die by suicide*. Cambridge, MA: Harvard University Press.

Kapson, H. S., & Haaga, D. A. F. (2010). Depression vulnerability moderates the effects of cognitive behavior therapy in a randomized controlled trial for smoking cessation. *Behavioral Therapy*, 41(4), 447–460.

Klingberg, S., Herrlich, J., Wiedemann, G., Wölwer, W., Meisner, C., Engel, C., . . . Wittorf, A. (2012). Adverse effects of cognitive behavioral therapy and cognitive remediation in schizophrenia: Results of the treatment of negative symptoms study. *Journal of Nervous and Mental Disease*, 200(7), 569–576.

Lai, M. H., Maniam, T., Chan, L. F., & Ravindran, A. V. (2014). Caught in the web: A review of web-based suicide prevention. *Journal of Medical Internet Research*, 16(1), e30.

Lincoln, N. B., & Flannaghan, T. (2003). Cognitive behavioral psychotherapy for depression following stroke: A randomized controlled trial. *Stroke*, 34(1):111–115.

Lynch, D., Laws, K. R., & McKenna, P. J. (2010). Cognitive behavioural therapy for major psychiatric disorder: Does it really work? A meta-analytical review of well-controlled trials. *Psychological Medicine*, 40(1), 9–24.

March, J. S., & Vitiello, B. (2009). Clinical messages from the treatment for adolescents with depression study (TADS). *American Journal of Psychiatry*, 166(10), 1118–1123.

McMahon, K., Herr, N. R., Zerubavel, N., Hoertel, N., & Neacsiu, A. D. (2016). Psychotherapeutic treatment of bipolar depression. *Psychiatric Clinics of North America*, 39(1), 5–56.

McMullin, R. (Ed.). (2000). *A new handbook of cognitive therapy techniques*. New York, NY: W.W. Norton.

Mewton, L., & Andrews, G. (2015). Cognitive behaviour therapy via the internet for depression: A useful strategy to reduce suicidal ideation. *Journal of Affective Disorder*, 170, 78–84.

Mewton, L., & Andrews, G. (2016). Cognitive behavioral therapy for suicidal behaviors: Improving patient outcomes. *Psychology Research and Behavior Management*, 9, 21–29.

Millings, A., & Carnelley, K. B. (2015). Core belief content examined in a large sample of patients using online cognitive behaviour therapy. *Journal of Affective Disorder*, 186, 275–283.

Morgan, K., Dixon, S., Mathers, N., Thompson, J., & Tomeny, M. (2004). Psychological treatment for insomnia in the regulation of long-term hypnotic drug use. *Health Technology Assessment*, 8, iii–iv, 1–68.

Neely, L. L., Irwin, K., Carreno Ponce, J. T., Perera, K., Grammer, G., & Ghahramanlou-Holloway, M. (2013). Post-admission cognitive therapy (PACT) for the prevention of suicide in military personnel with histories of trauma: Treatment development and case example. *Clinical Case Studies*, 12(6), 457–473.

Neimeyer, R. A., & Feixas, G. (1990). The role of homework and skill acquisition in the outcome of cognitive therapy for depression. *Behavior Therapy*, 21(3), 281–292.

Norrie, J., Davidson, K., Tata, P., & Gumley, A. (2013). Influence of therapist competence and quantity of cognitive behavioural therapy on suicidal behaviour and inpatient hospitalisation in a randomised controlled trial in borderline personality disorder: Further analyses of treatment effects in the BOSCOT study. *Psychology Psychotherapy*, 86(3), 280–293.

Persons, J. B. (2008). *The case formulation approach to cognitive behavior therapy*. New York, NY: Guilford Press.

Pollock, L. R., & Williams, M. G. (1998). Problem solving and suicidal behavior. *Suicide and Life-Threatening Behavior*, 28(4), 375–387.

Robinson, J., Hetrick, S., Cox, G., Bendall, S., Yung, A., Yuen, H. P., . . . Pirkis, J. (2014). The development of a randomised controlled trial testing the effects of an online intervention among school students at risk of suicide. *BioMed Central Psychiatry*, 14, 155–169.

Rotherman-Borus, M. J., Piacentini, J., Miller, S., Graae, F., & Castro-Blanco, D. (1994). Brief cognitive-behavioral treatment for adolescent suicide attempters and their families. *Journal of the American Academy of Child and Adolescent Psychiatry*, 33(4), 508–517.

Salkovskis, P. M., Atha, C., & Storer, D. (1990). Cognitive-behavioural problem solving in the treatment of patients who repeatedly attempt suicide: A controlled trial. *British Journal of Psychiatry*, 157, 871–876.

Scott, J. A. N., Paykel, E., Morriss, R., Bentall, R., Kinderman, P., Johnson, T., . . . Hayhurst, H. (2006). Cognitive–behavioural therapy for severe and recurrent bipolar disorders. *The British Journal of Psychiatry*, 188(4), 313–320.

Sharpe, L., Sensky, T., Timberlake, N., Ryan, B., Brewin, C. R., & Allard, S. (2001). A blind, randomized, controlled trial of cognitive-behavioural intervention for patients with recent onset rheumatoid arthritis: Preventing psychological and physical morbidity. *Pain, 89*(2), 275–283.

Spirito, A., Wolff, J. C., Seaboyer, L. M., Hunt, J., Esposito-Smythers, C., Nugent, N., . . . Miller, I. (2015). Concurrent treatment for adolescent and parent depressed mood and suicidality: Feasibility, acceptability, and preliminary findings. *Journal of Child and Adolescent Psychopharmacology, 25*(2), 131–139.

Stanley, B. H., Brown, G., Brent, D., Wells, K., Poling, K., Curry, J., . . . Hughes, J. (2009). Cognitive-behavioral therapy for suicide prevention (CBT-SP): Treatment model, feasibility, and acceptability *Journal of the American Academy of Child & Adolescent Psychiatry, 48*(10), 1005–1013.

Tarrier, N., Kelly, J., Maqsood, S., Snelson, N., Maxwell, J., Law, H., . . . Gooding, P. (2014). The cognitive behavioural prevention of suicide in psychosis: A clinical trial. *Schizophrenia Research, 156*(2–3), 204–210.

Tarrier, N., Taylor, K., & Gooding, P. (2008). Cognitive-behavioral interventions to reduce suicide behavior: A systematic review and meta-analysis. *Behavior Modification, 32*(1), 77–108.

Tundo, A., Salvati, L., Cieri, L., Daniele, M., Di Spigno, D., Necci, R., & Parena, A. (2014). Effectiveness and outcome predictors of cognitive-behavioural therapy for obsessive-compulsive disorder co-occurring with psychosis. *Journal of Psychopathology/Giornale di Psicopatologia, 20*(2), 127–133.

Turner, C., Heyman, I., Futh, A., & Lovell, K. (2009). A pilot study of telephone cognitive-behavioural therapy for obsessive-compulsive disorder in young people. *Behavioral Cognitive Psychotherapy, 37*(4), 469–474.

Van der Sande, R., Buskens, E., Allart, E., van der Graaf, Y., & van Engeland, H. (1997). Psychosocial intervention following suicide attempt: A systematic review of treatment interventions. *Acta Psychiatrica Scandinavica, 96*, 43–50.

Wagner, B., Horn, A. B., & Maercker, A. (2014). Internet-based versus face-to-face cognitive-behavioral intervention for depression: A randomized controlled non-inferiority trial. *Journal of Affective Disorders, 152–154*, 113–121.

Wagner, B., Nagl, M., Dölemeyer, R., Klinitzke, G., Steinig, J., Hilbert, A., & Kersting, A. (2016). Randomized controlled trial of an internet-based cognitive-behavioral treatment program for binge-eating disorder. *Behavior Therapy, 47*(4), 500–514.

Walkup, J. T., Albano, A. M., Piacentini, J., Birmaher, B., Compton, S. N., Sherrill, J. T., . . . Iyengar, S. (2008). Cognitive behavioral therapy, sertraline, or a combination in childhood anxiety. *New England Journal of Medicine, 359*(26), 2753–2766.

Weinberg, I., Gunderson, J. G., Hennen, J., & Cutter, C. J. (2006). Manual assisted cognitive treatment for deliberate self-harm in borderline personality disorder patients. *Journal of Personality Disorders, 20*, 482–492.

Weinstein, S. M., Henry, D. B., Katz, A. C., Peters, A. T., & West, A. E. (2015). Treatment moderators of child- and family-focused cognitive-behavioral therapy for pediatric bipolar disorder. *Journal of the American Academy of Child & Adolescent Psychiatry, 54*(2), 116–125.

Welch, T., Welch, M., Baer, J., Dias, J., Gurney, C., Van Dale, B., . . . Psiurski, S. (2010). Removed but not out of reach: Seniors with depression in smaller center, rural, and remote communities. *Psychiatric Annals, 40*(12), 616–623.

West, A. E., Weinstein, S. M., Peters, A. T., Katz, A. C., Henry, D. B., Cruz, R. A., & Pavuluri, M. N. (2014). Child- and family-focused cognitive-behavioral therapy for pediatric bipolar disorder: A randomized clinical trial. *Journal of the American Academy of Child & Adolescent Psychiatry, 53*(11), 1168–1178.

Wilson, K., Mottram, P. G., & Vassilas, C. (2008). Psychotherapeutic treatments for older depressed people. *The Cochrane Library*. doi:10.1002/14651858.CD004853.pub2

Wittouck, C., Van Autreve, S., Portzky, G., & van Heeringen, K. (2014). A CBT-based psychoeducational intervention for suicide survivors: A cluster randomized controlled study. *Crisis, 35*(3), 193–201.

Wolk, C. B., Kendal, P. C., & Beidas, R. S. (2015). Cognitive-behavioral therapy for child anxiety confers long-term protection from suicidality. *Journal of American Academy of Child & Adolescent Psychiatry, 54*(3), 175–179.

CHAPTER SEVENTEEN

DIALECTICAL BEHAVIORAL THERAPY AND SUICIDE

This chapter presents dialectical behavioral therapy (DBT) as a treatment model for working with suicidal individuals. DBT was originally developed by Marsha Linehan in 1987 as a treatment for borderline personality disorder (BPD; Linehan, 1987). In recent years, a strong evidence base has been established for the use of DBT for individuals experiencing suicidality. The theory behind DBT is explored in this chapter. Additionally, a thorough description of the key components and strategies of DBT is presented. Research examining the effectiveness of DBT across psychiatric disorders and settings is also explored. Lastly, recommendations for clinical practice when implementing DBT are provided.

GOALS AND OBJECTIVES

An understanding of:

- Theory behind DBT
- Major components of DBT
- Hierarchy of DBT goals
- Stages of DBT
- Treatment targets of DBT
- Core strategies used in DBT
- Evidence to support the use of DBT
- Populations for and settings in which DBT is supported
- Factors that impact the effectiveness of DBT
- Clinical considerations when conducting DBT

BPD, characterized by a pattern of instability in interpersonal relationships, self-image, affect, and marked impulsivity (American Psychological Association [APA], 2013), is highly associated with suicide attempts and completions (Pompili, Girardi, Ruberto, & Tatarelli, 2005). Individuals with BPD also engage in nonsuicidal self-injury at an alarmingly high rate (Gunderson, 2001; Linehan, 1993a). It is estimated that up to 85% of individuals suffering from BPD engage in nonsuicidal self-injury (Brickman, Ammerman, Look, Berman, & McCloskey, 2014; Gunderson, 2001; Hawton et al., 2016; Linehan, 1993). In an effort to address the high rate of suicide and deliberate self-harm in this group, Marsha Linehan developed a new treatment approach, *DBT* (Linehan, 1987). DBT is based on the principle that individuals struggle with the dialect of change and acceptance. Rather than emphasizing a purely changed oriented approach, Linehan recognized the importance of helping clients accept themselves as they are (Linehan, 1987). Given the difficulties that individuals with BPD have in tolerating distress and regulating affect and interpersonal relationships, DBT aims to help clients develop distress-tolerance and coping as well as acceptance-oriented skills, thereby helping clients to strike a balance between change and acceptance (Linehan, 1987).

DBT draws upon several theoretical and philosophical perspectives, including behavioral principles and social learning theory (Linehan & Wilks, 2015). Also, DBT incorporates acceptance-oriented strategies that are based on Zen principles, the client-oriented and emotion-focused treatment approaches. Change strategies stem from a combination of dialectical, philosophical, psychodynamic, cognitive, behavioral treatment approaches, and biopsychosocial theory (Linehan, 1993). According to Linehan, the focus of DBT has been built on a "life worth living" (Linehan & Wilks, 2015).

Mental health practitioners generally adhere to a particular or favored theoretical approach to clinical work. DBT is unique in that it represents a blending together of multiple treatment approaches and philosophies. In order to effectively implement DBT, it is important to explore one's openness to alternative treatment approaches to those to which one proscribes. If DBT is to be effective, the clinician as well as the client needs to accept the theoretical approach behind the evidence-based practice intervention.

Individual Exercise 17.1

1. From which perspective do you approach clinical work (i.e., psychodynamic, cognitive behavioral therapy [CBT], interpersonal psychotherapy [IPT], DBT)? Be as specific as possible. (If you are not currently in clinical practice, describe which approach you anticipate using or which approach resonates most strongly with you.)
2. What about this approach resonating with you as a mental health clinician?
3. What are the pros to using this approach?
4. What are the cons to using this approach?
5. List the major theoretical approach(es) to which you do not adhere or ascribe. (If you are not currently in clinical practice, describe which approaches you do not anticipate using or which do not resonate with you.)
6. What about this/these approaches do/does not resonate with you?
7. Are you able to identify any pros to these methods? Explain.
8. Under what circumstances do you feel this/these approaches might be useful?

Small Group Exercise 17.1

In small groups of two to three, please discuss, as you are comfortable, your responses to the questions in Individual Exercise 17.1. Remember, answers are personal and there are no correct or incorrect answers.

1. What were the response similarities in your group?
2. What were the response differences in your group?
3. Explore with group members who adhere to different treatment approaches than your own, and the pros and cons they identify regarding their approach.
4. Did you find any surprises in the group discussion? If so, what were they and how were you surprised?

DIALECTICAL BEHAVIORAL THERAPY

DBT serves four main functions in an attempt to reduce self-harm behaviors. It is designed to (a) help the client develop new skills, (b) address motivational obstacles to skills use, (c) help clients generalize the skills they learn in treatment to their daily lives, and (d) provide therapists with the support and supervision they need to remain motivated and skilled in treatment (Linehan, 1981, 1987, 1993).

The guiding principle of DBT is the *biosocial theory* of BPD. Proposed by Linehan (1987), the biosocial theory of BPD suggests that the emotional and behavioral dysregulation experienced by clients with BPD is both a byproduct of, and reinforced by, the transaction between an invalidating early childhood home environment and an inherent biological emotional vulnerability (Ivanoff, Linehan, & Brown, 2001; Linehan, 1993; Shearin & Linehan, 1994). In other words, the emotional and behavioral dysregulation of a client is considered a natural reaction to environmental reinforcers (Linehan, 1993).

This biosocial theory of BPD directly informs DBT as it provides the foundation for the stages of treatment. DBT involves four stages of treatment (Linehan, 1993; Linehan & Wilks, 2015; Shearin & Linehan, 1994). The goal of Stage 1 treatment is to address the severe behavioral dysregulation of clients by helping them to develop greater behavioral control. Behavior targets in this stage include decreasing imminent life-interfering behaviors (e.g., suicide attempts), reducing therapy-interfering behaviors (e.g., missing treatment), decreasing client-guided, quality-of-life-interfering behaviors (e.g., substance use), and increasing skillful behaviors to replace dysfunctional behaviors (also called "DBT skills training"). The goal of Stage 2 treatment is to develop emotional regulation, to increase the client's ability to experience an appropriate and full range of emotions. Stage 3 treatment decreases problems of daily living. Treatment goals are to facilitate the client's experience of happiness, to improve interpersonal relationships and self-esteem, and to improve problems in daily living. Stage 4 treatment emphasizes the development of an increased sense of connectedness, to find joy and freedom, and to reduce feelings of emptiness and loneliness (Ivanoff et al., 2001; Lynch, Trost, Salsman, & Linehan, 2007; Robins & Chapman, 2004).

Unlike other treatment models, a client can begin treatment at any one of the stages depending on his or her presentation and symptomatology. For example, a client experiencing extreme behavioral dysregulation (i.e., suicidal behaviors) would enter treatment at Stage 1 whereas a client struggling with emotional dysregulation without engaging in dangerous behaviors might enter treatment at Stage 2.

In addition to the biosocial theory of BPD, DBT is organized around the following hierarchy of goals: (a) eliminating life-threatening behaviors including suicide attempts and deliberate self-harm, (b) eliminating therapy-interfering behavior such as treatment nonadherence or not completing homework assignments, and (c) ameliorating behaviors and factors associated with poor quality of life, such as substance abuse (Linehan, 1993; Shearin & Linehan, 1994).

DBT also emphasizes skills training or the teaching of clients more adaptive ways of responding to stressors rather than engaging in self-harm behaviors. Four main sets of skills are the focus of this mode of treatment: (a) mindfulness, (b) interpersonal effectiveness, (c) emotion regulation, and (d) distress tolerance (Ivanoff et al., 2001; Linehan & Wilks, 2015; Robins & Chapman, 2004; Robins, Ivanoff, & Linehan, 2001). *Mindfulness* has to do with the quality of awareness that a client brings to what he or she is doing and experiencing. It encourages individuals to live in the here and now, to focus on the present, and to pay attention to what is happening in the moment. Clients learn to control their attention and limit distracting thoughts, images, and feelings associated with negative mood and anxiety. *Interpersonal effectiveness* seeks to improve the clients' communication skills and the way in which they manage interpersonal relationships. Both emotional regulation and interpersonal effectiveness skills are change oriented (Ivanoff et al., 2001; Linehan & Wilks, 2015; Robins et al., 2001). *Emotional regulation* involves helping clients to manage recent as well as longstanding difficult feelings. Clients are taught to observe their emotions and accept their emotions rather than to push them away. They are also taught not to judge their emotions, not to hang on to them, and not to intensify them. In addition, clients are taught to recognize where their emotions come from and how to describe their emotions. Emotional regulation skills also teach clients how to modulate their emotions should they desire to do so (Ivanoff et al., 2001; Linehan & Wilks, 2015; Robins et al., 2001). Lastly, *distress tolerance* involves helping clients to endure adverse situations, feelings, and/or thoughts. Both mindfulness and distress tolerance are acceptance-oriented skills (Linehan & Wilks, 2015; Robins et al., 2001).

The next mode of DBT focuses on helping clients to generalize the skills that they have learned in the previous mode and apply them to real-life situations. Typically via brief telephone sessions, sometimes referred to as "coaching calls" or "between-session coaching" (Lynch et al., 2007; Robins & Chapman, 2004), clinicians help clients to apply the aforementioned four skills to here-and-now situations.

The last mode of treatment is clinician centered. Given that DBT requires active participation of the clinician and 24-hour availability to clients, clinicians are highly susceptible to burnout. Furthermore, due to the nature of BPD, clinicians practicing DBT frequently encounter difficult and challenging cases. Thus, supervision and consultation is a major aspect of treatment. Clinicians are part of consultation teams where difficult cases can be discussed and feedback on treatment issues is provided (Linehan, 1993; Robins et al., 2001).

DBT involves once-weekly psychotherapy sessions during which a specific problematic behavior or event from the past week is examined in detail via a *behavioral chain analysis* (BCA). The BCA begins with identifying a specific situation or event and examining the chain of events leading up to the situation or event and how they may be related. The BCA continues then by exploring alternative solutions and adaptive responses (Linehan, 1993). Weekly individual sessions are supplemented with weekly 2.5-hour group therapy sessions during which interpersonal skills, mindfulness skills, distress tolerance skills, and emotional regulation skills are taught (Linehan, 1993).

EVIDENCE FOR DBT

Several randomized controlled trials (RCTs) have examined the efficacy of DBT for the treatment of BPD (Koons et al., 2001; Linehan, 1993; Linehan, Armstrong, Suarez, Allmon, & Heard, 1991; Linehan et al., 1999, 2002, 2006; Linehan, Tutek, Heard, & Armstrong, 1994; R. M. Turner, 2000; van den Bosch, Koeter, Stijnen, Verheul, & van den Brink, 2005; van den Bosch, Verheul, Schippers, & van den Brink, 2002; Verheul et al., 2003). In 1991, Linehan and colleagues conducted the first study examining the efficacy of DBT and compared 1 year of DBT to 1 year of treatment as usual (standard care received in the agency where treatment is occurring) in a group of 44 women diagnosed with BPD who experienced parasuicide. Participants who received DBT exhibited greater decreases in the frequency and severity of parasuicide as compared to participants who received treatment as usual. DBT participants also experienced greater reduction in the frequency and length of inpatient hospitalization and demonstrated higher rates of treatment adherence (Linehan et al., 1991).

Also important to recognize is the first RCT of a briefer form of DBT. Koons et al. (2001) conducted a randomized control trial of a 6-month version of DBT compared to 6 months of treatment as usual among a group of 20 female veterans, 40% of whom experienced suicidality. Again, DBT participants experienced greater reductions in suicidal ideation and parasuicidal behavior. They also experienced greater improvements in levels of hope-lessness, depression, and anger (Koons et al., 2001).

Stanley, Brodsky, Nelson, and Dulit (2007) also examined a brief 6-month course of dialectical behavioral therapy–brief (DBT-B), as to its effectiveness in improving rates of retention in treatment and reducing nondeliberate self-harm among 20 clients with BPD (Stanley et al., 2007). Results indicated that DBT-B led to vast improvement in treatment retention and a significant reduction in target behaviors (Stanley et al., 2007).

Recently, Linehan and Wilks (2015) examined the multiple components of DBT on out-comes, specifically individual therapy, skills training, telephone coaching, and a thera-pist consultation team (Linehan & Wilks, 2015). This study compared the skills training component of DBT by comparing skills training plus case management (DBT-S), DBT individual therapy plus activities group (DBT-I), and standard DBT that includes skills training and individual therapy; results highlight that DBT treatments that include DBT skills training are more effective than DBT without skills training, and standard DBT (Linehan et al., 2015). Another randomized trial sought to develop and evaluate the pre-liminary feasibility and effectiveness of a brief, one-time, DBT skills-based intervention with particular attention given to examining its acceptability among nontreatment seek-ers. Results of this study showed that the intervention is both acceptable to nontreatment seekers and that it significantly reduced suicidal ideation at the 1-month follow-up (Ward-Ciesielski, 2013). This single-session DBT skills–based intervention has also been shown to be more effective than relaxation training (Ward-Ciesielski, Jones, Wielgus, Wilks, & Line-han, 2016).

In an attempt to isolate the factors that may contribute to the efficacy of DBT, Linehan et al. (2002) conducted an RCT to determine the impact of the training, supervision, and monitoring of treatment fidelity associated with DBT versus treatment as usual. In this study, DBT was compared to "treatment by experts" who were received leaders in the field rather than to comparing it to treatment as usual. Results indicated that participants in the DBT group had a significantly lower rate of suicide attempts and severity of attempts. DBT participants also experienced lower rates of emergency room and inpatient hospitalization and higher rates of treatment adherence than those who received treat-ment by experts.

Harned et al. (2008) conducted a similar study and evaluated the efficacy of DBT ver-sus treatment by experts in psychotherapies other than behavioral treatment. This study also concluded that the efficacy of DBT cannot be attributed to general factors associated with therapist characteristics (Harned et al., 2008). Others seeking to compare DBT to treatment by experts using psychodynamically informed therapy in conjunction with symptom-targeted medication management found no differences in the effects of the two interventions across the groups on any of the outcome measures, including severity of suicidal and nonsuicidal self-injurious behavior, general health care utilization, number of emergency visits and psychiatric hospital days, improvements in BPD symptoms, symptom distress, depression, anger, and interpersonal functioning (McMain et al., 2009). This suggests that further RCTs are required to fully understand the effectiveness of DBT and the components that contribute to its effect.

A number of DBT models have been developed targeting adolescent clients with sui-cidal and self-injurious behavior and symptoms of BPD. Dialectical behavioral therapy for adolescents (DBT-A; Rathus & Miller, 2000, 2002) is one such model. DBT-A consists of 12 weeks of twice-weekly sessions comprising individual therapy and multifamily skills-training groups. Treatment focuses on addressing the three dialectical dilemmas specific to working with adolescents and their parents: (a) excessive leniency versus authoritarian control; (b) normalizing pathological behaviors versus pathologizing normative behavior; and (c) fostering dependence versus forcing autonomy. The intervention was shown to be effective at reducing suicidal ideation and improving general psychiatric symptoms as well as symptoms of BPD as compared to psychodynamic-supportive psychotherapy with family therapy sessions. However, no differences in the number of suicide attempts during follow-up across the two groups were found (Rathus & Miller, 2002). An adapted form of Dialectical Behavior Therapy for adolescents (A-DBT-A); Courtney & Flament, 2015) has also been tested as a treatment model for suicidal adolescents with borderline features. Results demonstrated a significant reduction in suicidal ideation and overall clinical improvement in adolescents who completed the 15-week A-DBT-A program (Courtney & Flament, 2015). Another model of DBT for adolescents has also been developed specifically for female/Latinas (German et al., 2015). The model presents supplemental dialectical corollaries to those in DBT-A that are frequently observed in Latino families. These dialects include (a) old school versus new school and (b) overprotecting versus underprotecting. The model suggests that the old school versus new school dialect is rooted in cultural and generational factors and may contribute to why some Latina adolescents, particularly those whose families recently immigrated to the United States, engage in suicidal behaviors. The overprotecting versus underprotecting dialect is linked to Latino parents who have experienced past abuse or life-threatening extreme adverse events, which then have critical consequences for their parenting behaviors. There have been no clinical trials focused on the effectiveness of the model for Latina youth; however, it is suggested that the added dialects unique to Latino families strengthen the model of DBT-A in general, and clinical strategies for use of the adapted model with both adolescents and their parents have been recommended (Germain, 2015).

Models of DBT have also been adapted for adolescents with various psychiatric disorders, mood disorders, externalizing disorders, eating disorders, trichotillomania across multiple settings, including outpatient, day program, inpatient, residential, and correctional facilities (MacPherson, Cheavens, & Fristad, 2013). Overall, studies examining DBT's effectiveness for at-risk adolescents have shown promising results in decreasing deliberate self-harm behaviors, psychiatric hospitalizations, suicidal ideation, severity of depression, level of hopelessness, and BPD symptomatology (Klein & Miller, 2011; MacPherson et al., 2013; Mehlum et al., 2014; Ougrin, Tranah, Stahl, Moran, & Asarnow, 2015; Rathus & Miller, 2002; Tørmoen et al., 2014). A recent, albeit preliminary, meta-analysis on nonsuicidal self-injury (NSSI) and DBT indicated decreased NSSI and improvement in depressive symptoms for adolescents following a course of DBT (Cook & Gorraiz, 2016).

There are also several uncontrolled trials and nonrandomized control trials of DBT and studies of modified courses of DBT based on setting and population. Overall, DBT has been shown to be effective not only at reducing NSSI (Mehlum et al., 2014; Ougrin, Tranah, Stahl, Moran, & Asarnow, 2015; B. J. Turner, Austin, & Chapman, 2014) as well as suicidality with adolescents, adults, and the elderly, particularly within the context of BPD (Davidson & Tran, 2014; Linehan et al., 1994, 2006; Linehan, Heard, & Armstrong, 1993), but also for depression (Cook & Gorraiz, 2016; Davidson & Tran, 2014; Inyang & Hua, 2015; Lynch, Morse, Mendelson, & Robins, 2003), attention deficit hyperactivity disorder (ADHD; Hesslinger et al., 2002), posttraumatic stress disorder (PTSD; Boritz, Barnhart, & McMain, 2016; Harned, Korslund, & Linehan, 2014; Krüger et al., 2014), substance abuse (Linehan et al., 1999, 2002; Verheul et al., 2003), bipolar disorders (Chesin & Stanley, 2013; Goldstein et al., 2015), intimate partner violence (Iverson, Shenk, & Fruzzetti, 2009), eating disorders (Chen, Matthews, Allen, Kuo, & Linehan, 2008; Fischer & Peterson, 2015; Safer, Telch, & Agras, 2001; Telch, Agras, & Linehan, 2000, 2001), and family members of suicide attempters (Rajalin, Wickholm-Pethrus, Hursti, & Jokinen, 2009). In addition, DBT also has evidence to support its use in inpatient settings (Barley et al., 1993; Bohus et al., 2004; Katz, Cox, Gunasekara, & Miller, 2004; McCann, Ball, & Ivanoff, 2000; Rathus & Miller, 2002; Rusch et al., 2008; Swenson, 2000; Trupin, Stewart, Beach, &

Boesky, 2002; van den Bosch & McDonell et al., 2010; Verheul, Schippers, & van den Brink, 2002). The efficacy of DBT is generally examined in the context of a year-long course of treatment. It is important to note that the greatest treatment effects have been found to occur during the first 4 months of treatment. The remaining 8 months, considered a period of skills consolidation (Linehan et al., 1991), require further examination.

RECOMMENDED CLINICAL GUIDELINES FOR DBT

DBT is an effective treatment approach for addressing suicidality that is flexible based on the level of pathology of the client (Comtois & Linehan, 2006; Lynch et al., 2007; Robins et al., 2001). Nonetheless, it is an intensive treatment modality for both clients and clinicians. Several important aspects have been emphasized in the literature examining DBT that require specific attention (Linehan, 1993; Robins et al., 2001). The following recommendations should be kept in mind when utilizing DBT with suicidal clients:

1. *Training.* DBT is a highly complex intervention. It is recommended that no clinician utilize DBT without proper training and that no modified or adapted versions be utilized until the full model has been mastered.
2. *Supervision.* DBT builds into the treatment process a supervision component. It is important that clinicians adhere to this component as it is critical for effective DBT. Proper supervision and consultation reduce the risk of clinician burnout and provide the opportunity to receive feedback and direction with difficult cases.
3. *Maintaining perspective on client functioning.* DBT operates from a clear perspective regarding clients. It approaches practice from the perspective that clients are doing the best they can, that they desire to do better, and that they can learn the skills they need to improve. It is essential for clinicians practicing DBT to maintain this perspective. If clinicians take the stance that clients already have the skills they need and choose not to use them or that clients are not interested in changing, then the DBT process will fail.
4. *Maintaining boundaries.* DBT requires intense therapist involvement in terms of time and active participation in treatment. That said, it is critical to set and maintain appropriate boundaries with clients in order to avoid burnout and to allow clients to enjoy the maximum benefit of treatment. For example, coaching calls are a standard part of DBT; however, clients should be provided with clear instructions as to under what circumstances it is appropriate/acceptable to page their therapist. Clients need the opportunity to retrieve and implement skills on their own and therapists need to know that they will not be receiving phone calls every hour.

ROLE-PLAY 17.1

You are a mental health clinician in an outpatient mental health center. A client you treated briefly 2 years prior for depression unexpectedly presents to your office expressing suicidal ideation with intent.

Using this scenario, break into groups of three and assume the roles of the mental health clinician and the client. The third member will act as a recorder and can be called upon to consult and assist the mental health clinician. Engage in a role-play in which you would implement DBT with this client.

ROLE-PLAY 17.2

You are a mental health clinician in an outpatient mental health center. A client you treated briefly 2 years prior for depression unexpectedly presents to your office expressing suicidal ideation with intent.

Using this scenario, break into groups of three and assume the roles of the mental health clinician and the supervisor. The third member will act as a recorder and can be called upon to consult and assist the mental health clinician. Engage in a role-play in which you discuss this client with your supervisor. What questions might you ask? What kind of support might you try to elicit? Is the supervision for you? The client? Both?

SUMMARY

Developed by Marsha Linehan, DBT is an evidence-based practice for the treatment of deliberate and nondeliberate self-harm. Initially introduced to target these behaviors in women with BPD, DBT now has evidence to support its use across a number of major diagnostic categories. DBT emphasizes the dialect of change and acceptance and provides clients with skills that target both of these goals. DBT is successful at reducing self-harm via teaching clients skills and adaptive techniques to experience their emotions, modulate affect and emotion, improve interpersonal relationships, and manage stressful life experiences. Supervision, training, and consultation are essential for any clinician practicing DBT.

KEY POINTS

1. DBT is based on a biosocial theory of BPD.
2. DBT represents a blending together of multiple theoretical orientations and philosophies.
3. There are four stages of DBT.
4. There is an overarching hierarchical order of goals associated with DBT.
5. DBT is skills focused.
6. DBT seeks to improve the behavioral and emotional dysregulation of clients.
7. DBT relies on active involvement of clinicians.
8. Supervision and consultation are essential to the practice of DBT.
9. DBT is typically delivered in a year-long period, and the greatest improvements are experienced in the first 4 months of treatment.
10. DBT has a strong evidence base for the treatment of suicidality.

ELECTRONIC RESOURCES

www.middle-path.org/DBT/dbtr-index.html
www.dbtselfhelp.com
www.bpdresourcecenter.org
www.depts.washington.edu/brtc/about/dbt

KNOWLEDGE ACQUISITION TEST (KAT)

True or False

1. Dialectical behavioral therapy (DBT) requires active participation of the clinician.
2. DBT has evidence to support its efficacy with individuals with borderline personality disorder (BPD) only.
3. Distress-tolerance strategies are change-oriented skills.
4. DBT is based on a biosocial theory of BPD.
5. Individuals treated with DBT rather than treatment as usual do not experience greater reduction in inpatient hospitalizations.
6. A behavior chain analysis focuses strictly on precipitating events.
7. DBT represents a blend of theoretical orientations, philosophies, and perspectives.
8. Individuals experiencing emotional dysregulation typically enter DBT at Stage 1.
9. Interpersonal effectiveness strategies are change-oriented skills.

Short Answer

10. What are the four main functions of DBT?
11. What are the four main skill sets taught in DBT?
12. Why is the last mode of DBT clinician centered?
13. Describe the skill of mindfulness.
14. What is the hierarchy of goals around which DBT is organized?
15. How are the individual and weekly sessions organized in DBT?

Multiple Choice

16. DBT has been shown to be effective at treating individuals with which of the following disorders?
    A. Eating disorders
    B. Depression
    C. Substance abuse
    D. BPD
    E. All of the above
    F. None of the above
17. Emotional regulation skills do not include:
    A. Helping clients to manage recent as well as long-standing difficult feelings
    B. Observing emotions
    C. Pushing away emotions
    D. Learning not to judge their emotions
    E. Recognizing where their emotions come from and how to describe them
18. Which of the following is not part of the hierarchy of goals of DBT?
    A. Eliminating life-threatening behaviors
    B. Eliminating therapy-interfering behaviors
    C. Ameliorating behaviors and factors associated with poor quality of life
    D. All of the above
    E. None of the above
19. The four main skill sets of DBT include:
    A. Mindfulness
    B. Distress tolerance

C. Emotional regulation
D. Medication management
E. Interpersonal effectiveness

20. Which of the following is not a goal of Stage 3 of DBT?
    A. Provide psychoeducation regarding diagnosis
    B. Facilitate the client's experience of happiness
    C. Improve interpersonal relationships
    D. Improve self-esteem
    E. Improve problems in daily living

REFERENCES

American Psychiatric Association. (2013). *Diagnostic and statistical manual of mental disorders* (5th ed.). Washington, DC: American Psychiatric Publishing.

Barley, W. D., Buie, S. E., Peterson, E. W., Hollingsworth, A. S., Griva, M., . . . Bailey, B. J. (1993). Development of an inpatient cognitive-behavioral treatment program for borderline personality disorder. *Journal of Personality Disorders, 7,* 232–240.

Bohus, M., Haaf, B., Simms, T., Limberger, M., Schmahl, C., Lieb, K., & Linehan, M. M. (2004). Effectiveness of inpatient dialectical behavioral therapy for borderline personality disorder: A controlled trial. *Behavior Research and Therapy, 42,* 487–499.

Boritz, T., Barnhart, R., & McMain, S. F. (2016). The influence of posttraumatic stress disorder on treatment outcomes of patients with borderline personality disorder. *Journal of Personality Disorders, 30*(3), 395–407.

Brickman, L. J., Ammerman, B. A., Look, A. E., Berman, M. E., & McCloskey, M. S. (2014). The relationship between non-suicidal self-injury and borderline personality disorder symptoms in a college sample. *Borderline Personality Disorder and Emotion Dysregulation, 1,* 1–14.

Chen, E. Y., Matthews, L., Allen, C., Kuo, J. R., & Linehan, M. M. (2008). Dialectical behavior therapy for clients with binge-eating disorder or bulimia nervosa and borderline personality disorder. *International Journal of Eating Disorders, 41*(6), 505–512.

Chesin, M., & Stanley, B. (2013). Risk assessment and psychosocial interventions for suicidal patients. *Bipolar Disorder, 15*(5), 584–593.

Comtois, K. A., & Linhean, M. M. (2006). Psychosocial treatments for suicidal behaviors: A practice-friendly review. *Journal of Clinical Psychology, 62*(2), 161–170.

Cook, N. E., & Gorraiz, M. (2016). Dialectical behavior therapy for nonsuicidal self-injury and depression among adolescents: Preliminary meta-analytic evidence. *Child and Adolescent Mental Health, 21*(2), 81–89.

Courtney, D. B., & Flament, M. F. (2015). Adapted dialectical behavior therapy for adolescents with self-injurious thoughts and behaviors. *Journal of Nervous and Mental Disease, 203*(7), 537–544.

Davidson, K. M., & Tran, C. F. (2014). Impact of treatment intensity on suicidal behavior and depression in borderline personality disorder: A critical review. *Journal of Personality Disorder, 28*(2), 181–197.

Fischer, S., & Peterson, C. (2015). Dialectical behavior therapy for adolescent binge eating, purging, suicidal behavior, and non-suicidal self-injury: A pilot study. *Psychotherapy, Special Section: Cognitive-Behavioral Psychotherapy, 52*(1), 78–92.

German, M., Smith, H. L., Rivera-Morales, C., Gonzalez, G., Haliczer, L. A., Haaz, C., & Miller, A. L. (2015). Dialectical behavior therapy for suicidal Latina adolescents: Supplemental dialectical corollaries and treatment targets. *American Journal Of Psychotherapy, 69*(2), 179–197.

Goldstein, T. R., Fersch-Podrat, R. K., Rivera, M., Axelson, D. A., Merranko, J., Yu, H., . . . Birmaher, B. (2015). Dialectical behavior therapy for adolescents with bipolar disorder: Results from a pilot randomized trial. *Journal of Child and Adolescent Psychopharmacology, 25*(2), 140–149.

Gunderson, J. G. (2001). *Borderline personality disorder: A clinical guide.* Washington, DC: American Psychiatric Publishing.

Harned, M. S., Chapman, A. L., Dexter-Mazza, E. T., Murray, A., Comtois, K. A., & Linehan, M. M. (2008). Treating co-occurring Axis I disorders in recurrently suicidal women with borderline personality disorder: A 2-year randomized trial of dialectical behavior therapy versus community treatment by experts. *Journal of Consulting and Clinical Psychology, 76*(6), 1068–1075.

Harned, M. S., Korslund, K. E., & Linehan, M. M. (2014). A pilot randomized controlled trial of Dialectical Behavior Therapy with and without the Dialectical Behavior Therapy Prolonged Exposure protocol for suicidal and self-injuring women with borderline personality disorder and PTSD. *Behaviour Research and Therapy, 55,* 7–17.

Hawton, K., Witt, K. G., Taylor Salisbury, T. L., Arensman, E., Gunnell, D., Hazell, P., . . . van Heeringen, K. (2016). Psychosocial interventions for self-harm in adults. *The Cochrane Database of Systematic Reviews, 12*(5), CD012189.

Hesslinger, B., Tebartz van Elst, L., Nyberg, E., Dykierek, P., Richter, H., Berner, M., & Ebert, D. (2002). Psychotherapy of attention deficit hyperactivity disorder in adults: A pilot study using a structured skills training program. *European Archives of Psychiatry and Clinical Neuroscience, 252,* 117–184.

Inyang, M., & Hua, L. L. (2015). Self-inflicted bilateral ocular perforation in an adolescent patient with major depressive disorder and borderline personality traits. *Adolescent Psychiatry, 5*(1), 64–69.

Ivanoff, A., Linehan, M. M., & Brown, M. (Eds.). (2001). *Dialectical behavior therapy for impulsive self-injurious behaviors.* Arlington, VA: American Psychiatric Publishing.

Iverson, K. M., Shenk, C., & Fruzzetti, A. E. (2009). Dialectical behavior therapy for women victims of domestic abuse: A pilot study. *Professional Psychology: Research and Practice, 40*(3), 242–248. doi:10.1037/a0013476

Katz, L. Y., Cox, B. J., Gunasekara, S., & Miller, A. L. (2004). Feasibility of dialectical behavior therapy for suicidal adolescent inpatients. *Journal of the American Academy of Child and Adolescent Psychiatry, 43,* 276–282.

Klein, D. A., & Miller, A. L. (2011). Dialectical behavior therapy for suicidal adolescents with borderline personality disorder. *Child and Adolescent Psychiatric Clinics of North America, 20*(2), 205–216.

Koons, C., Robins, C. J., Tweed, J. L., Lynch, T. R., Gonzelez, A. M., Morse, J. Q., . . . Bastian, L. A. (2001). Efficacy of dialectical behavior therapy in women veterans with borderline personality disorder. *Behavior Therapy, 32,* 371–390.

Krüger, A., Kleindienst, N., Priebe, K., Dyer, A. S., Steil, R., Schmahl, C., & Bohus, M. (2014). Non-suicidal self-injury during an exposure-based treatment in patients with posttraumatic stress disorder and borderline features. *Behavior Research and Therapy, 61,*136–141.

Linehan, M. M. (1987). Dialectical behavior therapy: A cognitive-behavioral approach to parasuicide. *Journal of Personality Disorders, 1,* 328–333.

Linehan, M. M. (1993a). *Cognitive behavioral treatment of borderline personality disorder.* New York, NY: Guilford Press.

Linehan, M. M. (1993b). *Skills training manual for treating borderline personality disorder.* New York, NY: Guilford Press.

Linehan, M. M., Armstrong, H. E., Suarez, A., Allmon, D., & Heard, H. L. (1991). Cognitive-behavioral treatment of chronically parasuicidal borderline patients. *Archives of General Psychiatry, 48,* 1060–1064.

Linehan, M. M., Comtois, K. A., Murray, A. M., Brown, M. Z., Gallop, R. J., . . . Lindenboim, N. (2006). Two year randomized controlled trial and follow-up of dialectical behavior therapy vs. therapy by experts for suicidal behaviors and borderline personality disorder. *Archives of General Psychiatry, 62,* 1–10.

Linehan, M. M., Dimeff, L. A., Reynolds, S. K., Comtois, K. A., Welch, S. S., Heagerty, P., & Kivlahan, D. R. (2002). Dialectical behavior therapy versus comprehensive validation therapy plus 12-step for the treatment of opioid dependent women meeting criteria for borderline personality disorder. *Drug and Alcohol Dependence, 67,* 13–26.

Linehan, M. M., Heard, H. L., & Armstrong, H. E. (1993). Naturalistic follow-up of a behavioral treatment for chronically parasuicidal borderline patients. *Archives of General Psychiatry, 50*(12), 971–974.

Linehan, M. M., Schmidt, H. I., Dimeff, L. A., Craft, J. C., Kanter, J., & Comtois, K. A. (1999). Dialectical behavior therapy for patients with borderline personality disorder and drug-dependence. *American Journal on Addictions, 8,* 279–292.

Linehan, M. M., Tutek, D. A., Heard, H. L., & Armstrong, H. E. (1994). Interpersonal outcome of cognitive behavioral treatment for chronically suicidal borderline patients. *American Journal of Psychiatry, 151,* 1771–1776.

Linehan, M. M., & Wilks, C. R. (2015). The course and evolution of dialectical behavior therapy. *American Journal of Psychotherapy, 69*(2, Special Issue: Dialectical behavior therapy: Evolution and adaptations in the 21st century), 97–110.

Lynch, T. R., Morse, J. Q., Mendelson, T., & Robins, C. J. (2003). Dialectical behavior therapy for depressed older adults: A randomized pilot study. *American Journal of Geriatric Psychiatry, 11,* 33–45.

Lynch, T. R., Trost, W. T., Salsman, N., & Linehan, M. M. (2007). Dialectical behavior therapy for borderline personality disorder. *Annual Review of Clinical Psychology, 3,* 181–205.

MacPherson, H. A., Cheavens, J. S., & Fristad, M. A. (2013). Dialectical behavior therapy for adolescents: Theory, treatment adaptations, and empirical outcomes. *Clinical Child and Family Psychology Review, 16*(1), 59–80.

McCann, R. A., Ball, E. M., & Ivanoff, A. (2000). DBT with an inpatient forensic population: The CMHIP forensic model. *Cognitive and Behavioral Practice, 7,* 447–456.

McDonell, M. G., Tarantino, J., Dubose, A. P., Matestic, P., Steinmetz, K., Galbreath, H., & McClellan, J. M. (2010). A pilot evaluation of dialectical behavioural therapy in adolescent long-term inpatient care. *Child and Adolescent Mental Health, 15*(4), 193–196.

McMain, S. F., Links, P. S., Gnam, W. H., Guimond, T., Cardish, R. J., Korman, L., & Streiner, D. L. (2009). A randomized trial of dialectical behavior therapy versus general psychiatric management for borderline personality disorder. *American Journal of Psychiatry, 166*(12), 1365–1374.

Mehlum, L., Tørmoen, A. J., Ramberg, M., Haga, E., Diep, L. M., Laberg, S., . . . Grøholt, B. (2014). Dialectical behavior therapy for adolescents with repeated suicidal and self-harming behavior: A randomized trial. *Journal of the American Academy of Child and Adolescent Psychiatry, 53*(10), 1082–1091.

Ougrin, D., Tranah, T., Stahl, D., Moran, P., & Asarnow, J. R. (2015). Therapeutic interventions for suicide attempts and self-harm in adolescents: Systematic review and meta-analysis. *Journal of the American Academy of Child and Adolescent Psychiatry, 54*(2), 97–107.

Pompili, M., Girardi, P., Ruberto, A., & Tatarelli, R. (2005). Suicide in borderline personality disorder: A meta-analysis. *Norwegian Journal of Psychiatry, 59*, 319–324.

Rajalin, M., Wickholm-Pethrus, L., Hursti, T., & Jokinen, J. (2009). Dialectical behavior therapy-based skills training for family members of suicide attempters. *Archives of Suicide Research, 13*(3), 257–263.

Rathus, J. H., & Miller, A. L. (2002). Dialectical behavior therapy adapted for suicidal adolescents. *Suicide and Life-Threatening Behavior, 32*, 146–157.

Robins, C. J., & Chapman, A. L. (2004). Dialectical behavior therapy: Current status, recent developments, and future directions. *Journal of Personality Disorder, 18*, 73–89.

Robins, C. J., Ivanoff, A. M., & Linehan, M. M. (2001). *Dialectical behavior therapy*. New York, NY: Guilford Press.

Rusch, N., Schiel, S., Corrigan, P. W., Leihener, F., Jacob, G. A., Olschewski, M., . . . Bohus, M. (2008). Predictors of dropout from inpatient dialectical behavior therapy among women with borderline personality disorder. *Journal of Behavior Therapy and Experimental Psychiatry, 39*(4), 497–503.

Safer, D. L., Telch, C. F., & Agras, W. (2001). Dialectical behavior therapy for bulimia nervosa. *American Journal of Psychiatry, 158*, 632–634.

Shearin, E. N., & Linehan, M. M. (1994). Dialectical behavior therapy for borderline personality disorder: Theoretical and empirical foundations. *Acta Psychiatrica Scandinavica, 379*(Suppl.), 61–68.

Stanley, B. H., Brodsky, B. S., Nelson, J. D., & Dulit, R. (2007). Brief dialectical behavior therapy (DBT_B) for suicidal behavior and non-suicidal self injury. *Archives of Suicide Research, 11*(4), 337–341.

Swenson, C. R. (2000). How can we account for DBT's widespread popularity? *Clinical Psychology, 7*, 87–91.

Telch, C. F., Agras, W., & Linehan, M. M. (2000). Group dialectical behavior therapy for binge eating disorder: A preliminary uncontrolled trial. *Behavioral Therapy, 31*, 569–582.

Telch, C. F., Agras, W., & Linehan, M. M. (2001). Dialectical behavior therapy for binge eating disorder. *Journal of Consulting and Clinical Psychology, 69*, 1061–1065.

Tørmoen, A. J., Grøholt, B., Haga, E., Brager-Larsen, A., Miller, A., Walby, F., . . . Mehlum, L. (2014). Feasibility of dialectical behavior therapy with suicidal and self-harming adolescents with multi-problems: Training, adherence, and retention. *Archives of Suicide Research, 18*(4), 432–444.

Trupin, E. W., Stewart, D. G., Beach, B., & Boesky, L. (2002). Effectiveness of dialectical behavior therapy program for incarcerated female juvenile offenders. *Child and Adolescent Mental Health, 7*, 121–127.

Turner, B. J., Austin, S. B., & Chapman, A. L. (2014). Treating nonsuicidal self-injury: A systematic review of psychological and pharmacological interventions. *Canadian Journal of Psychiatry, 59*(11), 576–585.

Turner, R. M. (2000). Naturalistic evaluation of dialectical behavior therapy–oriented treatment for borderline personality disorder. *Cognitive and Behavioral Practice, 7*, 413–419.

van den Bosch, L. M. C., Koeter, M. W. J., Stijnen, T., Verheul, R., & van den Brink, W. (2005). Sustained efficacy of dialectical behavior therapy for borderline personality disorder. *Behavior Research and Therapy, 43*, 1231–1241.

van den Bosch, L. M. C., Verheul, R., Schippers, G. M., & van den Brink, W. (2002). Dialectical behavior therapy of borderline patients with and without substance use problems: Implementation and long-term effects. *Addictive Behavior, 27*, 911–923.

Verheul, R., van den Bosch, L. M., Koeter, M. W., De Ridder, M. A., Stijnen, T., & van den Brink, W. (2003). Dialectical behavior therapy for women with borderline personality disorder: 12-month, randomised clinical trial in the Netherlands. *British Journal of Psychiatry, 182*, 135–140.

Ward-Ciesielski, E. F. (2013). An open pilot feasibility study of a brief dialectical behavior therapy skills-based intervention for suicidal individuals. *Suicide and Life-Threatening Behavior, 43*(3), 324–335.

Ward-Ciesielski, E. F., Jones, C. B., Wielgus, M. D., Wilks, C. R., & Linehan, M. M. (2016). Single-session dialectical behavior therapy skills training versus relaxation training for non-treatment-engaged suicidal adults: A randomized control trial. *BioMed Psychology, 4*, 13–20. doi:10.1186/s40359-016-0117-4

CHAPTER EIGHTEEN

INTERPERSONAL PSYCHOTHERAPY AND SUICIDE

Interpersonal psychotherapy (IPT) has been demonstrated to be an effective evidence-based practice (EBP) for depression in randomized controlled and open trials. The efficacy of IPT has further been demonstrated to be superior to treatment-as-usual (standard treatment provided by an organization) or wait-list controls (a comparison group of individuals not currently receiving treatment but awaiting service provision). The empirical support for IPT treatment has been found in a number of populations, but is only beginning to emerge as a potential EBP for individuals experiencing suicidality. This chapter outlines the IPT approach and its adaptation as an emergent model of intervention with individuals experiencing suicidality, specifically adolescents and older adults. The core elements and strategies of IPT are examined, along with evidence on the effectiveness of this EBP. Finally, this chapter provides core recommendations for clinical practice with IPT.

GOALS AND OBJECTIVES

An understanding of:

- ■ Background and key theories underlying IPT
- ■ Description of IPT
- ■ Core goals of IPT
- ■ Key strategies, skills, and techniques of IPT
- ■ Three phases of IPT treatment
- ■ Diverse applications of IPT
- ■ Evidence that supports the use of IPT
- ■ Evidence that is not supportive of the use of IPT
- ■ Emergent adaption of IPT with older adults
- ■ IPT and suicidality

IPT is a time-limited psychosocial treatment that was developed for adults with depression (Cuijpers et al., 2011; Klerman & Weissman, 1993; Klerman, Weissman, Rounsaville, & Chevron, 1984). IPT is a brief outpatient EBP (Klerman et al., 1984). It emerged out of *interpersonal theory* (Cuijpers et al., 2011), originating under Henry Stack Sullivan, which hypothesized that interpersonal experiences help in the formation of personality (Sullivan, 1953). In addition, IPT draws from Adolf Meyer's theory that postulates that an individual's psychological disorder comes from his or her adaptations to interpersonal relationships and the larger environment (Mufson & Sills, 2006). Difficulties in or loss of relationships occur through an individual's interpersonal interactions and can contribute to depression. IPT's psychological treatment of depression emphasizes current, not past, interpersonal relations of the client with specific focus on the individual's immediate social context (Klerman et al., 1984; Weissman & Markowitz, 1994). IPT is designed to help an individual resolve interpersonal problems through a range of techniques and strengthen his or her access to social support (Hetrick, Cox, Witt, Bir, & Merry, 2016). Further, IPT seeks to intervene in symptom formation and the social dysfunction associated with depression, but does not target aspects of an individual's personality (de Mello, de Jesus Mari, Bacaltchuk, Verdeli, & Neugebauer, 2005; Weissman & Markowitz, 1994).

Since its emergence in the 1970s, IPT has developed from an intervention that focused on adults with depression to an effective intervention that can be applied to a number of different populations and diagnoses. Recently, IPT has begun to focus directly on older adults experiencing suicidality.

Small Group Exercise 18.1

Discuss in small groups of three to four the following:

1. How can a client's current interpersonal difficulties contribute to his or her suicidal risk factors?
2. By working with a client's current interpersonal difficulties, how can a mental health clinician positively contribute to the client's protective factors against suicidality?

INTERPERSONAL PSYCHOTHERAPY

IPT was designed to treat adults with depression and was originally conceptualized as having three treatment phases (described in the following; de Mello et al., 2005; Klerman et al., 1984; Weissman & Markowitz, 1994, 1998). Specifically, IPT strived to treat depression through two central goals: (a) to reduce depressive symptoms and (b) to improve and restore interpersonal functioning (Mufson & Sills, 2006). The achievement of these goals revolves around three main overarching strategies: (a) identification of the problem area(s) that are identified in the first phase of treatment, (b) identification of effective communication and problem-solving skills for the client's problems that occur in the second phase of treatment, and (c) practicing these skills and techniques both in and out of treatment sessions. The practicing occurs in the second and third phases of treatment (Mufson & Sills, 2006).

Phase 1. An initial assessment phase centers on an evaluation of the client's psychiatric history, diagnoses and symptoms, current social functioning, existing social relationships, relational patterns, and any recent changes, and may also assess for the need for medication. The client is also given the "sick role" during this phase. This assessment provides the clinician a base understanding of the client's social and interpersonal context of his or her depressive symptoms and assists in setting the framework for treatment. The client's depressive symptoms are subsequently connected to his or her current situation with specific focus on the following four main problem area(s): grief, interpersonal role disputes, role transitions, and interpersonal deficits (de Mello et al., 2005; Weissman & Markowitz, 1994, 1998).

Phase 2. The middle or treatment phase centers on the development of specific strategies for the client's current interpersonal problem areas (grief, interpersonal role disputes, role transitions, and interpersonal deficits) as determined in Phase 1. Grief strategies facilitate mourning and assist in the development of new activities and relationships to compensate for the client's loss. Interpersonal role dispute strategies target the management and resolution of conflicts with significant others. Role transition strategies seek to help the client deal with the change-of-life status (e.g., career changes, new diagnoses, new or ending relationships) by recognizing the positives and negatives of his or her new role. Finally, interpersonal deficit strategies recognize the client's social skills limitations and seek to develop, maintain, and/or expand his or her social relationships (Weissman & Markowitz, 1994, 1998).

Phase 3. The final phase is one of consolidation and ending. Clients are provided support and encouragement to recognize and consolidate their therapeutic gains as a method to reassert their independence, efficacy, and competence. In addition, clinicians work with clients to be able to identify and counter depressive symptoms that may emerge or reemerge in the future (Weissman & Markowitz, 1994, 1998).

EVIDENCE FOR IPT

Initially, IPT was developed for the treatment of adult depression, and investigations soon demonstrated its efficacy in the treatment approach of depression (de Mello et al., 2005; Hetrick et al., 2016; Ryan, 2005; Weissman & Markowitz, 1994). The proven effectiveness of IPT and its time-limited manualized approach readily lent this EBP to be adapted to diverse populations and diagnostic disorders (de Mello et al., 2005).

Interpersonal psychotherapy for adolescents (IPT-A) has been adapted from the original approach to treat depressed adolescents (Brunstein-Klomek, Zalsman, & Mufson, 2007; Klomek & Mufson, 2006; Moreau, Mufson, Weissman, & Klerman, 1991; Mufson & Sills, 2006). IPT-A was developed originally in 1993, then revised in 2004 (Mufson et al. 2004). It is designed specifically for use with adolescents aged 12 to 18 years who have an acute onset of major depression. In IPT-A, the three primary goals are to (a) decrease the depressive symptoms, (b) improve the interpersonal problems associated with the onset of the depressive episode, and (c) help clients strengthen their social support networks.

IPT-A differs from traditional IPT in several ways: (a) it is often briefer; (b) it may involve parents or caregivers; (c) in addition to the three problem areas of grief and loss, interpersonal disputes, and role transition, IPT-A includes a fourth problem area of interpersonal gaps. In the IPT-A model, treatment focuses on developing adolescents' emotional and relationship literacy, increasing their understanding of depression, enhancing their social skills, and developing their ability to communicate their attachment needs to others. This treatment occurs via weekly sessions across a period of 12 to 16 weeks.

IPT-A has been demonstrated to be effective for treating adolescents with depression, including White, African American, and Latino/a youths (Gunlicks-Stoessel, Mufson, Jekal, & Turner, 2010; Mufson et al., 1994, 2004; Mufson & Fairbanks, 1996; Mufson, Weissman, Moreau, & Garfinkel, 1999; Santor & Kusumakar, 2001). Several other models of IPT-A have since been developed and have emerging evidence as to their effectiveness. These include IPT for bipolar disorder (based on Interpersonal and Social Rhythm Therapy [IPSRT]; Crowe et al., 2009), IPT for depression comorbid with anxiety (Young, Mufson, & Davies, 2006), and family-based IPT (FB IPT) for youths 9–12 years of age (Deitz, Weinberg, Brent, & Mufson, 2015).

Another model has gained some stronger support. Young and colleagues have developed interpersonal psychotherapy–adolescent skills training (IPT-AST) from positive IPT-A findings (Young et al., 2016; Young, Makover, Cohen, Mufson, Gallop, & Benas, 2012; Young, Mufson, & Gallop, 2010). IPT-AST is a group-based preventive intervention that develops interpersonal skills to address problematic relationships and facilitate positive ones (Young et al., 2010), but has not been applied to suicide.

Research has similarly found that IPT is effective in treating older adults with late-life depression in general practice, and uptake and satisfaction by clients, therapists, and physicians (van Schaik et al., 2006; van Schaik, van Marwijk, Beekman, de Haan, & van Dyck, 2007).

IPT has yielded empirical support for treatment of postpartum depression (O'Hara, Stuart, Gorman, & Wenzel, 2000). An adaptation of IPT, interpersonal and social rhythm therapy (IPSRT), has demonstrated early evidence to support the treatment of bipolar 1 disorders (Frank et al., 2005). Also, IPT has been found to be efficacious in the treatment of persistent chronic depression (Markowitz, 1994), and for individuals with persistent chronic depression and secondary alcohol abuse; however, only a small effect was found in increasing the percentage of days abstinent (Markowitz, Kocsis, Christos, Bleiberg, & Carlin, 2008).

IPT has also been successfully adapted to eating disorders (Fairburn, Jones, Peveler, Hope, & O'Connor, 1993; Wilfley et al., 2002). Emerging research has also found preliminary data that supports the effectiveness of IPT in treating posttraumatic stress disorder (PTSD; Bleiberg & Markowitz, 2005; Krupnick et al., 2008; Markowitz, Milrod, Bleiberg, & Marshall, 2009) and borderline personality disorder (BPD; Markowitz, Bleiberg, Pessin, & Skodol, 2007).

Although IPT has increasingly been applied effectively across a number of populations, it has not been efficacious in every application. For example, IPT has not demonstrated effectiveness in the treatment of substance disorder findings (Markowitz et al., 2008, 2009). In addition, IPT has not been found to be efficacious in the treatment of anxiety (adults), although a small open pilot study seemed promising (Lipsitz et al., 2008).

IPT AND SUICIDE

IPT has not yet been demonstrated to be an effective EBP for the treatment of suicidality. However, IPT has increasingly been adapted and investigated as a *potential* treatment of suicidality (Heisel, Duberstein, Talbot, Tu, & King, 2009; Weitz, Hollon, Kerkhof, & Cuijpers, 2014). In addition, since its inception, IPT has focused on depression, a major underlying risk factor for suicidality. Depression is the most common psychiatric disorder associated with suicide. Further, research has found that more than 90% of individuals who suicide fulfill the criteria for one or more psychiatric disorders (American Psychiatric Association, 2003), of which 60% of all suicides occur in persons with a mood disorder (Malone & Lartey, 2004). Although IPT was not developed to treat suicide, its approach and efficacious treatment of depression may position this EBP as a potential, promising, and emerging treatment that may provide a basis to be adapted more directly for the treatment of suicidality. Future research into IPT will indicate the potential of this intervention as a treatment for suicidality.

Currently there is some research investigating the adaptation of IPT as a treatment for suicidality, and this preliminary evidence is promising. A recent study demonstrated the specific effectiveness of IPT and medications in reducing suicidal ideation (vs. a placebo-only control group); however, most of the effect was on the treatment of depression (Weitz et al., 2014). This adds to the growing body of evidence that depression treatments, specifically IPT and medication, can also reduce suicidal ideation and serve to further our understanding of the complex relationship between depression and suicide.

A model of IPT-A has since been adapted to specifically target adolescents at risk for suicide. The Program of Intensive Interpersonal Psychotherapy for depressed adolescents with suicidal risk (IPT-A-IN) is a school-based intervention designed to reduce the severity of depression and decrease suicidal risk of adolescents who were identified as at-risk during in-school screening based on self-reports of high school students (Tang, Jou, Ko, Huang, & Yen, 2009). The IPT-A-IN model is based on the same principles of IPT-A, which targets symptoms related to current interpersonal problem areas, including interpersonal conflict, interpersonal sensitivity, role transition, and grief. In IPT-A-IN, however, suicide is considered a comorbid symptom of depression. Accordingly, when a depressed adolescent with suicidal risk also suffers interpersonal stress, depression worsens and thoughts of self-injury increase. Proper treatment for interpersonal stress should, therefore, both ameliorate depressive symptoms and reduce thoughts of self-injury. In IPT-A-IN, suicidal ideation and depression are connected as interpersonal problems, and adolescents and their families are educated about the reduction of suicide risk, which is achieved by resolution of interpersonal problems. In IPT-A-IN, treatment is modified to occur via two sessions per week for six consecutive weeks in order to respond to the urgency of suicidal risk.

A randomized trial was conducted comparing 35 high school students receiving IPT-A-IN to 38 high school students receiving treatment-as-usual. Results demonstrated that school-based IPT-A-IN was significantly more effective than treatment-as-usual at reducing severity of depression, suicidal ideation, anxiety, and hopelessness in depressed high school students at risk of suicide. This preliminary evidence is promising and suggests that further research is needed to better understand the populations for which IPT-A-IN may be effective and the mechanisms through which the intervention model effects change.

Research has also found that IPT adaption to the treatment depression in older adults is efficacious (Bruce et al., 2004; Heisel & Duberstein, 2005). As older adults have high rates of suicidality (Bruce et al., 2004; Heisel & Duberstein, 2005), researchers have started to recommend that IPT may be adaptable to the treatment of suicidality in older adults (Szanto, Mulsant, Houck, Dew, & Reynolds III, 2003). A recent pilot study investigated a modified IPT treatment for older outpatients at elevated risk for suicide and found a substantial reduction in participant suicide ideation (Heisel et al., 2009). This study investigated 17 participants enrolled in this open trial of a modified 16-weekly IPT intervention, and researchers adapted existing IPT treatment manuals and incorporated safety precautions to treat older persons experiencing suicidality (Heisel et al., 2009). Specifically, study IPT therapists were instructed to focus on suicidal risk factors (past and current suicide ideation, death ideation, suicide plan, intent, and self-injurious behaviors) and to educate participants to the potential connection of interpersonal difficulties and suicidal ideation and behaviors during the assessment sessions (Heisel et al., 2009). In particular, attention was given to associations between suicide ideation and four main problem areas: grief, interpersonal role disputes, role transitions, and interpersonal deficits.

During treatment, IPT therapists monitored suicidal thoughts and linked these symptoms to identified interpersonal problems. In addition, IPT therapists helped participants to clarify and improve their interpersonal needs, identified opportunities to enhance their positive social networks by encouraging more engagement in pleasant activities with others, while decreasing the participants' exposure to painful or self-defeating interpersonal interactions (Heisel et al., 2009).

The termination phase focused on participants continuing to develop positive interpersonal relationships and to utilize their social supports and professionals when feeling suicidal in the future. Throughout the intervention, safety precautions were also added to the IPT protocols, including routine monitoring of suicidal ideation, in-session focus on validation of their feelings and problem-solving strategies to alleviate ideation, and the provision of the 24-hour cellular phone number of the study's therapist to access in the event of imminent risk (Heisel et al., 2009).

In small groups of four to six, discuss the following:

1. As a practitioner, consider what strengths a researcher may consider important for future adaptations of IPT for suicidality?
2. What are some potential interesting or concerning elements of the emergent application of IPT for suicidal older adults?

RECOMMENDED CLINICAL GUIDELINES FOR IPT

Research has not established recommended clinical guidelines for the use of IPT in the treatment of suicidality. Research is adding to the nascent body of evidence that IPT can reduce levels of depression (often with medication) and may also reduce suicidal ideation (Weitz et al., 2014). However, ongoing research with this approach may shortly produce such guidelines. Currently, there exists very little research to support the use of IPT for suicidality, and preliminary investigations focus specifically on adolescents and older adults. Considering the nature of IPT, its manualized and established strategies, adaptations across numerous populations and issues, and early findings in the treatment of suicidal adolescents and older adults, this approach has considerable, albeit unexplored potential for working with clients at risk of suicide.

SUMMARY

Treating individuals is best achieved through the use of EBP that has been demonstrated to be effective in research with similar populations. It is important for mental health clinicians to be aware of and use EBPs in their work with clients. IPT is an empirically supported treatment for individuals experiencing depression. The core elements and strategies of IPT have been adapted and demonstrated effectiveness in the treatment of a number of populations and presenting issues. Recently, IPT has been modified to treat suicidal older adults and adolescents, but this emergent research is limited and not yet sufficient to support its application to suicidality. Current and future research may yield IPT as an effective future evidence-based treatment in the area of suicidality. Clinicians are encouraged to keep up-to-date on this intervention's positive and ongoing progress and developments in the treatment of suicidality.

KEY POINTS

1. IPT has been demonstrated to be an effective time-limited, EBP treatment for depression.
2. IPT treatment of depression seeks the reduction of depressive symptoms and improvement and restoration of interpersonal functioning.
3. IPT uses three main overarching strategies to achieve treatment goals.
4. There are three main phases in IPT treatment.
5. IPT has been effectively adapted to the treatment of depression in adolescent, adults, and older adults.

(continued)

<table>
</table>

KEY POINTS (*continued*)

6. Empirical research has supported the efficacious use of IPT in the treatment of several diagnoses and presenting problems including anxiety, postpartum depression, persistent chronic depression, bipolar disorder, BPD, eating disorders, and PTSD.
7. IPT has not demonstrated effectiveness in the treatment of some disorders or presenting problems (e.g., substance disorders).
8. A recent pilot study that investigated a modified IPT treatment for older outpatients at elevated risk for suicide found a substantial reduction in suicide ideation.
9. Adaptation to IPT for the treatment of suicidal older adults has been developed.
10. Although promising, IPT has not yet been sufficiently investigated to support its application to suicidality.

ELECTRONIC RESOURCES

www.interpersonalpsychotherapy.org
https://iptinstitute.com/ipt-for-adolescents
www.depressioncenter.org

KNOWLEDGE ACQUISITION TEST (KAT)

True or False

1. Interpersonal psychotherapy (IPT) is a long-term intervention.
2. IPT is an effective intervention for anxiety.
3. Youths, adults, and older adults can be effectively treated with IPT.
4. IPT is a well-developed, manualized EBP intervention.
5. IPT has found limited success as an intervention outside of mood disorders.
6. IPT was initially developed in the 1970s.
7. The treatment of IPT comprises eight discrete phases.
8. IPT focuses on an individual's personality.
9. Currently, IPT is an established empirically supported (evidence-based) intervention for all individuals experiencing suicidality.

Short Answer

10. What are the four main interpersonal problem areas on which IPT focuses?
11. IPT was originally conceptualized as having three treatment phases; describe Phase 1.
12. IPT was originally conceptualized as having three treatment phases; describe Phase 2.
13. IPT was originally conceptualized as having three treatment phases; describe Phase 3.
14. Describe how researchers have adapted IPT to the treatment of suicidal older adults.
15. Describe how researchers have adapted IPT to the treatment of suicidal adolescents.

Multiple Choice

16. IPT uses which of the following strategy/ies?
    A. Identification of the problem area(s)
    B. Identification of effective communication and problem-solving skills for the client's problems
    C. Practicing these skills and techniques both in and out of treatment sessions
    D. All of the above
    E. None of the above
17. IPT has been demonstrated to be an effective treatment for which of the following depressive disorder(s)?
    A. Major depressive disorder
    B. Bipolar 1 disorder
    C. Persistent chronic depression
    D. Postpartum depression
    E. All of the above
    F. None of the above
18. IPT has not demonstrated some effectiveness in the treatment for which of the following disorder(s)?
    A. Posttraumatic stress disorder
    B. Substance disorders
    C. Eating disorders
    D. Personality disorders

    E. All of the above

    F. None of the above

19. Very preliminary investigations into adapting IPT to suicidality have demonstrated positive findings in which of the following areas?

    A. Children

    B. Adolescents

    C. Adults

    D. Older adults

    E. All of the above

    F. None of the above

20. The use of IPT as an evidence-based practice for the treatment of suicidality is currently:

    A. Recommended

    B. Tentatively recommended

    C. Recommended only for mild suicidal ideation

    D. Recommended only for older adults

    E. Not recommended

REFERENCES

American Psychiatric Association. (2003). Assessing and treating suicidal behaviors: A quick reference guide. Retrieved from http://www.psychiatryonline.com/pracGuide/loadPracQuickRefPdf.aspx ?file=Suibehavs_QRG

Bleiberg, K. L., & Markowitz, J. C. (2005). Interpersonal psychotherapy for posttraumatic stress disorder. *American Journal of Psychiatry, 162,* 181–183.

Bruce, M. L., Ten Have, T. R., Reynolds III, C. F., Katz, I. I., Schulberg, H. C., Mulsant, B. H., . . . Alexopoulus, G. S. (2004). Reducing suicidal ideation and depressive symptoms in depressed older primary care patients: A randomized controlled trial. *Journal of the American Medical Association, 291*(9), 1081–1091.

Brunstein-Klomek, A., Zalsman, G., & Mufson, L. (2007). Interpersonal psychotherapy for depressed adolescents (IPT-A). *Israel Journal of Psychiatry and Related Sciences, 44*(1), 40–46.

Crowe, M., Inder, M., Joyce, P., Moor, S., Carter, J., & Luty, S. (2009). A developmental approach to the treatment of bipolar disorder: IPSRT with an adolescent. *Journal of Clinical Nursing, 18*(1), 141–149.

Cuijpers, P., Geraedts, A. S., van Oppen, P., Andersson, G., Markowitz, J. C., & van Straten, A. (2011). Interpersonal psychotherapy for depression: A meta-analysis. *American Journal of Psychiatry, 168,* 581–592.

de Mello, M. F., de Jesus Mari, J., Bacaltchuk, J., Verdeli, H., & Neugebauer, R. (2005). A systematic review of research findings on the efficacy of interpersonal therapy for depressive disorders. *European Archives of Psychiatry and Clinical Neuroscience, 255,* 75–82.

Dietz, L. J., Weinberg, R. J., Brent, D. A., & Mufson, L. (2015). Family-based interpersonal psychotherapy (FB-IPT) for depressed preadolescents: Examining efficacy and potential treatment mechanisms. *Journal of the American Academy of Child and Adolescent Psychiatry, 54*(3), 191–199. doi:10.1016/j .jaac.2014.12.01

Fairburn, C. G., Jones, R., Peveler, R. C., Hope, R. A., & O'Connor, M. (1993). Psychotherapy and bulimia nervosa: Longer-term effects of interpersonal psychotherapy, behavior therapy and cognitive behavior therapy. *Archives of General Psychiatry, 50,* 419–428.

Frank, E., Kupfer, D. J., Thase, M. E., Mallinger, A. G., Swartz, H., Fagiolini, A. M., . . . Monk, T. (2005). Two-year outcomes for interpersonal and social rhythm therapy in individuals with bipolar I disorder. *Archives of General Psychiatry, 62,* 996–1004.

Gunlicks-Stoessel, M., Mufson, L., Jekal, A., & Turner, B. (2010). The impact of perceived interpersonal functioning on treatment for adolescent depression: IPT-A versus treatment as usual in school-based health clinics. *Journal of Consulting and Clinical Psychology, 78*(2), 260–267.

Heisel, M. J., & Duberstein, P. R. (2005). Suicide prevention in older adults. *Clinical Psychology: Science and Practice, 12*(3), 242–259.

Heisel, M. J., Duberstein, P. R., Talbot, N. L., Tu, X. M., & King, D. A. (2009). Adapting interpersonal psychotherapy for older adults at risk for suicide: Preliminary findings. *Professional Psychology: Research and Practice, 40*(2), 156–164.

Hetrick, S. E., Cox, G. R., Witt, K. G., Bir, J. J., & Merry, S. N. (2016). Cognitive behavioural therapy (CBT), third-wave CBT and interpersonal therapy (IPT)-based interventions for preventing depression in children and adolescents. *Cochrane Database of Systematic Review, 9*(8), CD003380.

Klerman, G. L., & Weissman, M. M. (1993). *New applications of interpersonal psychotherapy.* Washington, DC: American Psychiatric Press.

Klerman, G. L., Weissman, M. M., Rounsaville, B. J., & Chevron, E. S. (1984). *Interpersonal psychotherapy of depression.* New York, NY: Basic Books.

Klomek, A. B., & Mufson, L. (2006). Interpersonal psychotherapy for depressed adolescents. *Child and Adolescent Psychiatric Clinics of North America, 15*(4), 959–975.

Krupnick, J. L., Green, B. L., Stockton, P., Miranda, J., Krause, E., & Mete, M. (2008). Group interpersonal psychotherapy with low-income women with post-traumatic stress disorder. *Psychotherapy Research, 18,* 497–507.

Lipsitz, J. D., Gur, M., Vermes, D., Petkova, E., Cheng, J., Miller, N., . . . Fyer, A. J. (2008). A randomized trial of interpersonal therapy versus supportive therapy for social anxiety disorder. *Depression and Anxiety, 25*(6), 542–553.

Malone, D. A., & Lartey, P. (2004). *Depression and suicide: Recognition and early intervention* (2nd ed.). Washington, DC: American Medical Association.

Markowitz, J. C. (1994). Psychotherapy of dysthymia. *American Journal of Psychiatry, 151*(8), 1114–1121.

Markowitz, J. C., Bleiberg, K., Pessin, H., & Skodol, A. E. (2007). Adapting interpersonal psychotherapy for borderline personality disorder. *Journal of Mental Health, 16*(1), 103–116.

Markowitz, J. C., Kocsis, J. H., Christos, P., Bleiberg, K., & Carlin, A. (2008). Pilot study of interpersonal psychotherapy versus supportive psychotherapy for dysthymic patients with secondary alcohol abuse or dependence. *Journal of Nervous and Mental Disease, 196*(6), 468–474.

Markowitz, J. C., Milrod, B., Bleiberg, K., & Marshall, R. D. (2009). Interpersonal factors in understanding and treating posttraumatic stress disorder. *Journal of Psychiatric Practice, 15*(2), 133–140.

Moreau, D., Mufson, L., Weissman, M. M., & Klerman, G. L. (1991). Interpersonal psychotherapy for adolescent depression: Description of modification and preliminary application. *Journal of the American Academy of Child and Adolescent Psychiatry, 30*(4), 642–651.

Mufson, L., Dorta, K. P., Wickramaratne, P., Nomura, Y., Olfson, M., & Weissman, M. M. (2004). A randomized effectiveness trial of interpersonal psychotherapy for depressed adolescents. *Archives of General Psychiatry, 61*(6), 577–584.

Mufson, L., & Fairbanks, J. (1996). Interpersonal psychotherapy for depressed adolescents: A one-year naturalistic follow-up study. *Journal of the American Academy of Child and Adolescent Psychiatry, 35*(9), 1145–1155.

Mufson, L., Moreau, D., Weissman, M. M., Wickramaratne, P., Martin, J., & Samoilov, A. (1994). Modification of interpersonal psychotherapy with depressed adolescents (IPT-A): Phase I and II studies. *Journal of the American Academy of Child and Adolescent Psychiatry, 33*(5), 695–705.

Mufson, L., & Sills, R. (2006). Interpersonal psychotherapy for depressed adolescents (IPT-A): An overview. *Nordic Journal of Psychiatry, 60*(6), 431–437.

Mufson, L., Weissman, M. M., Moreau, D., & Garfinkel, R. (1999). Efficacy of interpersonal psychotherapy for depressed adolescents. *Archives of General Psychiatry, 56*, 573–579.

O'Hara, M. W., Stuart, S., Gorman, L. L., & Wenzel, A. (2000). Efficacy of interpersonal psychotherapy for postpartum depression. *Archives of General Psychiatry, 57*, 1039–1045.

Ryan, N. (2005). Treatment of depression in children and adolescents. *Lancet, 366*(9489), 933–940.

Santor, D., & Kusumakar, V. (2001). Open trial of interpersonal therapy in adolescents with moderate to severe major depression: Effectiveness of novice IPT therapists. *Journal of the American Academy of Child and Adolescent Psychiatry, 40*(2), 236–240.

Sullivan, H. S. (Ed.). (1953). *The interpersonal theory of psychiatry.* New York, NY: W. W. Norton.

Szanto, K., Mulsant, H. B., Houck, P., Dew, M. A., & Reynolds III, C. F. (2003). Occurrence and course of suicidality during short-term treatment of late-life depression. *Archives of General Psychiatry, 60*, 610–617.

Tang, T. C., Jou, S. H., Ko, C. H., Huang, S. Y., & Yen, C. F. (2009). Randomized study of school-based intensive interpersonal psychotherapy for depressed adolescents with suicidal risk and parasuicide behaviors. *Psychiatry and Clinical Neuroscience, 63*(4), 463–470.

van Schaik, A., van Marwijk, H. W., Adèr, H., van Dyck, R., de Haan, M., Penninx, B., . . . Beekman, A. (2006). Interpersonal psychotherapy for elderly patients in primary care. *American Journal of Geriatric Psychiatry, 14*(9), 777–786.

van Schaik, D. J., van Marwijk, H. W., Beekman, A. T., de Haan, M., & van Dyck, R. (2007). Interpersonal psychotherapy (IPT) for late-life depression in general practice: Uptake and satisfaction by patients, therapists and physicians. *BioMed Central Family Practice, 8*, 52–59.

Weissman, M. M., & Markowitz, J. C. (1994). Interpersonal psychotherapy: Current status. *Archives of General Psychiatry, 51*, 599–606.

Weissman, M. M., & Markowitz, J. C. (1998). An overview of interpersonal psychotherapy. In J. Markowitz (Ed.), *Interpersonal psychotherapy* (pp. 1—33). Washington, DC: American Psychiatric Press.

Weitz, E., Hollon, S. D., Kerkhof, A., & Cuijpers, P. (2014). Do depression treatments reduce suicidal ideation? The effects of CBT, IPT, pharmacotherapy, and placebo on suicidality. *Journal of Affective Disorders, 167*, 98–103.

Wilfley, D. E., Welch, R. R., Stein, R. I., Spurrell, E. B., Cohen, L. R., Saelens, B. E., . . . Matt, G. E. (2002). A randomized comparison of group cognitive-behavioral therapy and group interpersonal psychotherapy for the treatment of overweight individuals with binge-eating disorder. *Archives of General Psychiatry, 59*, 713–721.

Young, J. F., Makover, H. B., Cohen, J. R., Mufson, L., Gallop, R. J., & Benas, J. S. (2012). Interpersonal psychotherapy–adolescent skills training: Anxiety outcomes and impact of comorbidity. *Journal of Clinical Child and Adolescent Psychology, 41*(5), 640–653.

Young, J. F., Mufson, L., & Davies, M. (2006). Efficacy of interpersonal psychotherapy–adolescent skills training: An indicated preventive intervention for depression. *Journal of Child Psychology and Psychiatry, 47*(12), 1254–1262.

Young, J. F., Mufson, L., & Gallop, R. (2010). Preventing depression: A randomized trial of interpersonal psychotherapy–adolescent skills training. *Depression and Anxiety, 27*(5), 426–433.

CHAPTER NINETEEN

MOTIVATIONAL INTERVIEWING AND SUICIDE

This chapter presents motivational interviewing (MI) as a treatment model to address suicidal individuals. MI was originally conceived of as a treatment for individuals struggling with alcohol use disorders (Beck, Rush, Shaw, & Emery, 1979; Rollnick & Miller, 1995). However, in recent years, an evidence base has been growing for the use of MI with individuals experiencing suicidality. This chapter explores the theory behind MI and provides a thorough description of the key components and strategies of MI. Research examining the effectiveness of MI among individuals experiencing suicidality is reviewed. Recommendations for clinical practice when implementing MI are also reviewed.

GOALS AND OBJECTIVES

An understanding of:

- Theory behind MI
- Major components of MI
- Goals of MI intervention
- Major tasks of MI
- Treatment targets of MI
- Core strategies used in MI
- Evidence to support the use of MI
- Populations for and settings in which MI is supported
- Factors that impact the effectiveness of MI
- Clinical considerations when conducting MI

MOTIVATIONAL INTERVIEWING

Developed by Drs. William R. Miller and Stephen Rollnick, MI has been defined as a directive, client-centered counseling style for eliciting behavioral change by helping clients explore and resolve ambivalence (Miller & Rollnick, 1991; Rollnick & Miller, 1995). MI is a client-centered counseling approach (Miller & Rollnick, 1991) with a central principle that motivation to change should be elicited from people, not somehow imposed on them (Rollnick & Allison, 2004). As an approach, MI is a well-researched and empirically supported evidence-based intervention used to evoke intrinsic motivation to change behaviors (Miller & Rollnick, 2013). Also, MI has often been used in conjunction with

Prochaska and DiClemente's Transtheoretical Model (TTM) to support clients as they move through the stages of the Transtheoretical Model of Change (six stages of change: precontemplation, contemplation, preparation, action, maintenance, and termination; Prochaska & DiClemente, 1984; Prochaska & Velicer, 1997). Initially developed for individuals with substance use disorders, MI has been expanded across a number of mental health diagnoses, presenting problems, and symptoms, including applications to clients with suicidal thoughts and behaviors (Britton, Conner, & Maisto, 2012; Britton, Patrick, Wenzel, & Williams, 2011; Burke, Arkowitz, & Menchola, 2003; Hoy, Natarajan, & Petra, 2016). To date, MI is not a supported evidence-based intervention for suicide ideation or attempts; however, research is beginning to show nascent support for its application in the field of suicidality.

Individual Exercise 19.1

In this exercise, we are going to ask you to think of a behavior that you engage in with which you are dissatisfied or displeased. This may evoke some distressing thoughts and feelings. You may consider skipping this exercise or reflecting on a less significant behavior. The intention of this exercise is one of reflection and understanding related to MI. It is not designed or intended for you to focus on a negative, upsetting self-characteristic.

1. Think of a behavior that you engage in that you have wanted to change (being late, procrastinating, nail biting, cigarette smoking, etc.). Describe the behavior with as much detail as possible.
2. What has kept you from making that change to date?
3. Have others told you it would be important to change that behavior?
4. Does their warning/advising/lecturing help you to want to make the change? Why or why not?
5. What would have to happen for you to take action toward change?
6. On a scale of 1 to 10, 1 being "not ready at all" and 10 being "very ready," how ready are you to make the change and stop that behavior?
7. On a scale of 1 to 10, 1 being "not at all confident" and 10 being "extremely confident," how confident are you that you can successfully change that behavior?
8. As you reflect on your answers to questions 1 to 7, does anything surprise you about your readiness to change?

Small Group Exercise 19.1

In small groups of two to three, please discuss, as you are comfortable, your responses to Individual Exercise 19.1. Remember, share only what you are comfortable to share. Answers are personal, and there are no correct or incorrect answers.

1. What were the response similarities in your group?
2. What were the response differences in your group?
3. Did you find any surprises in the group discussion? If so, what were they and how were you surprised?

As a directive, client-centered counseling style, MI seeks to elicit behavioral change by helping clients explore and resolve ambivalence (Miller & Rollnick, 1991; Rollnick & Miller, 1995). The processes that constitute the method of MI include four overlapping components: engaging, focusing, evoking, and planning (Miller & Rollnick, 2013).

Engaging process. Any therapeutic process begins with engagement, where the client and clinician establish a connection and working relationship, the formation of the therapeutic alliance. This process begins in the initial moments and can continue for weeks. Miller and Rollnick (2013) stress that much can be achieved in engaging conversations to build and foster engagement, as therapeutic engagement is a prerequisite for everything that follows (Miller & Rollnick, 2013).

Focusing process. Engagement will often facilitate a focusing on a particular therapeutic agenda that leads the client into treatment. According to Miller and Rollnick (2013), it is not only clients that have an agenda, but clinicians also have one, which may or may not coincide with each other. The focusing process is where the clinician and client develop and maintain a specific direction in the conversation about change (Miller & Rollnick, 2013). In this process, the direction frequently leads to the emergence of goals, which often require change. This collaborative and consultative process seeks to bring clarity and focus to the treatment and goals toward which the client wants to move.

Evoking process. After change goals have been focused upon, the next process involves evoking at the very core a client's inner motivations for these changes, striving to activate the client's own ideas and feelings about why and how he or she might make these changes (Miller & Rollnick, 2013). Rather than an expert clinician leading the change process, the clinician works to evoke the client's own argument for the needed change, as people tend to talk themselves into change. During this process, the clinician nurtures and fosters the client's inherent motivation for positive change (Miller & Rollnick, 2013).

Planning process. This process begins as clients' motivation ushers their thinking motivation to change to a readiness for change. Specifically, the client's conversation transitions from whether and why they may change to a more tangible when and how that change will be (Miller & Rollnick, 2013). Generally, the planning process has two core components: developing a commitment to change and formulating an action plan for that change.

EVIDENCE FOR MI

MI has a substantial body of research demonstrating its effectiveness at addressing alcohol use disorders (Burke et al., 2003; Miller & Rollnick, 1989; PROJECT MATCH Research Group, 1997, 1998; Vasilaki, Hosier, & Cox, 2006). Since its conceptualization, MI has been found to be effective for addressing substance use, then rapidly expanded to a wide range of problems. Currently, extensive evidence exists providing empirical support to the effectiveness of MI among individuals struggling with various health change behaviors such as smoking cessation (Burke et al., 2003; Stotts, DiClemente, & Dolan-Mullan, 2002), weight loss (Burke et al., 2003; Hettema, Steele, & Miller, 2005; Resnicow, Davis, & Rollnick, 2006), sobriety from a substance addiction (Apodaca & Longabaugh, 2009; Burke et al., 2003; Carroll et al., 2009; Jensen et al., 2011; Lundahl & Burke, 2009; Martino, Carroll, O'Malley, & Rounsaville, 2000; McCambridge & Strang, 2004; Stephens, Roffman, & Curtin, 2000; Sussman, Sun, Rohrback, & Spruiit-Metz, 2012; Vasilaki et al., 2006), HIV treatment (Dunn, Deroo, & Rivara, 2001; Outlaw et al., 2010; Parsons, Golub, Rosof, & Holder, 2007; Parsons, Rosof, Punzalan, & Maria, 2005), exercise (Harland et al., 1999; Hettema et al., 2005), medication adherence (Hettema et al., 2005; Rusch & Corrigan, 2002; Swanson, Pantalon, & Cohen, 1999), and treatment engagement (Carroll et al., 2009; Hettema et al., 2005; Lundahl & Burke, 2009).

Evidence for the effectiveness of MI at increasing engagement in treatment and improving treatment outcomes is widespread in terms of target populations. At present, research supports MI's effectiveness across age groups (Brown et al., 2003; Burke et al., 2003; Erickson, Gerstle, & Feldstein, 2005; Hettema et al., 2005; Jensen et al., 2011; McCambridge & Strang, 2004; Sussman, 2012; Vasilaki et al., 2006), ethnicities (Añez, Silva, Paris, & Bedregal, 2008; Befort et al., 2008; Interian, Martinez, Rios, Krejci, & Guarnaccia, 2012; Lundahl, Kunz, Brownell, Tollefson, & Burke, 2010; Ogedegbe et al., 2008; Spencer et al., 2011), and socioeconomic strata (Dishion et al., 2008; Hardcastle, Blake, & Hagger, 2012; Michie, Jochelson, Markham, & Bridle, 2009). MI has also been found to be effective at addressing change behaviors across physical illnesses and health care settings (Britt, Hudson, & Blampied, 2004; Knight, McGowan, Dickens, & Bundy, 2006; Malouff, Thorsteinsson, & Schutte, 2007; Martins & McNeil, 2009; Söderlund, Madson, Rubak, & Nilsen, 2011) and psychiatric illnesses and mental health settings (Baker et al., 2002; Burke et al., 2003; Hettema et al., 2005; Lundahl & Burke, 2009; Vasilaki et al., 2006).

MI has also been adapted to more current technologically based delivery models and has been shown to be effective as an online intervention across age groups and presenting problems (Hoek et al., 2011; King et al., 2015). One study, for example, examined the effect of adding MI to an Internet-based treatment for depression. Results indicate that the MI group demonstrated significantly fewer depressive episodes and reported less hopelessness as compared with the group that received only the Internet-based intervention (Hoek et al., 2011). Research has also demonstrated MI to be effective for increasing the treatment utilization of college students seeking online mental health treatment, specifically in the following areas: including greater readiness for help-seeking, especially readiness to talk to family, talk to friends, and see a mental health professional, lower stigma levels, and greater likelihood of linking to mental health treatment (King, 2015).

MI AND SUICIDE

Research has shown that suicidal individuals progress through stages of change as they move from suicidal thinking to a suicide attempt (Coombs, 2001; Hoy, Natarajan, & Petra, 2016), yet only recently has research begun to focus on the applicability of MI and the stages of change to suicidal individuals (Hoy, Natarajan, & Petra, 2016; Kress & Hoffman, 2008; Olfson, Marcus, & Bridge, 2014).

MI is often used in conjunction with Prochaska and DiClemnte's Transtheoretical Model of Change, which suggests that individuals move through various stages (stages of change: precontemplation, contemplation, preparation, action, maintenance, and termination) before behavioral change successfully occurs (Prochaska & DiClemente, 1984). It has similarly been proposed that levels of risk for suicide may, at times, be conceptualized as occurring in stages (i.e., ranging from no risk, low risk, moderate risk, or high risk of attempting suicide; Berman & Silverman, 2014). Evidence has been presented that suggests that stages of moving from not even considering suicide (precontemplation) to attempting or completing suicide (action) align with the stages delineated in the Transtheoretical Model of Change (Coombs, 2001; Hoy, 2016). In a retrospective descriptive study of 42 formerly suicidal individuals, the majority of participants reported progressing through the stages of change (i.e., precontemplation, contemplation, preparation, and action; Coombs, 2001). Findings indicated that an individual who is facing serious stressors such as mental health problems, financial issues, and interpersonal problems may initially not even consider suicide (precontemplation), but, as other coping mechanisms or attempts to address the stressors are rejected or perhaps not even considered, the person may then begin to consider suicide (contemplation). Further, if other coping/problem-solving attempts are deemed ineffective and problems begin to seem unsolvable, suicide then may become a viable option (Hoy, 2016).

MI has been examined as a conjunctive treatment to other evidence-based practices (EBPs). For example, Hettema et al. (2005) conducted a comprehensive meta-analysis of MI-based interventions that included 72 studies (Hettema et al., 2005). In seven studies, MI was added to other treatments such as psychopharmacological treatment and cognitive behavioral therapy (CBT), to increase engagement and adherence with alcohol and drug treatment and improve treatment outcomes. Overall, a strong support for the effectiveness of MI at increasing treatment engagement was found (Hettema et al., 2005). Another analysis of eight additional studies examining MI as a conjunctive treatment to CBT found that the use of MI in addition to CBT led to improvements in treatment engagement as well as treatment outcomes (Britton et al., 2011).

Different strategies for integrating MI and CBT have been proposed. Most commonly, one or two sessions of MI are implemented before CBT to help clients explore and resolve their ambivalence toward a desired change. However, additional strategies that require additional research support but have been proposed as useful are to (a) implement a course of MI once the client is motivated to transition to CBT, (b) incorporate one or two sessions of MI into treatment when the client's motivation wanes, and (c) assimilate principles of MI throughout the CBT process (Aharonovich, Amrhein, Bisaga, Nunes, & Hasin, 2008; Britton et al., 2011).

Given that it is difficult to engage clients who are at risk in treatment and that MI has been shown to be effective at increasing treatment engagement and improving treatment outcomes when used to complement other treatments (Hettema et al., 2005), Britton et al. (2011) examined the use of MI as a supplement to CBT, a treatment approach demonstrated to be effective at addressing suicidality. Britton et al. (2011) proposed that one explanation for why it is often challenging to engage at-risk individuals in treatment is that they may lack motivation to live and, consequently, lack interest in and energy for treatment. They further propose that resolving this ambivalence by increasing the motivation to live may be critical to reducing suicidal behavior and may serve to increase participation in life-sustaining behavior, such as treatment (Britton et al., 2011). The authors also suggest that the very stressors that influence client's suicidality may serve as barriers to treatment engagement (e.g., the low motivation that accompanies depression, poor interpersonal skills, and financial problems making it difficult to pay for treatment). These factors, in turn, can further influence the client's wish to live or wish to die. It is critical, then, to carefully differentiate the varying motivations that clients have to ensure that efforts to increase motivation in treatment simultaneously increase the wish to live (Britton et al., 2011). MI was specifically developed to help clients increase their motivation to change a harmful behavior, or engage in a beneficial behavior, and to increase the likelihood that they will do so. Given the significant ambivalence reported by individuals who are thinking about suicide and MI's focus on resolving ambivalence, MI appears to address some significant treatment needs of clients considering suicide (Britton et al., 2011; Hoy, 2016; Zerler, 2008).

Consequently, Britton et al. (2011) propose MI to address suicidal ideation (MI-SI). MI-SI has three treatment phases that occur across one session. It was originally developed to provide psychiatric emergency department clinicians with a means for tapping into and enhancing a client's motivation to live and engage in life-enhancing activities in one brief meeting. In Phase 1, the clinicians provide clients with an opportunity to share and explore their presenting problem and their reasons for thinking about suicide. In Phase 2, the focus is on eliciting and exploring reasons for living in order to enhance the client's motivation to live. In Phase 3, clinicians help strengthen the client's commitment to live by developing a personal plan to make life worth living. The phases are not intended to serve as a checklist, but rather as an outline to help clinicians structure MI-SI sessions (Britton et al., 2011).

Preliminary research on MI-SI provides support for its usefulness in emergency room settings (Britton, Patrick, Wenzel, & Williams, 2011). In a pilot study of 28 individuals presenting to the emergency room with severe suicidal ideation who received MI-SI, results demonstrated that clients were satisfied with MI-SI and that clinicians reported that MI-SI facilitated the discussion of both reasons for dying and reasons for living. Further, no adverse events were reported by the clinicians or unit staff during the trial study period (Britton, 2007).

Preliminary research has begun to demonstrate positive benefits of employing MI at reducing suicidal behavior among at-risk individuals in and of itself, not only as a supplemental treatment. For example, one study examined the use of MI for addressing suicidal ideation among psychiatrically hospitalized veterans (Britton et al., 2012). Although the sample size was quite small at only 13 veterans, nascent results provided some positive initial support for the use of MI in this population. Specifically, participants reported MI to be acceptable and that they experienced large reductions in the severity of suicidal ideation at posttreatment and follow-up (Britton et al., 2012). Another case study demonstrated positive results of MI at reducing the severity of a suicidal crisis (Zerler, 2008).

MI has also been examined as an intervention for improving means restriction as a form of addressing suicide risk. One study found that MI can be effective as a means-restriction counseling approach to increase the willingness of challenging and ambivalent clients to limit their access to lethal means (Britton, Bryan, & Valenstein, 2016).

Recommended Clinical Guidelines for MI

MI is increasingly building a body of research for application and use in addressing suicidality. It is a collaborative, client-centered approach that requires active participation of both the client and the therapist. As a mental health professional working with suicidal clients and implementing an MI approach, recommended practice guidelines to consider include the following:

1. *Expressing empathy.* The principle of empathy is fundamental to an MI approach. From an MI perspective, the helping process should be a humanistic (client-centered), accepting approach in which reluctance or ambivalence is framed as a normal part of the change process and human experience. Therefore, it is recommended that when practicing MI, accurate empathy is conveyed via reflective listening.

2. *Developing discrepancy.* According to MI, motivation increases as clients grows to see a discrepancy between their current behaviors and their future goals. When clients can recognize on their own that their current circumstances interfere with their values or desired goals, they are more likely to work toward making changes. Clinicians should aim to gradually help their clients become aware of how their current behaviors may lead them further away from, rather than toward, their identified goals.

3. *Rolling with resistance.* Although MI is intentionally directive, it is important that a clinician avoid explicit advocate for change; it is the client who needs to develop and present the reasons for change. Therefore, when a client expresses resistance to change, it is a signal for the clinician to respond differently. As such, resistance, in an MI approach, is conceptualized as an interpersonal variable, and it is recommended that the clinician not oppose it but rather accept and flow with it using reflective listening skills. Signs of resistance should not, therefore, be challenged but rather clinicians should avoid resistance and work to deescalate a negative interaction.

4. *Enhancing self-efficacy.* According to MI, in order for change to occur, two conditions are necessary: (a) the change has to be important to the client and (b) the

client has to have the confidence that he or she can be successful at making the change. Together, these conditions are considered the client's sense of self-efficacy. It is recommended that a clinician work not only to increase the sense of importance of change but also to enhance the client's confidence in his or her own ability to cope with barriers and to succeed in changing. Clinicians should, therefore, focus on previous successes the client has experienced and highlight the skills and strengths that the client already has.

5. *Open-ended questions.* The use of an open-ended question, rather than a closed-ended question, in MI is a specific tool as it facilitates a client's reflection and elaboration. An open-ended question supports client engagement by encouraging clients to discuss and explore their own thoughts and evoke/increase their intrinsic motivation. Therefore, it is recommended that clinicians emphasize the use of open-ended rather than closed-ended questions that serve more as an information gathering tool for the clinician rather than an opportunity for reflection and growth for the client.

6. *Affirmations.* MI focuses on a client's own personal strengths, efforts, and resources to elicit change. Thus, it is recommended that clinicians continually strive to affirm the client's way of thinking toward change, and his or her strengths and resources to make the desired change.

7. *Reflective listening.* Reflective listening is a skill in which the clinician reflects back to the clients their thoughts and feeling. In MI, reflective statements can support the clients' continued change process by encouraging their change talk and exploration. It is recommended that clinicians employ reflective listening in the evoking and planning process.

8. *Summaries.* Also a type of reflection, summaries serve to communicate interest and understanding and to highlight important elements of a discussion. It is recommended that clinicians use summaries to highlight moments where a client is expressing ambivalence about taking action toward change, or as opportunities to develop discrepancy by emphasizing certain information the client has shared while minimizing other information.

9. *Change talk.* Change talk is a moment in the session when the client is expressing a commitment to, motivation for, or consideration of taking action toward change, specifically in face of naturally occurring ambivalence to change. Clinicians are recommended to be attentive to the moments when the client is expressing change talk and purposively reflect on them when they occur. It is also recommended that clinicians work to elicit change talk from clients by exploring the pros and cons of changing one's behavior, examining one's current actions and future goals, and asking for examples to highlight desired changes being expressed.

ROLE-PLAY 19.1

You are a mental health clinician in an outpatient mental health center. A client you treated briefly 2 years prior for depression unexpectedly presents to your office expressing suicidal ideation with intent.

Using this scenario, break into groups of three and assume the roles of the mental health clinician and the client. The third member will act as a recorder and can be called upon to consult and assist the mental health clinician. Engage in a role-play in which you would implement MI with this client.

ROLE-PLAY 19.2

You are a mental health clinician in an outpatient mental health center. A client you treated briefly 2 years prior for depression unexpectedly presents to your office expressing suicidal ideation with intent.

Using this scenario, break into groups of three and assume the roles of the mental health clinician and the supervisor. The third member will act as a recorder and can be called upon to consult and assist the mental health clinician. Engage in a role-play in which you would discuss this client with your supervisor. What questions might you ask? What kind of support might you try to elicit? Is the supervision for you? The client? Both?

SUMMARY

MI is a directive, client-centered counseling style for eliciting behavioral change by helping clients explore and elicit their own intrinsic motivation to change. Currently, MI is not an evidence-based intervention for treating individuals with suicidal ideation or behaviors. However, MI has demonstrated wide applicability to a number of diagnoses and presenting problems, and preliminary research is beginning to generate early positive results in several areas including engaging clients who are at risk in treatment, suicidal ideation, and reducing suicidal behavior among at-risk individuals. Ongoing and future research may demonstrate that MI will become an effective, future, evidence-based treatment in the area of suicidality. Clinicians are recommended to monitor MI's development in the field of suicidality.

KEY POINTS

1. MI is a directive, client-centered counseling approach.
2. MI elicits behavioral change by helping clients explore and resolve ambivalence.
3. A central principle of MI recognizes that motivation to change should be elicited from the clients, not somehow imposed on them by the clinician.
4. The goal of MI is to help clients to positively change their behaviors.
5. The method of MI comprises four overlapping components (engaging, focusing, evoking, and planning).
6. Evidence for the effectiveness of MI at increasing engagement in treatment and improving treatment outcomes is widespread.
7. Research supports MI's effectiveness across age groups, ethnicities, and socioeconomic status.
8. MI is effective in engaging clients who are at risk in nonengagement to treatment.
9. Preliminary research has shown that MI may support clinicians' ability to work with a client's suicide ideation by tapping into and enhancing the client's motivation to live and engage in life-enhancing activities in one brief meeting.
10. Currently, MI is not an evidence-based treatment for clients experiencing suicide ideation or behaviors.

ELECTRONIC RESOURCES

www.motivationalinterviewing.org
www.centerforebp.case.edu/practices/mi

KNOWLEDGE ACQUISITION TEST (KAT)

True or False

1. Motivational interviewing (MI) is a long-term treatment approach.
2. MI focuses on personality development.
3. The connection between cognitions, affect, and behavior is central to MI.
4. MI believes that intrinsic motivation is necessary for change.
5. MI is an evidence-based practice (EBP) for reducing suicidality.
6. Rolling with resistance is a key strategy of MI.
7. MI consists of three main processes.
8. MI is an EBP for changing health-related behaviors.
9. MI is effective at increasing treatment adherence.
10. Cognitive restructuring is a key technique of MI.

Short Answer

11. Describe how the stages of change explain the stages of suicidality.
12. What is the role of developing discrepancy in MI?
13. What is the role of self-efficacy in MI?
14. Describe how MI manages open-ended questions.
15. Describe change talk.
16. How are affirmations used in MI?

Multiple Choice

17. Which of the following is *not* a key component of MI?
    A. Summaries
    B. Affirmations
    C. Reflection
    D. Activity scheduling
    E. None of the above
    F. All of the above
18. Which of the following is *not* a key process in MI?
    A. Engaging
    B. Focusing
    C. Reviewing
    D. Evoking
    E. None of the above
    F. All of the above
19. For which behavior has MI been shown to be effective?
    A. HIV
    B. Smoking cessation
    C. Weight loss
    D. Medication adherence
    E. All of the above
    F. None of the above

20. Which of the following is one of the Transtheoretical Model of Change?
    A. Contemplation
    B. Maintenance
    C. Precontemplation
    D. Action
    E. All of the above
    F. None of the above

REFERENCES

Aharonovich, E., Amrhein, P. C., Bisaga, A., Nunes, E. V., & Hasin, D. S. (2008). Cognition, commitment language, and behavioral change among cocaine dependent patients. *Psychology of Addictive Behaviors, 22,* 557–562.

Añez, L. M., Silva, M. A., Paris Jr, M., & Bedregal, L. E. (2008). Engaging Latinos through the integration of cultural values and motivational interviewing principles. *Professional Psychology: Research and Practice, 39*(2), 153–159.

Apodaca, T. R., & Longabaugh, R. (2009). Mechanisms of change in motivational interviewing: A review and preliminary evaluation of the evidence. *Addiction, 104*(5), 705–715.

Baker, A., Lewin, T., Reichler, H., Clancy, R., Carr, V., Garrett, R., & Terry, M. (2002). Motivational interviewing among psychiatric in-patients with substance use disorders. *Acta Psychiatrica Scandinavica, 106*(3), 233–240.

Beck, A. T., Rush, A. J., Shaw, B. F., & Emery, G. (1979). *Cognitive therapy of depression.* New York, NY: Guilford Press.

Befort, C. A., Nollen, N., Ellerbeck, E. F., Sullivan, D. K., Thomas, J. L., & Ahluwalia, J. S. (2008). Motivational interviewing fails to improve outcomes of a behavioral weight loss program for obese African American women: A pilot randomized trial. *Journal of Behavioral Medicine, 31*(5), 367–377.

Berman, A. L., & Silverman, M. M. (2014). Suicide risk assessment and risk formulation part II: Suicide risk formulation and the determination of levels of risk. *Suicide and Life-Threatening Behavior, 44,* 432–443.

Britt, E., Hudson, S. M., & Blampied, N. M. (2004). Motivational interviewing in health settings: A review. *Patient Education and Counseling, 53*(2), 147–155.

Britton, P. C., Bryan, C. J., & Valenstein, M. (2016). Motivational interviewing for means restriction counseling with patients at risk for suicide. *Cognitive and Behavioral Practice, 23*(1), 51–61.

Britton, P. C., Conner, K. R., & Maisto, S. A. (2012). An open trial of motivational interviewing to address suicidal ideation with hospitalized veterans. *Journal of Clinical Psychology, 68*(9), 961–971.

Britton, P. C., Patrick, H., Wenzel, A., & Williams, G. C. (2011). Integrating motivational interviewing and self-determination theory with cognitive behavioral therapy to prevent suicide. *Cognitive and Behavioral Practice, 18*(1), 16–27.

Brown, R. A., Ramsey, S. E., Strong, D. R., Myers, M. G., Kahler, C. W., Lejuez, C., & Abrams, D. B. (2003). Effects of motivational interviewing on smoking cessation in adolescents with psychiatric disorders. *Tobacco Control, 12*(Suppl. 4), iv3–iv10.

Burke, B. L., Arkowitz, H., & Menchola, M. (2003). The efficacy of motivational interviewing: A meta-analysis of controlled clinical trials. *Journal of Consulting and Clinical Psychology, 71,* 843–861.

Carroll, K. M., Ball, S. A., Nich, C., Martino, S., Frankforter, T. L., Farentinos, C., & Polcin, D. (2006). Motivational interviewing to improve treatment engagement and outcome in individuals seeking treatment for substance abuse: A multisite effectiveness study. *Drug and Alcohol Dependence, 81*(3), 301–312.

Coombs, R. H. (2001). *Substance abuse treatment and the stages of change: Selecting and planning interventions.* New York, NY: Guilford Press.

Dishion, T. J., Shaw, D., Connell, A., Gardner, F., Weaver, C., & Wilson, M. (2008). The family check-up with high-risk indigent families: Preventing problem behavior by increasing parents' positive behavior support in early childhood. *Child Development, 79*(5), 1395–1414.

Dunn, C., Deroo, L., & Rivara, F. P. (2001). The use of brief interventions adapted from motivational interviewing across behavioral domains: A systematic review. *Addiction, 96*(12), 1725–1742.

Erickson, S. J., Gerstle, M., & Feldstein, S. W. (2005). Brief interventions and motivational interviewing with children, adolescents, and their parents in pediatric health care settings: A review. *Archives of Pediatrics and Adolescent Medicine, 159*(12), 1173–1180.

Hardcastle, S., Blake, N., & Hagger, M. S. (2012). The effectiveness of a motivational interviewing primary-care based intervention on physical activity and predictors of change in a disadvantaged community. *Journal of Behavioral Medicine, 35*(3), 318–333.

Harland, J., White, M., Drinkwater, C., Chinn, D., Farr, L., & Howel, D. (1999). The Newcastle exercise project: A randomised controlled trial of methods 74 to promote physical activity in primary care. *British Medical Journal, 25,* 828–832.

Hettema, J., Steele, J., & Miller, W. R. (2005). Motivational interviewing. *Annual Review of Clinical Psychology, 1,* 91–111.

Hoek, W., Marko, M., Fogel, J., Schuurmans, J., Gladstone, T., Bradford, N., Domanico, R., . . . & Petra, M. M. (2016). Motivational interviewing and the transtheoretical model of change: Under-explored resources for suicide intervention. *Community Mental Health Journal, 52*(5), 559–567.

Hoy, J., Natarajan, A., & Petra, M. M. (2016). Motivational Interviewing and the Transtheoretical Model of Change: Under-Explored Resources for Suicide Intervention. *Community Mental Health Journal, 52*(5), 559–567.

Interian, A., Martinez, I., Rios, L. I., Krejci, J., & Guarnaccia, P. J. (2010). Adaptation of a motivational interviewing intervention to improve antidepressant adherence among Latinos. *Cultural Diversity and Ethnic Minority Psychology, 16*(2), 215–225. doi:10.1037/a0016072

Jensen, C. D., Cushing, C. C., Aylward, B. S., Craig, J. T., Sorell, D. M., & Steele, R. G. (2011). Effectiveness of motivational interviewing interventions for adolescent substance use behavior change: A meta-analytic review. *Journal of Consulting and Clinical Psychology, 79*(4), 433–440.

King, C. A., Eisenberg, D., Zheng, K., Czyz, E., Kramer, A., Horwitz, A., & Chermack, S. (2015). Online suicide risk screening and intervention with college students: A pilot randomized controlled trial. *Journal of Consulting and Clinical Psychology, 83*(3), 630–636.

Knight, K. M., McGowan, L., Dickens, C., & Bundy, C. (2006). A systematic review of motivational interviewing in physical health care settings. *British Journal of Health Psychology, 11*(2), 319–332.

Kress, V. E., & Hoffman, R. M. (2008). Non-suicidal self-injury and motivational interviewing: Enhancing readiness to change. *Journal of Mental Health Counseling, 30*, 311–329.

Lundahl, B. W., & Burke, B. L. (2009). The effectiveness and applicability of motivational interviewing: A practice-friendly review of four meta-analyses. *Journal of Clinical Psychology, 65*(11), 1232–1245.

Lundahl, B. W., Kunz, C., Brownell, C., Tollefson, D., & Burke, B. L. (2010). A meta-analysis of motivational interviewing: Twenty-five years of empirical studies. *Research on Social Work Practice, 20*(2), 137–160.

Malouff, J. M., Thorsteinsson, E. B., & Schutte, N. S. (2007). The efficacy of problem solving therapy in reducing mental and physical health problems: A meta-analysis. *Clinical Psychology Review, 27*(1), 46–57.

Martino, S., Carroll, K. M., O'Malley, S. S., & Rounsaville, B. J. (2000). Motivational interviewing with psychiatrically ill substance abusing patients. *American Journal on Addictions, 9*, 88–91.

Martins, R. K., & McNeil, D. W. (2009). Review of motivational interviewing in promoting health behaviors. *Clinical Psychology Review, 29*(4), 283–293.

McCambridge, J., & Strang, J. (2004). The efficacy of single-session motivational interviewing in reducing drug consumption and perceptions of drug-related risk and harm among young people: Results from a multi-site cluster randomized trial. *Addiction, 99*(1), 39–52.

Michie, S., Jochelson, K., Markham, W. A., & Bridle, C. (2009). Low-income groups and behaviour change interventions: A review of intervention content, effectiveness and theoretical frameworks. *Journal of Epidemiology and Community Health, 63*(8), 610–622.

Miller, W. R., & Rollnick, S. (1991). *Motivational interviewing: Preparing people to change addictive behaviour.* New York, NY: Guilford Press.

Miller, W. R., & Rollnick, S. (2013). *Motivational interviewing: Helping people change* (3rd ed.). New York, NY: Guilford Press.

Ogedegbe, G., Chaplin, W., Schoenthaler, A., Statman, D., Berger, D., Richardson, T., . . . Allegrante, J. P. (2008). A practice-based trial of motivational interviewing and adherence in hypertensive African Americans. *American Journal of Hypertension, 21*(10), 1137–1143. doi:10.1038/ajh.2008.240

Olfson, M., Marcus, S. C., & Bridge, J. A. (2014). Focusing suicide prevention on periods of high risk. *Journal of the American Medical Association, 311*, 1107–1108.

Outlaw, A. Y., Naar-King, S., Parsons, J. T., Green-Jones, M., Janisse, H., & Secord, E. (2010). Using motivational interviewing in HIV field outreach with young African American men who have sex with men: A randomized clinical trial. *American Journal of Public Health, 100*(S1), S146–S151.

Parsons, J. T., Golub, S. A., Rosof, E., & Holder, C. (2007). Motivational interviewing and cognitive-behavioral intervention to improve HIV medication adherence among hazardous drinkers: A randomized controlled trial. *Journal of Acquired Immune Deficiency Syndromes, 46*(4), 443–450.

Parsons, J. T., Rosof, E., Punzalan, J. C., & Maria, L. D. (2005). Integration of motivational interviewing and cognitive behavioral therapy to improve HIV medication adherence and reduce substance use among HIV-positive men and women: Results of a pilot project. *AIDS Patient Care and STDs, 19*(1), 31–39.

Prochaska, J. O., & DiClemente, C. C. (1984). *The transtheoretical approach: Crossing traditional boundaries of therapy.* Homewood, IL: Dow Jones Irwin.

Prochaska, J. O., & Velicer, W. F. (1997). The transtheoretical model of health behavior change. *American Journal of Health Promotion, 12*(1), 38–48.

Project MATCH Research Group. (1997). Matching alcoholism treatments to client heterogeneity: Project MATCH posttreatment drinking outcomes. *Journal of Studies on Alcohol, 58*, 7–29.

Project MATCH Research Group. (1998). Matching alcoholism treatments to client heterogeneity: Project MATCH three-year drinking outcomes. *Alcoholism: Clinical and Experimental Research, 23*, 1300–1311.

Resnicow, K., Davis, R., & Rollnick, S. (2006). Motivational interviewing for pediatric obesity: Conceptual issues and evidence review. *Journal of the American Dietetic Association, 106*(12), 2024–2033.

Rollnick, S., & Allison, J. (2004). Motivational interviewing. In N. Heather, T. Stockwell (Eds.), *The essential handbook of treatment and prevention of alcohol problems* (pp. 105–116). Chichester, UK: John Wiley.

Rollnick, S., & Miller, W. R. (1995). What is motivational interviewing? *Behavioural and Cognitive Psychotherapy, 23*, 325–334.

Rusch, N., & Corrigan, P. W. (2002). Motivational interviewing to improve in- sight and treatment adherence in schizophrenia. *Psychiatric Rehabilitation Journal, 26*, 23–32.

Söderlund, L. L., Madson, M. B., Rubak, S., & Nilsen, P. (2011). A systematic review of motivational interviewing training for general health care practitioners. *Patient Education and Counseling, 84*(1), 16–26.

Spencer, M. S., Rosland, A. M., Kieffer, E. C., Sinco, B. R., Valerio, M., Palmisano, G., . . . Heisler, M. (2011). Effectiveness of a community health worker intervention among African American and Latino adults with type 2 diabetes: A randomized controlled trial. *American Journal of Public Health, 101*(12), 2253–2260.

Stephens, R. S., Roffman, R. A., & Curtin, L. (2000). Comparison of extended vs brief treatments for marijuana use. *Journal of Consulting and Clinical Psychology, 68*, 898–908.

Stotts, A. L., DiClemente, C. C., & Dolan-Mullan, P. A. (2002). Motivational intervention for resistant pregnant smokers. *Addictive Behavior, 27*, 275–292.

Sussman, S., Sun, P., Rohrback, L. A., & Spruiit-Metz, D. (2012). One-year outcomes of a drug abuse prevention program for older teens and emerging adults: Evaluating a motivational interviewing booster component. *Health Psychology, 31*(4), 476–485. doi:10.1037/a0025756

Swanson, A. J., Pantalon, M. V., & Cohen, K. R. (1999). Motivational interviewing and treatment adherence among psychiatrically and dually diagnosed patients. *Journal of Nervous and Mental Disease, 187*, 630–635.

Vasilaki, E., Hosier, S., & Cox, W. (2006). The efficacy of motivational interviewing as a brief intervention for excessive drinking: A meta-analytic review. *Alcohol and Alcoholism, 41*, 328–335.

Zerler, H. (2008). Motivational interviewing and suicidality. In H. Arkowitz, A. Westra Henny, R. Miller William, & S. Rollnick (Eds.), *Motivational interviewing in the treatment of psychological problems* (pp. 173–193). New York, NY: Guilford Press.

PART VII

Surviving Suicide

CHAPTER TWENTY

FAMILY SURVIVORS

For every death by suicide, it is estimated that there are at least six bereaved people left behind (Lukas & Seiden, 1997; Peterson, Luoma, & Dunne, 2002; Trimble, Hannigan, & Gaffney, 2012). In the United States, approximately 186,000 to 250,000 individuals each year are left to cope with the death of a loved one by suicide (Bailley, Kral, & Dunham, 1999; Peterson et al., 2002). Until recently, it was generally thought that family survivors of suicide experienced no more difficulties than survivors from other forms of traumatic deaths, such as accidents or natural disasters. Research clearly informs us that family and friends surviving a suicide of a loved one have specific and unique reactions and responses. The concept of suicide postvention introduced by Shneidman (1972, 1981) refers to any intervention conducted following a suicide on surviving family members, friends, and others affected by the death; postvention targets two domains: (a) assist surviving and bereaved individuals through their grief process after a suicide and (b) prevent suicide within survivors, who may be at higher risk following the suicide of a close friend or family member (Shneidman, 1972, 1981). This chapter explores the impact of completed suicide on family survivors. An understanding of the grief process for this unique group is outlined. Family members are not the only survivors; clinical professionals are dramatically impacted by the death of a client. A review of the impact and influence of a client suicide on treating clinicians and an examination of professional important considerations following a client suicide are explored.

GOALS AND OBJECTIVES

An understanding of:

- Guidelines for postvention
- Stages of grief
- Complicated grief
- Spousal/partner reactions to suicide
- Parental reactions to suicide
- Offspring responses to suicide
- Sibling responses to suicide
- Stigma experienced by family survivors
- The impact of disclosing a loved one's suicide for survivors
- Mental health treatment utilization of survivors
- Evidence-based treatment for suicide survivors

Every day suicides are prevented. Individuals managing various difficulties—working alone or with the support of families, friends, and/or professionals—no longer consider suicide an option, necessity, or choice. However, for thousands of other individuals every year, suicide does become the final act. It is estimated that for every completed suicide, there are more than six to 10 survivors, people closely affected by the suicide (Lukas & Seiden, 1997; Peterson et al., 2002; Trimble et al., 2012).

To the thousands of family and friends left behind, the suicide of a loved one can be devastating and can cause severe negative consequences. Research has found that suicide survivors are at increased risk for experiencing psychiatric and physical reactions, including grief, complicated grief, stress, depression, rejection, anxiety, stigma, and somatic complaints. A qualitative study exploring the lived experience of survivors found that survivors were inconsistently connected with service providers and inadequately provided with information regarding available services; and the initial responses of professionals ranged from compassionate to cold and influenced the bereavement process (Mckinnon & Chonody, 2014).

A suicide death has levels of repercussion beyond the surviving family and friends. Research estimates that among individuals who complete suicide, approximately 33% had contact with a mental health professional within 1 year prior to their death, with 20% having had contact within 1 month (Luoma, Pearson, & Martin, 2002). Across their professional career, mental health practitioners are more likely than not to experience the death of a client due to suicide. Thus, professionals also become survivors of suicide. It is important for professionals to not only understand and work with survivors of suicide but also be able to effectively manage personally and professionally the impact of a client's suicide. It is similarly important that mental health professionals be able to support and work with their colleagues following the suicide of a client (see Chapter 21 for guidelines and recommendations for professional survivors).

The clinical implications for effectively working with family, friends, and professional survivors require mental health practitioners to have knowledge, understanding, and awareness of the unique issues confronted by survivors. Furthermore, it is essential for practitioners to be cognizant of their own personal attitudes, thoughts, judgments, and beliefs regarding those left behind following a suicide.

POSTVENTION GUIDELINES

Increasingly, postvention programs and interventions are being developed to assist survivors of suicide through the processes of grief and traumas experienced following the suicide of a family member or a friend. The essential guidelines for postvention were initially presented by Shneidman (1981), then subsequently augmented by Leenaars and Wenckstern (1998), and have been further adapted within the larger field (Aguirre & Slater, 2010; Campbell, Cataldie, McIntosh, & Millet, 2004; Leenaars & Wenckstern, 1998; Shneidman, 1981). The guiding principles for postvention implementation are: (a) initiate postvention within 24 hours; (b) anticipate opposition and resistance from survivors; (c) survivors may experience negative emotions, which should be addressed later in the process; (d) clinicians conducting postvention treatment may serve as links to reality and reason for survivors; (e) clinicians conducting postvention treatment need to assess and monitor survivors for negative changes in survivors' physical and mental health; (f) clinicians conducting postvention treatment should limit simple or superficial reassurances; (g) postvention treatment and the work for survivors often require extensive effort and time; and (8) postvention treatment often requires comprehensive care and should include prevention, intervention, and postvention strategies (Aguirre & Slater, 2010; Leenaars & Wenckstern, 1998; Shneidman, 1981).

1. A friend telephoned you at home during a weekend to inform you that his spouse completed suicide the night before. After offering your condolences and speaking with him for a few minutes, you end the call. Alone you think of the news and your years of knowing the woman who had suicided, who seemed so content and confident. What are some of your thoughts and reactions?
2. A friend telephoned you at work early Monday morning to inform you that one of her coworkers just completed suicide the night before. After offering your condolences and speaking with her for a few minutes, you end the call. Alone you ponder the news. What are some of your thoughts and reactions?
3. How are your thoughts, beliefs, assumptions, judgments, and/or reactions the same and how are they different between the two aforementioned scenarios presented?

In groups of two to four:

1. Review and discuss your answers to question 3 in Individual Exercise 20.1.
2. What are the similarities or differences in your responses?
3. How may your reactions influence your practice?

STAGES OF GRIEF

The process of grieving in the face of loss by natural and traumatic causes has been the focus of research for many years. Most notable, Elisabeth Kübler-Ross (1969) suggested a model of the *stages of grief* originally proposed to help dying patients cope with their own death. Her model then became widely accepted as a model of grief that individuals experience after the loss of a loved one. Kübler-Ross (1969) suggested that there are five stages of the grieving process: (a) denial, characterized by a refusal to accept that the loss has occurred; (b) anger, characterized by feelings of fury toward the deceased and those around the individuals; (c) bargaining, characterized by searching for a way out of the situation; (d) depression, characterized by feeling sad to continue with one's own life; and (f) acceptance, characterized by making peace with what has happened.

She explained that not all individuals experience each of the five stages, but all experience at least two stages. She also believes that the order of the stages experienced may vary across individuals. Kübler-Ross (1969) believes that individuals may get stuck in one of the first four stages until they are able to reach the stage of acceptance that may bring unbearable pain and suffering that negatively impacts their personal and interpersonal functioning. The stages of grief proposed by Kübler-Ross (1969) have led to several other models of grieving that describe the emotional processes that individuals experience after the loss of a loved one. The specific processes or stages may vary across models; however, Kübler-Ross's (1969) concept of the grief process as an individual journey through which a range of emotions are experienced ultimately ending in acceptance of reality remains a fundamental component within each model.

COMPLICATED GRIEF

Complicated grief is differentiated from the normal grieving process. Often, survivors bereaved by suicide may experience complicated grief (Spino, Kameg, Cline, Terhorst, &

Mitchell, 2016), which is defined as a group of symptoms that include longing for the deceased, preoccupation with thoughts of the deceased, futility about the future, disinterest in others, social isolation, difficulty accepting the death, feeling a lack of control, insecurity, and anger and resentment over the death (Prigerson et al., 1999; Shear, Frank, Houck, & Reynolds, 2005). Survivors of traumatic death of a family member are at increased risk for complicated grief and bereavement (Clements, DeRanieri, Vigil, & Benasutti, 2004). Research posits that the traumatic characteristics of suicide bereavement may inhibit the grieving process by increasing experiential avoidance and emphasizing a cognitive approach for complicated grief of people who have lost their loved one to death by suicide (Nam, 2016). This is especially true for family survivors of suicide (Bailey et al., 1999; Farberow, Gallagher-Thompson, Gilewski, & Thompson, 1992a; Knieper, 1999; Mitchell, Kim, Prigerson, & Mortimer, 2005a; Mitchell, Kim, Prigerson, & Mortimer-Stephens, 2004). When an individual completes suicide, severe consequences ensue for the family the individual leaves behind. This may be due to the sudden shock, confusion regarding why the act was committed, and/or the trauma of discovering the suicide. Survivors' grief reactions can become even more exacerbated by negative responses from the community regarding the suicide (Cvinar, 2005; Knieper, 1999).

Closely related survivors of suicide could be at risk of developing physical and/or mental health problems, including suicidal ideation (Mitchell et al., 2004). For example, among suicide survivors, grief and loneliness have been found to rise over time, whereas grief and loneliness decrease over time among accidental death survivors (Kovarsky, 1989). Additionally, complicated grief among suicide survivors is associated with increased suicidal ideation and behavior (Latham & Prigerson, 2004; Mitchell et al., 2005a; Szanto et al., 2006; Szanto, Prigerson, Houck, Ehrenpreis, & Reynolds, 1997).

Currently, there is limited research that examines how the process of complicated grief varies across ethnicities and cultures. Given that the rate of depression and suicide attempt vary across ethnicities (Brent et al., 2004; Harris, 2015; Kessler et al., 1994), it is reasonable to expect that the process of complicated grief may vary across ethnicities as well, particularly in respect to survivors of suicide, a group with elevated rates of depression and suicidality. Future research is needed to better understand grief processes of suicide survivors across ethnicities.

Case Vignette 20.1

On Friday night, at 2:30 a.m., the phone rang and Jessica was awakened. She had been expecting an earlier call from her son, Daniel, with an update on how her daughter-in-law, Michele, was doing. Michele had been struggling with some issues at work and they had spent many hours on the phone talking about the situation. Jessica tried to be supportive and periodically provided advice to Daniel and Michele. They had a very strong, close relationship and Jessica always felt like Michele was her own daughter, not just a daughter-in-law.

The phone call Jessica received was not the one she had expected. A male voice explained that he was calling from the police department in the town where Daniel and Michele lived. The officer explained that Michele had passed away. It appeared as though she had completed suicide. After the officer had explained the situation, Jessica hung up the phone in disbelief. She was unable to speak or move. As far as Jessica knew, Michele and Daniel were making plans to have a family and were planning a vacation, a long cruise to Alaska just 2 months away.

Jessica could not understand how this could have happened. Just yesterday she was on the phone with Michele and they were developing a plan of action for how to deal with what Michele believed to be gender discrimination at work that was affecting her ability to advance in her career. Michele was brilliant. She graduated summa cum laude from Harvard as an undergraduate and was first in her graduating class from Harvard Law School. She was recognized in her specific field of practice and should have been on her way to becoming partner in her firm.

Several months later, after Michele had been buried and Daniel had relocated to a new home (trying to forget the life he lost with Michele), Jessica was still desperately trying to understand how and why Michele had completed suicide. She was haunted by Michele's memory and the phone call they had prior to the day that she completed suicide. Did she miss something? Could she have been more attentive? If she had paid more attention would she have picked up on any clues that Michele had been contemplating suicide? She felt tremendous guilt both for not being able to stop Michele and for being unable to console Daniel during his difficult mourning due to her own struggles with Michele's death. Jessica also felt guilty about the anger she felt toward Daniel. Why did he not see the signs? They must have been there, and he was Michele's husband. If he had paid more attention, then Jessica would not be in this position now. She often wondered what was wrong with her; how could a mother feel so angry toward her own suffering child? Often, her thoughts were consumed with anger at both Michele and Daniel.

Jessica felt out of control and did not know where to turn. Five months after Michele's suicide, Jessica finally reached out for support and joined Parental Survivors of Suicide, a support group near her home.

1. *Does this case represent what is considered the normal grief process or, rather, complicated grief?*
2. *What factors may help to protect against the development of complicated grief?*
3. *What areas would you target in treatment with Jessica?*

ROLE-PLAY 20.1

Using Case Vignette 20.1, engage in a role-play in which you would assess for complicated grief and engage Jessica in treatment. Have one person take the role of client, and one take the role of Jessica.

FAMILY SURVIVORS

It is estimated that up to 250,000 individuals a year are left to cope with the death of a loved one by suicide (Bailley et al., 1999; Peterson et al., 2002). Research now indicates that family survivors of suicide experience heightened feelings of rejection, responsibility, and experience complicated grief (Bailley et al., 1999; Barlow & Morrison, 2002; Cerel, McIntosh, Neimeyer, Maple, & Marshall, 2014; Clements et al., 2004; Farberow et al., 1992a; Feigelman, Jordan, & Gorman, 2011; Gall, Henneberry, & Eyre, 2014; Mitchell et al., 2005a; Smith, Mitchell, Bruno, & Constantino, 1995; Young et al., 2012). Other studies indicate that severe stress results for the family survivors, especially if they find the body of the loved one (Callahan, 2000) or witness the final act (Callahan, 2000; Cvinar, 2005; Knieper, 1999; Lester, 1993; van Dongen, 1991a).

Suicide survivors are more prone to experience psychiatric and physical reactions. For example, risk of suicidal ideation (Mitchell et al., 2004; Mitchell, Kim, Prigerson, & Mortimer, 2005b), depression, anxiety, posttraumatic stress, and somatic complaints are increased among suicide survivors (Grossman, Clark, Gross, Halstead, & Pennington, 1995; Jordan & McMenamy, 2004; Rudestam, 1992; van Dongen, 1991b; Watson & Lee, 1993; Zhang, Hui, & Zhou, 2005). Research found that most survivors identify a need for help to manage their grief and that this need was great or significant (Pompili et al., 2013; Wilson &

Marshall, 2010). However, fewer than half actually received any help. Of those who did receive professional support, fewer than half felt satisfied with it (Wilson & Marshall, 2010).

Family survivors of suicide are also faced with stigma imposed by society (V. Alexander, 1991; Barlow & Coleman, 2003; Barlow & Morrison, 2002; Cvinar, 2005; Harwood, Hawton, Hope, & Jacoby, 2002; Feigelman, Gorman, & Jordan, 2009; Frey, Hans, & Cerel, 2016; McNiel, Hatcher, & Reubin, 1988; Range, 1998; Range, Bright, & Ginn, 1985; F. M. Reynolds & Cimbolic, 1988; Smith et al., 1995; Stillion, 1996; Sudak, 2007; Sveen & Walby, 2008). A recent study by Frey et al. (2016) found that family members with higher rates of disclosure predicted more positive family reactions, which in turn predicted less severe depression symptoms. This study supports how family members can play an essential role in their recovery process after an attempt occurs, specifically in their work with clinicians to decrease stigma (Frey et al., 2016). However, others found that parents who encountered harmful responses and strained relations with family members and non-kin report heightened grief difficulties (Feigelman et al., 2009). Thus, the response received following the disclosure is crucial. It has also been demonstrated that suicide-bereaved individuals receive more blame for the individual's death from those around them than non-suicide-bereaved survivors (Cvinar, 2005; McNiel et al., 1988; Smith et al., 1995; Sveen & Walby, 2008; Kramer et al., 2015). Calhoun and Allen (1991) found that suicide-bereaved survivors were thought of as less likeable and more blameworthy than non-suicide-bereaved survivors. Additionally, the range of negative responses to survivors of suicide varies by their relationship to the suicide victim; children survivors are viewed less negatively than parent survivors (F. M. Reynolds & Cimbolic, 1988).

Research has also recognized that the impact of a child suicide influences the parents across many situations within their lives including the workplace. It is estimated that annually 5% of a workforce will be affected by the death of a close family member (Wojcik, 2000). The impact of a child's suicide on parents' work is significant as their traumatic bereavement influences not only their physical but also their emotional and cognitive functioning. For example, physical and emotional reactions included long-term sleeping difficulties, fatigue, and anxiety, as well as potential cognitive deficits in concentration, thinking, and memory processes (Gibson, Gallagher, & Jenkins, 2010). Other changes include changes in parental perceptions and attitudes toward work and life (Gibson et al., 2010). Survivors of suicide also tend to experience difficulty resulting from evaluations of their relationships with the suicide victim (V. Alexander, 1991; Cleiren & Diekstra, 1994; Gyulay, 1989; Lester, 1993; Seguin, Lesage, & Kiely, 1995; Silverman, Range, & Overholser, 1994; Smith et al., 1995; Watson & Lee, 1993; Törnblom, Werbart, & Rydelius, 2013). They are inclined to appraise their relationship with the deceased relative as less intimate and less satisfactory (Cleiren & Diekstra, 1994). Additionally, self-directed anger for missing possible signs and/or being unable to prevent the suicide is often experienced (V. Alexander, 1991; Cleiren & Diekstra, 1994; Gyulay, 1989; Lester, 1993; Seguin et al., 1995; Silverman et al., 1994). Many studies also indicate that survivors of suicide suffer heightened feelings of shame (V. Alexander, 1991; Barlow & Morrison, 2002; Gyulay, 1989; Harwood et al., 2002; Lester, 1993; Seguin et al., 1995; Silverman et al., 1994; Smith et al., 1995; Watson & Lee, 1993). Heightened feelings of depression and guilt have also been found in some research (Kramer et al., 2015; Feigelman et al., 2011; Schneider, Grebner, Schnabel, & Georgi, 2011). However, research has found that the children of parents with alcohol use disorder who committed suicide were less likely to feel guilty or abandoned than children of non-alcohol-related suicide victims (Tall, Kõlves, Sisask, & Värnik, 2008).

Research has consistently demonstrated that one of the major factors associated with complicated grief among suicide survivors is being plagued with unanswerable questions (Gall, 2014; Lindqvist, 2008; van Dongen, 1990, 1991a). Suicide survivors agonize over why their loved one completed suicide. Family members often struggle to find a reason for the action of their loved one. This searching often results in feelings of powerlessness and helplessness accompanied by feelings of depression (Cleiren & Diekstra, 1994; Seguin et al., 1995).

Little research has explored the perceptions of family members regarding their experiences with their loved ones prior to their suicide. One study examined this and interviewed family survivors regarding the few weeks prior to their loved ones' suicide (Peters, Murphy, & Jackson, 2013). This study found that most family members believed their loved one expressed an intention to die. Results also revealed that family members felt disappointed with the health services they sought and that they felt excluded from the treatment process. Overall, mental health services were perceived of as unsupportive and unhelpful (Peters et al., 2013).

Limited research has examined protective factors against developing complicated grief as a suicide survivor. Most consistently, having a supportive friend and family network has been associated with a decrease in the likelihood of experiencing complicated grief and an increase in successful resolution of the grieving process (Callahan, 2000; Dyregrov, 2009; Farberow, Gallagher-Thompson, Gilewski, & Thompson, 1992b; Ratnarajah, Maple, & Minichiello, 2014; Reed, 1998; Seguin et al., 1995; K. E. Thompson & Range, 1991). Those who report experiencing personal growth following their loved one's suicide also have better mental health outcomes (Dyregrov, 2009). Some research has indicated that male and female survivors cope differently with the death of their loved one (Terhorst & Mitchell, 2012). Females tend to rely on seeking social support and positive reappraisal significantly more often than males (Terhorst & Mitchell, 2012). Research has also found that religion can serve as a protective factor for family survivors and play an important role in the bereavement process depending on the nature of (a) the survivor's personal religion (e.g., belief in an afterlife, endorsing a more spiritual perspective), (b) religious support received from family and friends (e.g., in-depth and ongoing spiritual support), and (c) established religious communities (e.g., support for the funeral service, public vigil, ongoing support from clergy/ministry; Vandercreek, 2009).

The Effect of Relationship to Suicide Victim

Research indicates that closeness of the survivor to the suicide victim is related to the degree of distress experienced. Closely related survivors are at increased risk for experiencing complicated grief (Mitchell et al., 2004; Mitchell, Sakraida, Kim, Bullian, & Chiappetta, 2009).

Limited research has examined differences in the impact of suicide across groups of survivors, specifically, parents, offspring, siblings, and spouses. Research on parental survivors indicates that parental survivors experience decreases in cohesion among remaining family members and decreases in adaption or the ability of the marital and/or family system to modify roles and relationships in the face of situational and developmental stress (Lohan, 2002). Research also demonstrates that parents bereaved by the suicide of a child also express heightened feelings of distrust with the health care system preventing them from seeking the help they may need to recover from their loss (Pettersen, Omerov, Steineck, & Nyberg, 2015). One study examining the needs of parents following the suicide of their child found that parents report six specific main domains of need: (a) support by listening and responding, (b) support from another suicide survivor, (c) support in finding direction, (d) support when viewing the deceased teen, (e) support in remembering the teen, and (f) support in parents giving back to the community (Miers, Abbott, & Springer, 2012).

Research has explored the impact of time on parents' experience of bereavement from the death of a child by suicide. One study, in particular, compared parents whose children died by suicide with parents who lost children from other traumatic death circumstances and others whose children died from natural causes. Results showed that suicide survivors struggle with more grief difficulties and other mental health problems in several areas. Results also showed that in the first 1 to 3 years following the loss, experiencing repeated suicide attempts prior to the completed suicide and prior to negative relationships with the decedent were associated with greater grief difficulties. However, between 3 and 5 years appeared to be a significant turning point at which acute grief difficulties accompanying a suicide loss began to subside (Feigelman, Jordan, & Gorman, 2008). Among spousal survivors, a study comparing spousal suicide survivors to spousal nonsuicide survivors found that women whose husbands had died by suicide experienced more guilt and blame than widows who lost a husband in an accident (McNiel et al., 1988). Additionally, Agerbo (2003) found that mortality in the suicide-surviving spouse is heightened.

In one study that examined sibling survivors of suicide (Brent et al., 1993), sibling survivors experienced increased rates of new-onset depression. This risk was increased in those sibling survivors with a history of psychiatric illness and in those with a family history of depression and/or other psychiatric disorders (Brent et al., 1993). Research has also found that sibling survivors are more likely to experience adverse physical health effects and to have elevated mortality rates (Rostila, Saarela, & Kawachi, 2014).

Although the exact number of child suicide survivors worldwide is not known, it is estimated that annually, in the United States, approximately 60,000 children experience death by suicide of a relative, 7,000 to 12,000 children experience the suicide of a parent, and 8,000 experience the suicide of a sibling (Cerel, Jordan, & Duberstein, 2008). Of the limited research that exists examining the impact of suicide on child survivors, findings suggest that suicide-bereaved children and adolescents are at increased risk for anxiety (Cerel, Fristad, Weller, & Weller, 1999; Shepherd & Barraclough, 1976), major depression (Pfeffer et al., 1997; Pfeffer, Karus, Siegel, & Jiang, 2000), posttraumatic stress disorder (Cerel et al., 1999; Pfeffer et al., 1997), impaired social adjustment (Cerel et al., 1999; Pfeffer et al., 1997, 2000; Ratnarajah & Schofield, 2008; Sethi & Bhargava, 2003), and internalizing problems (Cerel et al., 1999; Pfeffer et al., 1997, 2000).

Offspring have also been found to be at greater risk of attempting suicide themselves (Brent et al., 2015). While research highlights that mental health treatment reduces suicidal behavior, only an estimated 30% of suicide decedents will have received treatment within 1 month of their death (Mann et al., 2005; Niederkrotenthaler, Logan, Karch, & Crosby, 2014). Offspring who have lost a parent to suicide in childhood and young adulthood had earlier onset of hospitalization for their own suicide attempt compared with offspring who lost a parent to an unintentional injury (Kuramoto, Runeson, Stuart, Lichtenstein, & Wilcox, 2013). Furthermore, research indicates that male youth suicide survivors more often experience externalizing behaviors than female youth suicide survivors (Grossman et al., 1995). Research also indicates that surviving suicide as a child is associated with greater risk of unresolved grief that negatively impacts interpersonal functioning into and throughout adulthood (Demi & Howell, 1991).

Little research has focused on the impact of suicide on a work colleague. Kinder and Cooper (2009) note that publicity over a suicide at work can have negative effects for an organization particularly when there is a link to the individual's suicide and issues of work stress. Not only can the organization's image be damaged, but fellow employees may feel angered that the organization somehow played a contributing role in the individual's suicide. Kinder and Cooper (2009) describe the unique role that managers and the organization's health care team (i.e., Employee Assistance Counselors) can have in helping the organization and its employees to recover after the individual's suicide. It has been found that many managers may struggle with feelings of guilt and difficulty in leaving such workplace issues at the office and not bringing them home (Kinder & Cooper, 2009). Ensuring adequate access to mental health professionals who can provide counseling services to colleague survivors is among the leading recommendations for organizations facing the loss of an employee due to suicide (Hughes & Kinder, 2007). Having a clear policy regarding employee risk assessment and management is also essential (Kinder & Cooper, 2009).

When a Mental Health Professional Suicides

There are no suicide types. Research has demonstrated an elevated risk for suicide by mental health and health care professionals, including doctors, nurses, psychologists, psychiatrists, social workers, and counselors (Agerbo, Gunnell, Bonde, Mortensen, & Nordentoft, 2007; Boxer, Burnett, & Swanson, 1995; Nock, Borges, Bromet, Cha, Kessler, & Lee, 2008; Kleespies et al., 2011; Lindeman, Laara, Hakko, & Lonnqvist, 1996; Schernhammer, 2005; Stack, 2001). Although research in this area is minimal, case reports and studies have found that surviving clients will often recognize that their clinician had psychological problems; however, this awareness does not mitigate common client reactions of depression, shock, numbness, hopelessness, loss, abandonment, and distrust (Ballenger, 1978; Dunne, 1987; Kleespies et al., 2011; J. Reynolds, Jennings, & Branson, 1997). According to Reynolds and colleagues (1997), all of the former clients studied (*n* = 12) were reluctant to reenter therapy, as each was provided a referral to another therapist in the area but refused the referral (J. Reynolds et al., 1997). Surviving suicide can extend to individuals' responses to their clinicians' deaths, which can have the added burden of becoming a barrier for postvention treatment. Chapter 21 explores mental health professionals as survivors of suicide.

Empirically Supported Treatment for Suicide Survivors

While there is extensive literature examining bereavement interventions in general, limited research exists examining bereavement interventions specifically targeting suicide survivors (Jordan & McMenamy, 2004). There are several descriptive papers that describe support groups for suicide-bereaved individuals; however, only nine studies objectively assess the effectiveness of specific interventions for suicide survivors and not all of these studies incorporated control groups and used random assignment (Jordan & McMenamy, 2004). This limited research indicates that group support programs (Constantino & Bricker, 1996; Constantino, Sekula, & Rubinstein, 2001; Farberow, 1992; Murphy, 2000; Pfeffer, Jiang, Kakuma, Hwang, & Metsch, 2002; Renaud, 1995), family treatment with added group support (Rogers, Sheldon, Barwick, Letofsky, & Lancee, 1982), debriefing interventions (Mitchell & Kim, 2003), and writing interventions where individuals write about the suicide of a loved one (Range, Campbell, Kovac, Marion-Jones, & Aldridge, 2002) are effective interventions for treating survivors of suicide. Please see Chapters 16 to 19 for an in-depth discussion of evidence-based practices (EBPs) to address suicidal behavior.

SUMMARY

Following a suicide, many family members and friends become survivors devastated by the death of a loved one. The suicide of a family member, friend, or colleague is often profound and far reaching across many areas of life. The event raises numerous questions for survivors about themselves, their relationship with others, and how they interact and perceive their larger context and world. Survivors frequently struggle between trying to make sense of the loss, managing their grief, and living their lives. Unfortunately, the suicide of a loved one can become a risk factor for suicide for survivors. It is important for practitioners to be able to effectively work with the surviving family and friends.

KEY POINTS

1. Survivors are at a higher risk of suicide.
2. Postvention interventions are designed to assist survivors of suicide through the processes of grief and traumas experienced following the suicide of a family member or a friend.
3. Grief reactions of suicide survivors vary according to personal and contextual characteristics.
4. Survivors of suicide often suffer from complicated grief.
5. The nature of the relationship with a suicide victim impacts a survivor's reaction.
6. The stigma experienced by survivors of suicide is a major cause of the severe grief reactions experienced by suicide survivors across types of relationships with the suicide victim (parent, offspring, spouse, and peer).
7. A major factor contributing to the difficulty that suicide survivors experience in resolving the grief process is the question of why their loved one completed suicide.
8. Survivors of suicide often experience difficulties in returning to work.
9. Following a coworker's suicide, colleagues and associates in the work environment can often experience negative reactions, including grief and anger.
10. Despite the significant impact on survivors and an elevated risk of suicide, most survivors of suicide do not seek professional counseling or mental health treatment.

ELECTRONIC RESOURCES

FAMILY AND PEER SURVIVORS

Suicide Survivors Group

www.gvsl.org

AMERICAN FOUNDATION OF SUICIDE PREVENTION

Surviving Suicide Loss

www.afsp.org

PARENTS OF SUICIDE

www.parentsofsuicide.com

FRIENDS AND FAMILY OF SUICIDE

www.friendsandfamiliesofsuicide.com

SIBLING SURVIVORS

www.siblingsurvivors.com

PEER SUICIDE

www.friendsforsurvival.org

SUPPORT FOR SURVIVORS

survivingsuicide.com
www.forsuicidesurvivors.com
www.lovingoutreach.org

GRIEF SUPPORT FOLLOWING SUICIDE

www.heartbeatsurvivorsaftersuicide.org/index.shtml

REFERENCE FOR SUICIDE SURVIVORS

www.suicidology.org/suicide-survivors/suicide-loss-survivors

SURVIVORS OF BEREAVEMENT BY SUICIDE

www.sobs.admin.care4free.net

KNOWLEDGE ACQUISITION TEST (KAT)

True or False

1. All suicide survivors experience complicated grief.
2. Suicide survivors do not experience more stigma than survivors of other forms of traumatic death.
3. There are no differences between parental, offspring, and peer survivors of suicide.
4. There is a greater likelihood of suicidal ideation among survivors of suicide than among survivors of other forms of death.
5. Coworkers of individuals who die by suicide often experience feelings of guilt and anger at their organization.
6. Male and female survivors often use different coping mechanisms.
7. Religion may serve as a protective factor during the bereavement process based solely on the nature of the individual's personal religious beliefs.
8. Most survivors do not self-identify as needing formal mental health support.

Short Answer

9. What is complicated grief?
10. What are the grief reactions that distinguish between survivors of suicide and survivors of other forms of death?
11. What are the five stages of grief proposed by Kübler-Ross?
12. What are the most pressing needs following the suicide of a child as identified by parents?
13. How does the passing of time impact the bereavement process of survivors?
14. What are the guiding principles of suicide postvention?
15. In what way can disclosing a loved one's suicide impact a survivor?

Multiple Choice

16. Complicated grief is characterized by which of the following?
    A. Disinterest in others
    B. Lack of control
    C. Preoccupation with thoughts of the deceased
    D. Futility about the future
    E. All of the above
    F. None of the above
17. Compared to survivors of other forms of death, some report that suicide survivors experience greater:
    A. Depression
    B. Posttraumatic stress
    C. Anxiety
    D. Impaired social adjustment
    E. All of the above
    F. None of the above
18. Suicide survivors often experience:
    A. Shame
    B. Guilt
    C. Self-directed anger
    D. Depression

E. None of the above

F. All of the above

19. Following a loved one's suicide, survivors are most likely to:

    A. Not perceive a need for mental health support

    B. Perceive a need for mental health support and most often receive that support

    C. Perceive a need for mental health support but most often do not receive the needed treatment

    D. Be most often highly satisfied with mental health support received

    E. None of the above

    F. All of the above

20. Following an individual's suicide, the individual most likely to experience a complicated grief reaction is a:

    A. Friend

    B. Parent

    C. Coworker

    D. Classmate

    E. None of the above

REFERENCES

Agerbo, E. (2003). Risk of suicide and spouse's psychiatric illness or suicide: Nested case-control study. *British Medical Journal, 327*(7422), 1025–1026.

Agerbo, E., Gunnell, D., Bonde, J. P., Mortensen, P. B., & Nordentoft, M. (2007). Suicide and occupation: The impact of socio-economic, demographic and psychiatric differences. *Psychological Medicine, 37*, 1131–1140.

Aguirre, R. T. P., & Slater, H. (2010). Suicide postvention as suicide prevention: Improvement and expansion in the United States. *Death Studies, 34*(6), 529–540.

Alexander, V. (1991). Grief after suicide: Giving voice to the loss. *Journal of Geriatric Psychiatry, 24*(2), 277–291.

Bailley, S. E., Kral, M. J., & Dunham, K. (1999). Survivors of suicide do grieve differently: Empirical support for a common sense proposition. *Suicide and Life-Threatening Behavior, 29*(3), 256–271.

Ballenger, J. C. (1978). Patients' reactions to the suicide of their psychiatrist. *Journal of Nervous and Mental Disease, 166*, 859–867.

Barlow, C. A., & Coleman, H. (2003). The healing alliance: How families use social support after a suicide. *Omega: Journal of Death and Dying, 47*, 187–202.

Barlow, C. A., & Morrison, H. (2002). Survivors of suicide. Emerging counseling strategies. *Journal of Psychosocial Nursing and Mental Health Services, 40*(1), 28–39.

Boxer, P. A., Burnett, C., & Swanson, N. (1995). Suicide and occupation: A review of the literature. *Journal of Occupational and Environmental Medicine, 37*, 442–452.

Brent, D. A., Melhem, N. M., Oquendo, M., Burke, A., Birmaher, B., Stanley, B., . . . Mann, J. J. (2015). Familial pathways to early-onset suicide attempt: A 5.6-year prospective study. *Journal of the American Medical Association Psychiatry, 72*(2), 160–168.

Brent, D. A., Oquendo, M., Birmaher, B., Greeenhill, L., Kolko, D., Stanley, B., . . . Mann, J. J. (2004). Familial transmission of mood disorders: Convergence and divergence with transmission of suicidal behavior. *Journal of the American Academy of Child and Adolescent Psychiatry, 43*(10), 1259–1266.

Brent, D. A., Perper, J., Moritz, G., Baugher, M., Schweers, J., & Roth, C. (1993). Firearms and adolescent suicide: A community case-control study. *American Journal of Disorders of Childhood, 147*, 1066–1071.

Calhoun, L. G., & Allen, B. G. (1991). Social reactions to the survivor of a suicide in the family: A review of the literature. *OMEGA-Journal of Death and Dying, 23*(2), 95–107.

Callahan, J. (2000). Predictors and correlates of bereavement in suicide support group participants. *Suicide and Life-Threatening Behavior, 30*(2), 104–124.

Campbell, F., Cataldie, L., McIntosh, J., & Millet, K. (2004). An active postvention program. *Crisis, 25*, 30–32.

Cerel, J., Fristad, M. A., Weller, E. B., & Weller, R. A. (1999). Suicide-bereaved children and adolescents: A controlled longitudinal examination. *Journal of the American Academy of Child and Adolescent Psychiatry, 38*, 672–679.

Cerel, J., Jordan, J. R., & Duberstein, P. R. (2008). The impact of suicide on the family. *Crisis: The Journal of Crisis Intervention and Suicide Prevention, 29*(1), 38–44.

Cerel, J., McIntosh, J. L., Neimeyer, R. A., Maple, M., & Marshall, D. (2014). The continuum of "survivorship": Dnitional issues in the aftermath of suicide. *Suicide and Life-Threaening Behavior, 44*(6), 591–600.

Cleiren, M., & Diekstra, R. (1994). *After the loss: Bereavement after suicide and other types of death.* New York, NY: Springer Publishing.

Clements, P. T., DeRanieri, J. T., Vigil, G. J., & Benasutti, K. M. (2004). Life after death: Grief therapy after the sudden traumatic death of a family member. *Perspectives in Psychiatric Care, 40*(4), 149–154.

Constantino, R. E., & Bricker, P. L. (1996). Nursing postvention for spousal survivors of suicide. *Issues in Mental Health Nursing, 17*, 131–152.

Constantino, R. E., Sekula, L. K., & Rubinstein, E. N. (2001). Group intervention for widowed survivors of suicide. *Suicide and Life-Threatening Behavior, 31*(4), 428–441.

Cvinar, J. G. (2005). Do suicide survivors suffer social stigma? A review of the literature. *Perspectives in Psychiatric Care, 41*(1), 14–21.

Demi, A. S., & Howell, C. (1991). Hiding and healing: Resolving the suicide of a parent or sibling. *Archives of Psychiatric Nursing, 5*(6), 350–356.

Dunne, E. J. (1987). Surviving the suicide of a therapist. In E. J. Dunne, J. L. McIntosh, & K. L. Dunne-Maxim (Eds.), *Suicide and its aftermath: Understanding and counseling the survivors.* New York, NY: W. W. Norton.

Dyregrov, K. (2009). How do the young suicide survivors wish to be met by psychologists? A user study. *Omega, 59*(3), 221–238.

Farberow, N. (1992). The Los Angeles survivors-after-sucide program: An evaluation. *Crisis: The Journal of Crisis Intervention and Suicide Prevention, 13,* 23–34.

Farberow, N. L., Gallagher-Thompson, D., Gilewski, M., & Thompson, L. (1992a). Changes in grief and mental health of bereaved spouses of older suicides. *Journal of Gerontology, 47*(6), P357–P366.

Farberow, N. L., Gallagher-Thompson, D., Gilewski, M., & Thompson, L. (1992b). The role of social supports in the bereavement process of surviving spouses of suicide and natural deaths. *Suicide and Life-Threatening Behavior, 22*(1), 107–124.

Feigelman, W., Gorman, B. S., & Jordan, J. R. (2009). Stigmatization and suicide bereavement. *Death Studies, 33*(7), 591–608. doi:10.1080/07481180902979973

Feigelman, W., Jordan, J. R., & Gorman, B. S. (2008). How they died, time since loss, and bereavement outcomes. *Omega, 58*(4), 251–273.

Feigelman, W., Jordan, J. R., & Gorman, B. S. (2011). Parental grief after a child's drug death compared to other death causes: Investigating a greatly neglected bereavement population. *Omega (Westport), 63*(4), 291–316.

Frey, L. M., Hans, J. D., & Cerel, J. (2016). Suicide disclosure in suicide attempt survivors: Does family reaction moderate or mediate disclosure's effect on depression? *Suicide and Life-Threatening Behavior, 46*(1), 96–105.

Gall, T. L., Henneberry, J., & Eyre, M. (2014). Two perspectives on the needs of individuals bereaved by suicide. *Death Studies, 38*(7), 430–437.

Gibson, J., Gallagher, M., & Jenkins, M. (2010). The experiences of parents readjusting to the workplace following the death of a child by suicide. *Death Studies, 34*(6), 500–528.

Grossman, J. A., Clark, D. C., Gross, D., Halstead, L., & Pennington, J. (1995). Child bereavement after paternal suicide. *Journal of Child and Adolescent Psychiatric Nursing, 8*(2), 5–17.

Gyulay, J. (1989). What suicide leaves behind. *Issues in Comprehensive Pediatric Nursing, 12*(1), 103–118.

Harris, R. E. (2015). Suicide grief in African American mothers: The roles of suicide stigmatization, attitudes toward suicide, and John Henryism (Capella University, Harold Abel School of Social and Behavioral Sciences, U.S.) *Dissertation Abstracts International: Section B, The Sciences and Engineering, 76*(12-B)(E).

Harwood, D., Hawton, K., Hope, T., & Jacoby, R. (2002). The grief experiences and needs of bereaved relatives and friends of older people dying through suicide: A descriptive and case-control study. *Journal of Affective Disorders, 72,* 185–194.

Hughes, R., & Kinder, A. (2007). *Guidelines for counselling in the workplace.* Lutter-worth, UK: British Association of Counselling Psychology.

Jordan, J. R., & McMenamy, J. (2004). Interventions for suicide survivors: A review of the literature. *Suicide and Life-Threatening Behavior, 34*(4), 337–349.

Kessler, R. C., McGonagle, K. A., Zhao, S., Nelson, C. B., Hughes, M., & Eshelman, S. (1994). Lifetime and 12-month prevalence of *DSM-III-R psychiatric disorders in the United States: Results from the National Comorbidity Survey. Archives of General Psychiatry, 51,* 8–19.

Kinder, A., & Cooper, C. L. (2009). The costs of suicide and sudden death within an organization. *Death Studies, 33*(5), 411–419. doi:10.1080/07481180902805624

Kleespies, P. M., Van Orden, K. A., Bongar, B., Bridgeman, D., Bufka, L. F., Galper, D. I., . . . Yufit, R. I. (2011). Psychologist suicide: Incidence, impact, and suggestions for prevention, intervention, and postvention. *Professional Psychology: Research and Practice, 42*(3), 244–251.

Knieper, A. J. (1999). The suicide survivor's grief and recovery. *Suicide and Life-Threatening Behavior, 29*(4), 353–364.

Kovarsky, R. S. (1989). Loneliness and disturbed grief: A comparison of parents who lost a child to suicide or accidental death. *Archives of Psychiatric Nursing, 3*(2), 86–96.

Kramer, J., Boon, B., Schotanus-Dijkstra, M., van Ballegooijen, W., Kerkhof, A., & van der Poel, A. (2015). The mental health of visitors of web-based support forums for bereaved by suicide. *Crisis, 36*(1), 38–45. doi:10.1027/0227-5910/a000281

Kübler-Ross, E. (1969). *On death and dying.* New York, NY: MacMillan.

Kuramoto, S. J., Runeson, B., Stuart, E. A., Lichtenstein, P., & Wilcox, H. C. (2013). Time to hospitalization for suicide attempt by the timing of parental suicide during offspring early development. *Journal of the American Medical Association Psychiatry, 70*(2), 149–157.

Latham, A. E., & Prigerson, H. G. (2004). Suicidality and bereavement: Complicated grief as psychiatric disorder presenting greatest risk for suicidality. *Suicide and Life-Threatening Behavior, 34*(4), 350–362.

Leenaars, A., & Wenckstern, S. (1998). Principles of postvention: Applications to suicide and trauma in schools. *Death Studies, 22,* 357–391.

Lester, D. (1993). The effectiveness of suicide prevention centers. *Suicide and Life-Threatening Behavior, 23,* 263–267.

Lindeman, S., Laara, E., Hakko, H., & Lonnqvist, J. (1996). A systematic review on gender-specific suicide mortality in medical doctors. *British Journal of Psychiatry, 168,* 274–279.

Lindqvist, P., Johansson, L., & Karlsson. U. (2008). In the aftermath of teenage suicide: A qualitative study of the psychosocial consequences for the surviving family members. *BioMed Central Psychiatry, 8,* 26–33. doi:10.1186/1471-244X-8-26

Lohan, J. A. (2002). Family functioning and family typology after an adolescent or young adult's sudden violent death. *Journal of Family Nursing, 8,* 49–56.

Lukas, C., & Seiden, H. (1997). *Silent grief.* New York, NY: Charles Scribner's Sons.

Luoma, J. B., Pearson, J. L., & Martin, C. E. (2002). Contact with mental health and primary care prior to suicide: A review of the evidence. *American Journal of Psychiatry, 159,* 909–916.

Mann, J. J., Apter, A., Bertolote, J., Beautrais, A., Currier, D., Haas, A. . . . Hendin, H. (2005). Suicide prevention strategies: A systematic review. *Journal of the American Medical Association, 294,* 2064–2074.

McKinnon, J. M., & Chonody, J. (2014). Exploring the formal supports used by people bereaved through suicide: A qualitative study. *Social Work in Mental Health, 12*(3), 231–248.

McNiel, D. E., Hatcher, C., & Reubin, R. (1988). Family survivors of suicide and accidental death: Consequences for widows. *Suicide and Life-Threatening Behavior, 18*(2), 137–148.

Miers, D., Abbott, D., & Springer, P. R. (2012). A phenomenological study of family needs following the suicide of a teenager. *Death Studies, 36*(2), 118–133.

Mitchell, A. M., & Kim, Y. (2003). *Debriefing approach with suicide survivors.* Paper presented at the Survivors of Suicide Research Workshop, Washington, DC.

Mitchell, A. M., Kim, Y., Prigerson, H. G., & Mortimer, M. K. (2005a). Complicated grief and suicidal ideation in adult survivors of suicide. *Suicide and Life-Threatening Behavior, 35*(5), 498–506.

Mitchell, A. M., Kim, Y., Prigerson, H. G., & Mortimer, M. K. (2005b). Complicated grief and suicidal ideation in adult survivors of suicide. *Suicide and Life-Threatening Behavior, 35*(5), 498–506.

Mitchell, A. M., Kim, Y., Prigerson, H. G., & Mortimer-Stephens, M. (2004). Complicated grief in survivors of suicide. *Crisis: Journal of Crisis Intervention and Suicide, 25*(1), 12–18.

Mitchell, A. M., Sakraida, T. J., Kim, Y., Bullian, L., & Chiappetta, L. (2009). Depression, anxiety and quality of life in suicide survivors: A comparison of close and distant relationships. *Archives of Psychiatric Nursing, 23*(1), 2–10.

Murphy, S. A. (2000). The use of research findings in bereavement programs: A case study. *Death Studies, 24,* 585–602.

Nam, I. (2016). Suicide bereavement and complicated grief: Experiential avoidance as a mediating mechanism. *Journal of Loss and Trauma, 21*(4), 325–334.

Niederkrotenthaler, T., Logan, J. E., Karch, D. L., & Crosby, A. (2014). Characteristics of U.S. suicide decedents in 2005–2010 who had received mental health treatment. *Psychiatric Services, 165*(3), 387–390.

Nock, M. K., Borges, G., Bromet, E. J., Cha, C. B., Kessler, R. C., & Lee, S. (2008). Suicide and suicidal behavior. *Epidemiologic Reviews, 30,* 133–154.

Peters, K., Murphy, G., & Jackson, D. (2013). Events prior to completed suicide: Perspectives of family survivors. *Issues in Mental Health Nursing, 34*(5), 309–316.

Peterson, E. M., Luoma, J. B., & Dunne, E. (2002). Suicide survivors' perceptions of the treating clinician. *Suicide and Life-Threatening Behavior, 32*(2), 158–166.

Pettersen, A., Omerov, P., Steineck, G., & Nyberg, U. (2015). Lack of trust in the health-care system after losing a child to suicide. *Crisis: The Journal of Crisis Intervention and Suicide Prevention, 36*(3), 1–12.

Pfeffer, C. R., Jiang, H., Kakuma, T., Hwang, J., & Metsch, M. (2002). Group intervention for children bereaved by the suicide of a relative. *Journal of the American Academy of Child and Adolescent Psychiatry, 41,* 505–513.

Pfeffer, C. R., Karus, D., Siegel, K., & Jiang, H. (2000). Child survivors of parental death from cancer or suicide: Depressive and behavioral outcomes. *Psycho-Oncology, 9,* 1–10.

Pfeffer, C. R., Martins, P., Mann, J., Sunkenberg, M., Ice, A., Damore, J. P., Jr., . . . Jiang, H. (1997). Child survivors of suicide: Psychosocial characteristics. *Journal of the American Academy of Child and Adolescent Psychiatry, 36*(1), 65–74.

Pompili, M., Shrivastava, A., Serafini, G., Innamorati, M., Milelli, M., Erbuto, D., . . . Girardi, P. (2013). Bereavement after the suicide of a significant other. *Indian Journal of Psychiatry, 55*(3), 256–263.

Prigerson, H. G., Shear, M. K., Jacobs, S. C., Reynolds, C. F., III, Maciejewski, P. K., Davidson, J. R., . . . Zisook, S. (1999). Consensus criteria for traumatic grief: A preliminary empirical test. *British Journal of Psychiatry—Supplementum, 174*, 67–73.

Range, L. M. (1998). *When a loss is due to suicide: Unique aspects of bereavement.* Philadelphia, PA: Brunner/Mazel.

Range, L. M., Bright, P. S., & Ginn, P. D. (1985). Public reactions to child suicide: Effects of age and method used. *Journal of Community Psychology, 13*, 288–294.

Range, L. M., Campbell, C., Kovac, S. H., Marion-Jones, M., & Aldridge, H. (2002). No-suicide contracts: An overview and recommendations. *Death Studies, 26*, 51–74.

Ratnarajah, D., Maple, M., & Minichiello, V. (2014). Understanding family member suicide narratives by investigating family history. *Omega, 69*(1), 41–57. doi:10.2190/OM.69.1.c

Ratnarajah, D., & Schofield, M. J. (2008). Survivors' narratives of the impact of parental suicide. *Suicide and Life-Threatening Behavior, 38*(5), 618–630.

Reed, M. D. (1998). Predicting grief symptomatology among the suddenly bereaved. *Suicide and Life-Threatening Behavior, 28*(3), 285–301.

Renaud, C. (1995). *Bereavement after a suicide: A model for support groups.* New York, NY: Springer Publishing.

Reynolds, F. M., & Cimbolic, P. (1988). Attitudes toward suicide survivors as a function of survivors' relationship to the victim. *Omega: Journal of Death and Dying, 19*(2), 125–133.

Reynolds, J., Jennings, G., & Branson, M. L. (1997). Patients' reactions to the suicide of a psychotherapist. *Suicide and Life-Threatening Behavior, 27*, 176–181.

Rogers, J. R., Sheldon, A., Barwick, C., Letofsky, K., & Lancee, W. (1982). Help for families of suicide: Survivors' support program. *Canadian Journal of Psychiatry, 27*, 444–449.

Rostila, M., Saarela, J., & Kawachi, I. (2014). The psychological skeleton in the closet: Mortality after a sibling's suicide. *Social Psychiatry and Psychiatric Epidemiology, 49*(6), 919–927.

Rudestam, K. E. (1992). Research contributions to understanding the suicide survivor. *Crisis: The Journal of Crisis Intervention and Suicide Prevention, 13*(1), 41–46.

Schernhammer, E. (2005). Taking their own lives: The high rate of physician suicide. *New England Journal of Medicine, 352*, 2473–2476.

Schneider, B., Grebner, K., Schnabel, A., & Georgi, K. (2011). Is the emotional response of survivors dependent on the consequences of the suicide and the support received? *Crisis, 32*(4), 186–193.

Seguin, M., Lesage, A., & Kiely, M. C. (1995). Parental bereavement after suicide and accident: A comparative study. *Suicide and Life-Threatening Behavior, 25*(4), 489–492.

Sethi, S., & Bhargava, S. C. (2003). Child and adolescent survivors of suicide. *Crisis: Journal of Crisis Intervention and Suicide, 24*(1), 4–6.

Shear, K., Frank, E., Houck, P. R., & Reynolds, C. F., III. (2005). Treatment of complicated grief: A randomized controlled trial. *Journal of the American Medical Association, 293*, 2601–2608.

Shepherd, D. M., & Barraclough, B. M. (1976). The aftermath of parental suicide for children. *British Journal of Psychiatry—Supplementum, 129*, 267–276.

Shneidman, E. (1972). Foreword. In A. C. Cain (Ed.), *Survivors of suicide* (pp. ix–xi). Springfield, IL: Charles C. Thomas.

Shneidman, E. (1981). *Deaths of man.* New York, NY: Quadrangle Books.

Silverman, E., Range, L., & Overholser, J. (1994). Bereavement from suicide as compared to other forms of bereavement. *Omega: Journal of Death and Dying, 30*(1), 41–51.

Smith, B. J., Mitchell, A. M., Bruno, A. A., & Constantino, R. E. (1995). Exploring widows' experiences after the suicide of their spouse. *Journal of Psychosocial Nursing and Mental Health Services, 33*(5), 10–15.

Spino, E., Kameg, K. M., Cline, T. W., Terhorst, L., & Mitchell, A. M. (2016). Impact of social support on symptoms of depression and loneliness in survivors bereaved by suicide. *Archives of Psychiatric Nursing, 30*(5), 602–606.

Stack, S. (2001). Occupation and suicide [Proceedings paper]. *Social Science Quarterly, 82*, 384–396.

Stillion, J. (1996). *Survivors of suicide.* Washington, DC: Hospice Foundation of America.

Sudak, H. (2007). Encountering patient suicide: The role of survivors. *Academic Psychiatry, 31*(5), 333–335.

Sveen, C., & Walby, F. A. (2008). Suicide survivors' mental health and grief reactions: A systematic review of controlled studies. *Suicide and Life-Threatening Behavior, 38*(1), 13–29.

Szanto, K., Prigerson, H., Houck, P., Ehrenpreis, L., & Reynolds, C. F. (1997). Suicidal ideation in elderly bereaved: The role of complicated grief. *Suicide and Life-Threatening Behavior, 27*(2), 194–207.

Szanto, K., Shear, M. K., Houck, P. R., Reynolds, C. F., Frank, E., Caroff, K., & Silowash, R. (2006). Indirect self-destructive behavior and overt suicidality in patients with complicated grief. *Journal of Clinical Psychiatry, 67*(2), 233–239.

Tall, K., Kõlves, K., Sisask, M., & Värnik, A. (2008). Do survivors respond differently when alcohol abuse complicates suicide? Findings from the psychological autopsy study in Estonia. *Drug and Alcohol Dependence, 95*(1–2), 129–133.

Terhorst, L., & Mitchell, A. M. (2012). Ways of coping in survivors of suicide. *Issues in Mental Health Nursing, 33*(1), 32–38.

Thompson, K. E., & Range, L. M. (1991). Recent bereavement from suicide and other deaths: Can people imagine it as it really is? *Omega: Journal of Death and Dying, 22*, 249–259.

Törnblom, A. W., Werbart, A., & Rydelius, P. A. (2013). Shame behind the masks: The parents' perspective on their sons' suicide. *Archives of Suicide Research, 17*(3), 242–261. doi:10.1080/13811118.2013.805644

Trimble, T., Hannigan, B., & Gaffney, M. (2012). Suicide postvention: Coping, support and transformation. *Irish Journal of Psychology, 33*(2–3), 115–121.

Van Dongen, C. J. (1990). Agonizing questioning: Experiences of survivors of suicide victims. *Nursing Research, 39*(4), 224–229.

Van Dongen, C. J. (1991a). Experiences of family members after a suicide. *Journal of Family Practice, 33*(4), 375–380.

Van Dongen, C. J. (1991b). Survivors of a family member's suicide: Implications for practice. *Nurse Practitioner, 16*(7), 31–35.

Watson, W. L., & Lee, D. (1993). Is there life after suicide? The systemic belief approach for *"survivors" of suicide. Archives of Psychiatric Nursing, 7*(1), 37–43.

Wilson, A., & Marshall, A. (2010). The support needs and experiences of suicidally bereaved family and friends. *Death Studies, 34*(7), 625–640.

Wojcik, J. (2000). Bereavement leave policies strike a compassionate chord. *Business Insurance, 34*, 3–14.

Young, I. T., Iglewicz, A., Glorioso, D., Lanouette, N., Seay, K., Ilapakurti, M., & Zisook, S. (2012). Suicide bereavement and complicated grief. *Dialogues in Clinical Neuroscience, 14*(2), 177–186.

Zhang, J., Hui, Q., & ZHou, L. (2005). The effect of bereavement due to suicide on survivors' depression: A study of Chinese samples. *Omega: Journal of Death and Dying, 51*(3), 217–227.

CHAPTER TWENTY ONE

PROFESSIONAL SURVIVORS

In the United States, more than 40,000 individuals complete suicide every year. Approximately ten times that number attempt suicide. Of those who attempt, 64% visit a doctor in the month before their attempt, and 38% in the week before (Ahmedani, 2015). It is further estimated that for individuals who complete suicide, approximately 45% had contact with their primary care provider within 1 month of the suicide (Luoma, Martin, & Pearson, 2002). Mental health professionals are dramatically impacted by the death of a client. A review of the impact and influence of a client suicide on treating clinicians and an examination of important considerations for professionals following a client suicide are explored in this chapter.

GOALS AND OBJECTIVES

An understanding of:

- Prevalence of client suicide across mental health professions
- Professional reactions following a client suicide
- Preparing and training professionals for the possibility of a client suicide
- Supporting a colleague, coworker, or team after a client suicide
- Supporting oneself personally and professionally following the suicide of a client
- Ethical obligations following a client suicide
- Legal obligations following a client suicide
- Working with the surviving family members
- The role of a psychological autopsy
- Survivor's perceptions of treating professionals

Research has found that for every completed suicide, there are between six and 10 people closely affected by the suicide (Lukas & Seiden, 1997; Peterson, Luoma, & Dunne, 2002). While we tend to automatically think of family and friends as survivors, mental health professionals are also often left struggling with the death of a client and warrant significant consideration. Being able to support and work through a client's suicide or with professional colleagues following the suicide of their client is often ignored, but is a critical and difficult skill.

Although limited, research has examined clinicians' reactions to clients during their last contact prior to their attempted or completed suicide. Results indicated that clinicians treating imminently suicidal patients reported less positive feelings toward these clients than for nonsuicidal clients, but had higher hopes for their treatment. They also reported feeling notably more overwhelmed, distressed by, and avoidant of these clients. Further, results showed that there was a paradoxical combination of hopefulness and distress/avoidance that could significantly discriminate between suicidal patients and those who died unexpected nonsuicidal deaths with 90% sensitivity and 56% specificity (Yaseen et al., 2013). Little research has examined colleagues' reactions to clinicians who have a client who suicides. Being able to identify our beliefs and potential assumptions about what it means to have a client suicide and how it reflects on the treating clinicians is important in order to ensure we are able to provide appropriate and effective care to our colleagues in need.

Individual Exercise 21.1

1. A professional colleague telephoned you at home during a weekend to inform you that his spouse (or child) completed suicide the night before. After offering your condolences and speaking with him for some time, you end the call. Alone, you think of the news and your years of knowing the individual who had suicided, who never gave you any indication of being at risk. What are some of your thoughts and reactions?
2. A professional colleague telephoned you at work early Monday morning to inform you that one of her clients just completed suicide the night before. After offering your condolences and speaking with her for some time, you end the call. Alone, you ponder the news. What are some of your thoughts and reactions?
3. How are your thoughts, beliefs, assumptions, judgments, and/or reactions the same and how are they different between the two scenarios presented in questions 1 and 2?
4. Please complete again questions 1 to 3, but instead of a colleague telephoning you, you are telephoning a colleague for consolation. What would you say? What sort of reaction would you expect?

Small Group Exercise 21.1

In groups of two to four:

1. Review and discuss your answers to question 3 in Individual Exercise 21.1.
2. What are the similarities or differences in your responses?
3. How may your reactions affect your colleague and/or the larger work environment?
4. How might you contribute to the response of other colleagues and coworkers, as well as the organization's reaction?
5. How might this event and/or your thoughts influence your own practice?

PROFESSIONALS MANAGING AFTER A CLIENT'S SUICIDE

What happens to the practitioner when a client suicides? While professionals are very effective in assessing and treating suicidal patients, there will be clients under treatment who successfully complete suicide. This phenomenon is often neglected or minimized in practice and the literature regarding how professionals manage a client's suicide (Gitlin, 1999). Following a client's suicide, practitioners' reactions may vary from grief, shock, denial, distress, depression, isolation, self-blame, a sense of failure, strain on their personal and professional lives, fear of another suicide, loss of confidence, to avoidance of triggering stimuli (D. A. Alexander, Klein, Gray, Dewar, & Eagles, 2000; Collins, 2003; Cooper, 1995; Dewar, Eagles, Klein, Gray, & Alexander, 2000; Eagles, Klein, Gray, Dewar, &

Alexander, 2001; Fang et al., 2007; Farberow, 2005; Grad, 1996; Grad & Michel, 2005; Halligan & Corcoran, 2001; Maltsberger, 1992; Spiegelman & Werth, 2005; Strom-Gottfried & Mowbray, 2006; Sudak, 2007; J. Thompson & Brooks, 1990). Research suggests that exposure to a client's suicide can undermine professionals' functioning and feelings of competence, causing them to question their professional standing and contributing to their early burnout (Gaffney et al., 2009). In a study of general practitioners who had experienced a suicidal client, participants reported being struck by guilt, a feeling of failure, self-scrutiny, and a need to reformulate the situation (Davidsen, 2011). Interestingly, a common automatic reaction that emerged was the assumption that they had overlooked something (Davidsen, 2011). The study recommends training to assist professionals to manage not only the emotional turmoil following a client's suicide but also the cognitive assumptions and concerns that may develop after such a tragedy.

Another study of psychiatrists found that the most common reactions following the suicide attempt of a client included frustration, sadness, and impotence, while guilt and shame were not common reactions (Scocco, Corinto, & Pavan, 2008). This study also found that trainees experienced a greater emotional reaction than their senior colleagues (Scocco et al., 2008). This is consistent with another long-standing research that found trainees and/or junior clinicians experience greater negative reactions to a client's suicide than their senior clinicians (Brown, 1987). Yet another study of psychiatrists found that more than 50% of psychiatrists reported personally experiencing sadness, depression, hopelessness, and guilt in response to their client's suicide. Additionally, 74.5% reported professional reactions, including conducting a review of their practice, and 93.4% reported being more aggressive in the assessment of their remaining caseloads' suicide risk (Thomyangkoon & Leenaars, 2008).

A common myth is that all suicides can be prevented. Although professionals work diligently and effectively with individuals expressing various degrees of suicidality, individuals both receiving and not receiving treatment will suicide. Survey research across a number of mental health professionals has found that 86% of community mental health teams, 46% to 67% of psychiatrists, 35% of social workers, and 22% to 40% of psychologists have reported one or more clients' suicides (D. A. Alexander et al., 2000; Chemtob, Hamada, Bauer, Kinney, & Torigoe, 1988; Chemtob, Hamada, Bauer, Torigoe, & Kinney, 1988; Kleespies, 1993; Linke, Wojciak, & Day, 2002; Ruskin, Sakinofsky, Bagby, Dickens, & Sousa, 2004). One study of psychiatrists in Thailand found that 56% of psychiatrists had experienced a patient die by suicide, consistent with the rates found in similar large-scale studies in the United States and United Kingdom (Thomyangkoon & Leenaars, 2008).

Further, quantitative and qualitative research has similarly found that nurses and social workers experience the difficult reality of client suicides (Brown, 1987; Gilje, Talseth, & Norberg, 2005; Jacobson, Ting, Sanders, & Harrington, 2004; Ting, Sanders, Jacobson, & Power, 2006). Unfortunately, many professionals in training or educational programs will also experience this phenomenon (Coverdale, Roberts, & Louie, 2007; Dewar et al., 2000; Farberow, 2005; Kleespies, 1993; Ruskin et al., 2004; Sudak, 2007).

Even though literature is limited on the management of this issue, a number of professionals, including medical doctors (D. A. Alexander et al., 2000; Davidsen, 2011; Dewar et al., 2000; Eagles et al., 2001; Halligan & Corcoran, 2001; Talseth & Gilje, 2007), social workers (Feldman, 1987; Strom-Gottfried & Mowbray, 2006; Ting et al., 2006), nurses (Collins, 2003; Cooper, 1995; Gilje et al., 2005), and psychologists (Kleespies, 1993; Spiegelman & Werth, 2005), have begun to investigate the impact of a client suicide on their practitioners. Confronted with the reality that a majority of mental health clinicians will experience working with a client who completes suicide (D. A. Alexander et al., 2000; Grad, 1996), professionally, there are a number of areas that warrant consideration, including preparation and training, supporting other practitioners, managing the aftermath of a client suicide, and working with the surviving family members.

1. *Preparation and training.* It is important to work to prevent every suicide, but it may be unethical not to prepare practitioners and establish protocols to manage a future client suicide. All too often few organizations have established such protocols (Tsai, Moran, Shoemaker, & Bradley, 2012). Preparation can occur on a number of levels (D. A. Alexander et al., 2000; Farberow, 2005):

    *   One: Training and education on managing a client suicide should begin in educational institutions.
    *   Two: Intern, residence, and trainee programs for practitioners need to incorporate the realities of practicing with a suicidal client and how others may have managed a client's suicide.
    *   Three: Supervisors working in this field should be required to have specific training in how to respond, support, and supervise trainees who may experience this event.
    *   Four: Agencies, institutions, and programs that work with suicidality need to not only develop and implement protocols and procedures to manage the aftermath of a client suicide but also to inform and train new and existing practitioners on these procedures.
    *   Five: Professional bodies may need to become more active in establishing protocols and preemptively reach out to members who will work with clients who are suicidal.
    *   Six: Practitioners need to recognize that the suicide of a client may not be evidence of professional incompetence but a reality of their chosen profession and seek to develop various levels of support in their personal and professional lives.

In a national survey of psychiatry chief residents and program directors, Tsai et al. (2012) found that one in 20 residents experienced a patient suicide in a 12-month study period, and about 20% of psychiatry residency programs have written postvention protocols (Tsai et al., 2012). They also noted that the levels of such protocols have remained constant since 1994. The authors recommend that postvention protocols be fully developed to assist residents. Others have also found that most psychiatric training programs provide relatively little educational focus on helping trainees learn about and cope with the completed suicide of a patient (Fang et al., 2007; Pieters, De Gucht, Joos, & De Heyn, 2003; Ruskin et al., 2004). Furthermore, a national survey of chief residents of psychiatric residency programs found that a lack of audio or video teaching materials was a common barrier to providing trainees with education on suicide care (Melton & Coverdale, 2009).

One study sought to examine the effectiveness of an interactive curriculum to help psychiatrists, psychiatry residents, and training programs cope with patient suicide (Prabhakar et al., 2014). Specifically, the research developed a DVD that has four main components: (a) a video program containing such topics as vignettes based on patients who suicided and their clinicians' initial reactions (emotions, thoughts, and behaviors); a panel discussion of psychiatrists focusing on universal themes, processes, and procedures to follow in the aftermath of a patient's suicide; guidelines for working with the client's family; and the importance of counseling/supporting trainees and colleagues; (b) a PowerPoint presentation providing suicide-related facts such as suicide epidemiology, emotional reactions to patient suicide, and an overview of resources available to survivors; (c) a learning exercise to measure competencies; and (d) suggested pre- and posttests (Prabhakar et al., 2014). The DVD program was tested across several well-established psychiatric training programs. Although a need was identified by participants to include additional information regarding the legal ramifications of a client suicide, results of the study showed that, overall, the program was valuable in providing a broad curriculum for trainees/residents and in educating, guiding, and supporting those who will experience the suicide of a client and will be vulnerable to the guilt, anger, shame, powerlessness, helplessness, and feelings of abandonment that may follow (Prabhakar et al., 2014).

2. *Colleague and team support.* Although practitioners typically see clients alone, most professionals working with individuals who may be suicidal operate with others or in teams. The impact of a client's suicide affects the entire team. Research has found that following a suicide, the most helpful coping strategy is support from colleagues; conversely, formal inquiries although necessary were reported as unhelpful (D. A. Alexander et al., 2000; Dewar et al., 2000; Linke et al., 2002; Ting et al., 2006). Supervisors and colleagues need to discourage negative and critical comments toward the clinician survivors, as well as discourage the clinician from overworking and/or self-blaming (Collins, 2003). Working to develop a supportive, nonjudgmental, and nonblaming professional environment following the suicide of a colleague's client may directly enable the practitioner and the team to manage the suicide while continuing to provide effective services. In one study of psychiatrists, it was found that approximately 90% of psychiatrists reported that working through the event with colleagues was most helpful, followed by seeking support from family and friends. The study also found that more than 70% of psychiatrists surveyed used religiosity as a form of coping and reported praying for their deceased patient, with 87% reporting it as helpful (Thomyangkoon & Leenaars, 2008).

3. *Managing in the aftermath of a suicide.* The suicide of a client will frequently have immediate and potentially lasting emotional and professional impact on practitioners (D. A. Alexander et al., 2000; Anderson, 2005; Chemtob, Hamada, Bauer, Kinney, et al., 1988; Dewar et al., 2000; Linke et al., 2002). A practitioner's ability to relate to others' emotional state and cognitive processes and her or his clinical effectiveness can all be affected by a client's suicide. Practitioners will often overfocus or ruminate on the *psychological autopsy* of their client, that is a formal or informal procedure of examining a death by analyzing or reconstructing the events and motives leading up to the client's death. This process can be both helpful and detrimental to the practitioner.

The following suggestions for practitioners managing in the aftermath of a client's suicide are adapted from Spiegelman and Werth (2005, pp. 50–52).

- Meet with your supervisor or senior practitioner in your department.
- Review the case, and, if possible, discuss your emotional reaction to the suicide, and plan next steps.
- Discuss how to inform other staff members, coworkers, peers, and others.
- Document the event and supervision session.
- Do not make statements that may sound like an assumption of responsibility.
- If able, obtain facts of the event from a neutral party.
- Contact professional supports (legal, insurance, administration).
- Consider personal counseling and/or personal support from others.
- If supervisor and employer allow, consider contacting significant others of the client (e.g., make counseling referrals for the significant others).
- Consider appropriateness of attending the funeral, wake, or other ritual.
- Consider participating in a future psychological autopsy.

4. *Working with the surviving family members.* A client's suicide does not terminate our professional role. Beyond a responsibility to ourselves and our team, practitioners must decide how to continue working with the surviving family members. This is often the most difficult decision and process of professionals; however, it is often described as helpful and therapeutic to both family members and the practitioner (D. A. Alexander et al., 2000; Anderson, 2005; Strom-Gottfried & Mowbray, 2006). Although it is important for practitioners to determine for themselves, with their employer, and most importantly the surviving family members, on how to

negotiate and navigate this role, the following steps may serve as a helpful guide if continued work with the family is possible. Here are some points to consider:

- Some grieving family members may want to speak with the practitioner, others may not. It is important to respect the wishes of the individual family members. Initially, providing support and condolences can be helpful, but practitioners may want to avoid reviewing client details or conducting a psychological review with family members. The practitioner may also consider recommending counseling and providing referrals (Anderson, 2005; Spiegelman & Werth, 2005).
- Consider attending the memorial or funeral rituals. Both personally and professionally, grieving rituals and shared grief can be very important (D. A. Alexander et al., 2000; Anderson, 2005; Linke et al., 2002; Spiegelman & Werth, 2005; Strom-Gottfried & Mowbray, 2006). Current literature has indicated that both family members and professionals can benefit by the practitioner attending these rituals (D. A. Alexander et al., 2000; Anderson, 2005; Strom-Gottfried & Mowbray, 2006).
- In some circumstances, there may be some value in an ongoing connection or checking in with the family across time (Anderson, 2005).

In a study that surveyed suicide survivors' perceptions of the treating professional who had worked with their loved ones at the time of their deaths, it was found that the majority (74%) knew of the ongoing clinical treatment (Peterson et al., 2002). Despite recommendations that professionals should contact family members regarding the suicide risk of a client (Linehan, 1999), only a few (11%) reported being contacted by the clinician of their loved ones' suicide risk (Peterson et al., 2002). The majority of family members wanted to speak with the treating clinician and have her or him attend the funeral. Survivors who did not consider bringing lawsuits tended to rate the meetings with the clinicians as more meaningful and believed the clinicians to be straightforward and open (Peterson et al., 2002).

Individual Exercise 21.2

You arrive to work at an inpatient psychiatry unit Monday morning to learn that the client you and your interdisciplinary team had discharged on Friday had completed suicide the past evening. You hold a leadership position within the team. Like yourself, the other team members are experiencing a range of emotions and looking for support, yet concerned about blame.

1. What steps would you recommend for yourself and your colleagues?
2. How may you support your colleagues?
3. How do you manage your own affect, sense of responsibility, and any concerns for the inevitable formal assessment of the client's suicide?
4. Would your answers to the aforementioned questions change if the client had insisted to being discharged AMA (Against Medical Advice)? Why or why not?

Small Group Exercise 21.2

In groups of three to five,

1. As a group, review and discuss your answers to Individual Exercise 21.2.
2. What are the similarities and or differences between the responses of the two exercises?

PROFESSIONALS MANAGING AFTER A COLLEAGUE'S SUICIDE

Doctors, nurses, psychologists, psychiatrists, social workers, and other mental health and health care professionals are at increased risk of suicide (Agerbo, Gunnell, Bonde, Mortensen, & Nordentoft, 2007; Boxer, Burnett, & Swanson, 1995; Kleespies et al., 2011; Lindeman, Laara, Hakko, & Lonnqvist, 1996; Nock et al., 2008; Schernhammer, 2005; Stack, 2001). Although receiving scant attention in the research, some studies have sought to explore and examine the impact of a colleague's suicide on the mental health and health care professionals. O'Connor (2001) reported that half of the psychologists who suicided were thought to have had problems with depression or substance abuse and many experienced interpersonal, professional, or functional loss preceding the suicide (O'Connor, 2001). Kleespies et al. (2011) reported that colleagues were often surprised, stunned, or shocked at the news of a colleague's suicide (Kleespies et al., 2011). A colleague's suicide was frequently not expected or anticipated (Kleespies et al., 2011; O'Connor, 2001). Although often receiving less attention, training protocols on suicide for mental health professionals may need to extend beyond focusing solely on clients at risk of suicide to also include the management of suicidal colleagues.

SUMMARY

Mental health practitioners are likely to experience a client who completes suicide. It is essential for professionals to recognize that they themselves and or their colleagues may become a professional survivor after a client suicide. Organizational and professional protocols for managing a client suicide and supporting professional survivors are strongly recommended.

KEY POINTS

1. Across a professional discipline, mental health practitioners are likely to experience the death of a client due to suicide.
2. It is a myth that all suicides can be prevented.
3. Organizations should establish protocols for managing the aftermath of the death of a client due to suicide and provide training to new and existing clinical staff regarding the protocols established.
4. The death of a professional colleague to suicide can have lasting and significant impact for mental health professionals.
5. Following the suicide of a client, practitioners benefit from the support of their colleagues and supervisors.
6. Formal inquiries, although necessary, have been found to be less helpful to a professional survivor than support from colleagues.
7. As a professional survivor, it is important to avoid making statements that may sound like an assumption of responsibility even when experiencing heightened feelings of guilt and/or doubt.
8. Supervisors of clinicians working with high-risk clients should be required to have specific training in how to respond, support, and supervise trainees who may experience the suicide of a client.

(continued)

KEY POINTS (*continued*)

9. A client's suicide does not terminate our professional role. Beyond a responsibility to ourselves and our team, practitioners must decide how to continue work with the surviving family members.
10. The majority of family members want to speak with the treating clinician and have her or him attend the funeral.

ELECTRONIC RESOURCES

AMERICAN FOUNDATION OF SUICIDE PREVENTION

www.afsp.org

AMERICAN ASSOCIATION OF SUICIDALITY

www.suicidology.org

SUICIDE PREVENTION RESOURCE CENTER

www.sprc.org

KNOWLEDGE ACQUISITION TEST (KAT)

True or False

1. All suicides are preventable by mental health professionals.
2. Professional survivors of a client suicide experience a similar range of emotions as do surviving family and friends ranging from depression, guilt, doubt, shame, anger, to name a few.
3. Conducting a psychological autopsy always has a positive effect on professionals.
4. Professionals should never attempt to contact the family of a client who suicides.
5. Professionals will rarely experience a client suicide.
6. After a client suicide, a helpful coping strategy for professionals is the support from their colleagues.
7. A practitioner's ability to relate to others, emotional state, cognitive processes, and clinical effectiveness can all be affected by a client's suicide.
8. Practitioners should always attend the funeral rites of a client after his or her suicide.

Short Answer

9. What is the likelihood that a treating professional will experience the suicide of a client across helping disciplines?
10. What are the common reactions that research has found among professionals who experience the suicide of a client?
11. Should a professional attempt to contact the family of a client who suicides?
12. What is the impact of a clinician's suicide on a client?
13. Should professions/professionals prepare and train themselves to manage a potential future of a client suicide? Explain.
14. In considering question 13, what steps can professions or professionals take to prepare or train themselves for a future client suicide?
15. How can practitioners work with the surviving family members?

Multiple Choice

16. Which of the following mental health disciplines reports the greatest likelihood of experiencing a client suicide?
    A. Psychiatrists
    B. Social workers
    C. Psychologists
    D. Community health workers
    E. Nurses
    F. Medical students
17. Following the suicide of a colleague, clinicians most often report:
    A. Feeling shocked at the news
    B. Having no knowledge that their colleague was struggling
    C. Never having considered that suicide was a possibility for their colleague
    D. Experiencing a lasting personal impact from their colleague's death
    E. All of the above
    F. None of the above

18. Following a client's suicide, practitioners' reactions may include:
    A. Little affective response due to comprehensive professional training and education
    B. Professional suspension of their license and probable job loss
    C. A potential range of responses including grief, shock, denial, distress, depression, isolation, self-blame, a sense of failure, strain on their personal and professional lives, fear of another suicide, loss of confidence, and avoidance of triggering stimuli
    D. A cluster of their clients attempting or completing suicide
    E. None of the above
    F. All of the above

19. Following a client's suicide, some recommended management steps that practitioners may want to consider are:
    A. Maintain clear boundaries by not meeting with your supervisor or department head to review the case
    B. If you do meet with your supervisor, do not document this event
    C. Personal counseling or support is not helpful and may be interpreted as complicity to the suicide if a lawsuit is filed
    D. Avoid any further contact with the surviving family members
    E. None of the above
    F. All of the above

20. Following a client's suicide, professionals may want to consider:
    A. Contacting or supporting surviving family members
    B. Working with their colleagues and team to help each other manage this tragedy
    C. Attending memorial or funeral rites
    D. Periodically checking in with the surviving family members
    E. None of the above
    F. All of the above

REFERENCES

Agerbo, E., Gunnell, D., Bonde, J. P., Mortensen, P. B., & Nordentoft, M. (2007). Suicide and occupation: The impact of socio-economic, demographic and psychiatric differences. *Psychological Medicine, 37*, 1131–1140.

Ahmedani, B. K. (2015). Racial/ethnic differences in health care visits made before suicide attempt across the United States. *Medical Care, 53.5*, 430–435.

Alexander, D. A., Klein, S., Gray, N. M., Dewar, I. G., & Eagles, J. M. (2000). Suicide by patients: Questionnaire study of its effect on consultant psychiatrists. *British Medical Journal, 320*, 1571–1574.

Anderson, G. O. (2005). Who, what, when, where, how, and mostly why? A therapist's grief over the suicide of a client. *Women and Therapy, 28*(1), 25–34.

Boxer, P. A., Burnett, C., & Swanson, N. (1995). Suicide and occupation: A review of the literature. *Journal of Occupational and Environmental Medicine, 37*, 442–452.

Brown, H. N. (1987). The impact of suicide on therapists in training. *Comprehensive Psychiatry, 28*(2), 101–112.

Chemtob, C. M., Hamada, R. S., Bauer, G., Kinney, B., & Torigoe, R. Y. (1988). Patients' suicides: Frequency and impact on psychiatrists. *American Journal of Psychiatry, 145*(2), 224–228.

Chemtob, C. M., Hamada, R. S., Bauer, G., Torigoe, R. Y., & Kinney, B. (1988). Patient suicide: Frequency and impact on psychologists. *Professional Psychology: Research and Practice, 19*(4), 416–420.

Collins, J. M. (2003). Impact of patient suicide on clinicians. *Journal of the American Psychiatric Nurses Association, 9*(85), 159–162.

Cooper, C. (1995). Patient suicide and assault: Their impact on psychiatric hospital staff. *Journal of Psychosocial Nursing and Mental Health Services, 33*(6), 26–29.

Coverdale, J. H., Roberts, L. W., & Louie, A. K. (2007). Encountering patient suicide: Emotional responses, ethics, and implications for training programs. *Academic Psychiatry, 31*(5), 329–332.

Davidsen, A. N. (2011). "And then one day he'd shot himself. Then I was really shocked": General practitioners' reaction to patient suicide. *Patient Education and Counseling, 85*, 113–118.

Dewar, I. G., Eagles, J. M., Klein, S., Gray, N., & Alexander, D. A. (2000). Psychiatric trainees' experiences of, and reactions to, patient suicide. *Psychiatric Bulletin, 24*(1), 20–23.

Eagles, J. M., Klein, S., Gray, N. M., Dewar, I. G., & Alexander, D. A. (2001). Role of psychiatrists in the prediction and prevention of suicide: A perspective from north-east Scotland. *British Journal of Psychiatry, 178*, 494–496.

Fang, F., Kemp, J., Jawandha, A., Juros, J., Long, L., Nanayakkara, S., . . . , Anzia, J. (2007). Encountering patient suicide: A resident's experience. *Academic Psychiatry, 31*(5), 340–344.

Farberow, N. L. (2005). The mental health professional as suicide survivor. *Clinical Neuropsychiatry: Journal of Treatment Evaluation, 2*(1), 13–20.

Feldman, D. (1987). A social work student's reaction to client suicide. *Social Casework, 68*, 184–187.

Gaffney, P., Russell, V., Collins, K., Bergin, A., Halligan, P., Carey, C., & Coyle, S. (2009). Impact of patient suicide on front-line staff in Ireland. *Death Studies, 33*(7), 639–656.

Gilje, F., Talseth, A. G., & Norberg, A. (2005). Psychiatric nurses' response to suicidal psychiatric inpatients: Struggling with self and sufferer. *Journal of Psychiatric and Mental Health Nursing, 12*(5), 519–526.

Gitlin, M. J. (1999). A psychiatrist's reaction to a patient's suicide. *American Journal of Psychiatry, 156*(10), 1630–1634.

Grad, O. T. (1996). Suicide: How to survive as a survivor? *Crisis: The Journal of Crisis Intervention and Suicide Prevention, 17*(3), 136–142.

Grad, O. T., & Michel, K. (2005). Therapists as client suicide survivors. *Women and Therapy, 28*(1), 71–81.

Halligan, P., & Corcoran, P. (2001). The impact of patient suicide on rural general practitioners. *British Journal of General Practice, 51*(465), 295–296.

Jacobson, J. M., Ting, L., Sanders, S., & Harrington, S. (2004). Prevalence of and reactions to fatal and non-fatal client suicidal behavior: A national study of mental health social workers. *OMEGA: The Journal of Death and Dying, 49*(3), 237–248.

Kleespies, P. M. (1993). The stress of patient suicidal behavior: Implications for interns and training programs in psychology. *Professional Psychology: Research and Practice, 24*(4), 477–482.

Kleespies, P. M., Van Orden, K. A., Bongar, B., Bridgeman, D., Bufka, L. F., Galper, D. I., . . . Yufit, R. I. (2011). Psychologist suicide: Incidence, impact, and suggestions for prevention, intervention, and postvention. *Professional Psychology: Research and Practice, 42*(3), 244–251.

Lindeman, S., Laara, E., Hakko, H., & Lonnqvist, J. (1996). A systematic review on gender-specific suicide mortality in medical doctors. *British Journal of Psychiatry, 168*, 274–279.

Linehan, M. M. (1999). Standard protocol for assessing and treating suicidal behavior for patients in treatment. In D. G. Jacobs (Ed.), *The Harvard Medical School guide to suicide assessment and intervention* (pp. 146–187). San Fancisco, CA: Jossey-Bass.

Linke, S., Wojciak, J., & Day, S. (2002). The impact of suicide on community mental health teams findings and recommendations. *Psychiatric Bulletin, 26*, 50–52.

Lukas, C., & Seiden, H. (1997). *Silent grief.* New York, NY: Charles Scribner's Sons.

Luoma, J. B., Pearson, J. L., & Martin, C. E. (2002). Contact with mental health and primary care prior to suicide: A review of the evidence. *American Journal of Psychiatry, 159*, 909–916.

Maltsberger, J. T. (1992). The implications of patient suicide for the surviving psychotherapist. In D. Jacobs (Ed.), *Suicide and clinical practice* (Vol. Clinical Practice Number 21, pp. 169–182). Washington, DC: American Psychiatric Press.

Melton, B. B., & Coverdale, J. H. (2009). What do we teach psychiatric residents about suicide? A national survey of chief residents. *Academic Psychiatry, 33*, 47–50.

Nock, M. K., Borges, G., Bromet, E. J., Cha, C. B., Kessler, R. C., & Lee, S. (2008). Suicide and suicidal behavior. *Epidemiologic Reviews, 30*, 133–154.

O'Connor, M. (2001). On the etiology and effective management of professional distress and impairment among psychologists. *Professional Psychology: Research and Practice, 32*, 345–350.

Peterson, E. M., Luoma, J. B., & Dunne, E. (2002). Suicide survivors' perceptions of the treating clinician. *Suicide and Life-Threatening Behavior, 32*(2), 158–166.

Pieters, G., De Gucht, V., Joos, G., & De Heyn, E. (2003). Frequency and impact of patient suicide on psychiatric trainees. *European Psychiatry, 18*, 345–349.

Prabhakar, D., Balon, R., Anzia, J. M., Gabbard, G. O., Lomax, J. W., Bandstra, B. S., . . . Zisook, S. (2014). Helping psychiatry residents cope with patient suicide. *Academic Psychiatry, 38*(5), 593–597.

Ruskin, R., Sakinofsky, I., Bagby, R. M., Dickens, S., & Sousa, G. (2004). Impact of patient suicide on psychiatrists and psychiatric trainees. *Academic Psychiatry, 28*(2), 104–110.

Schernhammer, E. (2005). Taking their own lives: The high rate of physician suicide. *New England Journal of Medicine, 352*, 2473–2476.

Scocco, P., Corinto, B., & Pavan, L. (2008). The aftermath of a suicide attempt: The emotional impact on patient and psychiatrist: A pilot study. *Clinical Neuropsychiatry: Journal of Treatment Evaluation, 5*(5), 240–244.

Spiegelman, J. S., & Werth, J. L. (2005). Don't forget about me: The experiences of therapists-in-training after a client has attempted or died by suicide. *Women and Therapy, 28*(1), 35–57.

Stack, S. (2001). Occupation and suicide [proceedings paper]. *Social Science Quarterly, 82*, 384–396.

Strom-Gottfried, K., & Mowbray, N. D. (2006). Who heals the helper? Facilitating the social worker's grief. *Families in Society, 87*(1), 9–15.

Sudak, H. (2007). Encountering patient suicide: The role of survivors. *Academic Psychiatry, 31*(5), 333–335.

Talseth, A. G., & Gilje, F. (2007). Unburdening suffering: Responses of psychiatrists to patients' suicide deaths. *Nursing Ethics: An International Journal for Health Care Professionals, 14*(5), 620–636.

Thompson, J., & Brooks, S. (1990). When a colleague commits suicide: How the staff reacts. *Journal of Psychosocial Nursing and Mental Health Services, 28*(10), 6–11.

Thomyangkoon, P., & Leenaars, A. (2008). Impact of death by suicide of patients on Thai psychiatrists. *Suicide and Life-Threatening Behavior, 38*(6), 728–740.

Ting, L., Sanders, S., Jacobson, J. M., & Power, J. R. (2006). Dealing with the aftermath: A qualitative analysis of mental health social workers' reactions after a client suicide. *Social Work, 51*(1), 329–341.

Tsai, A., Moran, S., Shoemaker, R., & Bradley, J. (2012). Patient suicides in psychiatric residencies and postvention responses: A national survey of psychiatry chief residents and program directors. *Academic Psychiatry, 36*(1), 34–38.

Yaseen, Z. S., Briggs, J., Kopeykina, I., Orchard, K. M., Silberlicht, J., Bhingradia, H., & Galynker, I. I. (2013). Distinctive emotional responses of clinicians to suicide-attempting patients: A comparative study. *BioMed Central Psychiatry, 13*, 230–239.

INDEX